FOUNDATIONS OF
POTENTIAL THEORY

BY

OLIVER DIMON KELLOGG

PROFESSOR OF MATHEMATICS IN HARVARD UNIVERSITY
CAMBRIDGE · MASSACHUSETTS · U.S.A.

WITH 30 FIGURES

NEW YORK
DOVER PUBLICATIONS, INC.

Library of Congress Catalog Card Number: 54-10019

Manufactured in the United States of America

Dover Publications, Inc.
180 Varick Street
New York 14, N. Y.

Preface.

The present volume gives a systematic treatment of potential functions. It takes its origin in two courses, one elementary and one advanced, which the author has given at intervals during the last ten years, and has a two-fold purpose: first, to serve as an introduction for students whose attainments in the Calculus include some knowledge of partial derivatives and multiple and line integrals; and secondly, to provide the reader with the fundamentals of the subject, so that he may proceed immediately to the applications, or to the periodical literature of the day.

It is inherent in the nature of the subject that physical intuition and illustration be appealed to freely, and this has been done. However, in order that the book may present sound ideals to the student, and also serve the mathematician, both for purposes of reference and as a basis for further developments, the proofs have been given by rigorous methods. This has led, at a number of points, to results either not found elsewhere, or not readily accessible. Thus, Chapter IV contains a proof for the general regular region of the divergence theorem (Gauss', or Green's theorem) on the reduction of volume to surface integrals. The treatment of the fundamental existence theorems in Chapter XI by means of integral equations meets squarely the difficulties incident to the discontinuity of the kernel, and the same chapter gives an account of the most recent developments with respect to the Dirichlet problem.

Exercises are introduced in the conviction that no mastery of a mathematical subject is possible without working with it. They are designed primarily to illustrate or extend the theory, although the desirability of requiring an occasional concrete numerical result has not been lost sight of.

Grateful acknowledgements are due to numerous friends on both sides of the Atlantic for their kind interest in the work. It is to my colleague Professor COOLIDGE that I owe the first suggestion to undertake it. To Professor OSGOOD I am indebted for constant encouragement and wise counsel at many points. For a careful reading of the manuscript and for helpful comment, I am grateful to Dr. ALEXANDER WEINSTEIN, of Breslau; and for substantial help with the proof, I wish to thank my pupil Mr. F. E. ULRICH. It is also a pleasure to acknowledge the generous attitude, the unfailing courtesy, and the ready coöperation of the publisher.

Cambridge, Mass.   O. D. Kellogg.
August, 1929.

Contents.

Chapter I.
The Force of Gravity.

Chapter II.
Fields of Force.

Chapter III.
The Potential.

Chapter IV.
The Divergence Theorem.

Chapter V.
Properties of Newtonian Potentials at Points of Free Space.

Chapter VI.
Properties of Newtonian Potentials at Points Occupied by Masses.

Chapter VII.
Potentials as Solutions of Laplace's Equation; Electrostatics.

Chapter VIII.
Harmonic Functions.

Chapter IX.
Electric Images; Green's Function.

Chapter X.
Sequences of Harmonic Functions.

Chapter XI.
Fundamental Existence Theorems.

Chapter XII.
The Logarithmic Potential.

Chapter I.

The Force of Gravity.

1. The Subject Matter of Potential Theory.

While the theory of Newtonian potentials has various aspects, it is best introduced as a body of results on the properties of forces which are characterized by *Newtons Law of Universal Gravitation*[1]:

Every particle of matter in the universe attracts every other particle, with a force whose direction is that of the line joining the two, and whose magnitude is directly as the product of their masses, and inversely as the square of their distance from each other.

If, however, potential theory were restricted in its applications to problems in gravitation alone, it could not hold the important place which it does, not only in mathematical physics, but in pure mathematics as well. In the physical world, we meet with forces of the same character acting between electric charges, and between the poles of magnets.

But as we proceed, it will become evident that potential theory may also be regarded as the theory of a certain differential equation, known as LAPLACE'S. This differential equation characterizes the steady flow of heat in homogeneous media, it characterizes the steady flow of ideal fluids, of steady electric currents, and it occurs fundamentally in the study of the equilibrium of elastic solids.

The same differential equation in two dimensions is satisfied by the real and imaginary parts of analytic functions of a complex variable, and RIEMANN founded his theory of these functions on potential theory. Differential geometry, conformal mapping, with its applications to geographical maps, as well as other branches of mathematics, find important uses for Laplace's equation. Finally, the methods devised for the solution of problems of potential theory have been found to be of far wider applicability, and have exerted a profound influence on the theory of the differential equations of mathematical physics, both ordinary and partial, and on other branches of analysis[2].

---

[1] *Philosophiae Naturalis Principia Mathematica*, Book III, Propositions I—VII. Formulated as above in THOMSON and TAIT, *Natural Philosophy*, Pt. II, p. 9.

[2] Indications on the literature will be found at the end of the book.

2. Newton's Law.

It is our experience that in order to set bodies in motion, or to stop or otherwise change their motion, we must exert forces. Accordingly, when we see changes in the motion of a body, we seek a cause of the character of a force. As bodies about us, when free to do so, fall toward the earth, we are accustomed to attribute to the earth an attracting power which we call the force of gravity. It is not at all obvious that the smaller bodies on the earth attract each other; if they do, the forces must be exceedingly minute. But we do see the effects of forces on the moon and planets, since they do not move in the straight lines we are accustomed to associate with undisturbed motion. To NEWTON it occurred that this deviation from straight line motion might be regarded as a continual falling, toward the earth in the case of the moon, and toward the sun in the case of the planets; this continual falling could then be explained as due to an attraction by the earth or sun, exactly like the attraction of the earth for bodies near it. His examination of the highly precise description of planetary motion which KEPLER had embodied in three empirical laws led, not only to the verification of this conjecture, but to the generalization stated at the beginning of the first section. The statement that all bodies attract each other according to this law has been abundantly verified, not only for heavenly bodies, but also for masses which are unequally distributed over the earth, like the equatorial bulge due to the ellipticity of the earth, and mountains, and finally for bodies small enough to be investigated in the laboratory.

The magnitude of the force between two particles, one of mass m_1, situated at a point P, and one of mass m_2, situated at Q, is given by Newton's law as

$$F = \gamma \frac{m_1 m_2}{r^2},$$

where r is the distance between P and Q. The constant of proportionality γ depends solely on the units used. These being given, its determination is purely a matter of measuring the force between two bodies of known mass at a known distance apart. Careful experiments have been made for this purpose, an account of which may be found in the *Encyclopedia Britannica* under the heading *Gravitation*[1]. If the unit of mass is the gramme, of length, the centimetre, of time, the second, and

---

[1] See also ZENNECK: Encyklopädie der Mathematischen Wissenschaften, Vol. V, pp. 25—67. Recently, measurements of a high degree of refinement have been made by Dr. P. R. HEYL, of the U. S. Bureau of Standards. See *A Redetermination of the Constant of Gravitation*, Proceedings of the National Academy of Sciences, Vol. 13 (1927), pp. 601—605.

The value of γ there given has been adopted here, although it should be noted that further experiments by Dr. HEYL are still in progress.

of force, the dyne, it is found that $\gamma = 6\cdot664 \times 10^{-8}$. If we borrow the result (p. 7) that a homogeneous sphere attracts as if concentrated at its center, we see that this means that two spheres of mass one gramme each, with centers one centimetre apart, will attract eachother with a force of $\cdot00000006664$ dynes.

In order to avoid this inconvenient value of γ, it is customary in potential theory to choose the unit of force so that $\gamma = 1$. This unit of force is called the *attraction unit*.

Exercises.

1. If the unit of mass is the pound, of length, the foot, of time, the second, and of force, the poundal, show that γ has the value $1\cdot070 \times 10^{-9}$. One foot contains $30\cdot46$ cm., and one pound, $453\cdot6$ gm.

2. Two homogeneous lead spheres, of diameter 1 ft. are placed in contact with each other. Compute the force with which they attract each other. A cubic foot of lead weights 710 pounds. Answer, about $\cdot0000046$ lb. This is approximately the weight of a square of medium weight bond paper, of side $1/_4$ in.

3. Compute the mass of the earth, knowing the force with which it attracts a given mass on its surface, taking its radius to be 3955 miles. Hence show that the earth's mean density is about $5\cdot5$ times that of water. Newton inferred that the mean density lies between 5 and 6 times that of water.

4. Find the mass of the sun, it being given that the sun's attraction on the earth is approximately in equilibrium with the centrifugal force due to the earth's motion around the sun in a circle of $4\cdot90 \times 10^{11}$ feet. Answer, about 330,000 times the mass of the earth.

3. Interpretation of Newton's Law for Continuously Distributed Bodies.

Newton's law was stated in terms of particles. We usually have to deal, not with particles, but with continuously distributed matter. We then naturally think of dividing the body into small parts by the method of the integral calculus, adding the vector forces corresponding to the parts, and passing to the limit as the maximum chord of the parts approaches 0. This, in fact, is exactly what we shall do. But it should be pointed out that such a process involves an additional assumption. For no matter how fine the division, the parts are still not particles, Newton's law as stated is not applicable to them, and we have no means of determining the forces due to the parts.

The physical law which we shall adopt, and which may well be regarded simply as an amplified statement of Newton's law, is the following: *Given two bodies, let them be divided into elements after the manner of the integral calculus, and let the mass of each element be regarded as concentrated at some point of the element. Then the attraction which one body exerts on the other is the limit of the attraction which the corresponding system of particles exerts on the second system of particles, as the maximum chord of the elements approaches* 0. We shall revert to this assumption, and consider its legitimacy, on p. 22.

4. Forces Due to Special Bodies.

Because of their use in other problems of potential theory, because of the generalizations which they illustrate, and because of the practice which they give in dealing with Newtonian forces, the attractions due to special bodies are well worth study.

While each of two bodies attracts the other, the forces exerted are not equal vectors. Their magnitudes are equal, but they are oppositely directed. In order to avoid ambiguity it will be convenient to speak of one body as the attracting, and the other as the attracted body. This merely means that we are specifying the body the force on which we are determining. We shall also confine ourselves for the present to the case in which the attracted body is a unit particle. It will appear in § 11 (page 27) that the results are of wider significance than is at first evident. This section will be devoted to some illustrative examples.

Straight homogeneous segment. Let us consider a straight line segment, which we regard as having mass, so distributed that the mass on any interval is proportional to the length of the interval. The constant factor of proportionality λ is called the *linear density.* We have here an idealization of a straight wire, which is a better approximation the smaller the diameter of the wire relatively to its length and the distance away of the attracted particle.

Let axes be chosen so that the ends of the wire are the points $(0, 0, 0)$ and $(l, 0, 0)$. As a first case, let the attracted particle be in line with the wire, at $(x, 0, 0)$, $x > l$. Let the wire be divided into intervals by the points $\xi_0 = 0, \xi_1, \xi_2, \ldots \xi_n = l$ (fig. 1). Then the interval (ξ_k, ξ_{k+1}) carries a mass $\lambda \, \varDelta \, \xi_k$, which, by our physical law, is to be regarded as concentrated at some point ξ_k' of the interval. The force due to the particle thus constructed will lie along the x-axis, and will be given, in attraction units, by

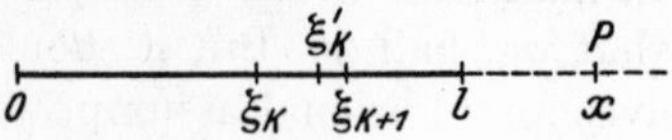

Fig. 1.

$$\varDelta X_k = - \frac{\lambda \, \varDelta \xi_k}{|x - \xi_k'|^2},$$

$$\varDelta Y_k = 0, \qquad \varDelta Z_k = 0.$$

The force due to the whole segment will be the limit of the sum of the forces due to the system of particles, or

$$X = - \int_0^l \frac{\lambda \, d\xi}{(x - \xi)^2}, \qquad Y = 0, \qquad Z = 0,$$

or

$$X = - \frac{\lambda l}{x \, (x - l)}, \qquad Y = 0, \qquad Z = 0.$$

The result may be given a more suggestive form by introducing the total mass $M = \lambda l$, and considering at what point of the segment a particle of that mass should be placed in order to yield the same attraction on a unit particle at $P(x, 0, 0)$. If c is the coördinate of this point,

$$X = -\frac{\lambda l}{x(x-l)} = -\frac{M}{c^2} \quad \text{and} \quad c = \sqrt{x(l-x)}.$$

Thus the wire attracts a unit particle at P as if the mass of the wire were concentrated at a point of the wire whose distance from P is the geometric mean of the distances from P of the ends of the wire.

As P approaches the nearer end of the wire, the force becomes infinite, but only like the inverse first power of the distance of P from this end, although a particle would produce a force which became infinite like the inverse square of the distance. The difference is that in the case of the particle, P draws near to the whole mass, whereas in the case of the wire the mass is distributed over a segment to only one of whose points does P draw arbitrarily near.

As P recedes farther and farther away, the *equivalent particle* (as we shall call the particle with the same mass as the wire, and with the same attraction on a unit particle at P) moves toward the mid-point of the wire, and the attraction of the wire becomes more and more nearly that of a fixed particle at its mid-point. An examination of such characteristics of the attraction frequently gives a satisfactory check on the computation of the force.

Let us now consider a second position of the attracted particle, namely a point $P\left(\frac{l}{2}, y, 0\right)$ on the perpendicular bisector of the material segment (fig. 2). The distance r of the attracted particle from a point $(\xi_k', 0, 0)$ of the interval (ξ_k, ξ_{k+1}) is given by

$$r^2 = \left(\xi_k' - \frac{l}{2}\right)^2 + y^2,$$

and the magnitude of the force at P, due to a particle at this point, whose mass is that on the interval (ξ_k, ξ_{k+1}) is

$$\Delta F_k = \frac{\lambda \Delta \xi_k}{\left(\xi_k' - \frac{l}{2}\right)^2 + y^2}.$$

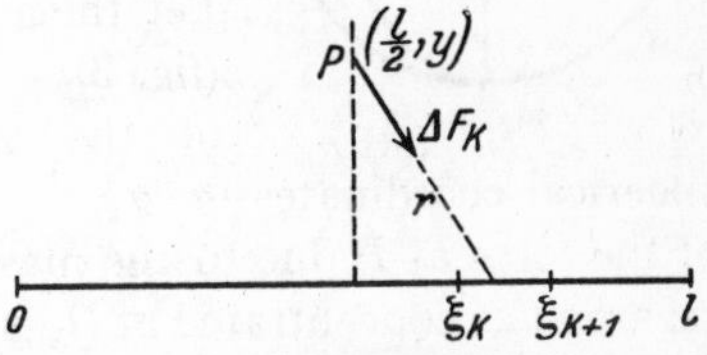

This force has the direction cosines

$$\frac{\xi_k' - \frac{l}{2}}{r}, \quad \frac{-y}{r}, \quad 0,$$

Fig. 2.

and therefore the components

$$\Delta X_k = \frac{\lambda\left(\xi_k' - \frac{l}{2}\right)\Delta \xi_k}{\left[\left(\xi_k' - \frac{l}{2}\right)^2 + y^2\right]^{\frac{3}{2}}}, \quad \Delta Y_k = \frac{-\lambda y \Delta \xi_k}{\left[\left(\xi_k' - \frac{l}{2}\right)^2 + y^2\right]^{\frac{3}{2}}}, \quad \Delta Z_k = 0.$$

The limits of the sums of these components give the components of the attraction of the segment

$$X = \lambda \int_0^l \frac{\left(\xi - \frac{l}{2}\right)d\xi}{\left[\left(\xi - \frac{l}{2}\right)^2 + y^2\right]^{\frac{3}{2}}}, \quad Y = -y\lambda \int_0^l \frac{d\xi}{\left[\left(\xi - \frac{l}{2}\right)^2 + y^2\right]^{\frac{3}{2}}}, \quad Z = 0 :$$

The first integral vanishes, since the integrand has equal and opposite values at points equidistant from $\xi = \frac{l}{2}$. The second integral is easily evaluated, and gives

$$Y = - \frac{\lambda l}{y\sqrt{\left(\frac{l}{2}\right)^2 + y^2}} = -\frac{M}{c^2},$$

if c is the geometric mean of the distances from P of the nearest and farthest points of the wire. The equivalent particle, is thus seen to lie *beyond* the wire as viewed from P. This fact is significant, as it shows· that there does not always exist *in* a body a point at which its mass can be concentrated without altering its attraction for a second body. Our physical law does not assert that such a point exists, but only that if one be assumed in each of the parts into which a body is divided, the errors thereby introduced vanish as the maximum chord of the parts approaches 0.

Spherical shell. Let us take as a second illustration the surface of a sphere with center at O and radius a, regarding it as spread with mass such that the mass on any part of the surface is proportional to the area of that part. The constant factor of proportionality σ is called the *surface density.* We have here the situation usually assumed for a charge of electricity in equilibrium on the surface of a spherical conductor[1]. Let the attracted particle be at $P(0,0,z)$, $z \neq a$ (fig. 3). Let ΔS_k denote a typical element of the surface, containing a point Q_k with spherical coördinates $(a, \varphi_k', \vartheta_k')$. Then the magnitude of the element of the force at P due to the mass $\sigma \Delta S_k$ of the element of surface ΔS_k, regarded as concentrated at Q_k is

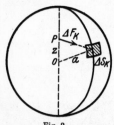

Fig. 3.

$$\Delta F_k = \frac{\sigma \Delta S_k}{r_k^2} + \frac{\sigma \Delta S_k}{a^2 + z^2 - 2az\cos\vartheta_k'}.$$

By symmetry, the force due to the spherical shell will have no component perpendicular to the z-axis, so that we may confine ourselves

---

[1] See Chapter VII (page 176).

to the components of the elements of force in the direction of the z-axis. The cosine of the angle between the element of force and this axis is

$$\frac{a \cos \vartheta'_k - z}{r},$$

so that

$$\varDelta Z_k = \frac{\sigma \, (a \cos \vartheta'_k - z) \, \varDelta S_k}{[a^2 + z^2 - 2\, a\, z \cos \vartheta'_k]^{\frac{3}{2}}},$$

and the total force is given by the double integral over the surface of the sphere

$$Z = \sigma \iint\limits_{S} \frac{(a \cos \vartheta - z) \, dS}{[a^2 + z^2 - 2\, a\, z \cos \vartheta]^{\frac{3}{2}}}.$$

This is equivalent to the iterated integral

$$Z = \sigma \, a^2 \int\limits_0^\pi \int\limits_0^{2\pi} \frac{(a \cos \vartheta - z) \, d\varphi \sin \vartheta \, d\vartheta}{[a^2 + z^2 - 2\, a\, z \cos \vartheta]^{\frac{3}{2}}},$$

$$= 2\pi \sigma \, a^2 \int\limits_0^\pi \frac{(a \cos \vartheta - z) \sin \vartheta \, d\vartheta}{[a^2 + z^2 - 2\, a\, z \cos \vartheta]^{\frac{3}{2}}}.$$

In evaluating this last integral (which may be done by introducing r as the variable of integration), it must be kept in mind that

$$r = \sqrt{a^2 + z^2 - 2\, a\, z \cos \vartheta}$$

is a distance, and so essentially positive. Thus, its value for $\vartheta = 0$ is $|a - z|$, that is $a - z$ or $z - a$ according as $a > z$ or $z > a$. The result is

$$Z = -\frac{4\pi a^2 \sigma}{z^2} = -\frac{M}{z^2} \quad \text{for} \quad z > a,$$

$$Z = 0 \qquad\qquad\qquad \text{for} \quad 0 \leqq z < a.$$

That is, *a homogeneous spherical shell attracts a particle at an exterior point as if the mass of the shell were concentrated at its center, and exercises no force on a particle in its interior.*

Homogeneous solid sphere. If a homogeneous solid sphere be thought of as made up of concentric spherical shells, it is a plausible inference that the whole attracts a particle as if the sphere were concentrated at its center. That this is so, we verify by setting up the integral for the attraction. Let $\varkappa$ denote the constant ratio of the mass of any part of the sphere to the volume of the part, that is, the *density*. The mass $\varkappa \varDelta V$ in the element $\varDelta V$, regarded as concentrated at the point

$Q\,(\varrho,\,\varphi,\,\vartheta)$ will exert on a unit particle at $P\,(z,\,0,\,0)$, a force whose magnitude is

$$\Delta F = \frac{\varkappa\,\Delta V}{\varrho^2 + z^2 - 2\,\varrho\,z\cos\vartheta}$$

and whose component in the direction of the z-axis is therefore

$$\Delta Z = \frac{\varkappa\,(\varrho\cos\vartheta - z)\,\Delta V}{[\varrho^2 + z^2 - 2\,\varrho\,z\cos\vartheta]^{\frac{3}{2}}}.$$

Hence, for the total force,

$$Z = \varkappa \int\limits_0^a \int\limits_0^\pi \int\limits_0^{2\pi} \frac{(\varrho\cos\vartheta - z)\,d\varphi\sin\vartheta\,d\vartheta\,\varrho^2\,d\varrho}{[\varrho^2 + z^2 - 2\,\varrho\,z\cos\vartheta]^{\frac{3}{2}}}.$$

The two inner integrals have been evaluated in the previous example. We have only to replace a by ϱ and evaluate the integral with respect to ϱ. The result is

$$Z = -\frac{4\,\pi\varkappa}{z^2}\int\limits_0^a \varrho^2\,d\varrho = -\frac{4\,\pi\varkappa\,a^3}{3\,z^2} = -\frac{M}{z^2},$$

as was anticipated.

Further examples will be left as exercises to the reader in the following sections. We take them up in the order of multiplicity of the integrals expressing the components of the force.

5. Material Curves, or Wires.

We take up first the case in which the attracting body is a material curve. Consider a wire, of circular cross-section, the centers of the circles lying on a smooth curve C. If we think of the mass between any pair of planes perpendicular to C as concentrated on C between these planes, we have the concept of a *material curve*. By the *linear density* λ of the material curve, or where misunderstanding is precluded, by the density, at a point Q, we mean the limit of the ratio of the mass of a segment containing Q to the length of the segment, as this length approaches 0.

Our problem is now to formulate the integrals giving the force exerted by a material curve C on a particle at P. Let the density of C be given as a function λ of the length of arc s of C measured from one end. We assume that λ is continuous. Let C be divided in the usual way into pieces by the points $s_0 = 0,\,s_1,\,s_2,\,\ldots,\,s_n = l$, and let us consider the attraction of a typical piece Δs_k. The mass of this piece will lie between the products of the least and greatest value of λ on the piece by the length of the piece, and therefore it will be equal to $\lambda_k'\,\Delta s_k$, where λ_k' is a properly chosen mean value of λ. A particle with this mass, situated at a point Q_k of the piece, will exert on a unit particle at $P(x, y, z)$ a force whose magnitude is

$$\Delta F = \frac{\lambda_k' \Delta s_k}{r_k^2}, \qquad r_k = \overline{P Q_k}.$$

If ξ_k, η_k, ζ_k are the coördinates of Q_k, the direction cosines of this force are

$$\cos \alpha = \frac{\xi_k - x}{r_k}, \qquad \cos \beta = \frac{\eta_k - y}{r_k}, \qquad \cos \gamma = \frac{\zeta_k - z}{r_k},$$

so that the components of the force due to the typical piece are

$$\Delta X_k = \frac{\lambda_k' (\xi_k - x) \Delta s_k}{r_k^3}, \qquad \Delta Y_k = \frac{\lambda_k' (\eta_k - y) \Delta s_k}{r_k^3}, \qquad \Delta Z_k = \frac{\lambda_k' (\zeta_k - z) \Delta s_k}{r_k^3}$$

The components in each of the three directions of the axes corresponding to all the pieces of the wire are now to be added, and the limits taken as the lengths of the pieces approach 0. The results will be the the components of the force on the unit particle at P due to the curve:

(1)
$$X = \int_C \frac{\lambda (\xi - x)}{r^3} \, ds,$$

$$Y = \int_C \frac{\lambda (\eta - y)}{r^3} \, ds,$$

$$Z = \int_C \frac{\lambda (\zeta - z)}{r^3} \, ds.$$

We shall sometimes speak of a material curve as a *wire*. We shall also speak of the attraction on a unit particle at P simply as the *attraction at P*. An illustration of the attraction of a wire was given in the last section. Further examples are found in the following exercises, which should be worked and accompanied by figures.

Exercises.

1. Find the attraction of a wire of constant density having the form of an arc of a circle, at the center of the circle. Show that the equivalent particle is distant $\sqrt{\dfrac{\alpha}{\sin \alpha}}$ from the center, where a is the radius of the arc and 2α is the angle it subtends at the center. The equivalent particle is thus not in the body. But there is a point on the wire such that if the total mass were concentrated there, the *component* of its attraction along the line of symmetry of the arc would be the actual attraction. Find this point.

2. Find the attraction of a straight homogeneous piece of wire, at any point P of space, not on the wire. Show that the equivalent particle lies on the bisector of the angle APB, A and B being the ends of the wire, and that its distance c from P is the geometric mean of the two quantities: the length of the bisector between P and the wire, and the arithmetic mean of the distances $\overline{PA}$ and $\overline{PB}$.

3. Show, by comparing the attraction of corresponding elements, that a straight homogeneous wire exercises the same force at P as a tangent circular wire with center at P, terminated by the same rays from P, and having the same linear density as the straight wire.

4. Find the attraction of a homogeneous circular wire at a point P on the axis of the wire. Show that the distance c of the equivalent particle is given by $c = d \sqrt{\dfrac{d}{d'}}$, where d is the distance of P from the wire, and d' its distance from the plane of the wire.

5. In Exercise 2, show that if the wire be indefinitely lengthened in both directions, the force approaches a limit in direction and magnitude (by definition, the force due to the infinite wire), that this limiting force is perpendicular to the wire, toward it, and of magnitude $\dfrac{2\lambda}{r}$, where λ is the linear density of the wire, and r the distance of P from it.

6. Material Surfaces, or Laminas.

Consider a thin metallic plate, or shell, whose faces may be thought of as the loci formed by measuring off equal constant distances to either side of a smooth surface S on the normals to S. We arrive at the notion of a *material surface* or *lamina* by imagining the mass of the shell concentrated on S in the following way: given any simple closed curve on S, we draw the normals to S through this curve; the mass included within the surface generated by these normals we regard as belonging to the portion of S within the curve, and this for every such curve. The *surface density*, or if misunderstanding is precluded, the density, of the lamina at Q is defined as the limit of the ratio of the mass of a piece of S containing Q to the area of the piece, as the maximum chord of the piece approaches 0. In addition to the terms material surface and lamina, the expressions *surface distribution*, and *surface spread*, are used.

As we have noted in studying the attraction of a material spherical surface, the notion of surface distribution is particularly useful in electrostatics, for a charge in equilibrium on a conductor distributes itself over the surface.

Now, according to Coulomb's law, two point charges of electricity in the same homogeneous medium, exert forces on each other which are given by Newton's law with the word mass replaced by charge, except that if the charges have like signs, they repel each other, and if opposite signs, they attract each other. A constant of proportionality will be determined by the units used and by the medium in which the charges are situated. Because of the mathematical identity, except for sign, between the laws governing gravitational and electric forces, any problem in attraction may be interpreted either in terms of gravitation or in terms of electrostatics. Thus, in the case of an electrostatic charge on a conductor, the force at any point will be that due to a surface distribution.

As an illustration of the determination of the attraction due to a material surface, let us take a homogeneous circular disk, and a particle at a point P of its axis. Let the (y, x)-plane coincide with that of the disk, the origin being at the center. Then Y and Z vanish, by symmetry. Instead of the coördinates η and ζ, let us use polar coördinates, ϱ and φ. If σ denotes the constant density, the element $\varDelta S_k$ of the disk, containing the point Q_k (ϱ_k, φ_k) will have a mass $\sigma \varDelta S_k$; if this mass be regarded as concentrated at Q_k, it will exert on a unit particle at P $(x, 0, 0)$ a force whose magnitude is

$$\varDelta F_k = \frac{\sigma \varDelta S_k}{r_k^2} \quad \left(r_k = \overline{PQ}_k = \sqrt{\varrho_k^2 + x^2} \right),$$

and which makes with the x-axis an angle whose cosine is

$$\frac{- x}{r_k}$$

Hence

$$X = \lim \sum_k \varDelta X_k = \lim \sum_k \frac{- \sigma x \varDelta S_k}{r_k^3} = - \sigma x \iint_S \frac{dS}{r^3}$$

$$= - \sigma x \int_0^{2\pi} \int_0^a \frac{\varrho \, d\varrho \, d\varphi}{[\varrho^2 + x^2]^{\frac{3}{2}}}.$$

The integral is easily evaluated, and yields

$$X = - 2 \pi \sigma x \left[\frac{1}{|x|} - \frac{1}{\sqrt{a^2 + x^2}} \right].$$

The absolute value sign is important, for $\sqrt{x^2}$ is not necessarily x.

As x becomes infinite, the ratio of the force to $\frac{- M}{x^2}$ approaches 1, as the reader may verify. At any two points on the axis and equidistant from the disk, the forces are equal and opposite. As P approaches the disk, the force does not become infinite, as it does in the cases of particle and wire. We can account for this, at least qualitatively, by noticing that a given amount of mass is no longer concentrated at a point, or on a segment of a curve, but over an area. The force does, however, have a sudden reversal of direction on passing through the disk; the component of the force in the direction of the x-axis has a sudden decrease of $4 \pi \sigma$ as P passes through the disk in the direction of increasing x.

Exercises.

1. Write as a simple integral the expression for the force, at a point of its axis, due to a disk whose density is any continuous function $\sigma = f(\varrho)$ of the dis-

tance from the center. Examine the behavior of the force, as is done in the illustration in the text, if $f(\varrho) = a + b\varrho^2$.

2. The *solid angle* subtended at P by a piece of surface, which is always cut at an angle greater than 0 by a variable ray from P, may be defined as the area of that part of the surface of the sphere with unit radius and center at P which is pierced by the rays from P to the given surface. Show that the component of the attraction at P, of a plane homogeneous lamina, in the direction of the normal to the lamina, is equal to the density times the solid angle which the lamina subtends at P. Verify the result of the example of the text by this theorem.

3. Find the attraction of a homogeneous plane rectangular lamina at a point on the normal to the plane of the lamina through one corner. The answer can be obtained by specialization of the results of the next exercise.

4. Find the attraction of a homogeneous plane rectangular lamina at any point not on the rectangle, by decomposing the rectangle into sums or differences of the rectangles obtained by drawing parallels to the sides of the given rectangle through the foot of the normal from P. The answer may be given as follows. Take y- and z-axes parallel to the sides of the rectangle, with origin at the foot of the perpendicular from P. Let the corners of the rectangle referred to these axes be (b, c), (b', c), (b', c') and (b, c'), in order, and let the distances from P $(x, 0, 0)$ of these four points be d_1, d_2, d_3, and d_4, respectively. Then

$$X = -\sigma \left[\tan^{-1} \frac{bc}{x\,d_1} - \tan^{-1} \frac{b'c}{x\,d_2} + \tan^{-1} \frac{b'c'}{x\,d_3} - \tan^{-1} \frac{bc'}{x\,d_4} \right],$$

$$Y = \sigma \log \left[\frac{d_2 + c}{d_1 + c} \cdot \frac{d_4 + c'}{d_3 + c'} \right], \quad Z = \sigma \log \left[\frac{d_4 + b}{d_1 + b} \cdot \frac{d_2 + b'}{d_3 + b'} \right].$$

It should be kept in mind that the numbers b, c, b', c' may have either sign, or vanish.

5. Show that if the dimensions of the lamina of the last exercise become infinite, the force will not, in general, approach a limit. Show, on the other hand, that if the ratios of the distances of the sides of the rectangle from the origin approach 1 as these distances become infinite, the force does approach a limit, and investigate the character of this limiting force.

6. If, in working Exercise 1, polar coördinates are used and the integration with respect to the angle is carried out first, the integrand of the remaining integral may be interpreted as the force due to a circular wire (see Exercise 4, p. 10). What is the significance of this fact? Does it illustrate any principle which can be of use in other problems?

7. Curved Laminas.

So far, the surface distributions considered have been on flat surfaces. There is no difficulty in setting up the integrals for the force on a unit particle due to distributions on any smooth surfaces. We shall keep to the notation $P\ (x, y, z)$ for the position of the attracted particle, and to $Q\ (\xi, \eta, \zeta)$ for the point of the distribution whose coördinates are the variables of integration. The distance between these two points will be denoted by r. If σ is the density, we have

$$X = \iint\limits_{S} \frac{\sigma\,(\xi - x)}{r^3}\,dS,$$

(2)
$$Y = \iint\limits_{S} \frac{\sigma\,(\eta - y)}{r^3}\,dS,$$

$$Z = \iint\limits_{S} \frac{\sigma\,(\zeta - z)}{r^3}\,dS,$$

for the components of the attraction. The derivation of these formulas follows lines already marked out, and is commended as an exercise to the reader.

A particular type of surface distribution may receive special mention. It is that in which the surface is one of revolution, and the density is independent of the angle which fixes the meridian planes. Let us suppose that the surface is given by the meridian curve in the (x, y)-plane, in parametric form, $\xi = \xi\,(s)$, $\eta = \eta\,(s)$, s being the length of arc (fig. 4). Then the position of a point Q on the surface S is determined by a value of s and by the angle φ which the meridian plane through Q makes with a fixed meridian plane. We need to know the area of an element ΔS of S, bounded by two meridian planes corresponding to an increment $\Delta\varphi$ of φ, and by two parallel circles corresponding to an increment Δs of s. A complete strip of S, bounded by parallel circles, has an area given by the formula from the calculus

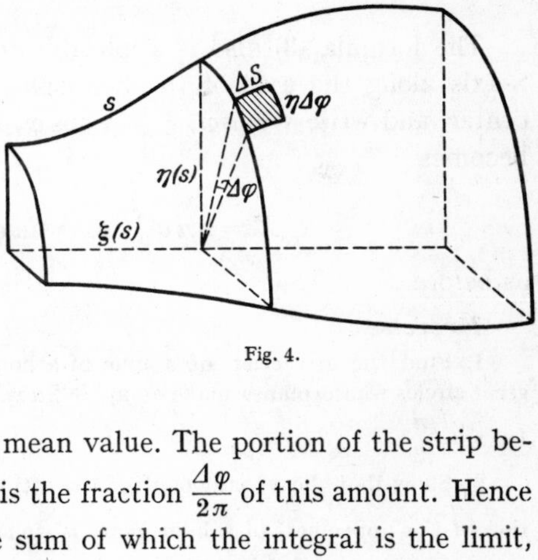

Fig. 4.

$$A = 2\pi \int\limits_{s}^{s+\Delta s} \eta\,ds = 2\pi\eta'\,\Delta s$$

where η' is a properly chosen mean value. The portion of the strip between the two meridian planes is the fraction $\dfrac{\Delta\varphi}{2\pi}$ of this amount. Hence $\Delta S = \eta'\,\Delta\varphi\,\Delta s$. Recalling the sum of which the integral is the limit, we see, then, that the first of the formulas (2) becomes

$$X = \int\limits_{s_1}^{s_2} \int\limits_{0}^{2\pi} \frac{\sigma\,(\xi - x)\,\eta}{r^3}\,d\varphi\,ds.$$

If the attracted particle is on the axis, at $P\,(x, 0, 0)$, we need only this component of the force, for the perpendicular components vanish. Moreover, in this case, the integrand is independent of φ, so that the formula becomes

(3)
$$X = 2\pi \int_{s_1}^{s_2} \frac{\sigma\,(\xi - x)\,\eta}{[(\xi - x)^2 + \eta^2]^{\frac{3}{2}}} ds.$$

As an illustration of the attraction of spreads on curved surfaces, let us consider that due to a homogeneous hemispherical lamina at its center. In order to give an example of different methods, we shall employ first the general formulas (2). If we take the z-axis along the axis of the hemisphere, $X = Y = 0$. Let us change the field of integration from the surface S itself, to its projection S' on the (x, y)-plane. Then for two corresponding elements of these fields, we have $\Delta S = \sec \gamma' \Delta S'$, where γ' is a suitable mean value of the angle between the normal to S and the z-axis. If a is the radius of the sphere, the third formula (2) becomes

$$Z = \sigma \iint_{S'} \frac{\zeta}{a^3} \sec \gamma\, dS'.$$

Since $\cos \gamma = \dfrac{\zeta}{a}$, this reduces to

$$Z = \frac{\sigma}{a^2} \iint_{S'} dS' = \frac{\sigma}{a^2} \cdot \pi a^2 = \pi\sigma.$$

The formula (3) also is applicable to this problem, if we take the x-axis along the axis of the hemisphere. We take the origin at the center, and write $s = a\varphi$, $\xi = a \cos \varphi$, $\eta = a \sin \varphi$. Then the formula becomes

$$X = 2\pi\sigma \int_0^{\frac{\pi}{2}} \cos \varphi \sin \varphi\, d\varphi = \pi\sigma.$$

as before.

Exercises.

1. Find the attraction of a lune of a homogeneous sphere, bounded by two great circles whose planes make an angle 2α with each other, at the center. Check for $\alpha = \dfrac{\pi}{2}$.

2. Show that the z-component of the attraction at the center due to any portion of the upper half of a homogeneous spherical surface, is $Z = \dfrac{\sigma A}{a^2}$, where a is the radius of the sphere, σ the density, and A the area of the projection of the portion in question on the (x, y)-plane. Check the result of the example of the text by this result.

3. Determine the attraction at the center due to the portion of the upper half of the homogeneous spherical surface $x^2 + y^2 + z^2 = a^2$ which is cut out by the cone

$$z^2 = \frac{x^2}{\alpha^2} + \frac{y^2}{\beta^2}.$$

Answer, $X = Y = 0$, $Z = \dfrac{\pi\sigma\alpha^2\beta^2}{(1 + \alpha^2)\,(1 + \beta^2)}$.

4. Find the attraction due to a homogeneous right circular cylindrical surface, at a point P of its axis. Check the result a) by taking P at the center, b) by taking P at a great distance, and c) by allowing the radius of the cylinder to approach 0, P being on the axis extended. Compare with the attraction of a straight wire, studied in § 4 (page 4).

5. Study the attraction due to a homogeneous spherical shell by means of the formula (3). Determine the break in the radial component of the force at the surface.

6. Obtain the formula (3) on the assumption that the attraction is correctly given by regarding the surface as the limiting form of a large number of circular wires.

7. Find the attraction of a homogeneous spherical cap, at a point of its axis. Check your result by allowing the cap to spread over the whole sphere. Draw a curve representing in magnitude and sign the component of the force in the direction of the axis as a function of the position of P when the cap comprises nearly the whole sphere. Compare it with the curve for the complete sphere.

8. Change the variable of integration in (3) to the abscissa ξ. Find the attraction at the focus of that portion of the homogeneous surface which is the paraboloid of revolution whose meridian curve is $\eta^2 = 2\,m\,\xi$, cut off by the plane $\xi = h$, the density being constant. Check by allowing h to approach zero, the total mass remaining constant. Find the value of h for which the force vanishes. Answers,

$$X = \frac{8}{3}\pi\sigma\left[1 - \frac{(m+6h)\sqrt{m}}{(m+2h)^{\frac{3}{2}}}\right], \qquad h = \frac{m}{2}\left(3 + 2\sqrt{3}\right).$$

9. Find the attraction, at the cusp, of that portion of the homogeneous lamina whose meridian curve is $\varrho = a\,(1 - \cos\varphi)$, $0 < \alpha \leqq \varphi \leqq \beta$. Show that this force remains finite as α approaches 0, and find, in particular, the force due to the whole closed surface.

8. Ordinary Bodies, or Volume Distributions.

Suppose we have a body occupying a portion V of space. By the *density* $\varkappa$ (or the volume density), of the body, at Q, we mean the limit of the ratio of the mass of a portion of the body containing Q to the volume of that portion, as its maximum chord approaches 0. It is customary to regard this limit as not existing unless the ratio approaches a limit independent of the shape of the portion for which it is calculated, and it is similar also with surface and linear densities. We shall assume, as usual, that the density exists and is continuous. The only physically important cases in which the densities are discontinuous may be treated by regarding the body as composed of several partial bodies in each of which the density is continuous.

The setting up of the integrals for the force due to volume distributions is so like the corresponding process for the distributions already treated that we may confine ourselves to setting down the results:

$$(4)\quad X = \iiint\limits_V \frac{\varkappa\,(\xi - x)}{r^3}\,dV, \quad Y = \iiint\limits_V \frac{\varkappa\,(\eta - y)}{r^3}\,dV, \quad Z = \iiint\limits_V \frac{\varkappa\,(\zeta - z)}{r^3}\,dV.$$

An illustration of the determination of the attraction of a volume distribution has been given in § 4 (p. 7). As a second example, let us consider the attraction of a homogeneous right circular cylinder, at a point of its axis, extended. Let us take the z-axis along that of the cylinder, with the origin at the point P the attraction at which is to be found. Cylindrical coördinates are most appropriate, that is, the coördinate ζ of Q, and the polar coördinates ϱ and φ of the projection of Q on the (x, y)-plane. The element of volume is then given by $\Delta V = \varrho' \Delta \varrho \Delta \varphi \Delta \zeta$, where ϱ' is a suitable mean value. Then, if a is the radius of the cylinder, and $\zeta = b$ and $\zeta = c$ the equations of the bounding planes $(0 < b < c)$, the third equation (4) becomes

$$Z = \varkappa \int\limits_{b}^{c} \int\limits_{0}^{2\pi} \int\limits_{0}^{a} \frac{\zeta \varrho}{[\zeta^2 + \varrho^2]^{\frac{3}{2}}} \, d\varrho \, d\varphi \, d\zeta \,.$$

The integral is easily evaluated. The result can be given the form

$$Z = \frac{2M}{a^2 h} [h + d_1 - d_2],$$

where M is the total mass, h the altitude and d_1 and d_2 the distances from P of the nearest and farthest points of the curved surface of the cylinder, respectively. It can be checked as was Exercise 4 of the last section. It will be observed that the force remains finite as P approaches the cylinder.

Exercises.

1. Find the attraction due to a homogeneous hollow sphere, bounded by concentric spheres, at points outside the outer and within the inner sphere.

2. Show that if the above hollow sphere, instead of being homogeneous, has a density which is any continuous function of the distance from the center, the attraction at any exterior point will be the same as that due to a particle of the same mass at the center, and that the attraction at any interior point will vanish.

3. Derive the following formula for the attraction of a body of revolution whose density is independent of the meridian angle φ, at a point of its axis:

$$X = 2\pi \int\limits_{\xi_1}^{\xi_2} \int\limits_{0}^{f(\xi)} \frac{\varkappa (\xi - x) \varrho}{[(\xi - x)^2 + \varrho^2]^{\frac{3}{2}}} \, d\varrho \, d\xi \,,$$

where ϱ is the distance of the point Q from the axis, ξ its distance from the (y, z)-plane, and $\varrho = f(\xi)$ the equation of a meridian curve of the bounding surface.

4. Show that if $\varkappa$ depends only on ξ, the formula of the last exercise becomes

$$X = 2\pi \int\limits_{\xi_1}^{\xi_2} \varkappa \left[\frac{\xi - x}{|\xi - x|} - \frac{\xi - x}{\sqrt{(\xi - x)^2 + f^2(\xi)}} \right] d\xi \,.$$

5. A certain text book contains the following problem. "Show that the attraction at the focus of a segment of a paraboloid of revolution bounded by a plane perpendicular to the axis at a distance b from the vertex is of the form

$$4 \pi a \varkappa \log \frac{a+b}{a} \text{ ''}.$$

Show that this result must be wrong because it does not give a proper limiting form as b approaches 0, the total mass remaining constant. Determine the correct answer. The latus rectum of the meridian curve is supposed to be $4a$.

6. Show that there exists in any body whose density is nowhere negative, corresponding to a given direction and a given exterior point P, a point Q, such that the component in the given direction of the force at P is unchanged if the body is concentrated at Q. Why does not this show that there is always an equivalent particle located *in* the body?

9. The Force at Points of the Attracting Masses.

So far, we have been considering the force at points outside the attracting body. But the parts of a body must attract each other. At first sight, it would seem that since the force varies inversely with the square of the distance, it must become infinite as the attracted particle approaches or enters the region occupied by masses, and so it is, with particles or material curves. We have seen, however, that surface and volume distributions are possible, for which this does not occur. This is less surprising if we think of the situation as follows. If P lies on the boundary of, or within, the attracting body, the matter whose distance from P lies between r and $2r$, say, has a mass not greater than some constant times r^3, and since its distance from P is not less than r, the magnitude of its attraction at P cannot exceed a constant times r. Thus the nearer masses exercise not more, but less attraction than the remoter.

Let us turn to the question of the calculation of the force at an interior or boundary point. The integrals (4) are then meaningless, in the ordinary sense, since the integrands become infinite. If, however, the integrals are extended, not over the whole of V, but over what is left after the removal of a small volume v containing P in its interior, they yield definite values. If these values approach limits as the maximum chord of v approaches 0 *these limits are regarded as the components of the force at P due to the whole body*. This amounts to a new assumption, or to an extension of Newton's law. It is found to be entirely satisfactory from the standpoint of physics. We may state it more briefly as follows: the formulas (4) still give the force at P, even though P is interior to, or on the boundary of V, provided the integrals, which are now improper integrals, converge.

We shall now show that in all cases in which the volume density is continuous—or even if it is merely integrable and bounded—the integrals always converge. Let us consider the z-component. The others admit of the same treatment. We may also confine ourselves to the case in which P is interior to the body, for we may regard the body as part of a larger one in which the density is 0 outside the given body. Let v be a small region, containing P in its interior. We have to show that

$$Z' = \iiint\limits_{V-v} \frac{\varkappa\,(\zeta - z)}{r^3}\,dV$$

approaches a limit as v shrinks down on P, v having any shape[1].

But how can we show that Z' approaches a limit unless we know what the limit is? If a variable approaches a limit, its various values draw indefinitely near each other. It is the converse of this fact that we need, and which may be stated as follows[2]: a necessary and sufficient condition that Z' approach a limit is that to any positive test number ε there corresponds a number $\delta > 0$ such that if v and v' are any two regions containing P and contained in the sphere of radius δ about P,

$$\left| \iiint\limits_{V-v} \frac{\varkappa\,(\zeta - z)}{r^3}\,dV - \iiint\limits_{V-v'} \frac{\varkappa\,(\zeta - z)}{r^3}\,dV \right| < \varepsilon .$$

Let us examine this inequality. If we take away from both regions of integration that part of V which lies outside the sphere σ of radius δ about P, the difference of the two integrals is unaltered. Our aim will then be attained if we can show that each of the resulting integrals can be made less in absolute value than $\frac{\varepsilon}{2}$ by proper choice of δ. The following treatment will hold for either.

$$I = \left| \iiint\limits_{\sigma-v} \frac{\varkappa\,(\zeta - z)}{r^3}\,dV \right| \leqq B \iiint\limits_{\sigma-v} \frac{|\zeta - z|}{r^3}\,dV ,$$

where B is an upper bound for $|\varkappa|$. We can easily obtain a bound for the last integral by replacing it by an iterated integral in spherical coördinates, with P as pole, and z-axis as axis. It then ceases to be improper, even when extended over the whole of σ, and as the integrand is nowhere

---

[1] The limit is not regarded as existing if it is necessary to restrict the shape of v in order to obtain a limit. The only restrictions on v are that it shall have a boundary of a certain degree of smoothness (be a regular region in the sense of Chapter IV, § 8, p. 100), that it shall contain P in its interior, and that its maximum chord shall approach 0.

[2] This test for the existence of a limit was used by CAUCHY, and is sometimes referred to as the Cauchy test. A proof of its sufficiency for the case of a function of a single variable is to be found in OSGOOD: *Funktionentheorie*, 4th ed., Leipzig, 1923, Chap. I, § 7, pp. 33—35; 5th ed. (1928), pp. 30—32. See also FINE, *College Algebra*, Boston, 1901, pp. 60—63. A modification of the proof to suit the present case involves only formal changes.

negative, this extension of the field cannot decrease its value. Hence

$$I < B \int\limits_{0}^{\pi} \int\limits_{0}^{2\pi} \int\limits_{0}^{\delta} \frac{\varrho \cos \vartheta \mid}{\varrho^3} \varrho^2 \, d\varrho \, d\varphi \sin \vartheta \, d\vartheta < B \int\limits_{0}^{\pi} \int\limits_{0}^{2\pi} \int\limits_{0}^{\delta} d\varrho \, d\varphi \, d\vartheta = 2 B \pi^2 \delta.$$

Hence I can be made less than $\frac{\varepsilon}{2}$ by taking $\delta < \frac{\varepsilon}{4 B \pi^2}$. The condition that Z' approach a limit is thus fulfilled, and the integrals (4) are convergent, as was to be proved.

When we come to the computation of the attraction at interior points of special bodies, we see the advantage of being unrestricted as to the shapes of the volumes v removed. For we may use any convenient system of coördinates, and remove volumes conveniently described in terms of these coördinates.

As an illustration, let us find the attraction of a homogeneous sphere S at the interior point P. We cut out P by means of two spheres S' and S'', concentric with S. The hollow sphere bounded by S'' and S then exercises no force at P, while the sphere bounded by S' attracts at. P as if concentrated at the center. As the region cut out, between the two spheres S' and S'', shrinks down, the attraction at P approaches as limit the attraction of a particle at the center whose mass is that of the concentric sphere through P. In symbols,

$$Z = - \frac{4}{3} \pi \varkappa z.$$

The attraction of a homogeneous sphere at an interior point is thus toward the center, and varies as the distance from the center.

It will be observed that the region v cut out in these considerations, did not shrink to 0 in its maximum chord. However, its volume did shrink to 0, and if an integral is convergent, the limit thus obtained is the same as if the maximum chord shrinks to 0. Indications as to the proof of this statement will be given in connection with Exercise 18, below.

Exercises.

1. Find the attraction, at an interior point on the axis, due to a homogeneous right circular cylinder. Answer,

$$F = 2 \pi \varkappa (h_2 - h_1 + d_2 - d_1),$$

where h_1, h_2 are distances of P from the centers, and d_1, d_2, from the circumferences of the bases.

2. Show that in Exercise 5, § 8, the quoted result must be wrong because it is incompatible with the fact that for $b < a$ the force must be to the left, while for $b > 2a$ it must be to the right, and so vanish at some intermediate point. This involves the justifiable assumption that the force varies continuously with b.

3. Show that the formula of Exercise 4 (page 16) holds when P is an interior point on the axis of the body. Are there any precautions to be observed in applying it?

4. Lack of homogeneity in the earth's crust produces variations in gravity. This fact has been used with some success in prospecting for hidden ore and oil deposits. An instrument used is the Eötvös[1] gravity variometer or torsion balance. A body of matter heavier than the surrounding material will change the field of force by the attraction of a body of the same size, shape, and position whose density is the difference between that of the actual body and the surrounding material. Investigate the order of magnitude of the change in the force produced by a sphere of density $1/2$, of radius 200 feet, imbedded in material of density $1/3$ and tangent to the earth's surface, the average density of the earth being taken as unity.

Answer, at the highest point of the sphere, gravity is increased by about 1.6×10^{-4} percent, and it falls off per foot of horizontal distance by about 4×10^{-9} percent.

5. Show that within a spherical cavity in a homogeneous sphere, not concentric with it, the force is constant in magnitude and direction. This should be done without further integrations, simply making use of the result of the example of the text.

6. Determine the attraction at interior points due to a sphere whose density is a function of the distance from the center.

7. Find the attraction of the homogeneous paraboloid of revolution whose meridian curve is $\eta^2 = 4\,a\,\xi$, cut off by the plane $\xi = h$, at any point of the axis. Answers,

$$X = 2\,\pi\varkappa\left[h - x - d + 2\,a\log\frac{h - x + 2\,a + d}{2\,a\,(x - a)}\right], \qquad \text{if } x \leqq 0,$$

$$X = 2\,\pi\varkappa\left[\,|\,x - h\,| - d + 2\,a\log\frac{h - x + 2\,a + d}{2\,a}\right], \qquad \text{if } x \geqq 0,$$

where d is the distance of the attracted point $P\,(x, 0, 0)$ from the edge of the solid.

8. Verify that the force changes continuously as the attracted particle moves into and through the masses in Exercises 1, 5 and 6.

9. Verify that the derivative of the axial component of the force in the direction of the axis experiences a break of $4\,\pi\varkappa$ as P enters or leaves the masses, in Exercises 1, 5 and 6.

10. Determine the attraction of a homogeneous spheroid, at a pole. Answers, for an oblate spheroid of equatorial radius b, the magnitude of the force is

$$F = \frac{3\,M}{b^2\,e^3}\,(e - \sqrt{1 - e^2}\,\sin^{-1} e)\,,$$

and for a prolate spheroid of polar radius a,

$$F = \frac{3\,M}{a^2\,e^3}\left[\log\sqrt{\frac{1 + e}{1 - e}} - e\right],$$

e being the eccentricity of the meridian curve.

11. A body is bounded by a) a conical surface which cuts from the surface of the unit sphere about the vertex P of the conical surface, a region Ω, and by b) a surface whose equation in spherical coördinates with P as pole is $\varrho = f\,(\varphi, \vartheta)$.

---

[1] For an account of this sensitive instrument, see F. R. Helmert, in the Encyklopädie der mathematischen Wissenschaften, Vol. VI, I, 7, p. 166; L. Oertling, Ltd., The Eötvös Torsion Balance, London 1925; or Stephen Rybar, in Economic Geology, Vol. 18 (1923), pp. 639—662.

Show that the component of the attraction at P in the direction of the polar axis is

$$Z = \iint\limits_{\Omega} \left[\int_0^{f(\varphi,\vartheta)} \varkappa \, d\varrho \right] \cos \vartheta \, d\Omega,$$

or, if the density is constant,

$$Z = \varkappa \iint\limits_{\Omega} f(\varphi, \vartheta) \cos \vartheta \, d\Omega.$$

12. Show that the attractions, at the center of similitude, of two similar and similarly placed bodies, have the same line of action, and are in magnitude as the linear dimensions of the bodies.

13. Find the attraction at the vertex due to a right circular cone of constant density. Answer, $2\pi\varkappa h \, (1 - \cos\alpha)$.

14. The same for a spherical sector, bounded by a right circular conical surface and a sphere with center at the vertex of the cone. Answer, $\pi a \varkappa \sin^2\alpha$.

15. By subtracting the results of the last two exercises, find the attraction at the center due to a spherical cap.

16. Find the attraction due to a homogeneous hemisphere at a point of the edge. Answer,

$$\frac{2}{3}\pi a\varkappa, \qquad \frac{4}{3} a\varkappa, \qquad 0.$$

17. A mountain has approximately the form of a hemisphere of radius a, and its density is $\varkappa'$. If higher powers of $\dfrac{a}{R}$ are neglected, show that the difference in latitude at the northern and southern edges of the mountain, as observed by the direction of gravity, is

$$\frac{a}{R} \left(2 + \frac{\varkappa'}{\varkappa} \right),$$

where R and $\varkappa$ are the radius and mean density of the earth.

18. (a) Show that if $f(Q)$ is an integrable function of the coördinates ξ, η, ζ of Q, and bounded in any portion of V which does not contain P, and if

$$\iiint\limits_V f(Q) \, dV$$

is convergent, then

$$\iiint\limits_v f(Q) \, dV$$

approaches 0 with the maximum chord of v, where v is any portion of V with P in its interior.

(b) On the same hypothesis, show that

$$\iiint\limits_V f(Q) \, dV = \lim \iiint\limits_{V-u} f(Q) \, dV$$

as the *volume* of u approaches 0, whether the maximum chord of u does, or does not, approach 0. Suggestion. It is required to show that

$$\iiint\limits_u f(Q) \, dV \to 0$$

with the volume of u. Consider the portions u_1 and u_2 of u, inside and outside a sphere of radius δ. Show first how the integral over u_1 can be made less than $\dfrac{\varepsilon}{2}$ in absolute value by properly choosing δ, and then how, with δ fixed, the integral over u_2 can be made less than $\dfrac{\varepsilon}{2}$ in absolute value.

Ellipsoidal Homoeoid. We have seen that a homogeneous body bounded by concentric spheres exercises no attraction in the cavity. NEWTON showed that the same is true for an ellipsoidal homoeoid, or body bounded by two similar ellipsoids having their axes in the same lines. To prove it, we first establish a lemma: let P be any point within the cavity; draw any line through P, and let A, A', B', B be its intersections with the ellipsoids, in order; then $A A' = B' B$ (fig. 5). The problem is reduced to the similar problem for two similar coaxial ellipses if we pass the plane through the center O of the ellipsoids and the line AB. In this plane, we take axes through O, with x-axis parallel to AB. The equations of the ellipses may then be written

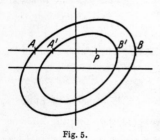

$$Ax^2 + 2Hxy + By^2 - a = 0,$$
$$Ax^2 + 2Hxy + By^2 - b = 0,$$

and the equation of AB will be $y = c$. The abscissas of A and B are then the roots of the equation obtained by eliminating y between $y = c$ and the equation of the first ellipse:

$$Ax^2 + 2Hcx + (Bc^2 - a) = 0,$$

Fig. 5.

so that the midpoint of the chord $A B$ has the abscissa $\dfrac{-Hc}{A}$. But this value is independent of a, and therefore the midpoints of the chords AB and $A'B'$ coincide. Hence $A A' = B'B$, as we wished to prove.

Now by Exercise 11, the z-component of the attraction at P may be written

$$Z = \varkappa \iint_{\Omega} [F(\varphi, \vartheta) - f(\varphi, \vartheta)] \cos \vartheta \, d\Omega,$$

where $\varrho = F(\varphi, \vartheta)$ and $\varrho = f(\varphi, \vartheta)$ are the equations of the ellipsoids in spherical coördinates with P as pole, and where Ω denotes the entire surface of the unit sphere about P. By the lemma, $F(\varphi, \vartheta) - f(\varphi, \vartheta)$ remains unchanged when the direction of a ray is reversed, *i. e.*, when φ is replaced by $\varphi + \pi$ and ϑ by $\pi - \vartheta$. On the other hand, $\cos \vartheta$ is replaced by its negative by this substitution. Thus the integral consists of pairs of equal and opposite elements, and so vanishes. As the z-axis may have any direction, it follows that the force in the cavity vanishes, as was to be proved.

10. Legitimacy of the Amplified Statement of Newton's Law; Attraction between Bodies.

We revert now to the amplified statement of Newton's law given in § 3 (page 3), and to a study of the attraction between bodies neither of which is a particle. The justification of the amplified statement must rest on the consistency of its consequences with observation and experiment. At the same time, it is hardly fair to call our physical assumption an amplified statement of Newton's law, unless it is consistent with this law. Our test of consistency will be this. As the dimensions of two bodies approach 0 in comparison with their distance apart, does their attraction, determined on the basis of the amplified statement, approach that given by Newton's law for particles? We shall see that this is indeed the case. Incidentally, we shall gain a deeper insight into the nature of the force between two bodies, and our inquiry will clothe the notion of particle with a broader significance.

The first point to be noticed is that a body does not, in general, exert a single force on another, but exerts forces on the parts of that body. In the case of a deformable body, these forces cannot, as a rule, be combined to form a system of even a finite number of forces. We shall therefore confine ourselves to rigid bodies, for present purposes. It is shown in works on statics[1] that the forces on a rigid body are equivalent to a single force at an arbitrarily selected point O of the body *and* a couple. The single force is the resultant of all the forces acting on the body, thought of as concurrent. The couple depends on the position of O, and its moment is the vector sum of the moments with respect to O of the forces acting on the body. If the forces acting are (X_i, Y_i, Z_i), applied at (x_i, y_i, z_i), $i = 1, 2, \ldots n$, we have for the single resultant force,

$$(5) \qquad X = \sum_i X_i, \quad Y = \sum_i Y_i, \quad Z = \sum_i Z_i,$$

and if the point O at which this force is assumed to act is the origin of coördinates, we have for the moment of the couple

$$(6) \qquad \begin{aligned} L &= \sum_i (y_i Z_i - z_i Y_i), \quad M = \sum_i (z_i X_i - x_i Z_i), \\ N &= \sum_i (x_i Y_i - y_i X_i). \end{aligned}$$

If the forces, instead of being finite in number, are continuously distributed, the summation signs are to be replaced by integrals. For the sake of simplicity, we continue for the present, with a finite number.

We are particularly interested in the case in which the couple is absent, so that the system reduces to a single force. Since the couple depends on the position of the point of application of the resultant force, it may be possible to choose O so that the moment of the couple vanishes. If we shift the point of application to the point (h, k, l), then in (6) x_i, y_i, z_i, must be replaced by $x_i - h, y_i - k, z_i - l$. This amounts

---

[1] See, for instance, APPELL: *Traité de mécanique rationelle*, Paris 1902, Vol. I, Chap. IV.

to adding to the couple (6) the couple

$$- (kZ - lY), \quad - (lX - hZ), \quad - (hY - kX).$$

The question is, can h, k, l be so chosen that the couple thus altered vanishes? That is, so that the following equations are satisfied?

(7)
$$
\begin{aligned}
kZ - lY &= L, \\
-hZ \quad\; + lX &= M, \\
hY - kX \quad\; &= N.
\end{aligned}
$$

It will be seen that if we eliminate two of the quantities h, k and l, the third disappears also, and we arrive at the following necessary condition

(8)
$$LX + MY + NZ = 0,$$

that is, the resultant (X, Y, Z) and the moment with respect to the origin (L, M, N) must be at right angles, or else one of them must vanish. In Newtonian fields, the force vanishes only at exceptional points, and if we assume now that the force is not 0, it will be found that two of the equations (7) can be solved for h, k, l (giving, in fact, a whole line of points), and that the solution will also satisfy the third equation if the condition (8) is fulfilled. *The equation (8) is therefore a necessary and sufficient condition that the forces acting on the body reduce to a single force, when the point of application is properly chosen.* One such point having been found, it will be seen that any other point on the line of action of the force will also serve.

With these preliminaries, we may proceed to the consideration of the attraction on a body B_1 due to a body B_2, the bodies occupying regions V_1 and V_2 of space. The first step is to divide the bodies into elements, concentrate each element at one of its points, and consider the attraction of the system of particles thus arising. Let ΔV_1 denote a typical element of V_1, containing the point P (x, y, z), and ΔV_2, a typical element of V_2 containing Q (ξ, η, ζ). Let $\varkappa_1$ and $\varkappa_2$ be suitably chosen mean values of the densities in these elements. Then the particle in ΔV_2 exerts on the particle in ΔV_1 a force whose x-component is

$$\Delta X = \varkappa_1 \varkappa_2 \, \Delta V_1 \, \Delta V_2 \, \frac{\xi - x}{r^3},$$

and whose point of application is P. The x-component of the moment with respect to the origin of this force is

$$\Delta L = \varkappa_1 \varkappa_2 \left[y \frac{\zeta - z}{r^3} - z \frac{\eta - y}{r^3} \right] \Delta V_1 \, \Delta V_2 = \varkappa_1 \varkappa_2 \, \frac{y \zeta - z \eta}{r^3} \Delta V_1 \, \Delta V_2.$$

These components, due to a pair of particles, are now to be summed over all pairs, one in each volume, and the limits are to be taken as the maximum chord of the elements of volume approaches 0. We arrive at the result:

In accordance with the amplified statement of Newton's law, the attraction exerted by the body B_2 on the body B_1, consists of a force

(9)
$$X = \iiint_{V_1} \iiint_{V_2} \frac{\varkappa_1 \varkappa_2 (\xi - x)}{r^3} \, dV_1 \, dV_2,$$

$$Y = \iiint_{V_1} \iiint_{V_2} \frac{\varkappa_1 \varkappa_2 (\eta - y)}{r^3} \, dV_1 \, dV_2,$$

$$Z = \iiint_{V_1} \iiint_{V_2} \frac{\varkappa_1 \varkappa_2 (\zeta - z)}{r^3} \, dV_1 \, dV_2,$$

applied at the origin of coördinates, and of a couple whose moment is

(10)
$$L = \iiint_{V_1} \iiint_{V_2} \frac{\varkappa_1 \varkappa_2 (y\zeta - z\eta)}{r^3} \, dV_1 \, dV_2,$$

$$M = \iiint_{V_1} \iiint_{V_2} \frac{\varkappa_1 \varkappa_2 (z\xi - x\zeta)}{r^3} \, dV_1 \, dV_2,$$

$$N = \iiint_{V_1} \iiint_{V_2} \frac{\varkappa_1 \varkappa_2 (x\eta - y\xi)}{r^3} \, dV_1 \, dV_2,$$

or, of course, any equivalent system. The above constitutes the analytical formulation of Newton's law in its amplified form. It is satisfactory from the standpoint of precision, and is, in fact, the actual, if usually the tacit, basis of all treatments of gravitation.

We are now in a position to consider the consistency of this statement with Newton's law for particles. Let the maximum chord of the bodies shrink toward 0, B_1 always containing the origin of coördinates, and B_2 always containing a fixed point $Q_0 (\xi_0, \eta_0, \zeta_0)$. Taking first the moment, and fixing our attention on the component L as typical, we may apply the law of the mean, on the hypothesis that the densities are never negative, and write

$$L = \frac{y'\zeta' - z'\eta'}{r^3} \iiint_{V_1} \iiint_{V_2} \varkappa_1 \varkappa_2 \, dV_1 \, dV_2 = \frac{y'\zeta' - z'\eta'}{r^3} \, m_1 m_2$$

where $P'(x', y', z')$ is a point in V_1 and $Q'(\xi', \eta', \zeta')$ in V_2. As the dimensions of the bodies—or even if the dimensions of B_1 alone—approach 0, x', y', z' approach 0, and L, and similarly, M and N, approach 0. Hence *the forces exerted by a body on a particle reduce to a single resultant force, applied at the particle.*

Treating the components of the force in a similar way, we find that when the bodies shrink down toward points, the origin and Q_0, the force approaches

$$X = \frac{\xi_0}{r_0^3} m_1 m_2, \quad Y = \frac{\eta_0}{r_0^3} m_1 m_2, \quad Z = \frac{\zeta_0}{r_0^3} m_1 m_2,$$

and this constitutes the statement of Newton's law for particles. Thus the consistency of the law in its broader form with the law for particles is established.

11. Presence of the Couple; Centrobaric Bodies; Specific Force.

We have seen that the gravitational effect of a body B_2 on a body B_1 is a force and a couple. In certain cases, if the force is applied at the right point, the couple disappears. This happens always when B_1 is a particle, also when it is a sphere, and the very name center of gravity implies that it happens in the case of any body B_1 when the attracting body is the earth, regarded as exerting a force constant in direction and proportional to the mass acted on. There are, indeed, many bodies such that the attraction of other bodies on them reduces in each case to a single force passing through a fixed point in the body. They are called *centrobaric bodies*[1] and have interesting properties. But centrobaric bodies are to be regarded as exceptional, for in general the attraction cannot be reduced to a single force. An illustration of this is provided in Exercise 3, below.

It would be disconcerting if, in the application of Newton's law as stated in the equations (9) and (10), we had to face sextuple integrals at every turn. Fortunately this is not the case. Moreover, it is only infrequently that we need consider the couple. The reason is that we usually confine ourselves to the study of the influence of a body B_2, abstracting from the shape and density of the body B_1 acted on. This is made possible by the notion of *specific* force, or force per unit of mass at a point.

Let us consider a small part of the body B_1 contained in a volume ΔV_1, and containing a fixed point P_0 (x_0, y_0, z_0). We compute the force on this part due to B_2. The component ΔX of this force is given by the first of the equations (9), where the region of integration V_1 is replaced by ΔV_1. We are assuming continuous densities and simple regions of integration, so that the multiple integral can be replaced by an iterated integral. Accordingly,

$$\Delta X = \iiint\limits_{\Delta V_1} \varkappa_1 \left[\iiint\limits_{V_2} \frac{\varkappa_2 \, (\xi - x)}{r^3} \, dV_2 \right] dV_1.$$

---

[1] See THOMSON and TAIT: *Natural Philosophy*. Vol. I, Part II, §§ 534—535.

The inner integral is a function of x, y, z only, and if $\varkappa_1$ does not change signs, this integral may be removed from under the outer signs of integration by the law of the mean:

$$\Delta X = \iiint\limits_{V_2} \frac{\varkappa_2\,(\xi - x')}{r'^3}\,dV_2 \iiint\limits_{\Delta V_1} \varkappa_1\,dV_1 = \iiint\limits_{V_2} \frac{\varkappa_2\,(\xi - x')}{r'^3}\,dV_2 \cdot \Delta m$$

where $P'\,(x',\,y',\,z')$ is some point in ΔV_1, r' its distance from the variable point $Q\,(\xi,\,\eta,\,\zeta)$ in V_2, and Δm the mass in ΔV_1. If now, we divide this force component by Δm and allow the maximum chord of ΔV_1 to approach 0 in such a way that P_0 remains within ΔV_1, we arrive at the limit

$$X_0 = \lim \frac{\Delta X}{\Delta m} = \iiint\limits_{V_2} \frac{\varkappa_2\,(\xi - x_0)}{r_0^3}\,dV_2,\quad r_0 = \overline{P_0 Q}.$$

This, with two other components, defines the *specific force* at P_0 due to the body B_2. But the components thus obtained are exactly those given by equations (4), § 8 for the attraction of a body B on a particle at P, except for the notation. We see thus that the expressions *force on a unit particle, specific force,* and *force at a point* are entirely synonymous.

The importance of the specific force lies in the fact that when it has been determined, we may find the force on a body B_1 by simply multiplying the components of the specific force at P by the density of B_1 at P and integrating the products over the volume occupied by B_1. For we then arrive at the integrals (9). In a similar manner we can construct the components (10) of the moment of the couple. It is for this reason that the knowledge of the force on a particle is so significant.

Should we care to define in a similar manner the *specific force per unit of attracting mass*, Newton's law could be stated: *the specific force at a point P of a body, per unit of mass at a point Q of a second body, is directed from P toward Q, and is equal in attraction units to the inverse square of the distance between P and Q.* This statement is very nearly of the form given in § 1, yet it implies, without further physical assumptions, the amplified statement of Newton's law given in § 3.

Exercises.

1. Determine the attraction due to a homogeneous straight wire, of unit linear density, terminating in the points $(0, 0)$, $(0, 12)$ of the (x, y)-plane, on a similar wire terminating in the points $(5, 0)$, $(9, 0)$. Show that the couple vanishes when the point of application of the force is properly taken, and find such a point, on the wire. Draw the wires and the force vector. Answer,

$$X = \log\left(\frac{3}{5}\right),\quad Y = \log\left(\frac{27}{20}\right),\quad x = \frac{2}{Y},\quad y = 0.$$

2. Show that if two plane laminas lie in the same plane, the attraction on either due to the other may always be given by a single force.

3. Let the "body" B_1 consist of a unit particle at $(0, 0, 1)$ and a unit particle at $(0, 0, -1)$; let the "body" B_2 consist of unit particles at $(0, a, 0)$ and $(1, a, 1)$.

a) Determine, for $a = .1$, the resultant force, regarded as acting at the origin, and the moment of the couple, which constitute the attraction of B_2 on B_1. Answer,

$$\frac{1 + 3\sqrt{3}}{6\sqrt{6}}, \quad \frac{1 + 9\sqrt{3}}{6\sqrt{6}}, \quad \frac{2}{6\sqrt{6}},$$

$$\frac{-3\sqrt{3} + 1}{6\sqrt{6}}, \quad \frac{3\sqrt{3} - 1}{6\sqrt{6}}, \quad 0.$$

b) Show, for $a = 1$, that the attraction is not equivalent to a single force.

c) Show that when a becomes great, the moment of the attraction, relative to the origin, is approximately $\left(-\frac{6}{a^4}, \frac{6}{a^5}, 0 \right)$, so that the moment falls off with the fourth power of the ratio of the dimensions of the bodies to their distance apart, while the force falls off only with the second power of this ratio.

Chapter II.

Fields of Force.

1. Fields of Force and Other Vector Fields.

The next step in gaining an insight into the character of Newtonian attraction will be to think of the forces at all points of space as a whole, rather than to fix attention on the forces at isolated points. When a force is defined at every point of space, or at every point of a portion of space, we have what is known as a *field of force*. Thus, an attracting body determines a field of force. Analytically, a force field amounts to three functions (the components of the force) of three variables (the coördinates of the point).

But in the analytical formulation, the particular idea of force has ceased to be essential. We have rather something which can stand for any *vector field*. The result is that any knowledge gained about fields of force is knowledge about any vector field, such as the velocity fields of moving matter, of heat flow, or the flow of electric currents in conductors. All these are simply interpretations of vector fields, or vector functions of a point in space.

2. Lines of Force.

We may picture a field of force by imagining needles placed at various points of space, each needle pointing in the direction of the force at the eye of the needle, and having a length proportional to the magnitude of the force. Thus, for a single particle, the needles would all point toward the particle, and their lengths would increase as they got nearer the particle. Indeed, the nearer needles would have to run way through the particle. The picture can be improved in many respects by the introduction of the idea of *lines of force*, a concept so fertile in suggestion that it led FARADAY to many of his important discoveries in electricity and magnetism.

A line of force is a curve which has at each of its points the direction of the field at that point. Thus the lines of force of a single particle are the straight lines through the particle. Another example is provided in Exercise 2, page 9, where it was found that the force at P due to a homogeneous straight wire bisects the angle subtended by the wire at P. Now we know that the tangent to a hyperbola bisects the angle between the focal radii. Hence in this case, the lines of force are hyperbolas with the ends of the wire as foci.

We are all familiar with the lines of force exhibited by the curves into which iron filings group themselves under the influence of a magnet. If the field, instead of being a field of force, is a velocity field, the lines are called *lines of flow*. A general term applicable in any vector field is *field lines*.

The determination of the lines of force, although in a few simple cases a matter of easy geometric reasoning, amounts essentially to the integration of a pair of ordinary differential equations. A tangent vector to a curve is (dx, dy, dz). If the curve is to be a line of force, this vector must have the direction of the force. Hence the differential equations of the lines of force are

(1)
$$\frac{dx}{X} = \frac{dy}{Y} = \frac{dz}{Z}.$$

Instead of the components of the force, we may, of course, use any quantities proportional to them. Thus, for a single particle at the origin of coördinates, we may take x, y, z as direction ratios of the force. The differential equations are

$$\frac{dx}{x} = \frac{dy}{y} = \frac{dz}{z},$$

which yield at once the integrals

$$\log y = \log x + \log c_1, \qquad \log z = \log x + \log c_2,$$
or
$$y = c_1 x, \qquad z = c_2 x.$$

We thus find as the lines of force, the straight lines through the origin. The lines in the (y, z)-plane are not given by the integrals written down. If it is desired, all the lines of force can be given by the parametric equations obtained by integrating the equations above with the equal ratios set equal, say, to $\frac{dt}{t}$.

The lines of force become more complicated, and more interesting, when more than one particle acts. Let us consider the case of two, with masses m_1 and m_2, located at the points $(-a, 0, 0)$ and $(a, 0, 0)$. The differential equations (1) become

$$\frac{dx}{m_1 \dfrac{-a-x}{r_1^3} + m_2 \dfrac{a-x}{r_2^3}} = \frac{dy}{-m_1 \dfrac{y}{r_1^3} - m_2 \dfrac{y}{r_2^3}} = \frac{dz}{-m_1 \dfrac{z}{r_1^3} - m_2 \dfrac{z}{r_2^3}}.$$

The equation involving dy and dz reduces at once to

$$\frac{dy}{y} = \frac{dz}{z},$$

the integral of which tells us that y and z are in a constant ratio. In other words, the lines of force lie in planes through the two particles, as we should expect from the symmetry of the field. Also, because of the symmetry of the field about the line through the particles, the lines of force lie on surfaces of revolution with this line as axis. This too is reflected in the differential equations. For, if the numerators and denominators in the second and third ratios are multiplied by y and z, respectively, the two numerators added, and the two denominators added, the equality of the resulting ratio with the first ratio in the differential equations constitutes a differential equation in x and $y^2 + z^2$, y and z entering only in this combination. The solution is therefore a relation between x, $y^2 + z^2$, and a constant, and thus represents a family of surfaces of revolution.

We may therefore confine ourselves to a meridian plane, say the (x, y)-plane. The differential equation involving dx and dy may then be integrated by collecting the terms in $\dfrac{1}{r_1^3}$ and $\dfrac{1}{r_2^3}$:

$$m_1 \frac{y\,dx - (x+a)\,dy}{r_1^3} + m_2 \frac{y\,dx - (x-a)\,dy}{r_2^3} = 0.$$

Since $z = 0$,

$$r_1^2 = (x+a)^2 + y^2, \quad \text{and} \quad r_2^2 = (x-a)^2 + y^2,$$

and the differential equation may be written

$$m_1 \frac{d\left(\dfrac{x+a}{y}\right)}{\left[1 + \left(\dfrac{x+a}{y}\right)^2\right]^{\frac{3}{2}}} + m_2 \frac{d\left(\dfrac{x-a}{y}\right)}{\left[1 + \left(\dfrac{x-a}{y}\right)^2\right]^{\frac{3}{2}}} = 0.$$

The integral is

$$m_1 \frac{x+a}{r_1} + m_2 \frac{x-a}{r_2} = C.$$

This equation can be expressed in still simpler form by introducing the angles ϑ_1 and ϑ_2 which the vectors from the particles to the point

(x, y) make with the positive x-axis. It then becomes

$$m_1 \cos \vartheta_1 + m_2 \cos \vartheta_2 = C.$$

The curves may be conveniently plotted by first drawing a set of rays, $u = \cos \vartheta_1$ corresponding to $u = -1, -\cdot 9, \ldots -\cdot 1, 0, \cdot 1, \ldots, \cdot 9, 1$, drawing a similar set of rays for $v = \cos \vartheta_2$, and numbering these rays with the corresponding values of u and v. It is then a simple matter to plot the linear equation $m_1 u + m_2 v = C$, for various values of C, on the coördinate paper thus prepared. It may be found necessary to inter-polate intermediate values of u and v and draw the corresponding lines in parts of the paper where those already drawn are sparse. Such coördi-nate paper being once prepared, curves corresponding to different values of m_1, m_2 and C can be drawn on thin paper laid over and attached to it by clips. The labor of repeating the ruling can thus be avoided.

Exercises.

1. Find the equations of, and describe, the lines of force of the field given by $X = x^2 - y^2$, $Y = -2xy$, $Z = 0$.

2. Find the equations of the lines of force for the field (Ax, By, Cz). This is the character of the field in the interior of a homogeneous ellipsoid.

3. Draw the lines of force of the field due to two particles of equal mass. Does any point of equilibrium appear? What can be said as to the stability of the equi-librium?

4. The same, when the masses of the particles are as 1 to 4.

5. The same, when the masses are equal and opposite. This case illustrates approximately the situation when iron filings are placed on a sheet of paper over the poles of a magnet.

6. Find the equations of the lines of force due to n particles in line.

3. Velocity Fields.

It has doubtless not escaped the reader that the lines of force do not give back a complete picture of the field, for they give only the direction, not the magnitude, of the force. However, in the case of certain fields, including the fields of Newtonian forces, this defect is only apparent, for it turns out that the spacing of the lines of force enables us to gauge the magnitude of the forces, or the *intensity* of the field. We shall be led to understand this best by interpreting the vector field as a velocity field. An incidental advantage will be an insight into the nature of the motion of a continuous medium, and into the relation of potential theory to such motions.

The motion of a single particle may be described by giving its coördi-nates as functions of the time:

$$x = x(t), \qquad y = y(t), \qquad z = z(t).$$

If, however, we have a portion of a gas, liquid, or elastic solid in motion, we must have such a set of equations, or the equivalent, for every particle of the medium. To be more specific, let us talk of a fluid. The particles of the fluid may be characterized by their coördinates at any given instant, say $t = t_0$. Then the equations of all the paths of the particles may be united in a single set of three, dependent on three constants:

(2) $\quad x = x (x_0, y_0, z_0, t), \quad y = y (x_0, y_0, z_0, t), \quad z = z (x_0, y_0, z_0, t),$

for these will tell us at any instant t the exact position of the particle of the fluid which at t_0 was at (x_0, y_0, z_0). The functions occuring in these equations are supposed to satisfy certain requirements as to continuity, and the equations are supposed to be solvable for x_0, y_0, z_0. In particular, x must reduce to x_0, y to y_0, and z to z_0 when $t = t_0$:

(3) $\quad x_0 = x (x_0, y_0, z_0, t_0), \quad y_0 = y (x_0, y_0, z_0, t_0), \quad z_0 = z (x_0, y_0, z_0, t_0).$

The velocities of the particles are the vectors whose components are the derivatives of the coördinates with respect to the time:

(4) $\quad \dfrac{dx}{dt} = x' (x_0, y_0, z_0, t), \quad \dfrac{dy}{dt} = y' (x_0, y_0, z_0, t), \quad \dfrac{dz}{dt} = z' (x_0, y_0, z_0, t).$

These equations give the velocity at any instant of a particle of the fluid in terms of its position at $t = t_0$. It is often more desirable to know the velocity at any instant with which the fluid is moving past a given point of space. To answer such a question, it would be necessary to know where the particle was at $t = t_0$ which at the given instant t is passing the given point (x, y, z). In other words, we should have to solve the equations (2) for x_0, y_0, z_0. The equations (4) would then give us the desired information. Let us suppose the steps carried out once for all, that is, the equations (2) solved for x_0, y_0, z_0, in terms of x, y, z and t, and the results substituted in (4). We obtain a set of equations of the form

(5) $\quad \dfrac{dx}{dt} = X (x, y, z, t), \quad \dfrac{dy}{dt} = Y (x, y, z, t), \quad \dfrac{dz}{dt} = Z (x, y, z, t).$

The right hand members of these equations define the velocity field. It differs from the fields of force we have considered so far, in that it varies, in general, with the time. This is not essential, however, for a field of force may also so vary, as for instance, the field of attraction due to a moving body. But what is the effect of the dependence of the field on the time, on the field lines? By definition, they have the direction of the field. As the field is changing, there will be one set of field lines at one instant and another at another. We mean by the field lines, a family of curves depending on the time, which at any instant have the direction of the field at every point at that instant. In other words, they are the integrals of the differential equations

$$\frac{dx}{X (x, y, z, t)} = \frac{dy}{Y (x, y, z, t)} = \frac{dz}{Z (x, y, z, t)}$$

on the assumption that t is constant. On the other hand, the paths of the particles are the integrals of (5), in which t is a variable wherever it occurs. Thus, in general, *the lines of flow (field lines) are distinct from the paths of the particles.* Evidently they do coincide, however, if the ratios of X, Y and Z are independent of the time, that is, if the direction of the field does not change. This includes the important case of a *stationary field,* or one in which the field is independent of the time. Thus, *in a stationary velocity field, the lines of flow and the paths of the particles coincide.*

To illustrate the above considerations, let us examine the flow given by

$$x = x_0 e^t, \qquad y = y_0 e^{-t}, \qquad z = z_0.$$

Here x, y, z reduce to x_0, y_0, z_0 for $t = t_0 = 0$. It will suffice to consider the motion of particles in the (x, y)-plane, since any particle has the same motion as its projection on that plane. The equations of the paths may be obtained by eliminating t. The paths are the hyperbolas

$$x y = x_0 y_0.$$

The velocities of given particles are furnished by

$$\frac{d x}{d t} = x_0 e^t, \qquad \frac{d y}{d t} = - y_0 e^{-t},$$

and the differential equations of the flow are obtained from these by eliminating x_0 and y_0:

$$\frac{d x}{d t} = x, \qquad \frac{d y}{d t} = - y.$$

The field is stationary, since the velocities at given points are independent of the time. The lines of flow are given by

$$\frac{d x}{x} = \frac{d y}{- y},$$

the integral of which is $x y = C$. The lines of flow thus coincide with the paths, as they should in a stationary field.

To take a simple case of a non-stationary flow, consider

$$x = x_0 + t, \qquad y = y_0 + t^2, \qquad z = z_0.$$

Here

$$\frac{d x}{d t} = 1, \qquad \frac{d y}{d t} = 2 t.$$

As x_0 and y_0 do not appear, these are already the differential equations of the motion in the $(x y)$-plane. The field depends on the time, and so is not stationary. The lines of flow are the integrals of

$$\frac{d x}{1} = \frac{d y}{2 t},$$

that is, the parallel straight lines $y = 2tx + C$, which become continually steeper as time goes on. From the equations of the paths, we see that the fluid is moving like a rigid body, keeping its orientation, and its points describing congruent parabolas.

Exercises.

1. Study the motions

a) $x = \dfrac{x_0 + y_0}{2} e^t + \dfrac{x_0 - y_0}{2} e^{-t}, \qquad y = \dfrac{x_0 + y_0}{2} e^t - \dfrac{x_0 - y_0}{2} e^{-t}, \qquad z = z_0,$

b) $x = x_0 + \sin t, \qquad y = y_0 + (1 - \cos t), \qquad z = z_0,$

c) $\dfrac{dx}{dt} = x, \qquad \dfrac{dy}{dt} = y, \qquad \dfrac{dz}{dt} = z,$

determining the nature of the paths, the velocity fields, and the lines of flow.

2. Show by a simple example that, in general, the path of a particle, moving under a stationary field of force, will not be a line of force.

4. Expansion, or Divergence of a Field.

An important concept in connection with a fluid in motion is its rate of expansion or contraction. A portion of the fluid occupying a region T_0 at time t_0, will, at a later time t, occupy a new region T. For instance, in the steady flow of the last section, a cylinder bounded at $t = 0$ by the planes $z_0 = 0$, $z_0 = 1$, and by the surface $x_0^2 + y_0^2 = a^2$, becomes at the time t the cylinder bounded by the same planes and the surface

$$\frac{x^2}{(a\,e^t)^2} + \frac{y^2}{(a\,e^{-t})^2} = 1,$$

as we see by eliminating x_0, y_0, z_0 between the equations of the initial boundary and the equations of the paths (fig. 6). Here the volume of the region has not changed, for the area of the elliptical base of the cylinder is πa^2, and so, independent of the time.

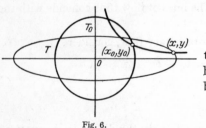

Fig. 6.

On the other hand, in the flow

$$x = x_0 + t, \qquad y = y_0 e^t,$$

the same cylinder at time $t = 0$, has at the time t the elliptical boundary

$$\frac{(x - t)^2}{a^2} + \frac{y^2}{(a\,e^t)^2} = 1,$$

so that the volume has increased to $\pi a^2 e^t$. The time rate of expansion of this volume is the derivative of this value, also $\pi a^2 e^t$. If we divide the rate of expansion of the volume by the volume, and find such a quotient for a succession of smaller and smaller volumes containing a given point, the limit gives us the time rate of expansion per unit of volume at that point. In the present instance, the quotient is 1, und by decreasing a, we may make the original volume as small as we please. Hence the time rate of expansion per unit of volume at the point originally at the origin is always 1. It is not hard to see that this characterizes the rate of expansion of the fluid at all points, for the chords of any portion of the fluid parallel to the x- and z-axes are constant, while those parallel to the y-axis are increasing at the relative rate 1. Thus every cubic centimetre of the fluid is expanding at the rate of a cubic centimetre per second.

Let us now consider the rate of expansion in a general flow. The volume at time t is

$$V(t) = \iiint_T dx\,dy\,dz.$$

We must relate this expression to the volume at t_0. By the equations (2), every point (x, y, z) of T corresponds to a point (x_0, y_0, z_0) of T_0. We may therefore, by means of this transformation, in which t is regarded as constant, change the variables of integration to x_0, y_0, z_0. According to the rules of the Integral Calculus[1], this gives

$$V(t) = \iiint_T dx\,dy\,dz = \iiint_{T_0} J(x_0, y_0, z_0, t)\,dx_0\,dy_0\,dz_0,$$

where J denotes the Jacobian, or functional determinant

$$J(x_0, y_0, z_0, t) = \begin{vmatrix} \dfrac{\partial x}{\partial x_0}, & \dfrac{\partial y}{\partial x_0}, & \dfrac{\partial z}{\partial x_0} \\[2ex] \dfrac{\partial x}{\partial y_0}, & \dfrac{\partial y}{\partial y_0}, & \dfrac{\partial z}{\partial y_0} \\[2ex] \dfrac{\partial x}{\partial z_0}, & \dfrac{\partial y}{\partial z_0}, & \dfrac{\partial z}{\partial z_0} \end{vmatrix}$$

of the transformation.

We are interested in the time rate of expansion of the volume. This is given, if the Jacobian has a continuous derivative with respect to the time, by

$$\frac{dV}{dt} = \iiint_{T_0} \frac{dJ}{dt}\,dx_0\,dy_0\,dz_0.$$

We can compute the derivative of the Jacobian for $t = t_0$ without difficulty, and as t_0 can be taken as any instant, the results will be general. First,

$$\frac{dJ}{dt} = S \begin{vmatrix} \dfrac{\partial^2 x}{\partial t\,\partial x_0}, & \dfrac{\partial^2 y}{\partial t\,\partial x_0}, & \dfrac{\partial^2 z}{\partial t\,\partial x_0} \\[2ex] \dfrac{\partial x}{\partial y_0}, & \dfrac{\partial y}{\partial y_0}, & \dfrac{\partial z}{\partial y_0} \\[2ex] \dfrac{\partial x}{\partial z_0}, & \dfrac{\partial y}{\partial z_0}, & \dfrac{\partial z}{\partial z_0} \end{vmatrix}$$

---

[1] See OSGOOD: *Advanced Calculus*, New York, 1925, Chap. XII, §§ 4—8, or COURANT: *Differential- und Integralrechnung*, Berlin, 1927—29, Vol. II, pp. 261, 264.

where the symbol S means that we are to add two more determinants in which the second and third rows of J, instead of the first, have been differentiated with respect to t. Let us assume that all derivatives appearing are continuous. Then, since x, y, z reduce to x_0, y_0, z_0, for $t = t_0$, at this instant

$$\frac{\partial x}{\partial x_0} = \frac{\partial y}{\partial y_0} = \frac{\partial z}{\partial z_0} = 1, \quad \frac{\partial x}{\partial y_0} = \frac{\partial x}{\partial z_0} = \frac{\partial y}{\partial x_0} = \frac{\partial y}{\partial z_0} = \frac{\partial z}{\partial x_0} = \frac{\partial z}{\partial y_0} = 0,$$

$$\frac{\partial^2 x}{\partial t \, \partial x_0} = \frac{\partial}{\partial x_0}\left(\frac{\partial x}{\partial t}\right) = \frac{\partial X}{\partial x_0}, \quad \frac{\partial^2 y}{\partial t \, \partial y_0} = \frac{\partial Y}{\partial y_0}, \quad \frac{\partial^2 z}{\partial t \, \partial z_0} = \frac{\partial Z}{\partial z_0}.$$

Accordingly

$$\frac{dJ}{dt}\Bigg]_{t=t_0} = \frac{\partial X}{\partial x_0} + \frac{\partial Y}{\partial y_0} + \frac{\partial Z}{\partial z_0}\Bigg]_{t=t_0}.$$

We may now drop the subscripts, since x, y, z coincide with x_0, y_0, z_0, at $t = t_0$, and t_0 may be any time. We then have, for the time rate of expansion of the fluid occupying a region T at time t,

$$(6) \qquad \frac{dV}{dt} = \iiint\limits_{T} \left(\frac{\partial X}{\partial x} + \frac{\partial Y}{\partial y} + \frac{\partial Z}{\partial z}\right) dV.$$

From this equation we may derive the relative rate of expansion, or the rate of expansion per unit of volume at a point. We remove the integrand from under the sign of integration, by the law of the mean, and divide by the volume:

$$\frac{\frac{dV}{dt}}{V} = \overline{\frac{\partial X}{\partial x} + \frac{\partial Y}{\partial y} + \frac{\partial Z}{\partial z}}.$$

If, now, the region T is made to shrink down on the point $P\,(x, y, z)$, the limit of the above expression gives us the *relative time rate of expansion of the fluid at P*:

$$(7) \qquad \operatorname{div} \boldsymbol{V} = \frac{\partial X}{\partial x} + \frac{\partial Y}{\partial y} + \frac{\partial Z}{\partial z},$$

or the *divergence* of the vector field $\boldsymbol{V}\,(X, Y, Z)$, as it is called. The expression (6) is called the *total divergence* of the field for the region T.

We see at once that if the rate of change of volume (6) is everywhere 0, the divergence (7) is everywhere 0, and conversely. Thus a fluid whose divergence vanishes everywhere is *incompressible*[1].

We are now in a position to see how the field lines can give us a picture of the intensity of the field. Consider all the field lines passing through a small closed curve. They generate a tubular surface called a *field tube*, or, in a field of force, a *tube of force*. If the flow is stationary,

---

[1] See, however, § 9 (p. 45).

the fluid flows in this tube, never crossing its walls. If, in addition, the fluid is incompressible, it must speed up wherever the tube is pinched down, and slow down when the tube broadens out. Interpreting the field as a field of force, we see that *in a stationary field of force whose divergence vanishes everywhere, the force at the points of a line of force is greater or less according as the neighboring lines of force approach or recede from it.* This qualitative interpretation of the spacing of the lines of force will be made more exact in § 6.

Exercises.

1. Verify that the field of Exercise 1, page 31, has a divergence which vanishes everywhere. Draw the lines of force $3x^2 y - y^3 = C$ for $C = -2, -1, 0, 1, 2$, and verify the relationship between intensity and spacing of the field lines.

2. Verify the fact that the total divergence vanishes for the field of force due to a single particle, for regions not containing the particle, bounded by conical surfaces with the particle as vertex, and by concentric spheres. Show that for spheres with the particle at the centers, the total divergence is $-4\pi m$, where m is the mass of the particle.

3. A *central field of force* is one in which the direction of the force is always through a fixed point, and in which the magnitude and sense of the force depends only on the distance from the point. The fixed point is called the *center* of the field. Show that the only field of force with Q as center, continuous except at Q, whose divergence vanishes everywhere except at Q, is the Newtonian field of a particle at Q. Thus Newton's law acquires a certain geometrical significance.

4. An *axial field of force* is one in which the direction of the force is always through a fixed line, and in which the magnitude and sense of the force depends only on the distance from this line. The line is called the *axis* of the field. If such a field is continuous, and has a vanishing divergence everywhere except on the axis, find the law of force. Find also the law of force in a field with vanishing divergence in which the force is always perpendicular to a fixed plane and has a magnitude and sense depending only on the distance from this plane.

5. Show that the divergence of the sum of two fields (the field obtained by vector addition of the vectors of the two fields) is the sum of the divergences of the two fields. Generalize to any finite sums, and to certain limits of sums, including integrals. Thus show that the divergence of Newtonian fields due to the usual distributions vanishes at all points of free space.

6. The definition of the divergence as

$$\lim_{V \to 0} \frac{\dfrac{dV}{dt}}{V}$$

involves no coördinate system. Accordingly, the expression (7) should be independent of the position of the coördinate axes. Verify that it is invariant under a rigid motion of the axes.

5. The Divergence Theorem.

The rate of expansion of a fluid can be computed in a second way, and the identity obtained by equating the new and old expressions will be of great usefulness. Let us think of the fluid occupying the region

T at a certain instant as stained red. We wish to examine the rate of spread of the red spot. Suppose, for the moment, that T has a plane face, and that the velocity of the fluid is perpendicular to this face, outward, and of constant magnitude V. Then the boundary of the red spot is moving outward at the rate of V centimetres per second, and $V \Delta S$ cubic centimetres per second are being added to the red spot corresponding to an element ΔS of the plane boundary of T. If the velocity is still constant in magnitude and direction, but no longer perpendicular to the plane face, the red fluid added per second, corresponding to ΔS will fill a slant cylinder, with base ΔS and slant height having the direction and magnitude of the velocity. Its volume will therefore be $V_n \Delta S$, where V_n is the component of the velocity in the direction of the outward normal to the face of T.

Giving up, now, any special assumptions as to T or the velocity, we may inscribe in T a polyhedron, and assume for each face a constant velocity which, at some point of the face coincides with the actual velocity of the field, and thus compute an approximate time rate of expansion of the red spot:

$$\left(\frac{dV}{dt}\right)' = \sum V_n \Delta S.$$

If the velocity field is continuous, and if the faces of the polyhedron are diminished so that their maximum chord approaches 0, while the faces approach more and more nearly tangency to the surface bounding T, the error in this approximation should approach 0. We are thus led to the second desired expression for the time rate of expansion, or total divergence

$$(8) \qquad \frac{dV}{dt} = \iint\limits_S V_n \, dS = \iint\limits_S (Xl + Ym + Zn) \, dS,$$

where l, m, n are the direction cosines of the normal to S, directed outward, S being the surface bounding T.

The identity of this expression with that given in equation (6) gives what is known as the **Divergence Theorem,** or as **Gauss' Theorem,** or **Green's Theorem**[1], and may be stated

---

[1] A similar reduction of triple integrals to double integrals was employed by LAGRANGE: *Nouvelles recherches sur la nature et la propagation du son*, Miscellanea Taurinensis, t. II, 1760—61, 45; *Oeuvres*, t. I, p. 263. The double integrals are given in more definite form by GAUSS, *Theoria attractionis corporum sphaeroidicorum ellipticorum homogeneorum methodo novo tractata*, Commentationes societatis regiae scientiarum Gottingensis recentiores, Vol. II, 1813, 2—5; *Werke*, Bd. V, pp. 5—7 A systematic use of integral identities equivalent to the divergence theorem was made by GEORGE GREEN in his *Essay on the Application of Mathematical Analysis to the Theory of Electricity and Magnetism*, Nottingham, 1828.

$$\iiint_T \operatorname{div} \boldsymbol{V}\, dV = \iint_S V_n\, dS,$$

(9)

$$\iiint_T \left(\frac{\partial X}{\partial x} + \frac{\partial Y}{\partial y} + \frac{\partial Z}{\partial z}\right) dV = \iint_S (Xl + Ym + Zn)\, dS,$$

or in words, *the integral of the divergence of a vector field over a region of space is equal to the integral over the surface of that region of the component of the field in the direction of the outward directed normal to the surface.*

The reasoning by which we have been led to this theorem is heuristic, and the result is so important that we shall devote special attention to it in Chapter IV. For the present we shall borrow the results there rigorously established, for we do not wish to interrupt our study of vector fields.

Exercises.

1. Verify the divergence theorem for the field $X = x$, $Y = 1$, $Z = 0$, and the regions (a) any cuboid $a \le x \le a'$, $b \le y \le b'$, $c \le z \le c'$, (b) the sphere $x^2 + y^2 + z^2 \le a^2$.

2. The same for the field $X = x^2$, $Y = y^2$, $Z = z^2$. For the sphere this may be done without the evaluation of any integrals.

3. Show by applying the divergence theorem to the field (x, y, z) that the volume of any region for which the theorem is valid is given by

$$V = \frac{1}{3} \iint_S r \cos (r, n)\, dS$$

where S is the boundary of the region, r the distance from a fixed point, and (r, n) the angle between the vector from this point and the outward directed normal to S. Apply the result to find the volume bounded by any conical surface and a plane. Find other surface integrals giving the volumes of solids.

4. Show that the projection on a fixed plane of a closed surface is 0, provided the surface bounds a region for which the divergence theorem holds.

5. By means of the divergence theorem, show that the divergence may be defined as

$$\lim \frac{\iint_S V_n\, dS}{V}$$

as the maximum chord of T approaches 0, V being the volume of T. With this definition alone, show that if the divergence exists, it must have the value (7). Suggestion. If the above limit exists, it may be evaluated by the use of regions of any convenient shape. Let T be a cube with edges of length a, parallel to the axes.

6. Show in a similar way that in spherical coördinates, the divergence is given by

$$\operatorname{div} \boldsymbol{V} = \frac{1}{\varrho^2} \frac{\partial}{\partial \varrho} \varrho^2 R + \frac{1}{\varrho \sin \vartheta} \frac{\partial \Phi}{\partial \varphi} + \frac{1}{\varrho \sin \vartheta} \frac{\partial}{\partial \vartheta} \sin \vartheta\, \Theta,$$

where R, Φ, Θ, are the components of the field $\boldsymbol{V}$ in the directions of increasing ϱ, φ, ϑ, respectively.

6. Flux of Force; Solenoidal Fields.

When a vector field is interpreted as a field of force, the integral $\iint V_n \, dS$, taken over any surface, open or closed, is called the *flux of force* across the surface. If the flux of force across every[1] closed surface vanishes, the field is called *solenoidal*. A necessary and sufficient condition for this is that the divergence vanishes everywhere, provided the derivatives of the components of the field are continuous. For, by the divergence theorem, if the divergence vanishes everywhere, the flux of force across any closed surface vanishes. On the other hand, if the flux across every closed surface vanishes (or even if only the flux across every sphere vanishes), the divergence vanishes. For suppose the divergence were different from 0 at P, say positive. Then there would be a sphere about P within which the divergence was positive at every point, since it is continuous. By the divergence theorem, the flux across the surface of this sphere would be positive, contrary to the assumption.

Newtonian fields are solenoidal at the points of free space. This has been indicated in Exercise 5, page 37. Let us examine the situation for volume distributions. Others may be treated in the same way. If P is a point where no masses are situated, the integrands in the integrals giving the components of the force have continuous derivatives, and we may therefore differentiate under the signs of integration. We find

$$\text{div } \boldsymbol{V} = \iiint\limits_{V} \varkappa \left[\frac{\partial}{\partial x} \frac{\xi - x}{r^3} + \frac{\partial}{\partial y} \frac{\eta - y}{r^3} + \frac{\partial}{\partial z} \frac{\zeta - z}{r^3} \right] dV$$

$$= \iiint\limits_{V} \varkappa \left[\frac{-3}{r^3} + 3 \frac{(\xi - x)^2 + (\eta - y)^2 + (\zeta - z)^2}{r^5} \right] dV$$

$$= 0.$$

Thus Newtonian fields are among those for which the spacing of the lines of force gives an idea of the intensity of the field. We can now state the facts with more precision, as was intimated at the close of § 4. Consider a region T of the field, bounded by a tube of force of small cross section, and by two surfaces S_1 and S_2 nearly normal[2] to the

---

[1] The word *every* here means without restriction as to size, position, or general shape. Naturally the surface must have a definite normal nearly everywhere, or the integral would fail to have a meaning. The kind of surfaces to be admitted are the regular surfaces of Chapter IV.

[2] It may not always be possible (although we shall see that it is in the case of Newtonian fields) to find surfaces everywhere normal to the direction of a field. Picture, for instance, a bundle of fine wires, all parallel, piercing a membrane perpendicular to them all. If the bundle be given a twist, so that the wires become helical, the membrane will be torn, and it seems possible that the membrane could not slip into a position where it is perpendicular to all the wires. In fact, the field $(-y, x, 1)$ has no normal surfaces.

field (fig. 7). The field being solenoidal, the flux of force across the surface bounding this region will be 0. The flux across the walls of the tube vanishes, since the component of the force normal to these walls is 0. Hence the flux across the two surfaces S_1 and S_2 is 0, or what amounts to the same thing, if the normals to these surfaces have their senses chosen so that on S_1 they point into T and on S_2 out from T,

$$(10) \qquad \iint_{S_1} V_n \, dS = \iint_{S_2} V_n \, dS.$$

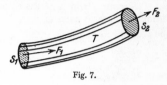

Fig. 7.

If A_1 and A_2 denote the areas of S_1 and S_2, and F_1 and F_2 the magnitudes of the forces at a point of each—say points where the forces are actually normal to the surfaces—we derive from the above an approximate equation,

$$A_1 F_1 = A_2 F_2,$$

in which the relative error approaches 0 with the cross section of the tube. That is, *the intensity of the force in a solenoidal field at the points of a tube of force of infinitesimal cross section, varies inversely as the area of the cross section.* The equation (10), of course, embodies the exact situation.

It is quite customary, in considering electrostatic fields, to speak of the *number of lines of force* cutting a piece of surface. This number means simply the flux across the surface, and need not be an integer. If a definite sense is attached to the normal to the surface, we speak of lines *leaving* the surface when the flux is positive, and of lines entering the surface when the flux is negative. The equation (10) tells us that in a solenoidal field, the number of lines in a tube of force is constant throughout the tube.

Since Newtonian fields are solenoidal in free space, ceasing to be so only at points where masses are situated, it is customary to say that *lines of force originate and terminate only at points of the acting masses.* But this should be understood in terms of tubes of force. For an individual line may fail to keep its continuity of direction, and even its identity throughout free space. As X, Y and Z are continuous, this may happen only when they vanish simultaneously, that is, at a point of equilibrium. But such points occur, as we have seen in Exercise 3, page 31. The straight line of force starting from one of the two equal particles toward the other (or, more properly, if we think of the lines of force having the sense as well as the direction of the field, arriving at one particle from the direction of the other), encounters the plane which bisects perpendicularly the segment joining the particles, any ray in which from the point of equilibrium may just as well be considered a continuating of the line of force as any other. Clearly any assertion that the lines of force continue and keep their identity beyond such a point of equilibrium must be a matter purely of convention. It is, however, always possible to find tubes of force which do continue on, for points of equilibrium can never fill volumes, or even surfaces, in free space, however restricted[1].

Exercise.

Determine which of the following fields are solenoidal, specifying the exceptional points, if such exist.

a) the field (x, y, z),

b) the field $(x, 0, 0)$,

c) the field $\left(\dfrac{x}{y^2 + z^2}, \ \dfrac{1}{z} \cot^{-1} \dfrac{y}{z}, \ \dfrac{1}{\sqrt{x^2 + y^2}}\right)$.

d) the attraction field due to a homogeneous sphere,

e) the field of the instantaneous velocities of a rigid body $(a + qz - ry, b + rx - pz, c + py - qx)$,

f) the field $\left(-\dfrac{y}{\varrho^2}, \dfrac{x}{\varrho^2}, 0\right)$, $\quad \varrho = \sqrt{x^2 + y^2}$.

In the cases in which the field is not solenoidal, alter, if possible, the intensity, but not the direction of the field, so that it becomes solenoidal.

7. Gauss' Integral.

In the field of force due to a particle of mass m, the flux of force across the surface of any sphere σ with center at the particle, is $-4\pi m$, the normal being directed outward. For the normal component of the field is the constant $\dfrac{m}{r^2}$, and the area of the surface is $4\pi r^2$. But the flux is the same for any other closed surface S containing the particle, to which the divergence theorem can be applied. For if we take the radius of σ so small that it lies within the region bounded by S, then in the region between σ and S, the field is solenoidal, and hence the flux across its entire boundary is 0:

$$\iint\limits_{\sigma} V_n \, dS + \iint\limits_{S} V_n \, dS = 0,$$

the normal pointing outward from the region. Reversing the sense of the normal on the sphere, so that in both cases it points outward from the surfaces, makes the two integrals equal. Thus the flux of this field across any closed surface containing the particle is $-4\pi m$.

If we have a field containing a number of particles, the flux across any closed surface S containing them all is the sum of the fluxes of the fields due to each singly, and is therefore $-4\pi M$, where M is the total mass within the surface. This remains true if there are also masses outside S, for since the field due to them is solenoidal within S, they contribute nothing to the flux across S.

---

[1] See Chapter X, § 9.

The result may be extended to fields due to continuous distributions which nowhere meet S. The fields due to masses outside S are still solenoidal inside of S, as we saw in § 6 (p. 40). Let us consider, as typical, the contribution to the flux of a volume distribution within S. It has the form

$$\iint_S V_n \, dS = \iint_S \iiint_V \varkappa \frac{-(\xi - x)\, l + (\eta - y)\, m + (\zeta - z)\, n}{r^3} \, dV \, dS,$$

and as S passes through no masses, r is never 0 and the integrand is continuous. So the order of integrations can be reversed, and

$$\iint_S V_n \, dS = \iiint_V \varkappa \iint_S \frac{(\xi - x)\, l + (\eta - y)\, m + (\zeta - z)\, n}{r^3} \, dS \, dV.$$

Here the inner integral is simply the flux of force across S due to a unit particle at $Q\,(\xi,\, \eta,\, \zeta)$, and so is equal to -4π. The iterated integral is therefore equal to $-4\pi M$, where M is the total mass of the volume distribution. In all cases then, in which S meets no masses,

(11) $$\iint_S V_n \, dS = -4\pi M.$$

The integral giving the flux is know as **Gauss' integral,** and the statement (11) is known as **Gauss' theorem,** or Gauss' integral theorem: *the flux outward across the surface bounding a region is equal to -4π times the total mass in the region*, provided the bounding surface meets no masses.

Gauss' theorem may even be extended, under certain conditions, to the case in which S passes through masses. Let us assume, for instance, that the mass within any closed surface sufficiently near S is arbitrarily close in total amount to that within S, as would be the case if the masses belonged to volume distributions with bounded volume density. Let us also assume that the flux of the field due to the masses within S, across any surface S'' enclosing S, varies continuously with the position of S'', and similarly, that the flux of forces due to the masses without S, across any surface S' enclosed by S, varies continuously with S'. Then

$$\iint_{S'} V_n'' \, dS = 0, \quad \text{and} \quad \iint_{S''} V_n' \, dS = -4\pi M,$$

where V'' and V' are the normal components on S' and S'' of the fields due to the masses outside of and within S respectively and M is the total mass within S. These equations are valid because the surfaces S' and S'' do not meet the masses producing the fields whose fluxes over the surfaces are computed. Now suppose that S' and S'' approach S. The right hand members of the above equations do not change, while, by hypothesis, the left hand members become the fluxes over S due to the fields of the exterior and interior masses, respectively. The sum of the limiting equations thus gives Gauss' theorem for S.

Implicit in the above reasoning is the assumption that S can bound a region for which the divergence theorem is valid (for the first equation of this section is derived from that theorem), and that it is possible to approximate S by surfaces S' and S'', arbitrarily closely, S' and S'' having the same character. This is evidently possible for spheres, and for many other simple surfaces. But a general assumption of the validity of Gauss' theorem for surfaces cutting masses is dangerous, and the application of the theorem in such cases, made in many text books, is unwarranted.

Exercise.

Determine the outward flux across the unit sphere about the origin in the fields (a), (b), (d), of the exercise of § 6 (p. 42). In (d), the origin is supposed to be the center of the sphere. For the field (d), verify Gauss' theorem for concentric spheres, with radii both less than, and greater than, that of the given sphere.

8. Sources and Sinks.

It is advantageous to keep before ourselves the various interpretations of vector fields, and the question arises, what is the significance of Gauss' theorem for velocity fields? Let us consider first the field of a single particle at Q, the components of the force now being thought of as components of velocity. The point Q is a point of discontinuity of the field. What is happening there? Everywhere else, the field is solenoidal, that is, incompressible in the sense that any portion keeps its volume unaltered. Yet into any region containing Q, by Gauss' theorem, $4\pi m$ cubic centimetres of fluid are pouring every second. As they are compressed nowhere, what becomes of them? It is customary to regard the fluid as absorbed at Q, and to call Q a *sink*, of *strength* $4\pi m$. If m is negative, so that the senses of the velocities are reversed, Q is called a *source*, of strength $4\pi |m|$.

The exact physical realization of sinks and sources is quite as impossible as the realization of a particle. For a fluid, we may imagine a small tube introduced into the field, with mouth at Q, through which fluid is pumped out from or into the field. In the case of electric currents, a source corresponds to a positive electrode at a point of a conducting body, and a sink to a negative electrode.

Suppose now that we have the Newtonian field due to a volume distribution with continuous density. We have already seen in examples, for instance, the homogeneous sphere, that the field due to such a distribution may be continuous everywhere. If the density is always positive,

Gauss' theorem tells us that the fluid with the corresponding velocity field pours into the region occupied by the distribution at the rate $4\pi M$ cubic centimetres per second, and, further, that it passes into any portion of this region at the rate $4\pi m$ cubic centimetres per second, where m is the mass in this portion in the corresponding field of force. If the portion is small, m will be small, so that the fluid may be thought of as absorbed continuously throughout the whole region. We then speak of a *continuous distribution of sinks*. Similarly, we may have a continuous distribution of sources, and we may also have sources and sinks distributed on surfaces. These concepts are useful. Thus, for instance, the heat generated by an electric current in a conductor because of the resistance, may be thought of as due to a continuous distribution of sources in the conductor. In problems in the conduction of heat and in hydrodynamics, flows satisfying preassigned conditions may often be produced by suitable distributions of sources and sinks, usually on bounding surfaces.

Exercises.

1. Show that the field (x, y, z) has continuously distributed sources by forming and evaluating Gauss' integral for cuboids. Show that the *source density* is 3, that is, that the flux out from any region is 3 times the volume of that region.

2. Show that for a field with continuously distributed sources, the *source density*, or rate of yield of fluid per unit volume at any point is equal to the divergence of the field at that point.

9. General Flows of Fluids; Equation of Continuity.

Thus far, we have been considering the kinematics of fluids, that is, purely the motion, the concept of mass of the fluid not having entered. To say that a fluid is incompressible has meant that any portion of the fluid, identified by the particles it contains, occupies a region of constant volume. But if sources are possible, this criterion of incompressibility is inadequate. For if fluid is poured into a region, particularly through continuously distributed sources, it is impossible to identify at a later instant the exact fluid which at a given instant occupies a given volume.

What then should be the definition of incompressibility? If a given body of fluid is introduced into a cylinder, and the volume decreased by means of a piston, the ratio of mass to volume increases. The same thing happens if new material is forced into the cylinder, the volume remaining unchanged. In either case, we should say that a compression has taken place. The density has increased. Thus a broader formulation of the notion of incompressibility may be founded on the density. It will not do, however, to say that incompressibility and constant density are synonymous. We might, for instance, have a flow of a layer of oil on a layer of water, both fluids being incompressible. The density would not be constant throughout the fluid. What would be constant is the *density of the fluid at a particular particle*, no matter where it moves, as long, at least, as the motion is continuous. So we must formulate analytically the meaning of this kind of constancy.

To say that a function, the density ϱ in the present instance, is constant at a *point of space*, means that

$$\frac{\partial}{\partial t} \varrho \, (x, y, z, t) = 0 \,,$$

x, *y and z being held constant.* To say that the density remains constant at a given particle is another matter. We must identify the particle, say by the equations (2). If ϱ were given as a function of x_0, y_0, z_0 and t, we should again equate to 0 the partial derivative with respect to the time, x_0, y_0, z_0 remaining fixed. But if ϱ is given as a function of x, y, z and t, this derivative must be computed by the rule for a function of several functions:

$$\frac{d\varrho}{dt} = \frac{\partial \varrho}{\partial x}\frac{\partial x}{\partial t} + \frac{\partial \varrho}{\partial y}\frac{\partial y}{\partial t} + \frac{\partial \varrho}{\partial z}\frac{\partial z}{\partial t} + \frac{\partial \varrho}{\partial t}.$$

If we introduce the components of the velocity, this becomes

(12) $$\frac{d\varrho}{dt} = X \frac{\partial \varrho}{\partial x} + Y \frac{\partial \varrho}{\partial y} + Z \frac{\partial \varrho}{\partial z} + \frac{\partial \varrho}{\partial t}.$$

The rate of change of density is thus in part due to the change at the point (x, y, z), and in part to the rate at which the fluid at this point is flowing to other parts of the field where the density is different. The process of forming this kind of derivative with respect to the time is known as *particle differentiation*. The symbol for the total derivative is employed to distinguish this time derivative from the time rate of change at a point fixed in space. The notation $\dfrac{D\varrho}{Dt}$ is also used.

The definition of incompressibility is now

$$\frac{d\varrho}{dt} = 0$$

throughout the region considered.

We shall see that in case no sources or sinks are present, this concept of incompressibility coincides with that of § 4 (p. 36). This will be a consequence of the equation of continuity, which we now derive. This equation amounts simply to an accounting for all the mass in the field. We shall assume that the components of the velocity and the density have continuous derivatives, and allow for continuously distributed sources, the density of the distribution of sources being denoted by $\sigma = \sigma\,(x, y, z, t)$. Thus at any point P, σ cubic centimetres of fluid per second per unit of volume at P are accounted for by the sources, as measured by the limit of the rate of efflux from a region containing P to the volume of the region, as the region shrinks to a point. More concretely, it means that $\varrho\sigma$ units of mass per second per unit of volume are added by the sources to the fluid. Thus, in the region T,

$$\iiint_T \varrho\,\sigma\,dV$$

units of mass per second are added by the sources.

The same region may gain in mass through the streaming in of fluid through its bounding surface S. Just as in § 5 (p. 37) we found

$$\iint_S V_n\,dS$$

for the rate at which a given portion of the fluid was expanding, so we may now show the number of units of mass entering T through S per second is

$$-\iint_S \varrho\,V_n\,dS.$$

Thus the total time rate of increase of mass in T is

$$\iiint_T \varrho\,\sigma\,dV - \iint_S \varrho\,V_n\,dS.$$

But the mass in T at any instant is the integral of the density over T, so that the time rate of increase of mass in T is the derivative of this integral, the region T being fixed

$$\frac{\partial}{\partial t}\iiint_T \varrho\,dV = \iiint_T \frac{\partial\varrho}{\partial t}\,dV,$$

differentiation under the integral sign being permitted on the hypothesis that the density has continuous derivatives. Equating the two expressions for the rate of gain in mass, we have

$$\iiint_T \varrho\,\sigma\,dV - \iint_S \varrho\,V_n\,dS = \iiint_T \frac{\partial\varrho}{\partial t}\,dV.$$

In order to draw conclusions as to the relation between density, source density and velocity, at a point, we must transform the surface integral to a volume integral. This service will be rendered by the divergence theorem. We replace, in that theorem as stated in the equations (9), X, Y, Z by $\varrho X, \varrho Y, \varrho Z$. It becomes

$$\iiint_T \left[\frac{\partial}{\partial x}\varrho X + \frac{\partial}{\partial y}\varrho Y + \frac{\partial}{\partial z}\varrho Z\right]dV = \iint_S \varrho\,V_n\,dS.$$

Accordingly, the preceding equation takes the form

$$\iiint_T \left[\frac{\partial\varrho}{\partial t} + \frac{\partial}{\partial x}\varrho X + \frac{\partial}{\partial y}\varrho Y + \frac{\partial}{\partial z}\varrho Z - \varrho\,\sigma\right]dV = 0.$$

This must hold for any region T. Accordingly, the integrand, being continuous, must vanish everywhere, in accordance with the reasoning at the beginning of § 6 (p. 40). Carrying out the indicated differentiations, we have

$$\frac{\partial \varrho}{\partial t} + X \frac{\partial \varrho}{\partial x} + Y \frac{\partial \varrho}{\partial y} + Z \frac{\partial \varrho}{\partial z} + \varrho \left[\frac{\partial X}{\partial x} + \frac{\partial Y}{\partial y} + \frac{\partial Z}{\partial z} \right] - \varrho \, \sigma = 0 \, ,$$

or, employing the formula (12) for the particle derivative, and dividing by ϱ, we may reduce this to

$$\frac{1}{\varrho} \frac{d\varrho}{dt} + \operatorname{div} \boldsymbol{V} - \sigma = 0 \, .$$

This is the desired *equation of continuity* of hydrodynamics.

We see from the equation of continuity that *in the absence of sources* ($\sigma = 0$), *the vanishing of the divergence is a necessary and sufficient condition that the fluid be incompressible.* Furthermore, we see that *in the case of an incompressible fluid, the divergence is equal to the source density.*

Chapter III.

The Potential.

1. Work and Potential Energy.

The properties of fields of force developed in the last chapter grouped themselves naturally about the divergence, and were concerned especially with solenoidal fields, among which are the fields due to matter acting in accordance with Newton's law. We are now to develop a second property of Newtonian fields and study its implications.

A particle of mass m, subject only to the force of a specific field $X, Y, Z)$ will move in accordance with Newton's second law of motion

$$m \frac{d^2 x}{dt^2} = \lambda \, m \, X \, , \qquad m \frac{d^2 y}{dt^2} = \lambda \, m \, Y \, , \qquad m \frac{d^2 z}{dt^2} = \lambda \, m \, Z \, ,$$

where λ is a constant depending on the units used. If these equations be multiplied by $\frac{dx}{dt}$, $\frac{dy}{dt}$ and $\frac{dz}{dt}$, respectively, and added, the result is

$$\frac{1}{2} \, m \frac{d}{dt} \left[\left(\frac{dx}{dt} \right)^2 + \left(\frac{dy}{dt} \right)^2 + \left(\frac{dz}{dt} \right)^2 \right] = \lambda \, m \left(X \frac{dx}{dt} + Y \frac{dy}{dt} + Z \frac{dz}{dt} \right).$$

The left hand member of this equation is the time derivative of the kinetic energy of the particle, $T = \frac{1}{2} \, m v^2$. If we integrate both sides of the equation with respect to t from t_0 to t, we have

$$T - T_0 = \lambda\, m \int_{t_0}^{t} \left(X \frac{dx}{dt} + Y \frac{dy}{dt} + Z \frac{dz}{dt} \right) dt$$

$$= \lambda\, m \int_{P_0}^{P} (X\, dx + Y\, dy + Z\, dz)$$

$$= \lambda\, m\, W\, (P,\, P_0;\, C),$$

C being the path of the particle. The expressions on the right,—the last a notation—, are known as the *work* done on the particle by the field during the motion, and the equation states that *the change in kinetic energy during a time interval is equal to the work done by the forces of the field during the motion in that interval.*

Let us examine whether the result is of value in determining the character of the motion. In order to determine the work done, we must evaluate the integral on the right. At first sight, it would seem that we must know the velocity of the particle at every instant of the motion. But the second expression shows that this is not necessary. It does, however, demand a knowledge of the path travelled by the particle, and this, as a rule, is not known in advance. We can, however, dispense with a knowledge of the path in the important special case in which the field is such that the integral is *independent of the path*, *i. e.* has the same values when taken over any two paths[1] connecting P_0 with P which can be continuously deformed one into the other, and this for any pair of points P_0, P. The work is then merely a function of the positions of P_0 and P, and we may drop the argument C in the notation. Under these circumstances, the field is called *conservative*, or *lamellar*. P_0 being thought of as a fixed point, the function of P (x, y, z), $- \lambda\, m\, W\, (P, P_0)$, is called the *potential energy* of the particle at P, and the above equation states that the total energy is constant during the motion. The energy equation, or the principle of the conservation of energy, is most useful in problems of mechanics, and the fact lends a special interest to conservative fields.

Let us now consider conservative fields. Furthermore, let us confine ourselves to a region in which the force is continuous, and which is *simply connected*, *i. e.* such that any two paths with the same end-points may be continuously deformed one into the other without leaving the region[2]. We take units for which $\lambda = 1$. The function

(1) $$W\, (P,\, P_0) = \int_{P_0}^{P} (X\, dx + Y\, dy + Z\, dz)$$

---

[1] Any two *regular* curves, in the sense of Chapter IV.
[2] See § 9, page 74.

is determined by the field only, and we may speak of it as the work per unit of mass, or the work of the specific field. We shall not even have to bother with its dependence on P_0. A change in the position of this point will merely mean adding a constant to the function, namely, the work between the two positions of P_0, taken with the proper sign.

We shall now show that the work function completely determines the field, assuming that it arises from a continuous field of force. But two preliminary remarks should be made.

The first is concerned with the notion of *directional* derivative. Let $W(P)$ be a function of the coördinates (x, y, z) of P, defined in a neighborhood of P_1, and let α denote a ray, or a directed straight line segment, issuing from P_1. We define the derivative of W in the direction α by

$$\frac{\partial W}{\partial \alpha} = \lim \frac{W(P) - W(P_1)}{PP_1}$$

as P approaches P_1 along the ray, provided this limit exists. The directional derivative is thus a *one-sided derivative*, since P is confined to the ray, which extends from P_1 in only one sense. The reader may show that if α has the direction cosines l, m, n, the derivative of W in the direction α has the value

$$\frac{\partial W}{\partial \alpha} = \frac{\partial W}{\partial x} l + \frac{\partial W}{\partial y} m + \frac{\partial W}{\partial z} n,$$

provided the derivatives which appear are continuous. He may also show that on the same hypothesis, the directional derivatives at P_1 in two opposite directions are numerically equal and opposite in sign.

The second remark is to the effect that the work integral (1) is independent of the coördinate system involved in its definition. Since it is the limit of a sum of terms of the form

$$X_k \Delta x_k + Y_k \Delta y_k + Z_k \Delta z_k,$$

it is only necessary to show that this expression can be given a form independent of the coördinate system. It is, in fact, a combination of two vectors, (X_k, Y_k, Z_k) and $(\Delta x_k, \Delta y_k, \Delta z_k)$, known as their *scalar product*[1], and whose value is the product of their magnitudes times the cosine of the angle between them. For if F_k is the magnitude, and l, m, n, are the direction cosines of the first vector, and if Δs_k and and l', m', n' are the corresponding quantities for the second, the above expression is equal to

$$F_k \Delta s_k (ll' + mm' + nn') = F_k \Delta s_k \cos(F_k, \Delta s_k),$$

as stated. Incidentally, we see that the expression for the work may be written

$$W(P, P_0) = \int_{P_0}^{P} F \cos \vartheta \, ds,$$

---

[1] See the footnote, page 123.

where ϑ is the angle between the force and the forward direction of the tangent to the path.

Let us suppose now that the work function is known, and that it belongs to a continuous field (X, Y, Z). We compute its derivative in the direction of the x-axis at P_1. We take the path from P_0 to P_1 (x, y, z) along any convenient curve, and the path from P_0 to P $(x + \Delta x, y, z)$ along the same curve to P_1, and then along the straight line to P. Then, by (1),

$$\frac{W(P) - W(P_1)}{\overline{PP_1}} = \frac{1}{\Delta x} \int_{x}^{x + \Delta x} X(x, y, z)\, dx = X(x + \vartheta \Delta x, y, z),$$

$$0 < \vartheta < 1, \quad \Delta x > 0,$$

by the law of the mean. This gives in the limit, as $PP_1 = \Delta x$ approaches 0,

$$X = \frac{\partial W}{\partial x}.$$

Since the work is independent of the axis system, it follows that the above result holds for any direction, that is, that *the component of the field in any direction is equal to the derivative of the work in that direction.* In particular,

$$X = \frac{\partial W}{\partial x}, \quad Y = \frac{\partial W}{\partial y}, \quad Z = \frac{\partial W}{\partial z}.$$

Thus a great advantage of a conservative field is that it can be specified by a single function W, whereas the general field requires three functions, X, Y, and Z, or their equivalents, to determine it. Because it determines the field in this way, the work is sometimes called the *force function.*

Any field which has a force function with continuous derivatives is obviously conservative. For if the field (X, Y, Z) has the force function Φ with continuous derivatives,

$$X = \frac{\partial \Phi}{\partial x}, \quad Y = \frac{\partial \Phi}{\partial y}, \quad Z = \frac{\partial \Phi}{\partial z},$$

and

$$W(P, P_0) = \int_{P_0}^{P} \left(\frac{\partial \Phi}{\partial x}\, dx + \frac{\partial \Phi}{\partial y}\, dy + \frac{\partial \Phi}{\partial z}\, dz \right) = \int_{P_0}^{P} d\Phi = \Phi(P) - \Phi(P_0),$$

and the integral is independent of the path because the last expression depends only on the end points.

Thus the notions of work and force function are equivalent, and both are essentially,—*i. e.* except for a positive constant factor, depending on the mass of the particle acted on and the units employed,—the negative of the potential energy. Hereafter, we shall consider the mass of the particle acted on as unity, and assume that the units have been so chosen that the potential energy is equal to the negative of the force function.

It is now easy to verify that *Newtonian fields have force functions*[1]. Taking first a unit particle at Q (ξ, η, ζ), we see that the force due to it at P (x, y, z) is given by

$$X = \frac{\xi - x}{r^3} = \frac{\partial}{\partial x} \frac{1}{r}, \quad Y = \frac{\eta - y}{r^3} = \frac{\partial}{\partial y} \frac{1}{r}, \quad Z = \frac{\zeta - z}{r^3} = \frac{\partial}{\partial z} \frac{1}{r},$$

so that $\frac{1}{r}$ is a force function. It follows also that the field of a system of a finite number of particles has a force function, namely the sum of the force functions of the fields due to the separate particles. Also, the fields of all the distributions we have studied have force functions, namely the integrals of the products of the density by $\frac{1}{r}$, provided it is permitted to differentiate under the signs of integration, and we know that this is the case at all points outside the masses. As a matter of fact, we shall see that in the case of the usual volume distributions, the force function continues to be available at interior points of the distribution (p. 152).

If a field had two force functions, the derivatives of their difference with respect to x, y and z would vanish, so that this difference would be constant. Hence the force function of any field which has one, is determined to within an additive constant.

We now introduce the idea of *potential*[2] of a field, which in some cases coincides with the force function, and in others with the negative of the force function. In the case of general fields of force not specifically due to elements attracting or repelling according to Newton's law, there is a lack of agreement of writers, some defining it as the work done by the field, and thus making it the same as the force function and so the negative of potential energy, while others define it as the work done *against* the field, and so identifying it with potential energy and the negative of the force function. In vector analysis, whenever abstract fields are considered, the first definition is usual. The field (X, Y, Z) is then called the *gradient* of the potential U,

$$(X, Y, Z) = \operatorname{grad} U = \left(\frac{\partial U}{\partial x}, \frac{\partial U}{\partial y}, \frac{\partial U}{\partial z} \right).$$

We shall adopt this definition in the case of abstract fields, general force fields, and velocity fields.

On the other hand, in the theory of Newtonian potentials, authori-

---

[1] This fact was first noticed by LAGRANGE, Mémoires de l'Académie Royale des Sciences de Paris, Savants étrangèrs, Vol. VII (1773); Oeuvres, Vol. VI, p. 348.

[2] Called *potential function* by GREEN, l. c. footnote, page 38, *potential* by GAUSS, *Allgemeine Lehrsätze in Beziehung auf die im verkehrten Verhältnis des Quadrates der Entfernung wirkenden Anziehungs- und Abstoßungskräfte*, Werke, Bd. V, p. 200 ff.

ties are in substantial agreement, defining the potential of a positive unit particle, point charge, or magnetic pole, as $\frac{1}{r}$, and the potentials of various distributions as the corresponding integrals of the densities times $\frac{1}{r}$ (see Exercise 4, below). This convention has as consequence the great convenience of a uniformity of sign in the formulas for the potentials of all the various types of distributions. It does result, however, in a difference in the relation of the potential to the field, according as the force between elements of like sign is attractive or repulsive. Because of the puzzling confusion which is likely to meet the reader, we summarize the conventions as follows.

In abstract fields, $(X, Y, Z) = \text{grad } U$; the potential corresponds to the force function and the negative of potential energy.

In Newtonian fields, the potential at P due to a unit element at Q is $\frac{1}{r}$, and

a) if elements of like sign attract, as in gravitation, $(X, Y, Z) = \text{grad } U$; the potential is the force function, and the negative of potential energy,

b) if elements of like sign repel, as in electricity and magnetism, $(X, Y, Z) = -\text{grad } U$; the potential is the negative of the force function, and is identical with potential energy.

Furthermore, in the theory of Newtonian potentials, it is customary to fix the additive constant which enters, by some convenient convention. In case the distribution is such that the potential approaches a limit as P recedes indefinitely far, no matter in what direction, the constant is fixed so that this limit shall be 0; in other words, so that the zero of potential shall be at infinity. This is always possible where the masses are confined to a bounded portion of space. Cases arise, especially in connection with the logarithmic potential (see page 63) where this is not the situation, and the convention must be modified.

Exercises.

1. Show that a constant force field $(0, 0, -g)$ is conservative, a) by exhibiting a force function, and b) by showing that the work is independent of the path.

2. The same for any central force field (see Exercise 3, page 37).

3. The same for any axial force field (see Exercise 4, page 37).

4. Show that the work done by the field in bringing a unit particle from P_0 to P, in the field of a unit particle at Q, is $\frac{1}{r} + C$. Show that as the distance of P_0 from Q becomes infinite, C tends toward 0.

5. Show that if the components of a field have continuous partial derivatives, a necessary condition that it be conservative is

$$\frac{\partial Z}{\partial y} = \frac{\partial Y}{\partial z}, \qquad \frac{\partial X}{\partial z} = \frac{\partial Z}{\partial x}, \qquad \frac{\partial Y}{\partial x} = \frac{\partial X}{\partial y}.$$

6. Show that the condition that a field be conservative in a region in which it is continuous is equivalent to this, that the work integral (1), taken over any closed path in the region, which can be continuously shrunk to a point without leaving the region, shall vanish.

7. Apply the result of Exercise 5 to the field $X = \dfrac{-y}{\varrho^2}$, $Y = \dfrac{x}{\varrho^2}$, $Z = 0$, where $\varrho = \sqrt{x^2 + y^2}$. Then show that the work done by the field in carrying a unit particle over the circle $x^2 + y^2 = a^2$, $z = 0$, in the counter clockwise sense, is 2π. Does any contradiction arise? Show that the work over any closed path which does not make a loop around the z-axis, is 0.

8. Find the work done by the field $(y, 0, 0)$ in moving a unit particle from $(0, 0, 0)$ to $(1, 1, 0)$ over the following paths in the (x, y)-plane: a) the broken line with vertices $(0,0)$, $(0,1)$, $(1,1)$, b) the broken line with vertices $(0,0)$, $(1,0)$, $(1,1)$, c) the parabolic arc $y = x^2$. Show how a path can be assigned which will give as large a value to the work as we please.

9. Show that the gradient of a function is the vector which points in the direction of the maximum rate of increase of the function, and whose magnitude is the rate of increase, or the directional derivative of the function, in this direction.

2. Equipotential Surfaces.

We are now in a position to form a second kind of picture of a force field in case it is conservative. If U denote the potential of the field, the surfaces $U = $ const. are called *equipotential surfaces* or equipotentials. At every point of the field (assumed continuous), its direction is normal to the equipotential surface through the point. For the equipotential surface has, as direction ratios of its normal, the partial derivatives of U with respect to x, y, z, and these are the components of the force. An exception arises only at the points where the three partial derivatives all vanish. Here the field cannot be said to have a direction. Such points are points of equilibrium.

But more than this, the equipotential surfaces give an idea of the intensity of the force. Let us imagine a system of equipotential surfaces, $U = k$, $U = k + c$, $U = k + 2c, \ldots$ corresponding to constant differences of the potential. Let P be a point on one of these surfaces, and let N denote the magnitude of the force at P. Then, since the force is normal to the equipotential surface, N is also the component of the force normal to the surface, and as such

$$\frac{\partial U}{\partial n} = N,$$

the normal being taken in the sense of increasing potential. If Δn is the distance along the normal from P to the next equipotential surface of the set constructed, the corresponding ΔU is c, and we have

$$N \Delta n = c + \zeta$$

where the ratio of ζ to c approaches 0, when c is given values approaching 0.

We see, then, from the approximate equation $N = \dfrac{c}{\Delta n}$, that the smaller c, the more accurate is the statement: *the intensity of the field is inversely proportional to the distance between equipotential surfaces.* Crowded equipotentials mean great force, and sparse equipotentials, slight force. The reliability of such a picture in a given region is the greater the more the equipotentials approximate, in the region, a system of equally spaced planes.

In certain cases, simple graphical representations of the equipotential surfaces are possible. If the direction of the field is always parallel to a fixed plane, the equipotential surfaces will be cylindrical, and the curves in which they cut the fixed plane will completely characterize them. Again, if the field has an axis of symmetry, such that the force at any point lies in the plane through that point and the axis, and such that a rotation through any angle about the axis carries the field into itself, the equipotential surfaces will be surfaces of revolution, with the axis of symmetry of the field as axis. A meridian section of an equipotential surface will then characterize it[1].

Exercises.

1. Draw equipotentials and lines of force for the pairs of particles in Exercises 3, 4 and 5 (page 31). Describe the character of the equipotential surfaces in the neighborhood of points of equilibrium, particularly of those which pass through such points. Show that in Exercise 4, one of the equipotential surfaces is a sphere.

2. In the above exercise, any closed equipotential surface containing the two particles, may be regarded as the surface of a charged conductor, and the field outside the surface will be the field of the charge. Inside the conductor there is no force (see Chapter VII, § 1, page 176), so that the lines of the diagram would have to be erased. Describe, at least qualitatively, the shapes of certain conductors the electrostatic field of charges on which are thus pictured.

3. Draw equipotentials and lines of force for the field obtained by superimposing the field of a particle on a constant field.

3. Potentials of Special Distributions.

We saw, in the last section, that the potentials of line, surface and volume distributions are

$$(2) \qquad U = \int_C \frac{\lambda}{r}\, ds,$$

$$(3) \qquad U = \iint_S \frac{\sigma}{r}\, dS,$$

$$(4) \qquad U = \iiint_V \frac{\varkappa}{r}\, dV,$$

---

[1] For a method of construction of equipotentials in certain cases of this sort, see MAXWELL, *A Treatise on Electricity and Magnetism*, 3d Ed., Oxford 1892, Vol. I, § 123. Interesting plates are to be found at the end of the volume.

valid at points of free space. The same integrals are regarded as defining the potential at points of the distributions, provided they converge. This is generally the case for surface and volume distributions, but not for line distributions. But the formulation and proof of theorems of this sort, and of theorems assuring us that the force components are still the derivatives of the potential at interior points, is a task which had better be postponed for a systematic study in a later chapter. We shall content ourselves for the present with the verification of certain facts of this sort in connection with the study of the potentials of special bodies in the following exercises.

Exercises.

1. Find the potential of a homogeneous straight wire segment. Answer, the value of the potential in the (x, z)-plane is

$$U = \lambda \log \frac{\sqrt{x^2 + (c_2 - z)^2} + c_2 - z}{\sqrt{x^2 + (c_1 - z)^2} + c_1 - z},$$

where $(0, 0, c_1)$ and $(0, 0, c_2)$ are the ends of the wire. Show also that this result may be given the form

$$U = \frac{2M}{l} \coth^{-1} \frac{r_1 + r_2}{l},$$

where l is the length of the wire, and r_1 and r_2 are the distances from P to its ends. Thus show that the equipotential surfaces are ellipsoids of revolution with their foci at the ends of the wire.

2. Show that at a point of its axis, a homogeneous circular wire has the potential $U = \frac{M}{d}$, where d is the distance of P from a point of the wire. Check the result of Exercise 4 (p. 10), by differentiating U in the direction of the axis.

3. Reverting to the potential of the straight wire of Exercise 1, verify the following facts: a) as P approaches a point of the wire, U becomes infinite; b) P, the density, and the line of the wire remaining fixed, U becomes infinite as the length of the wire becomes infinite in both directions. Note that in this case, the demand that the potential vanish at infinity is not a possible one. Show, however, that c) if the potential of the wire segment is first altered by the subtraction of a suitable constant (i. e. a number independent of the position of P), say the value of the potential at some fixed point at a unit distance from the line of the wire, the potential thus altered will approach a finite limit as the wire is prolonged infinitely in both directions, independently of the order in which c_2 and $- c_1$ become infinite. Show that this limit is

$$2 \lambda \log \left(\frac{1}{r}\right),$$

where r is the distance of P from the wire. Finally, show d) that this is the value obtained for the work done by the force field of the infinite wire (see Exercise 5, page 10) in moving a unit particle from P_0, at a unit distance from the wire, to P.

4. Find the potential at a point of its axis of a homogeneous circular disk. Verify the following facts: a) the integral for the potential at the center of the disk is convergent; b) the potential is everywhere continuous on the axis; c) the derivative of the potential in the direction of the axis, with a fixed sense, experiences an abrupt change of $- 4 \pi \sigma$ as P passes through the disk in the direction of differentiation (compare with § 6, page 11).

5. Find the potential of a homogeneous plane rectangular lamina at a point of the normal to the lamina through one corner. If O denotes this corner, B and C adjacent corners distant b and c from it, and D the diagonally opposite corner, the answer may be written

$$U = \sigma\left[c \log \frac{b + d_3}{d_2} + b \log \frac{c + d_3}{d_1} - x \tan^{-1}\frac{bc}{xd_3}\right],$$

where $x = \overline{PO}$, $d_1 = \overline{PB}$, $d_2 = \overline{PC}$,   and $d_3 = \overline{PD}$.

Note. In obtaining this result, the following formula of integration will prove useful:

$$\int \log (b + \sqrt{x^2 + b^2 + \zeta^2})\, d\zeta = \zeta \log (b + \sqrt{x^2 + b^2 + \zeta^2}) +$$
$$+ b \log (\zeta + \sqrt{x^2 + b^2 + \zeta^2}) - \zeta + x \tan^{-1}\frac{\zeta}{x} - x \tan^{-1}\frac{b\,x}{x\sqrt{x^2 + b^2 + \zeta^2}}.$$

It may be verified by differentiation, or derived by integration by parts.

6. By the addition or subtraction of rectangles, the preceding exercise gives, without further integrations, the potential at any point due to a homogeneous rectangular lamina. Let us suppose, however, that we have a rectangular lamina whose density is a different constant in each of four rectangles into which it is divided by parallels to its sides. Show that the potential is continuous on the normal through the common corner of the four rectangles of constant density, and that the derivative in the direction of the normal with a fixed sense changes abruptly by -4π times the average of the densities, as P passes through the lamina in the direction of differentiation.

7. Study the potential of an infinite homogeneous plane lamina, following the lines of Exercise 3. Take as a basis a plane rectangular lamina, and check the results by a circular lamina. The potential should turn out to be $2\pi\sigma\,(1-|x|)$, if the lamina lies in the (y, z)-plane.

8. Show that the potential of a homogeneous spherical lamina is, at exterior points, the same as if the shell were concentrated at its center, and at interior points, constant, and equal to the limiting value of the potential at exterior points. Determine the behavior with respect to continuity of the derivatives of the potential, in the directions of a radius and of a tangent, at a point of the lamina.

9. Find the potential of a homogeneous solid sphere at interior and exterior points. Show that the potential and all of its partial derivatives of the first order are continuous throughout space, and are always equal to the corresponding components of the force. Show, on the other hand, that the derivative, in the direction of the radius, of the radial component of the force, experiences a break at the surface of the sphere. Show, finally, that

$$\text{div}\,(X,\, Y,\, Z) = \frac{\partial^2 U}{\partial x^2} + \frac{\partial^2 U}{\partial y^2} + \frac{\partial^2 U}{\partial z^2}$$

is 0 at exterior points, and $-4\pi\varkappa$ at interior points.

10. Given a homogeneous hollow sphere, draw graphs of the potential, its derivative in the direction of a radius, and of its second derivative in this direction, as functions of the distance from the center on this radius. Describe the character of these curves from the standpoint of the continuity of ordinates, slopes and curvatures.

11. The density of a certain sphere is a continuous function, $\varkappa\,(s)$ of the distance s from the center. Show that its potential is

$$U = 4\pi \left[\frac{1}{s} \int\limits_0^s \varkappa(\varrho)\, \varrho^2\, d\varrho + \int\limits_s^a \varkappa(\varrho)\, \varrho\, d\varrho \right], \quad 0 < s \leqq a,$$

$$= 4\pi \frac{1}{s} \int\limits_0^a \varkappa(\varrho)\, \varrho^2\, d\varrho = \frac{M}{s}, \qquad\qquad a \leqq s.$$

Show that at any interior point,

$$\frac{\partial^2 U}{\partial x^2} + \frac{\partial^2 U}{\partial y^2} + \frac{\partial^2 U}{\partial z^2} = -4\pi\varkappa.$$

12. Show that in any Newtonian field of force in which the partial derivatives of the components of the force are continuous, the last equation of the preceding exercise holds. Use Gauss' theorem.

13. In a gravitational field, potential and potential energy are proportional, with a negative constant of proportionality, and the equation of energy of § 1 (p. 49) becomes $T - kU = C$, where $k > 0$, or

$$\frac{1}{2} mv^2 = kU + C.$$

The constant k can be determined, if the force at any point is known, by differentiating this equation, and equating mass times acceleration to the proper multiple of the force, according to the units employed. Thus if the unit of mass is the pound, of length, the foot, of time, the second, and of force, the poundal, then the mass times the vector acceleration is equal to the vector force, by Newton's second law of motion.

This being given, determine the velocity with which a meteor would strike the earth in falling from a very great distance (i. e. with a velocity corresponding to a limiting value 0 as the distance from the earth becomes infinite). Show that if the meteor fell from a distance equal to that of the moon, it would reach the earth with a velocity about $1/60$ less. The radius of the earth may be taken as 3955 miles, and the distance of the moon as 238000 miles. The answer to the first part of the problem is about 36700 feet per second. Most meteors, as a matter of fact, are dissipated before reaching the earth's surface because of the heat generated by friction with the earth's atmosphere.

14. Joule demonstrated the equivalence of heat with mechanical energy. The heat which will raise the temperature of a pound of water one degree Farenheit is equivalent to 778 foot pounds of energy. A mass of m pounds, moving with a velocity of v feet per second, has $\frac{1}{2} mv^2$ foot poundals, or $\dfrac{\frac{1}{2} mv^2}{g}$ $(g = 32\cdot2)$ foot pounds of kinetic energy.

Show that if all the energy of the meteor in the last exercise were converted into heat, and this heat retained in the meteor, it would raise its temperature by about 178000° Fahrenheit. Take as the specific heat of the meteor (iron), 0·15.

4. The Potential of a Homogeneous Circumference.

The attraction and potential of a homogeneous circular wire have been found, so far, only at points of the axis of the wire. While the potential at a general point may be expressed simply in terms of elliptic integrals, we pause for a moment to give a treatment of the problem due to GAUSS, partly because of the inherent elegance of his method, and partly because of incidental points of interest which emerge.

Let the (x, y)-plane be taken as the plane of the wire, with origin at the center, and with the (x, z)-plane through the attracted particle P (fig. 8). Let a denote the radius of the wire, and ϑ the usual polar coördinate of the variable point Q. The coördinates of P and Q are $(x, 0, z)$ and $(a \cos \vartheta, a \sin \vartheta, 0)$, so that the distance $r = \overline{PQ}$ is given by

$$r^2 = x^2 + a^2 + z^2 - 2ax \cos \vartheta.$$

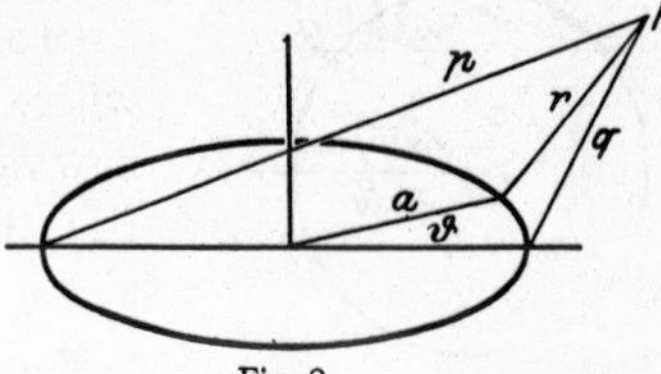

Accordingly,

Fig. 8.

$$(5) \quad U = 2a\lambda \int_0^\pi \frac{d\vartheta}{\sqrt{x^2 + a^2 + z^2 - 2ax \cos \vartheta}}.$$

We now express r in terms of its greatest value p for any position of Q, and its least value q. As

$$p^2 = (x + a)^2 + z^2, \qquad q^2 = (x - a)^2 + z^2,$$

we find, on forming half the sum and half the difference of these quantities, that

$$r^2 = \frac{p^2 + q^2}{2} - \frac{p^2 - q^2}{2} \cos \vartheta = p^2 \sin^2 \frac{\vartheta}{2} + q^2 \cos^2 \frac{\vartheta}{2}.$$

If this expression is substituted for the radicand in (5), and a new variable of integration introduced by the substitution $\vartheta = \pi - 2\varphi$, the result is

$$(6) \quad U = 4a\lambda \int_0^{\frac{\pi}{2}} \frac{d\varphi}{\sqrt{p^2 \cos^2 \varphi + q^2 \sin^2 \varphi}} = \frac{4a\lambda}{p} \int_0^{\frac{\pi}{2}} \frac{d\varphi}{\sqrt{\cos^2 \varphi + \frac{q^2}{p^2} \sin^2 \varphi}}.$$

The last integral depends only on the ratio $\frac{q}{p}$. Hence, if we can find the potential at any point where this ratio has a given value, we can find it at all points where it has this value. Now the locus of points of the (x, z)-plane for which $\frac{q}{p}$ is constant is a circle with respect to which the two points in which the wire cuts the (x, z)-plane are inverse[1]. Let P_1 be the point of this circle in the (x, y)-plane and interior to the circle of the wire. Then if p_1 denotes the maximum distance of P_1

---

[1] We shall have use again for the fact that the locus of points in a plane, the ratio of whose distances from two points A and B of the plane is constant, is a circle with respect to which A und B are inverse points, i. e. points on the same ray from the center, the product of whose distances from the center is the square of the radius of the circle. The reader should make himself familiar with this theorem if he is not so already.

from the wire, we see from (6) that $p\,U(P) = p_1 U(P_1)$, so that

(7) $$U(P) = \frac{p_1}{p}\,U(P_1).$$

Thus the problem is reduced to finding the potential at the points of a radius of the wire.

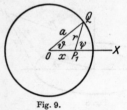

Fig. 9.

To do this, we return to the expression (5), where z is now 0, and $0 \leq x < a$. We introduce as new variable of integration the angle $\psi = \sphericalangle\,X P_1 Q$ (fig. 9). By the sine law of trigonometry,

$$a \sin (\psi - \vartheta) = x \sin \psi.$$

Differentiating this, we find

$$a \cos (\psi - \vartheta)\,(d\psi - d\vartheta) = x \cos \psi\,d\psi,$$

or,

$$[a \cos (\psi - \vartheta) - x \cos \psi]\,d\psi = a \cos (\psi - \vartheta)\,d\vartheta.$$

The coefficient of $d\psi$ is the projection of $P_1 O Q$ on $P_1 Q$, and is therefore equal to $P_1 Q$, or r. Thus

$$r\,d\psi = a \cos (\psi - \vartheta)\,d\vartheta,$$

and

$$\frac{d\vartheta}{r} = \frac{d\psi}{a \cos (\psi - \vartheta)} = \frac{d\psi}{\sqrt{a^2 - a^2 \sin^2 (\psi - \vartheta)}} = \frac{d\psi}{\sqrt{a^2 - x^2 \sin^2 \psi}}$$

$$= \frac{d\psi}{\sqrt{a^2 \cos^2 \psi + (a^2 - x^2) \sin^2 \psi}}.$$

The limits of integration for ψ are again 0 and π, but the substitution $\psi' = \pi - \psi$ shows that the integral from $\frac{\pi}{2}$ to π is equal to that from 0 to $\frac{\pi}{2}$, so we may write

$$U(P_1) = 4\,a\,\lambda \int\limits_0^{\frac{\pi}{2}} \frac{d\psi}{\sqrt{a^2 \cos^2 \psi + (a^2 - x^2) \sin^2 \psi}}.$$

If we introduce the maximum and minimum distances, p_1 and q_1 of P_1 from the wire, since $p_1 = a + x$ and $q_1 = a - x$, we see that

$$a = \frac{p_1 + q_1}{2} = p_2, \quad \text{and} \quad \sqrt{a^2 - x^2} = \sqrt{p_1 q_1} = q_2$$

are the arithmetic and geometric means of p_1 and q_1, and

$$U(P_1) = 4\,a\,\lambda \int\limits_0^{\frac{\pi}{2}} \frac{d\psi}{\sqrt{p_2^2 \cos^2 \psi + q_2^2 \sin^2 \psi}}.$$

Comparing this value with that given by (6), which is valid for $P = P_1$, $p = p_1$, $q = q_1$, we see that *the integral is unchanged by the substitution for p_1 of the arithmetic mean p_2 of p_1 and q_1, and for q_1 of the geometric mean q_2 of p_1 and q_1*. The substitution may now be repeated, with the result that $U(P_1)$ remains unchanged if we substitute

$$p_{n+1} = \frac{p_n + q_n}{2} \text{ for } p_n, \text{ and } q_{n+1} = \sqrt{p_n q_n} \text{ for } q_n,$$

for $n = 1, 2, 3 \dots,$. The significance of this remark lies in the fact that the sequences $[p_n]$ and $[q_n]$ tend to a common limit α as n becomes infinite, so that

$$(8) \qquad U(P_1) = 4 a \lambda \int_0^{\frac{\pi}{2}} \frac{d\psi}{\sqrt{\alpha^2 \cos^2 \psi + \alpha^2 \sin^2 \psi}} = \frac{4 a \lambda}{\alpha} \cdot \frac{\pi}{2} = \frac{M}{\alpha}.$$

To demonstrate the stated convergence, we observe first that p_2 lies midway between p_1 and q_1, and secondly that q_2 lies between q_1 and p_2, for

$$\frac{q_2}{q_1} = \sqrt{\frac{p_1}{q_1}} > 1, \text{ and } p_2 - q_2 = \frac{(p_1 + q_1 - 2\sqrt{p_1 q_1})}{2} = \frac{(\sqrt{p_1} - \sqrt{q_1})^2}{2} > 0.$$

Thus q_2 lies in the interval (q_1, p_2), whose length is half that of (q_1, p_1), and so $0 < p_2 - q_2 < \frac{(p_1 - q_1)}{2}$. As the same inequalities hold when the indices 1 and 2 are replaced by n and $n + 1$, we conclude that

$$0 < p_{n+1} - q_{n+1} < \frac{p_1 - q_1}{2^n}.$$

The sequences $[q_n]$ and $[p_n]$ are always increasing and always decreasing, respectively. The first is bounded above by p_1 and the second is bounded below by q_1. Hence they converge. The last inequality shows that their limits coincide. This limit α is called the *arithmetico-geometric* mean of the two positive quantities q_1, p_1. We have supposed q_1 and p_1 unequal. If they are equal, P_1 is at the center of the wire, and the potential at that point is $\frac{M}{a}$.

To determine the potential at P, then, we first determine the extreme values p and q of r. We then determine the numbers p_1 and q_1 by the equations $p_1 + q_1 = 2a$, $\frac{p_1}{q_1} = \frac{p}{q}$,

$$p_1 = \frac{2 a p}{p + q}, \qquad q_1 = \frac{2 a q}{p + q}.$$

We then determine the arithmetico-geometric mean of p_1 and q_1, to a suitable degree of accuracy, and this gives us the potential at P_1 to a corresponding degree of accuracy, by (8). Then (7) gives the potential at P.

Thus the problem is solved. The potential of a homogeneous circular wire will be found in another way in Chapter X, § 3.

Exercises.

1. Interpret the process of substituting means, as the reduction of the potential of the wire to that of a wire of the same mass and smaller radius, at a point relatively nearer the center, yielding in the limit, the potential at the center of a wire of radius α.

2. The last inequality given shows that the sequences of means converge at least as rapidly as a geometric sequence with common ratio $\frac{1}{2}$. Show, in fact, that the convergence is considerably more rapid by deriving the equation

$$p_{n+1} - q_{n+1} = \frac{p_n - q_n}{2} \cdot \frac{1 - \sqrt{\frac{q_n}{p_n}}}{1 + \sqrt{\frac{q_n}{p_n}}},$$

and noticing that $\frac{q_n}{p_n}$ is approaching 1.

3. Calculate the potential of a circular wire of unit radius and unit mass, at a point 2 units from the center in the plane of the wire. Answer, 0·5366.

4. From the equation (6), show that

$$U(P) = \frac{2M}{p} K(k), \quad k^2 = 1 - \frac{q^2}{p^2},$$

where p is the greatest, and q the least, distance of P from the wire, and where $K(k)$ is the complete elliptic integral of the first kind with modulus k [1]. Check in this way, by means of tables, the result of Exercise 3. Show also that the potential becomes infinite as P approaches a point of the wire.

5. Two Dimensional Problems; The Logarithmic Potential.

A problem involving the position of a point in space may be regarded as two dimensional whenever it may be made to depend on two real coördinates. Two cases of this sort have been mentioned in § 2, page 55. However, it is usual, in speaking of potential theory in two dimensions to understand the theory of potentials of fields of force which depend on only two of the *cartesian* coördinates of a point, and in which the directions of the field are always parallel to the plane of the corresponding coördinate axes. Then if these coördinates are taken as x and y, the components of the force will be independent of z, Z will be 0, and the whole field is characterized by the field in the (x, y)-plane.

The simplest distribution which produces such a field is the infinite straight wire, of constant density. We have seen (p. 10, Exercise 5) that the attraction of such a wire is perpendicular to it, and that its magnitude in attraction units is $\frac{2\lambda}{r}$, where r is the distance of the attracted unit particle from the wire. Confining ourselves to a normal plane, we may think

---

[1] See B. O. PEIRCE, *A short Table of Integrals*, Boston, 1929, p. 66 and 121.

of the point where the wire cuts the plane as the seat of a new sort of particle, of mass equal to that of two units of length of the wire, and attracting according to the law of the inverse *first* power of the distance. The potential of such a particle we have seen (p. 56, Exercise 3) to be $2\lambda \log\left(\frac{1}{r}\right)$. The constant, which may always be added to the potential, was here determined so that the potential vanishes at a unit distance from the particle. Continuous distributions of matter, attracting in accordance with this law of the inverse first power, are at once interpretable as distributions of matter attracting according to Newton's law on infinite cylinders, or throughout the volumes bounded by infinite cylinders, the densities being the same at all points of the generators of the cylinders, or of lines parallel to them.

The potentials of such distributions, if their total mass[1] does not vanish, will become infinite as the attracted particle recedes infinitely far. This deprives us of the possibility of making the convention that the potential shall vanish at infinity. The customary procedure is to allow the zero of the potential to be defined in the case of a particle, by making it at a unit distance from the particle, and in continuous distributions, by integrating the potential of a unit particle, thus fixed, multiplied by the density, over the curve or area occupied by matter. In other words, the potential is *defined* by the integrals

$$(9) \qquad U = \int_C \lambda \log \frac{1}{r}\, ds, \qquad U = \iint_A \sigma \log \frac{1}{r}\, dS,$$

for distributions on curves and over areas, respectively. To distinguish these potentials, regarded as due to plane material curves, or plane laminas, whose elements attract according to the law of the inverse first power, from the potentials of curves and laminas whose elements attract according to Newton's law, it is customary to call them *logarithmic potentials*. We shall also speak of *logarithmic particles*, when the law of attraction is that of the inverse first power.

Exercises.

1. Write the components of the force at $P(x, y)$ due to a logarithmic particle of mass m at $Q(\xi, \eta)$. Show that they are the derivatives of the potential in the corresponding directions.

2. Find the equations of the lines of force due to a logarithmic particle of mass m_1 at $Q_1(-a, 0)$ and one of mass m_2 at $Q_2(a, 0)$. Answer, $m_1 \vartheta_1 + m_2 \vartheta_2 = $ const., where $\vartheta_1 = \sphericalangle X Q_1 P$ and $\vartheta_2 = \sphericalangle X Q_2 P$. Plot these lines, and also the equipotential lines for $m_2 = m_1$, and for $m_2 = -m_1$. Show that in the first case the lines of force are equilateral hyperbolas through Q_1 and Q_2 and in the second case,

---

[1] The total mass means the integral of the density of the distribution in the plane, on a curve, or over an area, or, what is the same thing, the mass of the distribution on the surface or within a cylindrical surface, between two planes, perpendicular to their generators, and two units apart.

circles. The equipotentials are *Cassinian ovals* in the first case. What are they in the second?

3. Determine the rate of expansion, or the total divergence, for a region of the plane, in a plane velocity field. Interpret the result in terms of a field in three dimensions whose directions are always parallel to a fixed plane and whose components are independent of the distance from this plane.

4. State the divergence theorem for plane fields, and deduce it from equation (9) of Chapter II, (page 39).

5. By means of the divergence theorem for the plane, find two expressions for the area bounded by a plane curve, in terms of integrals around the curve.

6. Show that the fields of force due to logarithmic distributions are solenoidal at points distinct from those occupied by the distribution.

7. Determine the flux of force through a closed curve enclosing a logarithmic particle, and write the form which Gauss' theorem (p. 43) takes. Consider the possibility of deriving Gauss' theorem in the plane from Gauss' theorem in space.

8. Find the logarithmic potential of a straight homogeneous line segment. Answer,

$$U = \lambda \left[y_2 \log \frac{1}{d_2} - y_1 \log \frac{1}{d_1} + y_2 - y_1 - x \tan^{-1} \frac{(y_2 - y_1)\, x}{x^2 + y_1 y_2} \right],$$

where $(0, y_1)$ and $(0, y_2)$ are the end-points of the segment, and d_1 and d_2 are the distances of $P(x, 0)$ from them.

Show that the improper integral for the potential at a point of the segment is convergent, and that the potential is continous throughout the plane. Show that its normal derivative drops by $2\pi\lambda$ as P passes through the segment in the direction of differentiation. Does this result harmonize with that of Exercise 4, (p. 12), when the densities of the four rectangles there considered are the same?

9. Find the logarithmic potential of a homogeneous circumference, at interior and exterior points. Note the formula of integration

$$\int_0^{2\pi} \log (1 - e \cos \vartheta)\, d\vartheta = 2\pi \log \frac{1 + \sqrt{1 - e^2}}{2}, \qquad 0 \leqq e < 1, \quad \text{(Chap. XII, § 5)}.$$

The desired potential is

$$U = M \log \left(\frac{1}{a} \right), \qquad\qquad x^2 < a^2,$$

$$= M \log \left(\frac{1}{|x|} \right), \qquad\qquad x^2 > a^2.$$

10. Define the components of force due to logarithmic distributions on curves and over areas, as integrals. Find in this way the force due to the circumference in the above exercise. From the force, determine the potential to within an additive constant, on the assumption that the potential is everywhere continuous. The above formula of integration may be evaluated in this way, the additive constant in the potential being determined by its value at the center, for which point the integral for the potential can easily be evaluated.

11. Find the logarithmic potential of a homogeneous circular lamina at interior and exterior points. Show that this potential and its derivatives of the first order are everywhere continuous, but that

$$\frac{\partial^2 U}{\partial x^2} + \frac{\partial^2 U}{\partial y^2}$$

is 0 at exterior points, and $-2\pi\sigma$ at interior points.

12. Generalize the results of the above problem to the case in which the density is a continuous function of the distance from the center.

6. Magnetic Particles.

We are familiar with the attractions and repulsions which the poles of magnets exert on each other. The ordinary compass is a magnet, one pole, the positive, or north-seeking, being attracted toward the north magnetic pole of the earth, and the negative, or south-seeking pole being attracted toward the south magnetic pole of the earth. COULOMB established the fact that two unlike poles attract, and two like poles repel, according to Newton's law for particles, the masses of the particles being replaced by the *strengths* of the poles. The sense of the forces must be reversed, in the statement of this law, if, as is customary, the strengths of positive poles are regarded as positive quantities, and the strengths of negative poles as negative quantities.

It is found that the strengths of the poles of a single magnet are equal and opposite. If a long thin magnet is broken at any point, it is found that the two pieces are magnets, each with positive and negative poles, of strengths sensibly equal to the strengths of the original magnet. It is therefore natural to think of a magnet as made up of minute parts, themselves magnets, arranged so that their axes, or lines from negative to positive poles, are all approximately in the same direction. Then, at moderate distances from the magnet, the effects of the positive and negative poles in the interior of the magnet will very nearly counterbalance eachother. But at the ends, there will be unbalanced poles, and these will give to the magnet as a whole its ability to attract and repel. This view is further strengthened by a consideration of the process of magnetizing a piece of iron. Before magnetization, the particles may be thought of as having random orientations, and therefore no appreciable effect. Magnetization consists in giving them an orderly orientation.

The question which now confronts us, is to find a simple analytical equivalent for the field of this magnetic particle. Just as we idealize the element of mass in the notion of particle, we shall try to formulate a corresponding idealization of the minute magnet, or *magnetic particle*, as we shall call it. Actual magnets can then be built up of these magnetic particles by the process of integration. The natural thing to do is, perhaps, to take the field of two particles of equal and opposite mass, and interpret this as the field of a magnetic particle. But here, the distance between the particles seems to be an extraneous element. If we allow the distance to approach 0, the field approaches zero. We can, however, prevent this if at the same time we allow the masses to become infinite, in such a way that the product of mass by distance, or *moment*, approaches a limit, or more simply, remains constant. Let us try this. We are to have a mass $-m$ at Q, and a mass m at Q' on a ray from Q with a given direction α. The potential at P of the pair of masses is

$$U' = \frac{m}{r'} - \frac{m}{r},$$

or, in terms of the moment $\mu = mQQ'$,

$$U' = \mu \frac{\dfrac{1}{r'} - \dfrac{1}{r}}{QQ'}.$$

But the limit of this, as Q' approaches Q is nothing other than the directional derivative of the function $\dfrac{\mu}{r}$ of ξ, η, ζ in the direction α. Hence we find for the potential of the magnetic particle

$$U = \mu \frac{\partial}{\partial \alpha} \frac{1}{r} = \mu \left[l \frac{\partial}{\partial \xi} \frac{1}{r} + m \frac{\partial}{\partial \eta} \frac{1}{r} + n \frac{\partial}{\partial \zeta} \frac{1}{r} \right],$$

l, m, n being the direction cosines of the direction α. The direction is called the *axis* of the magnetic particle, and μ is called its *moment*. The components of the field of the magnetic particle are obtained at once by forming the derivatives of the potential with respect to x, y and z.

The field of a magnetic particle also plays a role when interpreted as a flow field in hydrodynamics or in the conduction of heat. It is then referred to as the field of a *doublet*.

Exercises.

1. Write the components of the force due to a magnetic molecule of moment 1 situated at the origin and having as axis the direction of the x-axis. Find the lines of force. Show that they consist of plane sets of similar and similarly placed curves, those in the (x, y)-plane having the equation $r = c \sin^2 \varphi$. Compare these lines of force at a considerable distance from the origin with those due to two particles of equal and opposite mass, drawn in connection with Exercise 5 (p. 31).

2. On a straight line segment of length a is a continuous distribution of magnetic particles of constant moment density μ per unit of length, and with axes along the line segment, all in the same sense. Show that the distribution has the same field as a single magnet, with poles at the ends of the segment, of strength $-\mu$ and μ.

3. Find the potential of a quadruplet, formed by placing poles of strength m at $(a, a, 0)$, $-m$ at $(-a, a, 0)$, m at $(-a, -a, 0)$ and $-m$ at $(a, -a, 0)$, and taking the limit of their combined potential as a approaches 0, while their strengths increase in such a way that $\mu = 4ma^2$ remains constant. Indicate an interpretation of any partial derivative of $\dfrac{1}{r}$ with respect to the coördinates ξ, η, ζ.

4. Define a logarithmic doublet in the potential theory of two dimensions, and determine its equipotentials and lines of flow, supplying a figure.

7. Magnetic Shells, or Double Distributions.

By means of magnetic particles or doublets, we may build up magnets or distributions of doublets of quite varied character. We confine ourselves here to one of particular usefulness. It may be regarded as the limiting form of a set magnetic particles distributed over a surface, with their axes always normal to the surface and pointing to one and the same[1] side, as the particles become more and more densely distributed and their moments decrease. We proceed as follows. Let a surface S be given, with a continuously turning tangent plane, and a continuous function μ of the position on the surface of a variable point Q. Let S be divided into elements ΔS. At some point of each such element, let a magnetic particle be placed, whose moment is the product of the value of the function μ at that point by the area of the element ΔS and whose axis has the direction of the positive normal ν. Let the potential of the field of these particles be denoted by U':

$$U' = \sum \mu \, \frac{\partial}{\partial \nu} \frac{1}{r} \, \Delta S.$$

The limit of such a distribution, as the maximum chord of the elements ΔS approaches 0, is a *magnetic shell* or *double distribution*. Its potential is

$$(10) \qquad U = \iint_S \mu \, \frac{\partial}{\partial \nu} \frac{1}{r} \, dS.$$

Here μ is called the *density of magnetization* of the magnetic shell, or the *moment* of the double distribution.

The potential can be given another form in the case of simple surfaces, which better reveals some of its properties. We shall think of P as fixed, for the moment, and suppose that in addition to having a continuously turning tangent plane, the surface S is cut by no ray from P more than once, and is tangent to no such ray (fig. 10). Let

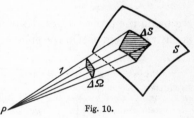

Fig. 10.

---

[1] The reader is doubtless aware that there exist surfaces for which it is not possible to speak of two distinct sides. One such is the Möbius strip. If a long, narrow rectangle of paper with corners A, B, C, D, in order, have its ends pasted together, so that B coincides with C and A with D, we have, approximately, a cylindrical surface, which is two sided. But if the ends are joined after turning one end through 180^0 in a plane roughly perpendicular to the initial plane of the paper, so that B falls on D and A on C, we have the Möbius strip, which is one sided. If we fix on a positive sense for the normal at some point P of the paper, and if we then pass once around the strip, keeping the sense of the normal so that its direction changes continuously, when we arrive at P again, we find the positive sense of the normal reversed. Any convention as to a positive side of the strip is thus impossible — at least as long as such circuits are allowed.

It is of interest to notice that the strip also has but one edge. It is also amusing to ask someone unacquainted with the situation to predict what will happen if the strip is cut along the line which in the original rectangle lay half way between the long sides until the cut closes. And similarly, if the cut be along a line which in the rectangle was one third the way from one long side to the other.

We shall understand, throughout, that one-sided surfaces are excluded, unless the contrary is distinctly stated.

ΔS be an element of S. We apply the divergence theorem to the region T bounded by ΔS, the conical surface joining the boundary of ΔS to P, and a small sphere σ about P to which S is exterior. We take

$$X = \frac{\partial}{\partial \xi} \frac{1}{r}, \qquad Y = \frac{\partial}{\partial \eta} \frac{1}{r}, \qquad Z = \frac{\partial}{\partial \zeta} \frac{1}{r},$$

the variables being ξ, η, ζ, and x, y, z being held constant. We have, then

$$\iiint_T \left(\frac{\partial^2}{\partial \xi^2} \frac{1}{r} + \frac{\partial^2}{\partial \eta^2} \frac{1}{r} + \frac{\partial^2}{\partial \zeta^2} \frac{1}{r} \right) dV = \iint_{S'} \frac{\partial}{\partial \nu} \frac{1}{r} dS,$$

S' being the boundary of T. As r does not vanish in T, the integrand in the volume integral vanishes, as may be seen by carrying out the differentiations. Moreover, the surface integral vanishes on the conical portion of the boundary because $\frac{1}{r}$ is constant in the direction of differentiation. Hence

$$\iint_{\Delta S} \frac{\partial}{\partial \nu} \frac{1}{r} dS + \iint_{\Delta \sigma} \frac{\partial}{\partial \nu} \frac{1}{r} dS = 0,$$

$\Delta \sigma$ being the projection of ΔS on the sphere σ. The sense of the normal is outward from T. On the sphere,

$$\frac{\partial}{\partial \nu} \frac{1}{r} = - \frac{\partial}{\partial \nu} \frac{1}{r} = \frac{1}{r^2},$$

so that

$$\iint_{\Delta S} \frac{\partial}{\partial \nu} \frac{1}{r} dS = - \iint_{\Delta \sigma} \frac{dS}{r^2} = - \Delta \Omega,$$

where $\Delta \Omega$ is the solid angle subtended at P by ΔS, to be regarded as positive when the positive normals to S make acute angles with the rays from P, and negative when these angles are obtuse.

We thus have a geometric interpretation of the double distribution in the case of a unit moment, namely the solid angle subtended at P by the surface on which the distribution is placed. To generalize the result, we apply the law of the mean to the above integral, and find

$$\left[\frac{\partial}{\partial \nu} \frac{1}{r} \right]_{Q'} \Delta S = - \Delta \Omega,$$

where Q' lies on ΔS. If now we multiply the two sides of this equation by the value of the moment μ at Q', sum over S, and pass to the limit as the maximum chord of the elements ΔS approaches 0, we obtain

$$U = \iint_S \mu \frac{\partial}{\partial \nu} \frac{1}{r} dS = - \iint_\Omega \mu \, d\Omega,$$

where Ω is the solid angle subtended at P by S.

This equation holds even if the rays from P are tangent to S at points of the curve bounding S, provided they are not tangent at interior points, as may be seen by applying it to an interior portion of S and allowing this portion to expand to the whole of S. Then by addition of portions, it can be extended to the case where P has any position off the surface S, provided there is a limit to the number of times any straight line cuts S. For such surfaces, then, U may be written

$$(11) \qquad U = - \iint_{\Omega} \mu \, d\Omega .$$

Exercises.

1. Find the potential at interior and exterior points of a closed magnetic shell of constant moment density for which the representation (11) is valid. Show that this potential has a sudden increase of $4\pi\mu$ as P moves out through the surface.

2. Show that the representation is valid for ellipsoids, right circular cones and cylinders, and polyhedra.

3. Compare the potential of a homogeneous double distribution on a plane area with the component, normal to the plane, of the force due to a homogeneous plane lamina occupying the same area (see Exercise 2, page 12).

4. Show that the potential of a double distribution of constant moment on an open surface may be regarded as everywhere continous, except on the edges of the surface, provided we admit multiply valued potentials, and that, in this case, the surface may be replaced, without changing the potential, by any other surface with the same boundary, into which it can be continuously warped. It is understood that we are restricting ourselves to surfaces for which the representation (11) is valid.

5. Define double distributions in the theory of logarithmic potentials, and develop their properties analogous to those of the double distributions considered in the text and exercises of this section.

6. Show that the double distribution may be interpreted in the following way. We draw the normals to the continuously curved surface S. On the normals we measure off the same distance a, to the same side of S, and call the locus of the points so constructed, S'. On S' we construct a simple distribution of density σ. On S we construct a simple distribution whose density at any point is the negative $-\sigma$ of the density of the distribution on S' at the point on the same normal. Let U' be the combined potential of these two spreads. Forming the function $\mu = a\sigma$, we now allow a to approach 0, σ increasing in such a way that μ keeps its value at each point. The limit U of U' is the potential of the double distribution on S of moment μ. This interpretation indicates the significance of the name double distribution.

8. Irrotational Flow.

We have considered the fields of flow which correspond to solenoidal fields of force. What are the characteristics of flows corresponding to conservative, or lamellar fields of force ? The line integral $\int (X \, dx + Y \, dy + Z \, dz)$ whose vanishing when taken over all closed paths defines a lamellar field, and which in a field of force means work, does not, in a field of flow, correspond to any concept familiar in elementary mechanics. It does, however, indicate the degree to which the general motion of the fluid is along the curve, and if its value when the curve is closed is different from 0, it indicates that there is a rotatory element in the motion, or a character of vortex motion. In a field of flow, the integral is called the *circulation* along the curve. If the integral vanishes when extended to all closed curves in a region, which can be shrunk to a point without leaving that region, the motion is said to be *irrotational*, or *free from vortices*, in the region.

Irrotational flows are characterized by the fact that they have a potential, that is, that the components of the velocity are the corresponding derivatives of one and the same function, called the *velocity potential*.

We have seen that a necessary condition for the existence of a potential is that

$$\frac{\partial Z}{\partial y} = \frac{\partial Y}{\partial z}, \quad \frac{\partial X}{\partial z} = \frac{\partial Z}{\partial x}, \quad \frac{\partial Y}{\partial x} = \frac{\partial X}{\partial y},$$

but is has not yet appeared that this condition is sufficient. It was the divergence theorem which showed us that the vanishing of the divergence of a field was necessary and sufficient that it be solenoidal. There is a corresponding integral identity which will answer in a similar way the question which now confronts us. The divergence theorem may be thought of as stating that the total divergence for a region is equal to the integral of the divergence at a point, over the region. Can we, in order to follow the analogy, define such a thing as the circulation at a point?

Let us consider first the case of a very simple flow, namely one in which the velocities are those of a rigid body rotating with unit angular velocity about the z-axis. The circulation around a circle about the origin in the (x, y)-plane, of radius a, is readily found to be $2\pi a^2$. Naturally, as a approaches 0, the circulation approaches 0, as it would in any continuous field. But if we first divide by the area of the circle, the limit is 2, and we should find this same limit if we followed the same process with any simple closed curve surrounding the origin in the (x, y)-plane. Suppose, however, that we take a closed curve in a vertical plane. The velocity is everywhere perpendicular to such a curve, and the circulation is 0. Thus we should get different values for the circulation at O according to the orientation of the plane in which the curves were drawn. Now when a concept seems to be bound up with a direction, it is natural to ask whether it has not the character of a vector. It turns out that this is the key to the present situation. The circulation at the origin in our case is a vector, whose component perpendicular to the (x, y)-plane is 2, and whose component in any direction in this plane is 0—it is the vector $(0, 0, 2)$.

We now formulate the definition of the circulation at a point, or as it is called, the *curl* of a field at a point. Let P denote a point, and n a direction (fig. 11). Through P we take a smooth surface S, whose normal at P has the direction n. On S we draw a simple closed curve C enclosing P, and compute the circulation around C, the sense of integration being counter-clockwise[1] as seen from the side of S toward which n points. We divide the value of the circulation by the area of the portion of S bounded by C, and allow the maximum chord of C to approach 0. *The limit defines the component of the curl in the direction* n:

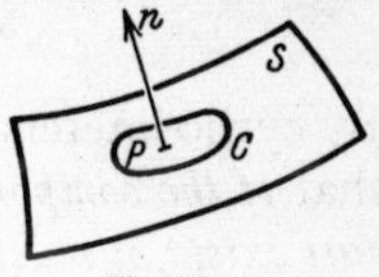

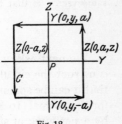

Fig. 11.

$$(12) \quad \mathrm{curl}_n\,(X,\,Y,\,Z) = \lim \frac{\displaystyle\int_C (X\,dx + Y\,dy + Z\,dz)}{A}.$$

This definition contains a double proviso. The limit of the ratio of circulation to area must exist—and it is understood that it shall be independent of the particular form of S and of C—and the components defined by the limits for various directions of n must actually be the components of a single vector (see the exercise, below). If these conditions are not fulfilled, the curl simply does not exist at P. But we shall see that they are fulfilled whenever the components of the field have continuous derivatives.

Let us now find an expression for the curl, on the hypothesis that it exists. This means, among other things, that we may specialize the curves C so that they have any convenient shape. We take the point P as origin of coördinates, and compute the x-component of the curl. We find first the circulation around the square in the (y, z)-plane which is bounded by the lines $y = \pm a$, $z = \pm a$ (fig. 12). It is

Fig. 12.

$$\int_{-a}^{a} Z\,(0,\,a,\,z)\,dz + \int_{a}^{-a} Y\,(0,\,y,\,a)\,dy + \int_{a}^{-a} Z\,(0,\,-a,\,z)\,dz$$
$$+ \int_{-a}^{a} Y\,(0,\,y,\,-a)\,dy.$$

We assemble the two integrals with respect to z and the two with respect to y, and apply the law of the mean:

$$\int_{-a}^{a} [Z\,(0,\,a,\,z) - Z\,(0,\,-a,\,z)]\,dz - \int_{-a}^{a} [Y\,(0,\,y,\,a) - Y\,(0,\,y,\,-a)]\,dy$$
$$= [Z\,(0,\,a,\,z') - Z\,(0,\,-a,\,z')]\,2a - [Y\,(0,\,y',\,a) - Y\,(0,\,y',\,-a)]\,2a.$$

---

[1] This convention is the one adopted when the system of coördinate axes is a right-hand system, *i. e.* such that a counter-clockwise rotation about the z-axis, as seen from the side of positive z, through an angle 90^0 carries the positive x-axis into the positive y-axis. For a left-hand system of axes, the convention as to the sense of integration around C is usually the opposite of that given above.

Applying the law of the mean for differences, we find for the circulation around the square C

$$\left[\frac{\partial Z}{\partial y}\bigg|_{P'} - \frac{\partial Y}{\partial z}\bigg|_{P''}\right]4a^2,$$

where P' and P'' are points of the surface of the square. If we divide by the area $4a^2$ of the square, and pass to the limit as a approaches 0, we find

$$\text{curl}_x(X, Y, Z) = \frac{\partial Z}{\partial y} - \frac{\partial Y}{\partial z}.$$

By cyclic interchanges we find the two other components. The result is that *if the components of the field have continuous derivatives, and if the curl exists, it must be given correctly by*

$$(13) \qquad \text{curl}(X,\ Y,\ Z) = \left(\frac{\partial Z}{\partial y} - \frac{\partial Y}{\partial z},\ \frac{\partial X}{\partial z} - \frac{\partial Z}{\partial x},\ \frac{\partial Y}{\partial x} - \frac{\partial X}{\partial y}\right).$$

In the case of an irrotational field, the curl of course exists, and vanishes. We thus find again the necessary condition for an irrotational field given at the beginning of the section.

Exercise.

Show that a necessary and sufficient condition that a set of vectors, finite or infinite in number, drawn from a point O, shall be the components of one and the same vector, is that they shall all be chords of the same sphere.

9. Stokes' Theorem.

We next ask, whether, knowing the curl at every point, we can reconstruct the circulation around a smooth curve C. We suppose C such that it can be spanned by a smooth simple surface S. Let a positive sense for the normals to S be decided upon, and let S be divided into elements by a net-work of simple curves. Then if the boundary of each element ΔS_k be given a sense, such that it is counter-clockwise when seen from the side of the positive normal to S, the sum of the circulations around the boundaries of the elements will be the circulation around C. For the parts of this sum that correspond to the common boundary to two adjacent elements will destroy each other, because this common boundary is described twice in opposite senses, and what remains after these common boundaries have been accounted for, is simply the curve C, described in a counter-clockwise sense as seen from the positive side of S. But, if the curl exists, the circulation around the boundary of an element ΔS_k is approximately equal to the normal component of the curl at one of the points of the element, multiplied by tha area of the element. For the equation (12) may be written

$$\text{curl}_n(X,\ Y,\ Z) = \frac{\int\limits_{C_k}(X\,dx + Y\,dy + Z\,dz)}{\Delta S_k} + \zeta_k,$$

C_k being the boundary of $\varDelta S_k$ and ζ_k a quantity which approaches 0 with the maximum chord of $\varDelta S_k$. If this equation be multiplied by $\varDelta S_k$, and the result summed over the whole of S, we have

$$\int_C (X\,dx + Y\,dy + Z\,dz) = \sum \operatorname{curl}_n (X, Y, Z)\,\varDelta S_k - \sum \zeta_k \varDelta S_k.$$

This gives, in the limit, as the maximum chord of the elements approaches 0, the equation

$$\int_C (X\,dx + Y\,dy + Z\,dz) = \iint_S \operatorname{curl}_n (X, Y, Z)\,dS.$$

We are thus led, granting any assumptions necessary to justify the reasoning, to the identity known as **Stokes' theorem**[1], which may be stated in various ways

$$\iint_S \operatorname{curl}_n V dS = \int_C V_s\,ds,$$

(14)
$$\iint_S \left[\left(\frac{\partial Z}{\partial y} - \frac{\partial Y}{\partial z}\right) l + \left(\frac{\partial X}{\partial z} - \frac{\partial Z}{\partial x}\right) m + \left(\frac{\partial Y}{\partial x} - \frac{\partial X}{\partial y}\right) n\right] dS$$
$$= \int_C (X\,dx + Y\,dy + Z\,dz),$$

or, in words, *the circulation around a simple closed curve is equal to the integral over any simple surface spanning the curve, of the normal component of the curl, the positive sense on the curve being the counter-clockwise sense as seen from the side of the surface toward which the positive normal points.* This is on the assumption that X, Y, Z are the components of the field referred to a right-hand set of axes. If a left hand set of axes is used, the sense of integration around the curve must be reversed, or else a minus sign introduced on one side of the equation.

A rigorous establishment of Stokes' theorem will be given in the next chapter. Assuming that it has been established, let us make some applications. First, as to the existence of the curl. Taking the definition (12), we express the curvelinear integral as a surface integral over the portion of S within C, by means of Stokes' theorem. We then apply the law of the mean to the surface integral, divide by the area of the portion of S within C, and pass to the limit as the maximum chord of C approaches 0. Because of the continuity of the derivatives of the components of the field, and of the direction cosines l, m, n of the normal, this limit exists, and is the value of

$$\left(\frac{\partial Z}{\partial y} - \frac{\partial Y}{\partial z}\right) l + \left(\frac{\partial X}{\partial z} - \frac{\partial Z}{\partial x}\right) m + \left(\frac{\partial Y}{\partial x} - \frac{\partial X}{\partial y}\right) n$$

at P. That is, the component of the curl in any direction is the component in that same direction of the vector given by the right hand

---

[1] STOKES, G., *A Smith's Prize Paper*. Cambridge University Calendar, 1854.

member of (13). Thus the components of the curl as given by (12) do exist, they are the components in various directions of one and the same vector, and the equation (13) is valid.

Secondly, we may show that the vanishing of the curl at every point of a region is a sufficient condition—as we have seen it to be a necessary condition—that the field be irrotational, at least on the hypothesis of a field with continuously differentiable components. For if C is any smooth curve that can be continuously shrunk to a point without leaving the region, it can be spanned by a simple smooth surface S, and applying Stokes' theorem we see that the vanishing of the curl at every point has as consequence the vanishing of the circulation around C.

Multiply connected regions. Both in the present section, and in § 1, we have mentioned curves which can be shrunk to a point without leaving a given region. A region such that any simple closed curve in it can be shrunk to a point without leaving the region is called *simply connected*. Such, for example, are the regions bounded by a sphere, a cube, a right circular cylinder, and the region between two concentric spheres. On the other hand, a torus, or anchor ring, is not simply connected. For the circle C, which is the locus of the midpoints of the meridian sections of the torus cannot be continuously shrunk to a point without leaving the region. What peculiarities are presented by conservative, or irrotational fields in such *multiply connected* regions? Let us take the region T, occupied by a torus, as an example. Suppose we cut it, from the axis outward, by a meridian curve, and regard the portion of this plane within the torus as a barrier, or *diaphragm*, and denote the new region with this diaphragm as part of its boundary, which must not be crossed, by T'. In T', the circulation around any closed curve is 0, for the field is irrotational, and any closed curve in T' may be continuously shrunk

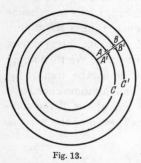

Fig. 13.

to a point without leaving T'. We shall later see in exercises that the circulation in T around the circle C need not vanish. What we can say, however, is that the circulation in T around all curves which can be continuously warped into C without leaving T, is the same, it being understood, of course, that the senses on these curves go over continuously into the sense on C. We may see this as follows. Let the point where C cuts the diaphragm have two designations, A, regarded as the point where C leaves the diaphragm, and A', the point where it arrives at the diaphragm (fig. 13). Let C' be a curve which can be continuously deformed into C, and let B and B' be notations for the point at which it leaves and arrives at the diaphragm. Consider the following circuit: the curve C from A to A' in the positive sense, the straight line segment in the diaphragm from A' to B', the curve C' in the negative sense from B' to B, the straight line segment from B to A. The circulation around this circuit vanishes. For, although it is true that it does not lie in T', the slightest separation of the segment $A'B' \equiv AB$ into two segments, one on either side of the diaphragm, will reduce the circuit to one in T', and since the circulation around such circuits vanishes, it vanishes also in the limiting case of the circuit $AA'B'BA$. But since the circulations along $A'B'$ and AB destroy each other, it follows that the circulation around C and that around C' in the negative sense have the sum 0, that is, that the circulations around the two curves in the same sense are equal. This is what we wished to prove.

In T', the field has a potential U. It is determined save for an additive constant, as the work over any path in T' connecting P_0 with P. What we have just seen amounts to this, that in the case of fields with vanishing curl, the differences of the values which the potential approaches, as P approaches a point on the diaphragm from opposite sides, is one and the same constant k, over the whole diaphragm, namely, the circulation around C. But the diaphragm is after all an artificial thing, and might have had other shapes and positions. So the potential U may be continued across it in either direction. Only, the function so determined is not uniquely determined at each point, but its values will differ by k, the value of the circulation around C. If the potential be continued along a circuit cutting the diaphragm a number of times, always in the same sense, its values will increase by an integral multiple of k. It is thus infinitely many valued, its branches at any point differing by integral multiples of k. This number k is called the *modulus* of the diaphragm (or of any equivalent diaphragm). Of course k may be 0 for the given field, in which case the potential is one-valued.

The torus is typical of regions which can be rendered simply connected by the introduction of a single diaphragm. Such regions are called *doubly connected*. If a bar runs across the hole in the ring, so as to form a sort of link like those used in some heavy anchor chains, two diaphragms will be necessary in order to reduce the region to a simply connected one. An irrotational field in such a region will have a potential which, in general, is multiple value with two moduli. It is clear how the situation is generalized to regions of higher connectivity. In a multiply connected region, fields whose potentials have moduli different from 0 are called *cyclic*, whereas those whose moduli all vanish are called *acyclic*.

Exercises.

1. Show, by means of (13), that for a velocity field given by the velocities of the points of a rigid body, rotating with constant angular velocity about a fixed axis, the curl is twice the vector angular velocity.

2. The curl can be different from 0 in a field of constant direction, and can vanish in a field in which the particles all move in the same sense along circles

with a common axis. Show that these situations occur in the fields a) $(y, 0, 0)$
and b) $\left(\dfrac{-y}{\varrho^2}, \dfrac{x}{\varrho^2}, 0\right)$, respectively.

3. The field (b) of Exercise 2 is not everywhere continuous. If the discontinuities are excluded by an appropriate enveloping surface, show that the rest of space is not a simply connected region. Introduce a diaphragm to produce a simply connected region, and find the corresponding modulus and the potential.

4. Show that in two dimensions, the divergence theorem and Stokes' theorem are identical in content, i. e. that they differ only in notation.

5. Show that in a field whose components have continuous partial derivatives of the first order, the integral of the normal component of the curl over a closed region vanishes. Again, assuming sufficient differentiability, show that div curl $V = 0$ and curl grad $U = 0$.

6. Granting always sufficient differentiability, show that any solenoidal field is the curl of some field. Suggestion. Let (F, G, H) denote the given solenoidal field. The desired end will be attained if we can find a field (X, Y, Z) whose curl is (F, G, H). Write down the differential equations for X, Y and Z, and attempt to integrate them on the hypothesis $Z = 0$. It will be found to be possible. What is the most general solution?

7. Show that any field, sufficiently differentiable, is the sum of a gradient and a curl.

8. Show that an open magnetic shell, of constant moment-density, not 0, produces an irrotational cyclic field, and determine the modulus. Construct in a similiar fashion an irrotational cyclic field with several moduli.

9. In Exercise 6 (p. 37), it was shown that the divergence of a field with continuous derivatives was invariant under a rigid motion of the axes. Show in the same way that grad U and curl V are invariant under a rigid motion of the axes.

10. Discuss the relation of the problem of integrating the differential equation $X\,dx + Y\,dy + Z\,dz = 0$ to the theory of irrotational fields. In particular, give the geometric significance of the usual condition for integrability

$$X\left(\frac{\partial Z}{\partial y} - \frac{\partial Y}{\partial z}\right) + Y\left(\frac{\partial X}{\partial z} - \frac{\partial Z}{\partial x}\right) + Z\left(\frac{\partial Y}{\partial x} - \frac{\partial X}{\partial y}\right) = 0.$$

11. In footnote 2, page 40, the question was raised as to when a field admitted surfaces orthogonal to it. Show that any Newtonian field does, and find a condition that is at once necessary and sufficient.

10. Flow of Heat.

Suppose we have a solid all of whose points are not at the same temperature. The cooler parts become warmer, and the warmer parts become cooler, and it is possible to picture what goes on as a flow of heat from the warmer to the cooler parts. The rate of flow may be represented as a vector (u, v, w), whose direction at any point is that in which heat is flowing, and whose magnitude is obtained by taking an element $\varDelta S$ of the plane through the point P in question, normal to the direction of flow, determining the number of calories per second flowing through this element, dividing this number by the area of $\varDelta S$, and taking the limit of this quotient as the maximum chord of $\varDelta S$ approaches 0. It is natural to assume that the velocity of flow is proportional to the rate of fall of temperature, U, at P. The constant of proportionality would depend on the character of the material of the solid, and would measure its *conductivity*. In certain bodies, like crystals, the conductivity may differ in different directions at one and the same point. We shall avoid such materials, and confine ourselves to bodies that are *thermally iso-tropic*. Then we should expect the flow vector to have the same direction as the gradient of the temperature, and, of course, the opposite sense:

$$(15) \qquad u = -k \frac{\partial U}{\partial x}, \qquad v = -k \frac{\partial U}{\partial y}, \qquad w = -k \frac{\partial U}{\partial z}.$$

These equations constitute our first physical assumption, for which there is ample experimental justification. Though k may vary from point to point, and even vary with the temperature, it is determinate at any point when the temperature is known, and may usually be regarded as constant for homogeneous bodies and moderate ranges of tempera-ture. The flow field is obviously always normal to the *isothermal sur-faces* $U =$ const. and, if k is constant, lamellar.

We are led to a second physical assumption by considering a region T in the body, and balancing the rate of flow of heat into it against the rise in temperature. The rate of flow into T in calories per second, is the negative of the flux of the field (u, v, w) out from the bounding sur-face, or

$$- \iint_S V_n \, dS = - \iint_S (u \, l + v \, m + w \, n) \, dS.$$

A calorie of heat will raise a unit mass of the body c degrees, if c is the *specific heat* of the material. Thus the number of calories per second re-ceived per unit of mass is measured by

$$c \frac{\partial U}{\partial t},$$

and the number of calories per second received by the whole mass in T is

$$\iiint_T c \varrho \frac{\partial U}{\partial t} \, dV.$$

We now equate these two expressions for the rate of flow of heat into T, transforming the first to a volume integral by the divergence theorem;

$$\iiint_T \left[c \varrho \frac{\partial U}{\partial t} + \frac{\partial u}{\partial x} + \frac{\partial v}{\partial y} + \frac{\partial w}{\partial z} \right] dV = 0.$$

Assuming that the integrand is continuous, we conclude by reasoning now familiar, that the integrand must vanish, since the integral vanishes for every region T. Hence we have our second physical assumption,·

$$(16) \qquad \frac{\partial U}{\partial t} = - \frac{1}{c \varrho} \left(\frac{\partial u}{\partial x} + \frac{\partial v}{\partial y} + \frac{\partial w}{\partial z} \right).$$

The flow of heat in a body may be stationary, *i. e.* such that the temperature at each point is independent of the time. Such, for instance, might be the situation in a bar, wrapped with insulating material, one end of which was kept in boiling water, and the other end in ice-water. Though heat would be constantly flowing, the temperatures might not vary sensibly with the time. If the flow is stationary, the equation (16) shows that it is solenoidal. Thus the fields of stationary flows of heat in isotropic bodies of constant conductivity have two important properties of Newtonian fields. We shall see later that these two properties characterize Newtonian fields, so that the theory of stationary flows of heat in isotropic bodies of constant conductivity and the theory of Newtonian fields is identical.

We may eliminate the components of the field between the equations (15) and (16), and obtain the differential equation which the temperature must satisfy:

$$(17) \qquad \frac{\partial U}{\partial t} = \frac{1}{c\,\varrho} \left[\frac{\partial}{\partial x} k \frac{\partial U}{\partial x} + \frac{\partial}{\partial y} k \frac{\partial U}{\partial y} + \frac{\partial}{\partial z} k \frac{\partial U}{\partial z} \right].$$

If k, c and ϱ are constant, this reduces to

$$(18) \qquad \frac{\partial U}{\partial t} = a^2 \left[\frac{\partial^2 U}{\partial x^2} + \frac{\partial^2 U}{\partial y^2} + \frac{\partial^2 U}{\partial z^2} \right], \qquad a^2 = \frac{k}{c\,\varrho},$$

and if the flow is stationary,

$$(19) \qquad \frac{\partial^2 U}{\partial x^2} + \frac{\partial^2 U}{\partial y^2} + \frac{\partial^2 U}{\partial z^2} = 0.$$

The situation is similar in the stationary flow of electric current in a conductor. In such a flow, we have

$$\boldsymbol{i} = - \lambda \operatorname{grad} U,$$

$$\operatorname{div} \boldsymbol{i} = 0,$$

where $\boldsymbol{i}$ is the current vector, λ the electrical conductivity, and U the potential. In particular, if the conductivity is constant the potential satisfies Laplace's equation (19).

Exercises.

1. Show that in a stationary flow of heat in an isotropic solid with constant conductivity, the only distribution of temperatures depending on a single cartesian coördinate is one in which U is a linear function of that coördinate.

2. If the stationary temperatures in a spherical solid of the same material depend only on the distance from the center, show that they must be constant. Determine the possibilities in a hollow sphere for temperatures depending only on the distance from the center.

3. Describe the flow of heat in an isotropic solid of constant conductivity when the temperatures are given by $U = \frac{1}{r}$. Determine the strength of such a source

of heat in calories per second. Interpret as fields of flow of heat the fields of the exercises of § 2 (p. 31).

4. Determine the relation which takes the place of (16) when continuously distributed sources are present, and find also the corresponding differential equation for the temperatures.

11. The Energy of Distributions.

If a distribution of matter, of electricity, or of magnetism, is altered, work will, in general, be done, and there will result a change in the energy of the system. Such changes can readily be computed if we know the energy of a distribution compared with some standard distribution. The standard distribution which is most convenient is one of infinite dispersion of all its elements. The energy change in assembling the distribution from such a state of infinite distribution is known as the energy of the distribution. We proceed to show how it may be found.

Let us first take the case of n distinct particles. There being no field of force to start with, no work is done in bringing the first particle, of mass m_1 to P_1. There is now a field of force whose potential is $\dfrac{m_1}{r}$ and this potential is the work done by the field of force in bringing a unit particle from an infinite distance to P. The work done in bringing a particle of mass m_2 to P_2 will therefore be

$$\frac{m_1 m_2}{r_{12}}$$

where r_{12} is the distance $\overline{P_1 P_2}$. The two particles now produce a field whose potential is

$$\frac{m_1}{r_1} + \frac{m_2}{r_2} \qquad r_1 = \overline{P_1 P}, \quad r_2 = \overline{P_2 P}.$$

and the work done in bringing the third particle of mass m_3 from infinity to P_3 is m_3 times the value of this potential at P_3. Thus, the total amount of work done in assembling the three particles is

$$\frac{m_1 m_2}{r_{12}} + \frac{m_1 m_3}{r_{13}} + \frac{m_2 m_3}{r_{23}}.$$

Proceeding in this way, we find for the work done in assembling the n particles

$$W = \sum' \frac{m_i m_j}{r_{ij}}$$

where the first index runs through all integral values from 1 to n and the second runs through all greater values to n. It is convenient to remove the restriction on the indices. If we do so, and let i and j run through all pairs of different values, we simply count each term twice, and we have

$$W = \frac{1}{2} \sum \frac{m_i m_j}{r_{ij}},$$

where i and j run through all pairs of different integers from 1 to n.

Since the fields are conservative, the work done in changing the configuration of the particles is simply $W_2 - W_1$, where W_1 and W_2 are the values of the above sum in the first and second positions of the particles. The expression W is called the *self-potential* of the system of particles. If the field is interpreted as a gravitational field, so that the particles attract, the work is done *by* the field, and is the *negative* of the potential energy. If the field is an electrostatic or magnetic field, W is the work done against the field, and is equal to the potential energy. Of course, a positive factor of proportionality, depending on the units used, may enter. For instance, in order to express W in foot pounds, we should have to multiply the above sum, the masses being measured in pounds and the distances in feet, by $\frac{\gamma}{g}$ where γ is the constant of gravitation (see Exercise 1, page 3), and g the acceleration due to gravity at the earth's surface, measured in the foot pound second system.

When it comes to determining the work done in assembling a continuous distribution, something of the nature of an additional hypothesis is inevitable. For no matter how small the masses of the elements brought up to their final positions from infinity, they are brought up as wholes, and the work of assembling each of them is ignored. We do not even know in advance that this work is a finite quantity, to say nothing of being able to neglect, as an error which vanishes in the limit, the sum of all such elements of work. We shall therefore set down *as the hypothesis itself* that the work is the expression, analogous to that found for particles,

$$(20) \qquad W = \frac{1}{2} \iiint\limits_{(TT)} \iiint \frac{\varkappa(P) \varkappa(Q)}{r} \, d(VV).$$

The test of the hypothesis, like all others of a physical nature, rests on the consistency of its consequences with measurements. By this test, the hypothesis is satisfactory.

The integral (20) is improper. Because it is sextuple, the verification that it converges involves either a geometric intuition concerning regions of six dimensions, or else dealing with systems of inequalities which would vex rather than enlighten the reader at this point, unless he happened to have an interest for this very sort of problem, in which case he would be able to supply the reasoning. We therefore ask him to accept the facts, first that the integral is convergent when the density is continuous, or bounded, and continuous in a finite number of regions into which T can be divided; and secondly, that it is equal to the iterated integral, obtained first by integrating over the region T with respect to the coördinates ξ, η, ζ of Q, and then over T with respect to the coördinates x, y, z of P. It may then be expressed in the form

$$(21) \qquad W = \frac{1}{2} \iiint_T \varkappa \, U \, dV,$$

where U is the potential of the distribution.

Exercises.

1. Show that the energy of a charge e in equilibrium (*i. e.* distributed with constant density) on a conducting sphere of radius a is $\frac{\frac{1}{2} e^2}{a}$.

2. Show that the work done by the field in assembling from a state of infinite dispersion a homogeneous sphere of mass m and radius a is $\frac{\frac{3}{5} m^2}{a}$. Note that this is also the work done when the sphere contracts from one of infinite radius to one of radius a, always remaining homogeneous.

3. Show that the energy expended in drawing together into a sphere of radius one foot, of the density of lead, its material, from a very finely divided and diffused state, is about 0.000177 foot pounds. Lead weighs about 710 pounds per cubic foot.

4. If the sun were homogeneous, the shrinkage of its radius by one foot would release about 7.24×10^{31} foot pounds of energy. Verify this statement, using the following data: the radius of the sun is about $432\,200$ miles, its mean density is about 1.4 times that of water, one cubic foot of water weighs 62.4 pounds.

5. The heat annually radiated from the sun has been estimated, on the basis of the heat received by the earth, as 6×10^{30} times the amount which will raise one pound of water one degree centigrade[1].

Show that the sun's age cannot have exceeded $20\,000\,000$ years, on the assumption that it is homogeneous. The energy whose equivalent in heat will raise the temperature of a pound of water one degree centigrade is at least 1400 foot pounds. Geological evidence is to the effect that the age of the earth is at least 60 times the above figure for the sun, and for this, among other reasons, the theory which accounts for the energy radiated by the sun on the basis of its contraction is no longer regarded as satisfactory[2].

6. If two bodies are brought, without change of form, from an infinite distance apart to a given position, show that the work done, or their *mutual potential*, is the integral over either body of the product of its density by the potential of the other. Show that the self-potential of the system of the two bodies is the sum of the self potentials of the bodies separately and their mutual potential.

7. Two straight homogeneous wires of length l and masses m_1 and m_2 form two parallel sides of a rectangle of width x_1. Show that the work necessary to increase the width of the rectangle to x_2 is

$$\frac{2 m_1 m_2}{l} \left[\frac{\sqrt{x^2 + l^2} - x}{l} - \log \frac{\sqrt{x^2 + l^2} + l}{x} \right]_{x = x_1}^{x = x_2}.$$

---

[1] See THOMSON and TAIT, *Natural Philosophy*, Vol. I, Part. II, Appendix E. More recent estimates somewhat exceed this figure.

[2] See EDDINGTON, *Stars and Atoms*, New Haven, 1927, pp. 96—98.

12. Reciprocity; Gauss' Theorem of the Arithmetic Mean.

The property that two bodies attract each other with equal and opposite forces is reflected in the potential. The potential is symmetric in the coördinates of the two points involved, so that the potential at Q of a unit particle at P is the same as the potential at P of a unit particle at Q. From this fact a number of theorems follow, which are of great use in the theory and applications of the potential. We shall now derive two of them, and suggest further consequences in exercises.

The potential

$$U(P) = \frac{1}{4\pi a^2} \iint_S \frac{dS}{r}$$

of a homogeneous spherical shell of radius a and total mass 1, is, as we have seen, equal at exterior points to the potential of the unit particle at the center, that is, to $\frac{1}{\varrho}$, while at interior points it is constant and equal to $\frac{1}{a}$. But we see from the formula that this potential can also be interpreted as the average, or arithmetic mean[1], over the surface of the sphere, of the potential at Q of a unit particle at P. Thus, remembering the values of $U(P)$ at exterior and interior points, the above equation has the interpretations

a) the average over the surface of a sphere of the potential of a unit particle outside the sphere, is equal to the value of that potential at the center of the sphere $\left(\text{namely } \frac{1}{\varrho}\right)$, and

---

[1] The arithmetic mean of a set of numbers is their sum divided by the number of them, or

$$m = \frac{a_1 + a_2 + a_3 + \cdots + a_n}{1 + 1 + 1 + \cdots + 1}.$$

If, instead of a finite set of numbers, we have a function f defined on a surface (and the process would be the same for other regions of definition), we may divide the surface into n equal portions, take a value of the function at some point of each portion, and form the arithmetic mean of these values, which we may write

$$m' = \frac{f_1 \varDelta S + f_2 \varDelta S + f_3 \varDelta S + \cdots + f_n \varDelta S}{\varDelta S + \varDelta S + \varDelta S + \cdots + \varDelta S}.$$

We may eliminate the arbitrariness in the choice of the points in the regions at which the values of f are taken, by passing to the limit as the maximum chord of the elements $\varDelta S$ approaches 0:

$$m = \frac{\iint_S f \, dS}{S}.$$

This constitutes the usual definition of the arithmetic mean of a function f on a surface S.

b) the average over the surface of a sphere of the potential of a unit particle within the sphere, is independent of the position of the particle within the sphere, and is equal to the value at any point of the surface of the potential of the particle when located at the center $\left(\text{namely } \dfrac{1}{a}\right)$.

Suppose now that we have a number of particles, or even one of the usual continuous distributions of matter either entirely exterior or entirely interior to the sphere. We have merely to sum the equations stated above in words, or in case of continuous distributions, sum and pass to the limit, in order to have the two following generalizations:

a) **Gauss' theorem of the Arithmetic Mean;** *the average over the surface of a sphere of the potential of masses lying entirely outside of the sphere is equal to the value of that potential at the center of the sphere,* and

b) **A Second Average Value Theorem;** *the average over the surface of a sphere of the potential of masses lying entirely inside of the sphere is independent of their distribution within the sphere, and is equal to their total mass divided by the radius of the sphere* [1].

The second theorem gives a means of determining the total mass of a bounded distribution when its potential is known. It therefore plays a role similar to that of Gauss' integral (p. 43). As a rule, however, it is less convenient than Gauss' integral, since the surface of integration must be a sphere.

Exercises.

1. Show that the value of a Newtonian potential (not a constant) at a point P of free space is strictly intermediate between the extreme values which it has on the surface of any sphere about P which has no masses within it or on its surface.

2. Show that a Newtonian potential can have neither maximum or minimum in free space, and deduce a theorem due to EARNSHAW with respect to the possibility of points of stable equilibrium in a Newtonian field of force.

3. According to the second average value theorem,

$$\iint\limits_{S} U(P)\, dS = 4\pi m a,$$

where $U(P)$ is the potential of a distribution of total mass m within the sphere S of radius a. Write a similar equation for the concentric sphere of radius $a + \Delta a$, and from the two deduce Gauss' integral (p. 43) for spheres.

4. Charges in equilibrium on conductors are always so distributed that the potential throughout each conductor is a constant (p. 176). Suppose that we have a set of conductors, $B_1, B_2, \ldots B_n$, and that charges $e_1, e_2, \ldots e_n$ are imparted to them. Let the potential of these charges when in equilibrium have the values $V_1, V_2, \ldots V_n$ on the conductors. Show that if a different system of charges,

---

[1] The first of these theorems is given in GAUSS' *Allgemeine Lehrsätze*, Collected Works, Vol. V, p. 222; reprinted in OSTWALDS *Klassiker der Exacten Wissenschaften*, No. 2. We shall meet with it again (Chap. VIII, § 6). The second theorem is less current, although also in GAUSS' work (l. c.).

$e'_1, e'_2, \ldots e'_n$ produce a potential with values $V'_1, V'_2, \ldots V'_n$ on the conductors, then

$$\sum_i e_i V'_i = \sum_i e'_i V_i.$$

5. State a theorem on the average value on a sphere of the potential due to masses both within and without (but not on) the sphere. Apply it to prove that if a spherical conductor is brought into the presence of various charges, the value on its surface of the resulting potential is the sum of the potential due to the initial charge of the conductor, and the value at its center of the potential of the field into which it was introduced.

6. Assuming the applicability of Gauss' theorem (p. 43), — as is often done in text books, without justification — derive the following results, already verified in certain special cases:

$$\text{a)} \quad \frac{\partial^2 U}{\partial x^2} + \frac{\partial^2 U}{\partial y^2} + \frac{\partial^2 U}{\partial z^2} = -4\pi\varkappa$$

where $\varkappa$ is the density of the distribution whose potential is U,

$$\text{b)} \quad \frac{\partial U}{\partial n_+} - \frac{\partial U}{\partial n_-} = -4\pi\sigma$$

where these derivatives represent the limits of the derivatives of the potential of a surface distribution with density σ, in the direction of the positive normal at P_0, as the point P approaches P_0 along the normal, from the positive and from the negative side, respectively.

c) the corresponding results in the theory of logarithmic potentials.

7. Write an exposition of the theory of potentials in one dimension, starting with the force due to an infinite plane. Derive a standard form for the potential, consider continuous distributions on a line segment, consider solenoidal and lamellar fields, derive an analogue of Gauss' integral, consider the analogue of the divergence theorem, and consider mean value theorems.

8. Write an exposition of the theory of potentials in n dimensions, determining the law of force in a way analogous to the method of Exercise 3 (p. 37).

Chapter IV.

The Divergence Theorem.

1. Purpose of the Chapter.

We have already seen something of the role of the divergence theorem and of Stokes' theorem in the study of fields of force and other vector fields; we shall also find them indispensable tools in later work. Our first task will be to prove them under rather restrictive assumptions, so that the proofs will not have their essential features buried in the minutiae which are unescapable if general results are to be attained.

The theorems will thus be established under circumstances making them available for fairly large classes of problems, although not without the possibility of difficulty in verifying the fulfillment of the hypotheses. Both because of this situation, and because of the desirability of being able to enunciate in simple terms general results based on these theorems, it is important that they be demonstrated under broad conditions the applicability of which is immediately evident. The later sections of this chapter will therefore be concerned with the exact formulation of certain essential geometric concepts, and then with the desired general proofs.

In the preceding chapters, we have used certain geometric concepts, like curve and surface, as if they were familiar and sharply defined ideas. But this is not the case, and at times we have had to specify that they should have certain properties, like continuously turning tangent lines or planes. This was not done with meticulousness, because such a procedure would have obscured the main results in view at the time. The results however, subsist. We shall have only to understand by curve, regular curve, by surface, regular surface, and by region, regular region, as these concepts are defined in the present chapter.

The reader approaching the subject for the first time will do well to study carefully only the first four sections of the chapter. The rest should be read rapidly, without attention to details of proof, but with the object merely of obtaining adequate ideas of the definitions and the content of the theorems. When he comes to a realization of the need of a more critical foundation of the theorems, and hardly before then, the reader should study the whole chapter for a mastery of its contents.

2. The Divergence Theorem for Normal Regions.

The divergence theorem involves two things, a certain region, or portion of space, and a vector field, or set of three functions X, Y, Z of x, y, z, defined in this region.

The regions which we shall consider are those which we shall call *normal regions*. A region N is normal if it is a convex polyhedron, or if it is bounded by a surface S consisting of a finite number of parts of planes and one curved surface F, and is such that for some orientation of the coördinate axes, the following conditions are fulfilled (fig. 14):

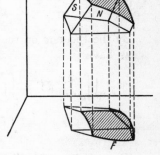

Fig. 14.

a) the projection $\overline{F}$ of F on the (x, y)-plane is bounded by a simple closed curve consisting of a finite number of arcs, each with continuously turning tangent; the projection of all the edges of S on the (x, y)-plane divide that plane into a finite number of regions, each bounded by a simple closed curve;

b) any parallel to the z-axis containing an interior point of N has in common with N a single segment and no other point, and F is given by an equation of the form $z = f(x, y)$, where $f(x, y)$ is one-valued and continuous, together with its partial derivatives of the first order, in $\overline{F}$:

c) these same conditions are fulfilled when the x, y and z-axes are interchanged in any way.

A sphere is not a normal region, because it does not satisfy condition (b). But it is made up of a finite number of normal regions. For the region bounded by a spherical triangle and the planes through its sides and the center of the sphere will be normal if the angular measures of the sides are sufficiently small. The situation is similar for the usual surfaces met with, and we shall see that the divergence theorem is applicable to regions made up of normal pieces.

As to the field (X, Y, Z) we shall assume that its components and their partial derivatives of the first order are continuous within and on the boundary of N.

For a normal region N and a field satisfying the above requirements in N, the divergence theorem holds:

$$(1) \qquad \iiint\limits_{N} \left(\frac{\partial X}{\partial x} + \frac{\partial Y}{\partial y} + \frac{\partial Z}{\partial z} \right) dV = \iint\limits_{S} (Xl + Ym + Zn)\, dS.$$

Let $\overline{\sigma}$ denote one of the regions into which the projection of the edges of S divides the (x, y)-plane, and let v denote the portion of N whose projection is $\overline{\sigma}$; v will be bounded by a surface σ consisting of a vertical cylindrical surface through the boundary of $\overline{\sigma}$, and by two surfaces $z = \varphi(x, y)$ and $z = f(x, y)$, $\varphi(x, y) \leqq f(x, y)$, one of them being plane, and thus both satisfying condition (b). We start by establishing the divergence theorem for the region v and the field $(0, 0, Z)$:

$$(2) \qquad \iiint\limits_{v} \frac{\partial Z}{\partial z}\, dV = \iint\limits_{\sigma} Zn\, d\sigma.$$

By the theorem on the equivalence of multiple and iterated integrals[1] we have

$$(3) \qquad \iiint\limits_{v} \frac{\partial Z}{\partial z}\, dV = \iint\limits_{\sigma} \left[\int_{\varphi(x, y)}^{f(x, y)} \frac{\partial Z}{\partial z}\, dz \right] d\overline{\sigma}$$

$$= \iint\limits_{\overline{\sigma}} Z[x, y, f(x, y)]\, d\overline{\sigma} - \iint\limits_{\overline{\sigma}} Z[x, y, \varphi(x, y)]\, d\overline{\sigma}.$$

We now change the field of integration in the surface integrals from the projection $\overline{\sigma}$ to the surface σ bounding v. If $\varDelta\sigma$ is an element of the upper portion $z = f(x, y)$ of σ, and $\varDelta\overline{\sigma}$ the corresponding portion of $\overline{\sigma}$, *i. e.*

---

[1] See, for instance, Osgood, *Advanced Calculus*, p. 90. —Courant, *Differential- und Integralrechnung*, Bd. II, pp. 175—183.

its projection, we have, by the familiar formula for areas,

$$\Delta\sigma = \iint_{\Delta\bar{\sigma}} \sec\gamma\, d\bar{\sigma} = \sec\gamma'\Delta\bar{\sigma}, \qquad \Delta\bar{\sigma} = \cos\gamma'\Delta\sigma.$$

γ' being a mean value of the acute angle between the normal to the surface and the z-axis. The application of the law of the mean is justified because of the condition (b) on $f(x, y)$. Thus the first integral on the right of (3) may be written

$$\lim \sum_k Z[x_k, y_k, f(x_k, y_k)]\,\Delta\bar{\sigma}_k = \lim \sum_k Z[x_k, y_k, f(x_k, y_k)]\cos\gamma_k\,\Delta\sigma_k$$
$$= \iint_{\sigma''} Z\cos\gamma\, d\sigma,$$

where σ'' is the portion of σ in the surface $z = f(x, y)$. The second integral on the right in (3) may be transformed in the same way. On σ'', $\cos\gamma$ is exactly the direction cosine n, since here the outward normal makes an acute angle with the z-axis. On the portion σ' of σ in the surface $z = \varphi(x, y)$, however, the outward normal makes an obtuse angle with the z-axis, namely the supplement of γ, and hence $\cos\gamma = -n$. We therefore obtain

$$\iiint_v \frac{\partial Z}{\partial z}\, dV = \iint_{\sigma''} Zn\, d\sigma + \iint_{\sigma'} Zn\, d\sigma.$$

The parts of σ not comprised in σ' and σ'' are vertical cylindrical walls. On them $n = 0$, so the last equation is equivalent to (2).

We may now establish the corresponding equation for the region N. For, if we add equations (2) corresponding to the finite number (by condition (a)) of regions of type v into which N is divided, the sum of the left hand members is exactly

$$\iiint_N \frac{\partial Z}{\partial z}\, dV,$$

while the surface integrals have as sum the integral over the surface S of N, the surface integrals over the vertical walls being 0. Thus

$$\iiint_N \frac{\partial Z}{\partial z}\, dV = \iint_S Zn\, dS.$$

Now, because of condition (c), we can derive in the same way, the equations

$$\iiint_N \frac{\partial X}{\partial x}\, dV = \iint_S Xl\, dS, \qquad \iiint_N \frac{\partial Y}{\partial y}\, dV = \iint_S Ym\, dS,$$

and the sum of the last three equations gives the divergence theorem (1) for N and for the particular orientation of the axes involved in the hypothesis on N. However, from the first form of the divergence theorem in equation (9), page 39, we know that both sides are invariant under a rigid motion of the axes, so that it holds for N with any position of the axes (see also Exercise 6, page 37).

3. First Extension Principle.

Any region which can be cut into normal regions by a finite number of planes, is also one for which the divergence theorem holds, the hypotheses on the field being maintained. For if the equations expressing the divergence theorem for the parts are added, the left hand members add up to the integral, over the whole region, of the divergence. The surface integrals add up to the integral of the normal component of the field over the surface of the whole region, plus integrals over surfaces each of which is part of the boundary of two adjacent partial regions. As the normal is outward from each, it is in opposite senses on such a surface, according as the surface is regarded as bounding one or the other of the partial regions. The surface integrals over such common boundaries therefore destroy each other, leaving only the outer surface of the whole region.

Thus the divergence theorem holds for any region which, in this sense, is the sum of normal regions. The principle of adding regions in this way we call the first extension principle.

Exercise.

1. Show that a right circular cylinder, an ellipsoid, a torus, a truncated right circular cone, are all sums of normal regions   Show, on the other hand, that any portion of a right circular cone containing the vertex is not the sum of normal regions.

By means of the first extension principle, we may assert the validity of the divergence theorem for a broad class of regions. It is easy to show that it holds also for right circular cones. It is the vertex which causes the difficulty. But the vertex can be cut out by means of a plane near to it, and normal to the axis, and the divergence theorem holds for what is left. Then, as the plane is made to approach the vertex, the divergence theorem for the truncated cone has as limiting form, the same theorem for the full cone. This is a special case of the second extension principle which we shall meet later.

Exercises.

2. Show that the divergence theorem in two dimensions

$$\iint_S \left(\frac{\partial P}{\partial x} + \frac{\partial Q}{\partial y}\right) dS = \int_C (Pl + Qm)\, ds = \int_C (P\,dy - Q\,dx)$$

holds, provided P and Q are continuous, together with their partial derivatives of the first order, in S and on its boundary C, and if S is the sum of a finite number of polygons and regions bounded by simple closed curves, each of which consists of a finite number of straight sides and one curved side with continuously turning tangent, the tangent never turning through as much as a right angle.

3. Show that the hypothesis on the field (X, Y, Z) in the divergence theorem may be lightened as follows. X, Y and Z shall be continuous in the region R, and on its boundary, and R can be broken up into a finite number of regions for which the divergence theorem holds, and in each of which X, Y and Z have derivatives which are continuous, the boundary included. This means that as P approaches the boundary from the interior of one of the partial regions, each derivative approaches a limit, and that these limits together with the values in the interior form a continuous function. The limits, however, need not be the same as P approaches a common boundary of two partial regions from the two sides.

4. Stokes' Theorem.

Stokes' theorem deals with an open, two sided surface S (see the footnote, p. 67), bounded by a simple closed curve C, and with a field X, Y, Z. A positive sense is assigned to the normal to S, and the direction cosines of the normal with this sense are assumed to vary continuously with the position of the foot of the normal on S. A positive sense is assigned to the curve C in accordance with the conventions of § 9, page 72. The condition on the continuity of the direction of the normal will be lightened.

We first prove Stokes' theorem for a simple class of surfaces S, corresponding to the normal regions for the divergence theorem. We assume, namely, that S satisfies the conditions imposed on the curved face F of a normal region, in (a), (b), and (c) of § 2, page 85, and that its projection on each of the coördinate planes is a region for which the divergence theorem in two dimensions holds.

As to the field, we assume that in a region of space with S in its interior, X, Y, Z and their partial derivatives of the first order are continuous.

For surfaces S and fields (X, Y, Z) satisfying these requirements, Stokes theorem holds:

$$(4) \qquad \iint\limits_{S} \left[\left(\frac{\partial Z}{\partial y} - \frac{\partial Y}{\partial z}\right) l + \left(\frac{\partial X}{\partial z} - \frac{\partial Z}{\partial x}\right) m + \left(\frac{\partial Y}{\partial x} - \frac{\partial X}{\partial y}\right) n\right] dS$$

$$= \int\limits_{C} (X\,dx + Y\,dy + Z\,dz).$$

Considering first the terms involving X, we shall show that

$$(5) \qquad \iint\limits_{S} \left(\frac{\partial X}{\partial z} m - \frac{\partial X}{\partial y} n\right) dS = \int\limits_{C} X\,dx.$$

Here X is given as a function of x, y and z, but as its values on the surface S, $z = f(x, y)$, are all that are involved, we may substitute for it the function

$$X[x, y, f(x, y)] = \Phi(x, y).$$

Then

$$\frac{\partial \Phi}{\partial y} = \frac{\partial X}{\partial y} + \frac{\partial X}{\partial z} \frac{\partial f}{\partial y} = \frac{\partial X}{\partial y} - \frac{\partial X}{\partial z} \cdot \frac{m}{n},$$

since

$$-\frac{\frac{\partial f}{\partial x}}{l} = -\frac{\frac{\partial f}{\partial y}}{m} = \frac{1}{n}.$$

Hence

$$\iint_S \left(\frac{\partial X}{\partial z} m - \frac{\partial X}{\partial y} n \right) dS = -\iint_S \left(\frac{\partial X}{\partial y} - \frac{\partial X}{\partial z} \cdot \frac{m}{n} \right) n \, dS = -\iint_S \frac{\partial \Phi}{\partial y} n \, dS$$

$$= -\iint_{\overline{S}} \frac{\partial \Phi}{\partial y} d\overline{S},$$

where $\overline{S}$ is the projection of S on the (x, y)-plane. The last integral we now transform into a line integral over the curve γ which is the projection of C on the (x, y)-plane, by means of the divergence theorem in two dimensions[1]. Writing $P = 0$, $Q = \Phi$, we see that the last integral is equal to

$$\int_\gamma \Phi(x, y) \, dx,$$

and since the values of Φ on γ are identical with those of X at the corresponding points of C, this integral is equal to

$$\int_C X \, dx,$$

so that the identity (5) is established. Since the conditions on S hold also when the axes are interchanged, we have two similar identities, found from (5) by cyclic permutation of the letters, the sum of which yields Stokes' theorem (4), for the particular orientation of the axes used. But by the first formula (14), page 73, we see that the two members of the equation expressing Stokes' theorem are independent of an axis system, and hence (4) holds for any orientation of the axes.

The theorem may now be extended. Let us call surfaces satisfying the conditions imposed on S *normal surface elements*. Then if a surface can be resolved, by means of a system of curves, into a finite number of normal surface elements, and if senses are assigned to the normals and bounding curves of these elements in according to the convention we

---

[1] See Exercise 2 of the last section. The formula is derived in Osgood's *Advanced Calculus*, pp. 222—223.

have established, the convention for two adjacent elements being such that their common boundaries are described in opposite senses, the sum of the identities (4) for the separate normal surface elements will yield the identity (4) for the whole surface. It is not necessary that S should have continuously changing normal directions throughout. This direction may break on the common boundary of two of the normal surface elements. The connection between the sense of the normal and the bounding curve permits us to decide on how the convention as to the positive side of S is to be continued from one element to the next. Only, the surface must be two sided, or a contradiction may be arrived at.

The result is that *we may now assert the validity of Stokes' theorem under the following conditions: the surface S is two sided, and can be resolved into a finite number of normal surface elements. The functions X, Y, Z are continuous at all points of S, and their partial derivatives are continuous at all points of the normal surface elements into which S is divided* (see Exercise 3 of the last section, page 89).

5. Sets of Points.

We turn now to the discussion of the geometric concepts which underlie any theory of integration, and which are especially important in the cases of line, surface, and volume integrals. Curves, volumes and portions of space are certain specified collections of points. By a *set of points*, we mean the aggregate of all points which are given by a definite law or condition, and only those points. Some examples of sets of points are given in Exercise 1, below.

If the points of a set E lie in a plane, E is called a *plane* set of points, and if the points of E lie on a straight line, E is called a *linear* set of points. Of course plane and linear sets of points lie in space, and it is sometimes important to know whether such sets are to be regarded as parts of space, or as parts of the planes or lines in which they lie. We shall point out the cases in which such distinctions arise.

A set of points is said to be *finite* or *infinite* according as it contains a finite or an infinite number of distinct points.

A set of points is said to be *bounded* if all of its points lie in some sphere.

A point P is said to be a *limit point* of the set E provided there are points of E, other than P, in every sphere with P as center. A limit point may belong to the set, or it may not. Thus if E consists of all the points within a given sphere, but not on its surface, all the points of the sphere, including its surface, are limit points of E. Thus some of its limit points belong to E and some do not.

Finite sets do not have limit points. On the other hand, an impor-

tant theorem known as the **Bolzano-Weierstrass Theorem** assures us
that *every bounded infinite set of points has at least one limit point*[1].

The set of points consisting of all the limit points of E is called the
derivative of E, and is denoted by E'. Thus if E is the set within a sphere,
E' consists of the points of the sphere, the boundary included. The derivative of a finite set is *empty*, that is, it contains no points.

A point P of E is said to be an *interior* point of E, provided there is a
sphere about P all the points in which belong to E.

A point P of a plane set of points E is said to be an *interior* point of
E *with respect to the plane* (or, if we are dealing only with a single plane,
and misunderstanding is precluded, simply an interior point of E), provided there is a circle in the plane with center at P all the points in
which belong to E.

Thus, if E consists of the points of the (x, y)-plane for which
$-a < x < a$, $-a < y < a$, any of its points is interior with respect
to the plane. But none of its points are interior when it is considered a
set of points in space.

A point P of a linear set of points E is said to be an *interior* point of
E *with respect to the line* (or, if misunderstanding is precluded, simply
an interior point of E) provided it is the mid-point of a segment of the
line, all the points of the segment belonging to E.

A point P is said to be *exterior* to a set E provided it is the center of
a sphere none of whose points belong to E.

The *boundary* of a set of points E is the set of all limit points of E
which are not interior to E. As this definition involves the notion of
interior points, we must know in the case of plane and linear sets whether
they are being considered as parts of space, or of the planes or lines
in which they lie. Thus the set of points in a plane consisting of the
surface of a circle, if regarded as a set in the plane, would have as boundary the circumference of the circle. If it is regarded as a set in space,
all its points are boundary points, since it has no interior points. Unless
explicit statement is made to the contrary, we shall understand that
the word interior, when used in connection with a plane set, means
interior with respect to the plane, and similarly with respect to linear
sets.

The *frontier* of a set E is the set of points which are not exterior to E
but are limit points of exterior points. Thus if E consists of the points
interior to a circle and not on a given radius, the circumference of the
circle belongs both to the boundary and to the frontier. The points of the
radius, other than the extremity, belong to the boundary, but not the
frontier.

---

[1] For a proof, see Osgood, *Funktionentheorie*, Leipzig, 1923 4th ed., p. 38,
5th ed. 1928, p. 35.

A *closed* set of points is one which contains all its limit points.

An *open* set of points is one all of whose points are interior points. The set $x^2 + y^2 + z^2 \leqq a^2$ is closed. If we suppress the sign of equality, the set becomes open. The set of all points whose coördinates are positive proper rational fractions is neither open nor closed.

A function of one or more variables is defined for certain values of the variable or variables, and these values constitute the coördinates of the points of a set. Such sets, in the case of functions occurring in mathematical physics, are of somewhat special character, and the names *region* and *domain* are employed for them. The usage is not uniformly established; we shall employ the words as follows.

A *domain*, or *open continuum* is an open set, any two of whose points can be joined by a polygonal line, of a finite number of sides, all of whose points belong to the set.

A *region* is either a domain, or a domain together with some or all of its boundary points. It is thus a broader term than domain. Usually it will be a domain with *all* its boundary points, in which case it will be called, as a rule, a *closed region*.

A *neighborhood* of a point is a domain containing that point.

Any bounded set S of numbers has a *least upper bound*. This is a number with the properties, that it is exceeded by no number of the set, while in any neighborhood of it, there is at least one number of the set. The existence of the least upper bound may be proved as follows. Let a_0 denote a number less than some number of S, and b_0 a number which exceeds all the numbers of S. We form the arithmetic mean of a_0 and b_0, and define a_1 and b_1 as follows:

$$a_1 = \frac{a_0 + b_0}{2}, \quad b_1 = b_0, \quad \text{or} \quad a_1 = a_0, \quad b_1 = \frac{a_0 + b_0}{2},$$

according as this mean is exceeded by some number of S or not. Similary, we define a_2, b_2, a_3, b_3, ..., . In general

$$a_n = \frac{a_{n-1} + b_{n-1}}{2}, \quad b_n = b_{n-1}, \quad \text{or} \quad a_n = a_{n-1}, \quad b_n = \frac{a_{n-1} + b_{n-1}}{2},$$

according as $\frac{a_{n-1} + b_{n-1}}{2}$ is exceeded by some number of S or not. We thus construct two sequences

(a) $\qquad\qquad a_0, \ a_1, \ a_2, \ a_3, \ \ldots$

(b) $\qquad\qquad b_0, \ b_1, \ b_2, \ b_3, \ \ldots .$

The first is never decreasing and bounded by b_0, and the second is never increasing and bounded below by a_0. Both therefore converge, and since $b_n - a_n$ approaches 0, to the same limit l. It is easily verified that l is the least upper bound of S.

Exercises.

1. Examine the following sets of points as to whether they are finite, bounded, open, closed, domains, regions. Specify also their limit points, derivatives, their interior points, their exterior points, and their boundaries and frontiers. The answers can be given conveniently in tabular form.

a) the points whose coördinates are integers less in absolute value than 10,

b) the points whose coördinates are integers,

c) the points whose coördinates are rational numbers less in absolute value than 10,

d) the points of the x-axis given by $0 < x \leq 1$,

e) the same, with the point $x = \frac{1}{2}$ removed,

f) the points of the x-axis given by $x = \dfrac{1}{n}$, where n assumes all integral values,

g) the points of the plane given by $\varrho^2 \leq a^2 \cos 2\varphi$,

h) the points whose coördinates satisfy either of the inequalities $(x-2)^2 + y^2 < 1$, $(x+2)^2 + y^2 < 1$.

i) the points $x^2 + y^2 + z^2 \leq 1$ and the points $x = 0$, $y = 0$, $1 \leq z \leq 2$.

2. Prove that the boundary of any set of points is closed.

3. Show that if any two points A and B of an open set E can be connected by a continuous curve (see page 98, Exercise 5) lying in E, they can also be connected by a polygonal line with a finite number of sides, also lying in E. Thus in the definition of domain, we may replace the polygonal line by any continuous curve in E.

Suggestion. About the point A there is a sphere, entirely in E. Consider the last point of the curve which belongs to this sphere. About it there is a second sphere in E. Thus a chain of spheres can be constructed, finite in number, in the last of which the point B lies. Having proved this, construct the polygon. The reasoning can be abbreviated by use of the Heine-Borel theorem of the next section.

4. If R is a closed region, and E is a set of points in R, containing at least one, but not all, of the interior points of R, show that there must be a frontier point of E in the interior of R.

Suggestion. Let P_1 and P_2 be interior points of R, P_1 belonging to E, and P_2 not. Consider a polygonal line connecting P_1 and P_2, and let l denote the least upper bound of the values of the length s of arc, measured from P_1, corresponding to points in E. Show that $s = l$ gives a frontier point of E.

6. The Heine-Borel Theorem.

The idea of uniformity is fundamental in analysis, and the reader who has not a clear appreciation of this concept should lose no time in obtaining one[1]. Generally speaking, a function is said to possess a certain property *uniformly*, or uniformly with respect to a certain variable, when the inequalities defining that property can be so chosen as to hold independently of that variable. Thus the series

$$u_1(x) + u_2(x) + u_3(x) + \cdots$$

---

[1] See the first eight sections of Chapter III of OSGOOD's *Funktionentheorie*, or COURANT's Differential- und Integralrechnung, under the heading *Gleichmäßige Annäherung* etc., in the index.

defines, by means of the sum of its first n terms, a function $s_n(x)$. To say merely that the series converges, in the interval $a \leq x \leq b$, to $l(x)$, means that to any x in the interval, and to any $\varepsilon > 0$, there corresponds an N such that for this value of x,

$$|s_n(x) - l(x)| < \varepsilon,$$

provided $n > N$.

To say that the series converges *uniformly* in the interval to $l(x)$ means that to any number $\varepsilon > 0$, there corresponds a number N *independent of x*, such that

$$|s_n(x) - l(x)| < \varepsilon,$$

for *all* x in the interval, provided $n > N$.

To say that a function $f(P)$ of the coördinates of P, defined in a region R, is continuous in the region, means that to any point P of R and any $\varepsilon > 0$, there corresponds a $\delta > 0$, such that

$$|f(Q) - f(P)| < \varepsilon,$$

provided Q is in R and the distance $\overline{QP}$ is less than δ.

To say that the above function is *uniformly* continuous in R means that to any $\varepsilon > 0$ there corresponds a $\delta > 0$, *independent of P*, such that

$$|f(Q) - f(P)| < \varepsilon,$$

where P and Q are *any* points of R, provided the distance $\overline{PQ}$ is less than δ.

The reasoning establishing many theorems on uniformity has a common part which can be formulated as a theorem on sets of points and proved once for all. This theorem is known as

The Heine-Borel Theorem[1]: *Let E be any closed bounded set of points, and S a set of domains, such that each point p of E is in one of the domains T_p of the set. Then there is a subset S', consisting of a finite number of the domains T_p, such that every point of E lies in one of the domains of S'.*

To prove this, we show first that there is a number $\alpha > 0$, such that each point of E lies in one of the domains of S whose boundary points all have a distance from that point greater than α. Suppose this were not the case. Then for each positive integer n, there would be a point p_n such that all the domains of the set S containing p_n had boundary points within a distance of $\frac{1}{n}$ from p_n. An infinite sequence of such points, since E is bounded, would have at least one limit point p_0, by

---

[1] Borel, Annales de l'Ecole Normale Supérieure, 3d Ser. Vol. 12 (1895) p. 51. Heine, *Die Elemente der Funktionentheorie*, Journal für Mathematik und Physik, Vol. 74 (1872), p. 188.

the Bolzano-Weierstrass theorem. And as E is closed, p_0 would be a point of E. It would therefore lie in one of the domains T_0 of S. We have here a contradiction. For if δ were the radius of a sphere about p_0, lying entirely in T_0, there would be points in the sequence $p_1, p_2, p_3, \ldots$ lying within a distance $\frac{\delta}{3}$ of p_0, with index n such that $\frac{1}{n} < \frac{\delta}{3}$. For such a point there was no domain of S which did not have boundary points within a distance $\frac{1}{n}$ of p_n. But T_0 would be a domain whose boundary points all lay at a greater distance from p_n, and this is the contradiction. Hence the number α exists.

Suppose now that e is a set of a finite number of the points of E, with the property that each point of E has a distance less than α from some point of e. Then for each point p of e there is a domain of the set S whose boundary points are all at a distance greater than α from p. The set of domains consisting of one such for each point of e is a set S' of a finite number of domains, such that each point of E is in one of them, and it has therefore the character demanded by the theorem.

Should there be any doubts about the existence of the set e, they may be set at rest by the following considerations. Let space be divided into cubes with diagonals of length $\frac{\alpha}{2}$, by three systems of parallel planes. The points of E can lie in but a finite number of these cubes, since E is bounded. Any set e consisting of one point of E in each cube which contains points of E, within it or on its boundary, has the required properties.

This proof of the Heine-Borel theorem has been given for sets in space. The changes to be made for plane or linear sets of points are only of a formal nature.

As an application, we prove the theorem *if $f(P)$ is continuous in the closed region R, then it is uniformly continuous in R.* Let $\varepsilon > 0$ be given. By hypothesis, there is a sphere $\sigma(P)$ about each point P of R, such that for any point Q of R in the sphere,

$$|f(Q) - f(P)| < \frac{\varepsilon}{2}.$$

Consider the domains attached to the points of R, defined thus: the domain corresponding to P is the interior of the sphere about P whose radius is half that of $\sigma(P)$. By the Heine-Borel theorem, every point of R is interior to one of a finite number of these domains. If δ denotes the least of their radii, then

$$|f(Q) - f(P)| < \varepsilon$$

if P and Q are *any* two points of R whose distance apart is less than δ. For P lies in one of the finite set of domains, say that about P_0. Hence both P and Q lie in the sphere $\sigma(P_0)$, of radius at least $2\,\delta$. Thus both $f(P)$ and $f(Q)$ differ from $f(P_0)$ by less than $\frac{\varepsilon}{2}$, and so differ from each other by less than ε. The above inequality therefore holds independently of the positions of P and Q, and the continuity is uniform.

7. Functions of one Variable; Regular Curves.

We shall be concerned with one-valued functions, defined for values of variables which are the coördinates of points of domains or regions. In the case of functions of one variable, the domains or regions are intervals, without, or with, their end-points.

Let I denote a closed interval $a \leqq x \leqq b$ of the x-axis. We say that $f(x)$ is *continous in* I if it is continuous at every point of I.

We say that $f(x)$ has a *continuous derivative*, or is *continuously differentiable in* I provided it is continuous in I and its derivative exists at all interior points of I, and coincides at all such points with a function which is continuous in I.

Some such definition is necessary, if we are to speak of the derivative in a *closed* interval, for the ordinary definition of the derivative is not applicable at the endpoints of an interval in which a function is defined (see Exercise 2, below).

We say that $f(x)$ is *piecewise continuous in* I provided there is a finite set of points of division, $a = a_0 < a_1 < a_2 \cdots < a_n = b$, of the interval I, such that in the interior of each of the intervals (a_i, a_{i+1}), $f(x)$ coincides with a function which is continuous in the closed sub-interval.

We say that $f(x)$ is *piecewise differentiable in* I provided there is a set of sub-intervals of I of the above sort in each of which it has a continuous derivative (the sub-intervals being regarded as closed).

Exercises.

1. Characterize, with respect to the above definitions, the following functions: a) $f(x) = \sqrt{a^2 - x^2}$, on $(-a, a)$, on $\left(-\dfrac{a}{2}, \dfrac{a}{2}\right)$; b) $f(x) = [x]$, where $[x]$ means the greatest integer not exceeding x, on various intervals; c) $f(x) = \int\limits_0^x [x]\,dx$, on various intervals.

2. Show that the above definition of continuously differentiable functions is equivalent to the following: a) $f(x)$ shall have a derivative at every interior point of I, and one-sided derivatives at the end-points, and the function thus defined shall be continuous in the closed interval I; b) the derivative is continuous in the open interval, and approaches limits at the end-points.

A *regular arc* is a set of points which, for some orientation of the axes, admits a representation

$$y = f(x), \qquad z = \varphi(x), \qquad a \leqq x \leqq b \quad (I),$$

where $f(x)$ and $\varphi(x)$ are continuous and have continuous derivatives in I. We call such a representation a *standard representation* of the arc.

We shall need several facts about regular arcs, some of which will be left to the reader as exercises, and some of which we shall prove as theorems.

Exercises.

3. A regular arc admits a parametric representation in terms of the length of arc s, $x = x(s)$, $y = y(s)$, $z = z(s)$, $0 \leq s \leq l$, where $x(s)$, $y(s)$, $z(s)$ are continuous and continuously differentiable in $0 \leq s \leq l$.

4. A curve $x = x(s)$, $y = y(s)$, $z = z(s)$, $0 \leq s \leq l$, where $x(s)$, $y(s)$, $z(s)$ are continuous and continuously differentiable in the interval $0 \leq s \leq l$, admits a standard representation provided there is an orientation of the axes for which no tangent to the curve is perpendicular to the x-axis. The curve is then a regular arc.

5. A continuous curve is a set of points given by $x = x(t)$, $y = y(t)$, $z = z(t)$, $a \leq t \leq b$, where $x(t)$, $y(t)$, $z(t)$ are continuous functions of t in the closed interval (a, b). Show that such a curve is a closed bounded set of points. Show hence that a function which is continuous in a closed interval actually takes on, at points in the interval, its least upper bound, its greatest lower bound, and any intermediate value. Notice that the bounds are not necessarily taken on if the interval is open.

Theorem I. *Given a regular arc C, and a number $\alpha > 0$, there exists a number $\delta > 0$, such that no two tangents to C at points on any portion of length less than δ, make with each other an angle greater than α.*

By Exercise 3 the direction cosines $x'(s)$, $y'(s)$, $z'(s)$ of the tangent to C at the point s are continuous in the closed interval $(0, l)$, and hence are uniformly continuous. There is therefore a number $\delta > 0$ such that if s and t are any two points for which $|s - t| < \delta$,

$$[x'(s) - x'(t)]^2 + [y'(s) - y'(t)]^2 + [z'(s) - z'(t)]^2 < 4\sin^2\frac{\alpha}{2}.$$

If the parentheses are expanded, we find for the cosine of the acute angle (s, t) between the tangents at s and t

$$(6) \qquad \cos(s, t) = x'(s) x'(t) + y'(s) y'(t) + z'(s) z'(t) > \cos\alpha,$$

and this angle is therefore less than α on any portion of C of length less than δ.

For plane regular arcs, we could infer that the tangents at such a portion of C make angles less than α with the chord joining the end-points of the portion, for one of these tangents is parallel to the chord. But for arcs which are not plane, there need not be a tangent parallel to a chord, as may be seen by considering several turns of a helix. The fact subsists however as we now prove.

Theorem II. *Given a regular arc C, and a number $\alpha > 0$, there is a number $\delta > 0$, such that the tangent to C at any point of a portion of length less than δ, makes with the chord joining the end-points of that portion an angle less than α.*

The same δ as that determined in the proof of the previous theorem will serve. In fact, if we integrate both sides of the inequality (6) with respect to s from s_1 to s_2, $0 < s_2 - s_1 < \delta$, we find

$$(x_2 - x_1) x'(t) + (y_2 - y_1) y'(t) + (z_2 - z_1) z'(t) > (s_2 - s_1) \cos \alpha.$$

If we divide by c, the length of the chord joining s_1 and s_2, we have on the left the cosine of the acute angle (c, t) between the chord and the tangent at t, and on the right something not less than $\cos \alpha$. Hence if $s_1 \leqq t \leqq s_2$, the angle (c, t) is less than α, as was to be proved.

Theorem III. *The projection of a regular arc on a plane to which it is nowhere perpendicular consists of a finite number of regular arcs.*

We take for the regular arc C the parametric representation of Exercise 3, the plane of projection being the (x, y)-plane. This is possible, since the properties there given for $x(s)$, $y(s)$, $z(s)$ subsist if the axes are subjected to a rigid displacement. Since the arc is nowhere perpendicular to the (x, y)-plane, $|z'(s)| < 1$, and hence, by Exercise 5[1], the maximum μ of $|z'(s)|$ is less than 1. Then, if σ is the length of arc of the projection C_1 of C,

$$\sigma'^2(s) = x'^2(s) + y'^2(s) = 1 - z'^2(s) \geqq 1 - \mu^2.$$

Hence, with the proper sense chosen for the positive direction on C_1, σ is an always increasing function of s for $0 \leqq s \leqq l$, with continuous, nowhere vanishing derivative. The inverse function $s(\sigma)$ therefore exists, and if 0 and λ are the values of σ corresponding to 0 and l of s, $s(\sigma)$ is continuous and has a continuous derivative $\left(\text{namely } \dfrac{1}{\sigma'(s)}\right)$ in the closed interval $(0, \lambda)$. Hence C_1 is given by $x = x[s(\sigma)]$, $y = y[s(\sigma)]$, $z = 0$, the coördinates being continuous and continuously differentiable functions of σ on the closed interval $(0, \lambda)$.

It remains to show that C_1 can be divided into a finite number of pieces on each of which the tangent turns by less than a right angle, for corresponding to each such piece there will be an orientation of the axes such that no tangent to the piece is perpendicular to the x-axis. The pieces will then be regular arcs, by Exercise 4. But the coördinates of C_1 expressed as functions of σ fulfill the conditions used in the proof of Theorem I, hence that theorem is applicable to C_1, and C_1 has the required property for $\alpha = \dfrac{\pi}{2}$.

A *regular curve* is a set of points consisting of a finite number of regular arcs arranged in order, and such that the terminal point of each arc (other than the last) is the initial point of the next following arc. The arcs have no other points in common, except that the terminal point

---

[1] Or, see Osgood, *Funktionentheorie*, Chap. I, § 4, Theorem 2.

of the last arc may be the initial point of the first. In this case, the regular curve is a *closed curve*. Otherwise it is an *open curve*. Regular curves have no double points. This means that if $x = x(s)$, $y = y(s)$, $z = z(s)$, $0 \leq s \leq l$, is a parametric representation of the curve in terms of its length of arc, the equations

$$x(s) = x(t), \quad y(s) = y(t), \quad z(s) = z(t)$$

have no solutions other than $s = t$ for s and t in the closed interval $(0, l)$ if the curve is open, and only the two additional solutions $s = 0$, $t = l$, and $s = l$, $t = 0$, if the curve is closed. A curve without double points is called a *simple* curve.

Exercise.

6. Show that the following is an equivalent definition of regular curve: a regular curve is a set of points which admits a representation $x = x(t)$, $y = y(t)$, $z = z(t)$, $a \leq t \leq b$, where $x(t)$, $y(t)$, $z(t)$ are continuous and have piecewise continuous derivatives in the closed interval (a, b), these derivatives never vanishing simultaneously, and where the equations $x(s) = x(t)$, $y(s) = y(t)$, $z(s) = z(t)$ have no common solutions for $a \leq s < t \leq b$, except possibly the solution $s = a$, $t = b$.

8. Functions of Two Variables; Regular Surfaces.

Functions of two variables will usually be defined at the points of plane regions. Of primary importance will be regular regions.

A *regular region* of the plane is a bounded closed region whose boundary is a closed regular curve.

Exercise.

1 Which of the following are regular regions? a) the surface and circumference of a circle; b) the points exterior to and on the boundary of a circle; c) the points between two concentric circles, with the circumferences; d) the points $e^{\vartheta} \leq \varrho \leq e^{\vartheta + \pi}$, $\vartheta \geq 0$; e) the region $x^2 + y^2 \leq 4$, $y \geq x \sin \dfrac{1}{x}$ for $x \neq 0$, $y \geq 0$ for $x = 0$.

A regular region R is the *sum* of the regular regions $R_1, R_2, \ldots R_n$, provided every point of R is in one of the regions R_i, every point of each R_i is in R, and no two of the regions R_i have common points other than as follows: a regular arc of the boundary of one of these regions and a regular arc of the boundary of another may either coincide, or have one or both end points in common.

Let R denote a regular region of the (x, y)-plane. We say that $f(x, y)$ is *continuous in* R provided it is continuous at every point of R.

We say that $f(x, y)$ is *continuously differentiable in* R, or has *continuous partial derivatives of the first order in* R, provided it is continuous in R and provided its partial derivatives of the first order with respect to x and y exist at all interior points of R and there coincide each with a function which is continuous in R.

We say that $f(x, y)$ is *piecewise continuous* in R, provided R is the sum of a finite number of regular regions in the interior of each of which $f(x, y)$ coincides with a function which is continuous in that sub-region. It may be noted that on the common boundary of two sub-regions, $f(x, y)$ need not be defined. A function which is 1 for $x^2 + y^2 \leqq a^2$, $y > 0$, and -1 for $x^2 + y^2 \leqq a^2$, $y < 0$, is piecewise continuous in the circle.

We say that $f(x, y)$ *is piecewise differentiable*, or *has piecewise continuous partial derivatives of the first order* in R, provided R is the sum of a finite number of regular regions in each of which $f(x, y)$ is continuously differentiable.

The above definitions concerning functions depend on a system of axes in the (x, y)-planes, although they deal with functions defined on sets of points whose coördinates may well be measured from other axes. It is important for us to know that a function satisfying any of these definitions continues to do so when the axes undergo a rigid displacement. This is the case. For if we make such a change of axes

$$x = a + \xi \cos \alpha - \eta \sin \alpha,$$
$$y = b + \xi \sin \alpha + \eta \cos \alpha,$$

$f(x, y)$ will become a function $\Phi(\xi, \eta)$. If $f(x, y)$ is continuous in any region, $\Phi(\xi, \eta)$ will be continuous in that region. If $f(x, y)$ has continuous partial derivatives of the first order in the interior of any region, $\Phi(\xi, \eta)$ will have the derivatives

$$\frac{\partial \Phi}{\partial \xi} = \frac{\partial f}{\partial x} \cos \alpha + \frac{\partial f}{\partial y} \sin \alpha,$$
$$\frac{\partial \Phi}{\partial \eta} = -\frac{\partial f}{\partial x} \sin \alpha + \frac{\partial f}{\partial y} \cos \alpha,$$

in the interior of that region, and they will also be continuous there. If in one case the derivatives coincide with functions which are continuous in the closed region, they will also in the other case.

The Triangulation of Regular Regions. A regular region may be complicated in character, and it will be useful to have a means of dividing it into simple parts. We proceed to a consideration of this question.

Theorem IV. *Given a regular region R, and a number $\delta > 0$, it is possible to resolve R into a sum of regular sub-regions σ with the properties*

    a) *each sub-region is bounded by three regular arcs.*
    b) *no sub-region has a reëntrant vertex,*
    c) *the maximum chord of the sub-regions is less than δ.*

A regular region has a *reëntrant vertex* at P if, as its boundary is traversed with the region to the left, the forward pointing tangent vector has at P an abrupt change in direction toward the right. The process of resolving R into the sub-regions of the theorem will be referred to as the *triangulation* of R.

The triangulation is accomplished by first cutting off triangular regions at the vertices of R, and then cutting out triangular regions along the edges, so that what is left of R is bounded by straight lines. The polygonal region is then easily triangulated.

We first interpolate vertices on the boundary C of R, finite in number, and such that between two adjacent vertices, C turns by less than 15^0 (fig. 15a). This is possible, by Theorem I. We then determine a number $\eta > 0$, which does not exceed the minimum distance between any two non-adjacent arcs of C, the arcs being regarded as terminated by the original and the interpolated vertices. With a radius r, less than either δ. or $\frac{\eta}{3}$, we describe about each vertex a circle. These circles will have no points in common, and each will be cut by no arcs of C other than the two terminating at its center.

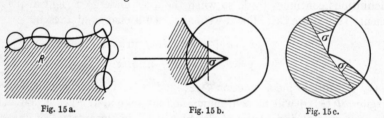

Fig. 15 a.   Fig. 15 b.   Fig. 15 c.

Suppose the arcs entering one of these circles meet at an angle not greater than 60^0 (fig. 15b). Then the tangents to these arcs at points within the circle will make with the bisector of the angle at the vertex, angles which never exceed 45^0. A perpendicular to the bisector, at a distance $\frac{r}{2}$ from the vertex, will cut off from R a region σ with the required properties. The rest of R will have a straight line segment as a portion of its boundary, met by the adjacent arcs at angles differing from a right angle by not more than 45^0.

If the arcs entering a circle meet at an angle greater than 60^0, we draw from the vertex into R two radii, each making an angle 30^0 with one of the arcs at the center (fig. 15c). We then cut off from R two triangles σ in the way just indicated, each bounded by an arc and two straight lines. The rest of R in the neighborhood of the vertex has a polygonal boundary.

After all such triangular regions have been removed from R at its vertices, the boundary C' of the portion R' of R which remains has the property that such of its arcs as remain never turn by more than 15^0, and are flanked by straight lines which meet them at angles which are not reëntrant and differ from right angles by not more than 45^0. No two curved arcs of C' have common points. No curved arc has points

other than its end-points in common with a straight line segment of
C' because all such segments are interior to the circles, and the construction within the circles has avoided this. Hence there is a number $\eta' > 0$,
such that any curved arc of C' has a distance greater than η' from any
non-adjacent arc of C', curved or straight.

We now interpolate on the curved arcs of C' a finite number of vertices so that these arcs are divided into parts whose chords never exceed
the smaller of the numbers, $\frac{\eta'}{3}$ or δ. With the chords of the sub-arcs as

diagonals, we construct rhombuses
whose sides make with the chords
angles of 30^0 (fig. 15d). As the arcs do
not differ in direction from their chords
by more than 15^0, the rhombuses do
not contain points of the straight line

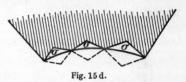

Fig. 15 d.

segments of C' in their interiors. As each rhombus lies within a
distance $\frac{\eta'}{3}$ of its arc, none has points in common with another belonging
to a different arc of C'. Finally, the rhombuses belonging to a single
arc of C' have no interior points in common, since that arc, on which
their longer diagonals lie, turns by less than 15^0.

The regions common to R' and the rhombuses are regular regions σ.
After their removal, the rest of R' is bounded by a finite number of
straight line segments. If the lines of these segments are prolonged
through R', they cut the polygonal region into a finite number of convex polygons. Each of these may then be triangulated by joining its
vertices to an interior point. If the resulting triangles are too large, they
may be quartered by joining the mid-points of their sides, and this process repeated, if necessary, until their maximum chord is less than δ.
The triangulation of R is thus accomplished.

The triangular regions σ have further properties, one of which we
shall need. It is as follows.

Theorem V. *If A and B are any two points of an arbitrary one of
the regions σ, they can be connected by a regular curve γ, all of whose
points, with the possible exception of A and B, are interior to this region σ,
and whose length does not exceed $2\,c$, where c is the length of the chord $A\,B$.*

The regions σ are of three types, the construction of γ varying
according to the type. First, there are the regions cut out, from the
region R which was triangulated, at the vertices (fig. 16a). These can
be characterized as follows, the x-axis being taken along the bisector
of the angle at the vertex:

a) $f(x) \leqq y \leqq \varphi(x), \quad 0 \leqq x \leqq a,$

where $f(0) = \varphi(0) = 0, \quad f(x) < \varphi(x) \quad \text{for} \quad 0 < x \leqq a,$

The Divergence Theorem.

and where $f(x)$ and $\varphi(x)$ are continuously differentiable in the closed interval $(0, a)$. Moreover, the curves $y = f(x)$ and $y = \varphi(x)$ turn by less than 15^0.

Secondly, we have the parts of rhombuses (fig. 16b). Choosing the chord of the curved side as x-axis, we may characterize σ as follows:

b) $$f(x) \leqq y \leqq \frac{1}{\sqrt{3}} x, \quad 0 \leqq x \leqq \frac{a}{2},$$

$$f(x) \leqq y \leqq \frac{1}{\sqrt{3}} (a - x), \quad \frac{a}{2} \leqq x \leqq a,$$

where

$$f(0) = f(a) = 0, \quad f(x) < \frac{1}{\sqrt{3}} x, \quad f(x) < \frac{1}{\sqrt{3}} (a - x) \quad \text{for} \quad 0 < x < a,$$

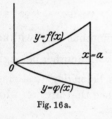

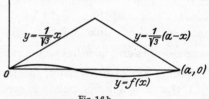

Fig. 16a.

Fig. 16b.

and where $f(x)$ is continuously differentiable in the closed interval $(0, a)$. Moreover, the curve $y = f(x)$ turns by less than 15^0.

Finally, we have the type

c) σ is bounded by three straight lines.

We first reduce the problem of constructing σ to the case in which A and B are interior to σ, if they are not so at the outset. Suppose A is a boundary point. Unless it is a vertex at which the sides are tangent, we can draw a straight line segment into σ, and take on it an interior point A' distant from A less than $0 \cdot 1 c$. If A is a vertex where the sides are tangent, σ must be of type (a), and A must be the origin in the representation given. We may then draw into σ the regular curve

$$y = \frac{f(x) + \varphi(x)}{2},$$

and take upon it a point A' whose distance from A along the curve is less than $0 \cdot 1 c$. If B is also a boundary point, we construct in the same way an interior point B'. The chord $c' = A'B'$ cannot then exceed $1 \cdot 2 c$. The theorem will be proved when it has been shown possible to connect A' and B' by a curve γ' whose length does not exceed $1 \cdot 8 c$, and this will be the case if its length does not exceed $1 \cdot 5 c'$. Let us therefore drop the primes, and show that any two interior points A and B of σ can be connected by a regular curve γ entirely interior to σ and of length not more than $1 \cdot 5 c$, c being the distance AB.

If σ is of type (c), the chord $A\,B$ will serve for γ. If σ is of type (b), the chord $A\,B$ cannot have points in common with the upper, or straight line parts of the boundary, and hence will again serve as γ unless it meets the curve $y = f\,(x)$. This cannot occur if $A\,B$ is vertical, so that $A\,B$ has a representation $y = a\,x + b$, $x_1 \leqq x \leqq x_2$. Now the distance $a\,x + b - f\,(x)$ of a point of $A\,B$ above the lower boundary of σ, measured vertically, is positive at x_1 and x_2. Let $\eta > 0$ be less than the smaller of the values of this function at x_1 and x_2, and also less than the minimum of the differences

$$\frac{1}{\sqrt{3}}\,x - f\,(x) \quad \text{and} \quad \frac{1}{\sqrt{3}}\,(a - x) - f\,(x) \quad \text{for} \quad x_1 \leqq x \leqq x_2.$$

Then the curve $y = f\,(x) + \eta$ is interior to σ for $x_1 \leqq x \leqq x_2$, and lies below A and B, but above $A\,B$ at some intermediate points. Let A' and B' be its intersections with $A\,B$ with least and greatest x, respectively. We take as γ the straight piece $A\,A'$, the arc of $y = f\,(x) + \eta$ between A' and B', and the straight piece $B'\,B$. Then γ is regular, is entirely interior to σ, and its direction never deviates from that of the x-axis by more than 15^0, because $A\,B$ is a secant of the curve $y = f\,(x)$, and so is parallel to a tangent, and the same is true of the x-axis. Hence the length of γ does not exceed $c \sec 15^0 < 1 \cdot 5\,c$, as required.

If σ is of type (a), the chord will again serve unless it meets one or both of the arcs $y = f\,(x)$, $y = \varphi\,(x)$. If it meets the first, say, a portion of the chord $A\,B$ may be replaced by a curve $y = f\,(x) + \eta$, between the points A' and B' of $A\,B$. If the chords $A\,A'$ or $B'\,B$ or both, are met by the curve $y = \varphi\,(x)$, portions of such a chord may be replaced by a curve $y = \varphi\,(x) - \eta$. We shall then have a regular curve γ, entirely within σ, connecting A and B, whose direction never deviates from that of the x-axis by more than 45^0, and whose length therefore does not exceed $\sqrt{2}\,c < 1 \cdot 5\,c$. The theorem is thus established.

Regular Surface Elements. We now turn to the definition and the consideration of the more important properties of regular surface elements, from which regular surfaces are built as were regular curves from regular arcs.

A *regular surface element* is a set of points which, for some orientation of the axes, admits a representation

$$(7) \qquad\qquad z = f\,(x, y), \qquad (x, y) \text{ in } R,$$

where R is a regular region of the (x, y)-plane, and where $f\,(x, y)$ is continuously differentiable in R.

We call such a representation a *standard representation*. The *boundary* of the regular surface element is the set of those of its points (x, y, z) for which (x, y) is on the boundary of R.

Exercises.

1. Let γ be a plane regular arc all of whose points are interior to R. Show that γ is the projection of a regular arc on the regular surface element.

2. Show that the direction cosines of the upward pointing normal to the regular surface element are continuous functions of (x, y) in R.

Theorem VI. *The boundary of a regular surface element E is a regular curve C.*

Consider one of the regular arcs of the boundary of R. As $f(x, y)$ remains continuously differentiable when the axes of x and y are rotated, we may assume that this arc γ has the standard representation

$$y = \varphi(x), \quad 0 \leqq x \leqq a,$$

where $\varphi(x)$ has a continuous derivative in the closed interval $(0, a)$. The corresponding portion of C is given by

$$y = \varphi(x), \quad z = f[x, \varphi(x)], \quad 0 \leqq x \leqq a,$$

and $f[x, \varphi(x)]$ is clearly continuous. It must be shown to have a continuous derivative in the closed interval $(0, a)$.

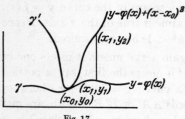

Fig. 17.

Let (x_0, y_0) be a point of γ, for the present not an end point, and let us suppose the axes chosen so that R lies above γ in the neighborhood of (x_0, y_0) (fig. 17). Then, since the boundary of R is free from double points, the curve γ'

$$y = \varphi(x) + (x - x_0)^2,$$

lies, for sufficiently small $|x - x_0|$, within R except for $x = x_0$. Now let (x_1, y_1) be a second point of γ, near (x_0, y_0), and let (x_1, y_2) be the point of γ' with the same abscissa. Let $z_0 = f(x_0, y_0)$, $z_1 = f(x_1, y_1)$, and $z_2 = f(x_1, y_2)$. Then

$$z_1 - z_2 = \int_{y_2}^{y_1} \frac{\partial f(x_1, y)}{\partial y} \, dy = f_y(x_1, y')(y_1 - y_2) = -f_y(x_1, y')(x_1 - x_0)^2,$$

where we have used the law of the mean and the values $y_1 = \varphi(x_1)$ and $y_2 = \varphi(x_1) + (x_1 - x_0)^2$. Also, integrating along γ', we find

$$z_2 - z_0 = \int_{x_0}^{x_1} \frac{df}{dx} \, dx = \int_{x_0}^{x_1} \left\{ \frac{\partial f}{\partial x} + \frac{\partial f}{\partial y} [\varphi'(x) + 2(x - x_0)] \right\} dx$$

$$= f_x(x'', y'')(x_1 - x_0) + f_y(x'', y'')[\varphi'(x'') + 2(x'' - x_0)](x_1 - x_0).$$

Adding the last two equations and dividing by $x_1 - x_0$, we find

$$\frac{z_1 - z_0}{x_1 - x_0} = f_x(x'', y'') + f_y(x'', y'')[\varphi'(x'') + 2(x'' - x_0)] - f_y(x_1, y')(x_1 - x_0).$$

As x_1 approaches x_0 the points at which mean values are taken approach (x_0, y_0), and since $f(x, y)$ is continuously differentiable, its partial derivatives approach values which we may regard as defining these derivatives on the boundary of R. The result is

$$\frac{dz}{dx} = \frac{\partial f}{\partial x} + \frac{\partial f}{\partial y} \, \varphi'(x).$$

Thus at points of γ other than end-points, z has a derivative with respect to x which is given by the ordinary rules for composite functions. From the form of the result, it is clear that this derivative coincides in the interior of $(0, a)$ with a function which is continuous in the closed interval. Hence z has a continuous derivative with respect to x in the closed interval and the part of C corresponding to γ is a regular arc. As C is made up of a finite number of regular arcs, suitably ordered, with only end points in common, it is a regular curve, as was to be proved.

We have seen that a regular arc admits a standard representation with any orientation of the axes such that the curve is nowhere perpendicular to the x-axis (Exercises 3 and 4, p. 98). A similar situation is not present in the case of regular surface elements. Consider, for example, the helicoidal surface

$$z = \tan^{-1} \frac{y}{x}, \quad -\pi < z \leqq \pi, \quad (x, y) \text{ in } R,$$

where R is given in polar coördinates by

$$-\pi + \alpha \leqq \varphi \leqq \pi - \alpha, \quad 1 \leqq \varrho \leqq 2, \quad (0 < \alpha).$$

If α is very small, it is possible to tilt the axes very slightly in such a way that the new z-axis cuts the surface element twice, so that a standard representation is not possible with the new orientation of the axes. It is true, however, that any regular surface element can be divided into a finite number of regular surface elements, such that each admits a standard representation, with much latitude of choice in the orientation of the axes. We proceed to a study of this question, deriving first a lemma which will be of repeated use to us.

Schwarz' Inequality. *Let $f(x)$ and $\varphi(x)$ be two real functions, piecewise continuous on (a, b). Then*

$$(8) \qquad \left[\int_a^b f(x)\, \varphi(x)\, dx \right]^2 \leqq \int_a^b f^2(x)\, dx \int_a^b \varphi^2(x)\, dx.$$

A similar relation holds for functions of several variables, and functions less restricted than the above. But for present needs the formulation given is sufficient. To derive the inequality, we introduce two real parameters, λ and μ, and observe that the integral

$$\int_a^b [\lambda f(x) + \mu \varphi(x)]^2\, dx$$

is never negative, the integrand being the square of a real function. Accordingly, the quadratic function of λ and μ obtained by expanding the integrand,

$$\lambda^2 \int_a^b f^2(x)\,dx + 2\lambda\mu \int_a^b f(x)\,\varphi(x)\,dx + \mu^2 \int_a^b \varphi^2(x)\,dx$$

cannot have real distinct factors, for otherwise λ and μ could be chosen so that these factors would have opposite signs. Hence the square of the coefficient of $\lambda\mu$ is less than or equal to the product of the coefficients of λ^2 and μ^2, and this gives the desired relation.

Theorem VII. *Any regular surface element E can be divided into a finite number of regular surface elements e, each with the property that if any system of coördinate axes be taken, in which the z-axis does not make an angle of more than 70^0 with any normal to e, e admits a standard representation with this system of axes.*

Starting with the standard representation (7) for E, we determine a number $\delta > 0$, such that if (x_1, y_1) and (x_2, y_2) are any two points of R whose distance apart does not exceed δ,

$$(9) \qquad (f_{x_2} - f_{x_1})^2 + (f_{y_2} - f_{y_1})^2 < \frac{1}{16}\cos^2 75^0.$$

This is possible since the partial derivatives of $f(x, y)$ are uniformly continuous in R. We then triangulate R in accordance with Theorem IV, so that the maximum chord of the sub-regions σ of R is less than δ. Then the surface element e

$$z = f(x, y), \qquad (x, y) \text{ in } \sigma$$

is regular, σ being any one of the sub-regions of R given by the triangulation. We shall show that e has the properties required by the theorem.

We first seek limits to the angle which any chord AB of e makes with the normal to e at A. Let A have the coördinates (x_1, y_1, z_1) and B, (x_2, y_2, z_2), and let c denote the length of the chord. The direction cosines of the chord, and of the normal to e at A are

$$\frac{x_2 - x_1}{c}, \quad \frac{y_2 - y_1}{c}, \quad \frac{z_2 - z_1}{c},$$

and

$$\frac{-f_{x_1}}{\sqrt{1 + f_{x_1}^2 + f_{y_1}^2}}, \quad \frac{-f_{y_1}}{\sqrt{1 + f_{x_1}^2 + f_{y_1}^2}}, \quad \frac{1}{\sqrt{1 + f_{x_1}^2 + f_{y_1}^2}},$$

so that the acute angle (c, n) between chord and normal is given by

$$\cos(c, n) = \left| \frac{(z_2 - z_1) - f_{x_1}(x_2 - x_1) - f_{y_1}(y_2 - y_1)}{c\,\sqrt{1 + f_{x_1}^2 + f_{y_1}^2}} \right|.$$

The points (x_1, y_1) and (x_2, y_2) can be connected, by Theorem V, by a regular curve γ, interior, except possibly for its end-points, to σ, and of length not more than twice the distance of these points, and so certainly not more than $2c$. Let $x = x(s)$, $y = y(s)$ be the parametric equations of γ, the length of arc s being measured from (x_1, y_1). Then $x(s)$, $y(s)$ and $z = f[x(s), y(s)]$ are continuously differentiable in the closed interval $(0, l)$, l being the length of γ. Hence

$$z_2 - z_1 = \int_0^l \frac{dz}{ds}\, ds = \int_0^l [f_x x'(s) + f_y y'(s)]\, ds.$$

The remaining terms in the numerator of the expression for $\cos(c, n)$ can also be expressed as an integral over γ. For f_{x_1} and f_{y_1} are constants, and

$$x_2 - x_1 = \int_0^l x'(s)\, ds, \qquad y_2 - y_1 = \int_0^l y'(s)\, ds,$$

so that

$$f_{x_1}(x_2 - x_1) + f_{y_1}(y_2 - y_1) = \int_0^l [f_{x_1} x'(s) + f_{y_1} y'(s)]\, ds,$$

and

$$\cos(c, n) = \frac{\left| \int_0^l [(f_x - f_{x_1}) x'(s) + (f_y - f_{y_1}) y'(s)]\, ds \right|}{c\sqrt{1 + f_{x_1}^2 + f_{y_1}^2}}.$$

Applying Schwarz' inequality to the integral of the first term in the numerator, we find

$$\left[\int_0^l (f_x - f_{x_1}) x'(s)\, ds \right]^2 \leqq \int_0^l (f_x - f_{x_1})^2\, ds \int_0^l x'^2(s)\, ds < \frac{1}{16} \cos^2 75^0\, l \cdot l,$$

because of the inequality (9) and the fact that $|x'(s)| \leqq 1$. Hence

$$\left| \int_0^l (f_x - f_{x_1}) x'(s)\, ds \right| < \frac{l}{4} \cos 75^0.$$

A similar inequality holds for the integral of the second term, and hence

$$\cos(c, n) < \frac{l}{2c} \cos 75^0 \leqq \cos 75^0,$$

since $l \leqq 2c$. *Thus the angle between any chord of e and the normal to e at one end of the chord differs from a right angle by less than 15^0.*

Suppose now that the axes of the system of coördinates (ξ, η, ζ) are selected in any way subject to the restriction that the ζ-axis does not make an angle of more than 70^0 with any normal to e (fig. 18). Then no chord of e can make with the ζ-axis an angle of less than 5^0, and hence *no parallel to the ζ-axis can meet e twice.*

This means that if τ is the set of points which is the projection of e on the (ξ, η)-plane, and (ξ, η, ζ) are the coördinates of a variable point on e, $\zeta = \varphi(\xi, \eta)$ is a one valued function of ξ and η in τ.

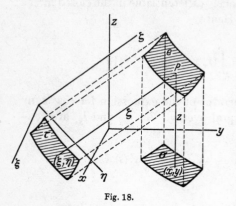

Fig. 18.

Our object is now to show that

$$\zeta = \varphi(\xi, \eta), \qquad (\xi, \eta) \text{ in } \tau$$

is a standard representation of e.

The correspondence between the points $P(x, y)$ of σ and the points $P'(\xi, \eta)$ of τ which are the projections of the same point p of e, is one-to-one, since parallels to the z-axis and the ζ-axis each meet e but once. It is also continuous. First, ξ and η are continuous functions of x and y, because $z = f(x, y)$ is continuous, and ξ and η are continuous functions of x, y and z. Conversely, x and y are continuous functions of ξ and η. This will follow in a similar way if it is shown that $\zeta = \varphi(\xi, \eta)$ is continuous in τ. Suppose this were not the case. This would mean that there was a point $P_0(\xi_0, \eta_0)$, and a number $\alpha > 0$, such that in every neighborhood of P_0 there would be points at which $\varphi(\xi, \eta)$ differed from $\zeta_0 = \varphi(\xi_0, \eta_0)$ by more than α. Let P_1, P_2, P_3, ... be an infinite sequence of such points with P_0 as limit point. The corresponding points of e would have at least one limit point, by the Bolzano-Weierstrass theorem. This limit point would lie on e, since e is closed, and its ordinate ζ' would differ from ζ_0 by at least α. Thus e would have a chord parallel to the ζ-axis, namely that joining (ξ_0, η_0, ζ_0) to (ξ_0, η_0, ζ'). This we know does not happen. Hence $\varphi(\xi, \eta)$ is continuous in τ, and the correspondence is continuous in both senses.

In such a correspondence between the closed bounded sets σ and τ, interior points correspond to interior points. Thus, let P_0 be an interior point of σ, and let γ be a circle about P_0, lying, with its interior, in σ. As the correspondence is continous and one-to-one, γ corresponds to a simple closed curve γ' in τ. By the Jordan theorem[1], such a curve separates the plane into two domains, a bounded interior one, and an infinite one. The points within γ all correspond to points in one of these domains only, for otherwise the continuity of the correspondence would be violated. This domain cannot be the infinite one, because τ being bounded, the set of points corresponding to the interior of γ would have

---

[1] See OSGOOD, *Funktionentheorie*, Chap. V, §§ 4—6. For the sake of simplicity of proof, the theorem there given is restricted to regular curves. References to the more general theorem are given.

to have boundary points other than those of γ', and this would violate the one-to-one character of the correspondence. For the same reason, the points corresponding to the interior of γ must fill the whole interior of γ'. As the point P_0' corresponding to P_0 must lie in the interior of γ', it is interior to τ. Similarly, interior points of σ correspond to interior points of τ. It follows that the boundary points of σ and τ also correspond.

Because of the correspondence of interior points, the interior of τ is a domain, and hence τ is a closed region. From Theorem III, it follows that the boundary of τ is made up of regular arcs, finite in number. These are ordered, corresponding to the boundary of e, in such a way that each has an end-point in common with the next following, and none has any other point in common with any other, since e has no chords parallel to the ζ-axis. Hence τ is a regular region.

We have seen that $\zeta = \varphi(\xi, \eta)$ is one-valued and continuous in τ. It remains to show that it is continuously differentiable. The equations determining the coördinates ξ, η, ζ of p are those giving the transformation from one orthogonal set of axes to another, and may be written

$$
\begin{aligned}
\xi &= a + l_1 x + m_1 y + n_1 f(x, y), \\
\eta &= b + l_2 x + m_2 y + n_2 f(x, y), \\
\zeta &= c + l_3 x + m_3 y + n_3 f(x, y).
\end{aligned}
$$
(10)

The first two, according to the theorem on implicit functions[1], determine x and y as continuous functions of ξ and η. The third then determines the function $\zeta = \varphi(\xi, \eta)$. We have seen that the first two equations have a solution corresponding to any interior point (ξ, η) of τ. It remains to verify that the Jacobian does not vanish.

But this has the value

$$
J = \begin{vmatrix} l_1 + n_1 f_x, & m_1 + n_1 f_y \\ l_2 + n_2 f_x, & m_2 + n_2 f_y \end{vmatrix},
$$

and if it be recalled that in the determinant of an orthogonal substitution (both systems being right-hand, or both left-hand) each minor is equal to its co-factor, it will be found that

$$
J = -l_3 f_x - m_3 f_y + n_3,
$$

But this reduces to

$$
J = \sqrt{1 + f_x^2 + f_y^2} \cos(n, \zeta),
$$

and so is never less in absolute value than $\sin 5°$.

The theorem on implicit functions now assures us that the derivatives exist at interior points of τ, and are given by the ordinary rules

---

[1] See Osgood, *Lehrbuch der Funktionentheorie*, Chap. II, § 5.

for differentiating implicit functions. Thus, from (10) we find, by differentiating with respect to ξ,

$$1 = (l_1 + n_1 f_x) \frac{\partial x}{\partial \xi} + (m_1 + n_1 f_y) \frac{\partial y}{\partial \xi}$$

$$0 = (l_2 + n_2 f_x) \frac{\partial x}{\partial \xi} + (m_2 + n_2 f_y) \frac{\partial y}{\partial \xi}$$

$$\frac{\partial \zeta}{\partial \xi} = (l_3 + n_3 f_x) \frac{\partial x}{\partial \xi} + (m_3 + n_3 f_y) \frac{\partial y}{\partial \xi},$$

from which we find, on eliminating the derivatives of x and y,

$$\frac{\partial \zeta}{\partial \xi} = - \frac{- l_1 f_x - m_1 f_y + n_1}{- l_3 f_x - m_3 f_y + n_3},$$

with a corresponding expression for the derivative with respect to η. Since the denominator, which is the Jacobian considered above, does not vanish in the closed region τ, the continuously differentiable character of $\zeta = \varphi(\xi, \eta)$ in τ follows from that of $z = f(x, y)$ in σ. The proof of Theorem VII is thus completed.

Regular Surfaces and Regular Regions of Space.

A *regular surface* is a set of points consisting of a finite number of regular surface elements, related as follows:

a) two of the regular surface elements may have in common either a single point, which is a vertex for both, or a single regular arc, which is an edge for both, but no other points;

b) three or more of the regular surface elements may have, at most, vertices in common;

c) any two of the regular surface elements are the first and last of a chain, such that each has an edge in common with the next, and ·

d) all the regular surface elements having a vertex in common form a chain such that each has an edge, terminating in that vertex, in common with the next; the last may, or may not, have an edge in common with the first.

Here *edge* of a regular surface element means one of the finite number of regular arcs of which its boundary is composed. A *vertex* is a point at which two edges meet. The boundary of a regular surface element need not experience a break in direction at a vertex, but the number of vertices must be finite. One of the regular surface elements is called a *face* of the regular surface.

If all the edges of the regular surface elements of a regular surface belong, each to two of the elements, the surface is said to be *closed*. Otherwise it is *open*.

Exercise.

2. Show that the following are regular surfaces: a) any polyhedron, b) a sphere, c) the finite portion of an elliptic paraboloid cut off by a plane, d) a torus, e) the boundary of the solid interior to two right circular cylindrical surfaces of equal radii, whose axes meet at right angles.

9. Functions of Three Variables.

A *regular region of space* is a bounded closed region whose boundary is a closed regular surface.

A regular region R of space is the *sum* of the regular regions R_1, R_2, ... R_n, provided each point of R is in one of the R_i, and each point of any R_i is in R, and provided no two of the R_i have points in common other than a single point which is a vertex of each, or a single regular arc which is an edge of each, or a single regular surface, which is a face of each.

If R is a regular region of space, and $f(x, y, z)$ is a one-valued function defined at the points of R, then $f(x, y, z)$ is *continuous in R*, is *continuously differentiable* or *has continuous partial derivatives of the first order in R*, is *piecewise continuous in R*, or has *piecewise continuous partial derivatives of the first order* or is *continuously differentiable in R*, according to the definitions of § 8. We have merely to substitute x, y and z for x and y.

10. Second Extension Principle; The Divergence Theorem for Regular Regions.

The object of this section is to establish the divergence theorem for any regular region R and for functions (X, Y, Z) with continuous derivatives in R. The foundation of the argument is the theorem for normal regions, established in § 2. In the light of the intervening study of functions and regions, we may characterize more sharply the notions there employed. All that need be added to the definition of normal regions is that they are regular regions of space, and that the projections referred to are regular regions of the plane. All that need be said of the functions X, Y, Z is that they are continuously differentiable in the region N, and of $f(x, y)$, that it is continuously differentiable in F,

A first extension principle was established in § 3, which may now be stated thus: *the divergence theorem holds for any regular region which is the sum of a finite number of normal regions, the functions X, Y, Z being continuously differentiable in each of the normal regions*. If it were possible to show that the general regular region was such a sum, the desired end would be attained. But this programme presents serious difficulties, and it is easier to proceed through a second extension principle.

Second Extension Principle: the divergence theorem holds for the regular region R, provided to any $\varepsilon > 0$, there corresponds a regular region R', or set R' of a finite number of regular regions without common points other than vertices or edges, related to R as follows:

a) every point of R' is in R;

b) the points of R not in R' can be enclosed in regions of total volume less than ε;

c) the points of the boundary S of R which are not points of the boundary S' of R' are parts of surfaces of total area less than ε, and the points of S' not in S are parts of surfaces of total area less than ε;

d) the divergence theorem holds for R'.

Here, the functions X, Y, Z, are assumed to have continuous partial derivatives of the first order in R.

To establish the principle, we start from the identity

$$(11) \qquad \iiint\limits_{R'} \left(\frac{\partial X}{\partial x} + \frac{\partial Y}{\partial y} + \frac{\partial Z}{\partial z}\right) dV = \iint\limits_{S'} (X l + Y m + Z n) \, dS,$$

which holds, by hypothesis. As X, Y, Z are continuously differentiable in R, there is a number M such that these functions and their partial derivatives of the first order are all less in absolute value than M in R. Then

$$(12) \qquad \left| \iiint\limits_{R} \left(\frac{\partial X}{\partial x} + \frac{\partial Y}{\partial y} + \frac{\partial Z}{\partial z}\right) dV - \iiint\limits_{R'} \left(\frac{\partial X}{\partial x} + \frac{\partial Y}{\partial y} + \frac{\partial Z}{\partial z}\right) dV \right|$$

$$= \left| \iiint\limits_{R-R'} \left(\frac{\partial X}{\partial x} + \frac{\partial Y}{\partial y} + \frac{\partial Z}{\partial z}\right) dV \right| \leqq \iiint\limits_{R-R'} 3 M \, dV < 3 M \varepsilon.$$

Also

$$(13) \qquad \left| \iint\limits_{S} (X l + Y m + Z n) \, dS - \iint\limits_{S'} (X l + Y m + Z n) \, dS \right|$$

$$= \left| \iint\limits_{\sigma} (X l + Y m + Z n) \, dS - \iint\limits_{\sigma'} (X l + Y m + Z n) \, dS \right|$$

$$\leqq \iint\limits_{\sigma} 3 M \, dS + \iint\limits_{\sigma'} 3 M \, dS < 6 M \varepsilon,$$

where σ is the part of S not in S' and σ' the part of S' not in S. From the equation (11) and the inequalities (12) and (13), it follows that

$$\left| \iiint\limits_{R} \left(\frac{\partial X}{\partial x} + \frac{\partial Y}{\partial y} + \frac{\partial Z}{\partial z}\right) dV - \iint\limits_{S} (X l + Y m + Z n) \, dS \right| < 9 M \varepsilon.$$

But the left hand member is independent of ε, and ε may be taken as small as we please. This member is therefore 0, and the divergence theorem holds for R, as was to be shown.

Approximate Resolution of the General Regular Region into Normal Regions. We now attack the problem of showing that any regular region can be approximated to, in the sense of the second extension principle. We first divide the regular surface elements of which the surface S of R is composed into regular surface elements such that for each no two normals make an angle of more than 15^0, and such that each admits a standard representation with any orientation of the axes such that the z-axis makes with no normal to the surface element an acute angle exceeding 70^0. These requirements can be met, the first because of the uniform continuity of the direction cosines of the normal in the coördinates x, y of the standard representation, and the second by Theorem VII. These smaller elements we call the *faces* of S, the regular arcs bounding them, the *edges* of S, and the end-points of these arcs, the *vertices* of S. Let N denote the sum of the number of faces, edges, and vertices.

We next introduce a system Σ_η of spheres, not for the purpose of sub-dividing R, but as an aid in establishing the inequalities of the second extension principle. On each edge of S, we mark off points, terminating chords of length η, beginning with one end, until we arrive at a point at a distance less than or equal to η from the second end. About each of these points, and about the second end point of the edge, we describe a sphere of radius η. This is done for every edge, and the resulting system of spheres is Σ_η. The essential property of Σ_η is that it encloses all the edges of S. This will be assured, if as a first requirement on η, we demand that it be chosen so that no edge, between successive centers of spheres, deviates in direction from its chord by more than 15^0, this being possible by Theorem II. For no arc can deviate in distance from its chord by more than it would if it constantly made with it the maximum angle permitted, and hence all the points of the arc are distant from the chord not more than $\eta \tan 15^0$. But any two successive spheres contain in their interiors all points whose distances from the chord of centers are less than $\eta \tan 60^0$. Any point of an edge is thus interior to some sphere of Σ_η.

We need an upper bound for the total volume of all the spheres of Σ_η, and also one for the total area of a system of great circles of the spheres, namely as many for each sphere as there are faces of S with points interior to that sphere.

The number of spheres corresponding to a given edge, that is, the number of vertices of the polygon connecting successive centers, is not more than two more than the length of the polygon divided by η, for at most one side of the polygon is less than η in length. If l is the length of the longest edge, the number of spheres with centers on any edge does not, therefore, exceed $\left(\dfrac{l}{\eta}\right) + 2$. Thus the total number of spheres does not exceed $N\left[\left(\dfrac{l}{\eta}\right) + 2\right]$. Accordingly, since it is legitimate to assume $\eta < l$, the number does not exceed $3 N\left(\dfrac{l}{\eta}\right)$, and if we set $N_1 = 4\pi N l$, *the total volume of the spheres of Σ_η does not exceed $N_1 \eta^2$.*

The sum of the areas of a system of great circles, one for each sphere, is $\frac{3}{\eta}$ times the volume just considered, and so does not exceed $3 N_1 \eta$. As the number of faces with points interior to any sphere is less than N, if we write $N_2 = 3 N N_1$, *the area of a system of great circles of Σ_η, as many for each sphere as there are faces S with points in that sphere, does not exceed $N_2 \eta$*.

We now subdivide R. We notice that since the edges are interior to Σ_η, the distance between the portions outside of Σ_η of any two different faces of S has a positive minimum k, for otherwise two faces would have a common point other than a point of an edge. Let a be a positive number, such that $\sqrt{3}\, a < \frac{k}{3}$, and $\sqrt{3}\, a < \eta$. Starting with one of the faces f_1 of S, and with some normal to this face as diagonal, we construct a cubic lattice of side a, by means of three sets of parallel planes a distance a apart, the lattice covering the whole of space. Let c_1 denote the cubes of this lattice having points of f_1 within them or on their boundaries. All other cubes of the lattice are discarded. Similarly, we construct a lattice for each of the other faces, and retain those cubes and only those having points in common with the corresponding faces. We thus obtain a set $c_1, c_2, \ldots, c_n$ of sets of cubes, which together contain all the points of S, no cube being free from points of S. The portion K of R, not interior to any of these cubes, consists of one or more regions bounded by plane faces.

The cubes of the sets $c_1, c_2, \ldots, c_n$ may now be reclassified:

the set c' of cubes none of which has any point on or within any of the spheres of Σ_η, and

the set c'' of cubes each of which has a point on or within some sphere of Σ_η.

No two cubes of c' have interior points in common. For if two cubes belong to the same face of S, they belong to the same lattice, and are separated by a plane of the lattice. If two cubes belong to different faces, each contains one of a pair of points a distance k or more apart, and this is more than three times their diagonal. No cube of c' has an interior point in K. The region, or regions K, together with the portions of R in the cubes c' constitute the approximating region, or set of regions R'. It remains to show that R' is made up of normal regions, and that η can be so chosen as to make the approximation arbitrarily close.

It is simple to show that K is made up of normal regions, for if its bounding planes are indefinitely extended, they divide it into a finite number of convex polyhedra, which are normal regions.

Now let r denote the portion of R in one of the cubes c of the set c'. If we take coördinate axes along three properly chosen edges of c, the face f of S which meets c has at some point a normal with direction cosines $\left(\dfrac{1}{\sqrt{3}}, \dfrac{1}{\sqrt{3}}, \dfrac{1}{\sqrt{3}}\right)$. As f turns by at most 15^0, none of its normals make with any coördinate axis an angle exceeding $\cos^{-1}\left(\dfrac{1}{\sqrt{3}}\right)+15^0 < 70^0$. Hence f admits a standard representation with the orientation of the axes chosen, no matter which is taken as z-axis. It follows that each face of c cut by f is severed into two plane regions, separated by a single regular arc. Moreover, as the normal to f makes an angle never greater than 70^0 with any coördinate axis, the normal to the arc in the plane never makes an angle greater than 70^0 with an edge of c in that plane. Thus the arc in which f cuts a face of c is never parallel to an edge of that face, and cannot cut an edge twice.

If f contains no interior points of c, either there are no points of R interior to c, and the cube may be discarded, or the whole cube belongs to R, and is a normal region. Suppose f cuts the face $z = a$ of c, but not the face $z = 0$. Then the projection on the (x, y)-plane of the portion of f in c is a regular region τ, and so is the rest τ' of the face of c in this plane (it is understood, of course, that the boundary between τ and τ' is counted as belonging to both). As the portion of f in c is a regular surface element, the conditions (a) and (b) for a normal region are met.

If f cuts the lower but not the upper face of c, the situation is the same, as is seen by reversing the senses of the axes. If f cuts neither face, its projection on the (x, y)-plane is a square, and conditions (a) and (b) are again met. If f cuts both the upper and lower faces, the projection of the part of f in c is bounded by two regular arcs and not more than four straight line segments, forming a regular curve, for the only damaging possibility would be that the curved arcs had common points other than end points. But as this would mean a vertical chord for f, it is not a possibility. The rest of the face of c in the (x, y)-plane consists also of regular regions. Hence in this case also r fulfills conditions (a) and (b) for normal regions. And as we have considered the only possibilities with respect to the direction of the z-axis, which may have any of the three perpendicular directions of the edges of c, the condition (c) for normal regions is also met.

Hence R' is made up entirely of normal regions, and hence the divergence theorem holds for their sum, R'. The first part of our task is accomplished.

We now study the closeness of the approximation to R of R'. Let $\Sigma_{2\eta}$ denote the system of spheres obtained from Σ_η by doubling their radii, while keeping their centers. Then all points of R not in R' lie within spheres of the system $\Sigma_{2\eta}$, for they are in cubes of the set c'' which contain points of the spheres of Σ_η, and since the diagonals of these cubes are less than η, the cubes all lie within $\Sigma_{2\eta}$. But the total volume of the spheres of $\Sigma_{2\eta}$ is 8 times that of the spheres Σ_η, and hence is not greater than $8 N_1 \eta^2$. Thus the volume of the part of R not in R' is less than ε if $\eta < \sqrt{\dfrac{\varepsilon}{8 N_1}}$.

As to the portion σ of the boundary S of R which is not a part of the boundary S' of R', that also lies in $\Sigma_{2\eta}$, since R and R' coincide outside these spheres. A bound for the area of the portion of a single face of S within one of these spheres, may be found by considering the fact that its projection on its tangent plane at the center of the sphere has an area not greater than that of a great circle, and as its normals differ in direction by not more than 15^0, the area of the portion of the face within the sphere is not more than the area of a great circle times sec 15^0. Thus, since the area of a system of great circles, each of radius 2η, as many for each sphere as there are faces of S with points in that sphere, does not exceed $4 N_2 \eta$, the total area of σ will not exceed $4 N_2 \eta$ sec 15^0. Thus if $\eta < \dfrac{\varepsilon \cos 15^0}{4 N_2}$, the area of σ will be less than ε.

Finally, the area of the portion σ' of S' not in S may be treated similarly. For σ' is a part of the faces of the cubes of the set c'', all of which lie in $\Sigma_{2\eta}$. Considering first those belonging to a single face of S, it is clear that there is at most one of these cubes on a single diagonal of the corresponding lattice, if cubes having a single point in common with R are discarded, as has been done. These diagonals cut a perpendicular plane in the vertices of a lattice of equilateral triangles. A point of one of these triangles can have over it but one cube for each lattice diagonal through its vertex, and hence not more than three cubes. Thus the projection of the faces of the cubes corresponding to a single face of S, on a plane perpendicular to the diagonal which is somewhere normal to f, can cover any portion of this plane at most six times. The secant of the angle between the faces of the cubes and this plane is $\sqrt{3}$. Hence if we multiply by $6\sqrt{3}$ the expression for the area of the system of great circles, we shall have a bound for the area of σ'. Such a bound, then, is $6\sqrt{3}\cdot 4 N_2 \eta = 24\sqrt{3} N_2 \eta$. If $\eta < \dfrac{\varepsilon}{24\sqrt{3} N_2}$, the area of σ' will be less than ε.

All the conditions required by the second extension principle can thus be met in the case of a regular region, the field being continuously differentiable. But the first extension principle permits us then to assert that the results hold for fields which are continuous and have piecewise continuous partial derivatives of the first order. Thus we may state:

The divergence theorem holds for any regular region R, with functions X, Y, Z which are continuous and piecewise continuously differentiable in R.

This is the degree of generality we set out to attain. It is true that conical points, cannot, in general, occur on the boundary of a regular region. But by means of the second extension principle it is clear that a finite number of conical points may be admitted. More generally, if a region becomes regular by cutting out a finite number of portions by means of spheres of arbitrarily small radius, the areas of the portions of S cut out vanishing with the radius, then the theorem holds for that region.

11. Lightening of the Requirements with Respect to the Field.

It is sometimes desirable to dispense with the hypothesis that the partial derivatives of the first order of X, Y, Z are continuous in the closed region R, and assume only that they are continuous in the interior of R. The divergence theorem subsists under the following hypothesis on the field

X, Y, Z are continuous in R and have partial derivatives of the first order which are continuous in the interiors of a finite number of regular regions of which R is the sum, and the integral

$$(14) \qquad \iiint\limits_{R} \left(\frac{\partial X}{\partial x} + \frac{\partial Y}{\partial y} + \frac{\partial Z}{\partial z} \right) dV$$

is convergent.

This integral, in fact, may well be improper, for there is no reason why the partial derivatives may not become infinite at points of the boundary of R. In order to say what we mean by the convergence of the integral, let us, for the purposes of this section only, understand that when we use the word region, without qualification, we mean a regular region, or a set of a finite number of regular regions without common interior points, or the difference of two such sets, one containing the other. By the difference, we mean the points of the including set which are not in the included set, plus their limit points. Such a region lacks the property, in general, that its interior is connected, as required by the definition of § 5, but for the present that is unessential.

The integral (14) is *convergent*, then, if when R' is any region interior to R, and containing all the points of R whose distance from the boundary S of R exceeds δ, the integral extended over R' approaches a limit as δ approaches 0.

We now indicate the proof that the divergence theorem subsists for a regular region R under the stated conditions on the field.

In the first place, as a consequence of the definition of convergence, it follows that the difference of the integrals over two regions R' and R'', both interior to R and both containing all points of R at a distance greater than δ from S, vanishes with δ. It follows that the integral over any region interior to R and lying within a distance δ of S, vanishes with δ, and this holds also, by a limit process, if the region contains boundary points of R. From this again it follows that the integral is convergent if extended over any region contained in R.

The integral is also additive. That is, if R_1 and R_2 are any two regions in R without common interior points, the sum of the integrals over R_1 and R_2 is the integral over the region consisting of the points of both. For if we cut off from R_1 and R_2 regions close to S, the integrand is continuous in the remaining regions, and here the additive property is a consequence of the definition of integral. Hence, in the limit, the additive property holds for R_1 and R_2.

With these preliminary remarks, it is a simple matter to verify that the divergence theorem holds. We have simply to review the argument of the last section. In the first place, the second extension principle holds. For although the bound M for the derivatives of X, Y, Z may no longer exist, we know that the region $R - R'$ will lie within a distance η of S, and hence the integral over this region can be made arbitrarily small by sufficiently restricting η. No change need be made in the treatment of the surface integrals.

Thus the divergence theorem will hold for R if it holds for R' under the present conditions on the field. And, by the first extension principle, it will hold for R' if it holds for the normal regions from which such a region R' can always be built because of the additive property of the volume integral. We may assume that the derivatives of X, Y, Z are continuous in the interior of R; the extension to the case in which they are continuous in the interiors of a finite number of regular regions of which R is the sum will then follow by the first extension principle.

Now let r be one of the normal regions of which R' is composed. To fix ideas, let it be of the first type considered in the last section:

$$r: \quad 0 \leqq z \leqq f(x, y), \quad (x, y) \text{ in } \tau, \quad 0 \leqq z \leqq a, \quad (x, y) \text{ in } \tau'.$$

With a sufficiently small positive α, we replace r by the normal region r', obtained from r by substituting $f(x, y) - \alpha$ for $f(x, y)$. The divergence theorem holds for r', since all its points are interior to R, where the field is continuously differentiable. Also, by hypothesis, the volume integral over r' converges to that over r as α approaches 0; and because of the continuity of the field, it is a simple matter to show that the surface integral over the boundary of r' approaches the surface integral over the boundary of r. This will show that the divergence theorem holds for r. Similar considerations apply to the other types of region r, and thus the reasoning is completed.

12. Stokes' Theorem.

In section 4, Stokes' theorem was shown to hold for surfaces made up of normal surface elements. Now a normal surface element is a regular surface element bounded by plane arcs. But if we have any regular surface element, by triangulation of its projection on the (x, y)-plane of its standard representation, we may approximate to it arbitrarily closely by a normal surface element. As Stokes' theorem holds for this approximating normal surface element, and as the field is continuously differentiable, it must hold also for the limiting regular surface element. Then by the juxtaposition of regular surface elements, we conclude that

Stokes' theorem holds for any two-sided regular surface, the functions X, Y, and Z being continuously differentiable in a region containing the surface in its interior.

Generalizations will suggest themselves, but the above formulation will be sufficient for our purposes.

Chapter V.

Properties of Newtonian Potentials at Points of Free Space.

1. Derivatives; Laplace's Equation.

So far, we have studied potentials arising from given distributions of matter. But in many problems, the distribution is not known, and the potential must be determined by means of other data. Thus in higher geodesy, very little is known of the distribution of the masses except at the surface. But the forces can be measured on the surface, and from these the potential can be determined, approximately, at least. In order to solve problems given in terms of data other than the distribution of acting matter, we need more information on the properties of potentials. We first consider such properties at points exterior to the regions occupied by the distributions. Such points are called *points of free space*.

We have seen on page 52, that the partial derivatives of the first order of the potential exist at the points of free space, and give the corresponding components of the force. We now go farther, and show that at such points, the partial derivatives of all orders exist and are continuous.

It is easy to prove this for a particle by induction. The partial derivatives of the first order are linear polynomials in x, y, z, divided by r^3. The partial derivatives of order n are polynomials of degree n in x, y, z, divided by r^{2n+1}. For if P_n denote such a polynomial of degree n,

$$\frac{\partial}{\partial x}\frac{P_n}{r^{2n+1}} = \frac{P'_{nx}}{r^{2n+1}} - (2n+1)\frac{P_n}{r^{2n+2}}\frac{x-\xi}{r}$$

$$= \frac{P'_{nx}[(x-\xi)^2 + (y-\eta)^2 + (z-\zeta)^2]}{r^{2n+3}} - \frac{(2n+1)P_n(x-\xi)}{r^{2n+3}} = \frac{P_{n+1}}{r^{2n+3}},$$

where P_{n+1} is a polynomial of degree $n+1$. Thus if the statement holds for one value of n, it holds for the next greater. It holds for $n = 1$, and so for any positive integral value of n. Now as the quotient of two continuous functions is continuous except at the points where the denominator vanishes, we see that the potential of a unit particle has continuous partial derivatives of all orders at all points of free space.

We notice that the polynomials in the numerators of the expressions for the partial derivatives are also polynomials in ξ, η and ζ. Thus the derivatives are continuous in all six variables as long as $r \neq 0$. This remark finds its application when we consider the potentials of various continuous distributions. For, if we differentiate under the sign of integration, in the expression for the potential of such a distribution, we find that the resulting integrand is the density times the corresponding derivative of the potential of a unit particle at the point $Q(\xi, \eta, \zeta)$ of integration. Hence, if the density is continuous, the integrand is continuous in all six variables, as long as $P(x, y, z)$ is confined to a closed region having no points in common with the distribution, and the differentiation under the integral sign is justified. As the integrand is continuous, so are the partial derivatives. The same holds for the case in which the densities are piecewise continuous, for the distributions are then sums of distributions with continuous densities. Hence we have

Theorem I. *The potentials of the distributions of all the types studied in the preceding chapters have partial derivatives of all orders, which are continuous at all points of free space.*

Exercise.

Can the same be said of the potential of a distribution consisting of an infinite number of discrete particles? Consider, for instance the potential

$$U = \sum_{n=1}^{\infty} \frac{m_n}{\sqrt{(x-n)^2 + y^2 + z^2}}, \qquad \left(\sum_{1}^{\infty}\frac{m_n}{n} \text{ convergent}\right).$$

We shall see later that the derivatives are analytic functions of x, y and z. But before turning to questions of this sort, we should emphasize the important relation existing between the second derivatives of a Newtonian potential. We saw on page 40 that the force field of a Newtonian distribution was solenoidal in free space, and on page 52 that it has a potential, U, whose derivatives give the components of the field.

It follows that this potential satisfies the differential equation

$$\nabla^2 U = \frac{\partial^2 U}{\partial x^2} + \frac{\partial^2 U}{\partial y^2} + \frac{\partial^2 U}{\partial z^2} = 0,$$

known as *Laplace's differential equation*[1].

---

[1] The differential equation in polar coördinates, to which the above is equivalent was found by LAPLACE as a condition on the potential of a Newtonian distribution in the Histoire de l'Académie des Sciences de Paris (1782/85), p. 135, reprinted in the *Oeuvres de Laplace*, Vol. 10, p. 362. Later LAPLACE gave the equation in the above form, *ibid.* (1787/89), p. 252, *Oeuvres*, Vol. 11, p. 278. In connection with a hydrodynamical problem, the equation had already been used by LAGRANGE, Miscellanea Taurinesia, Vol. 2, (1760/61), p. 273, *Oeuvres*, Vol. 1, p. 444.

As LAPLACE'S equation occurs frequently, an abbreviation for the left hand member is convenient. The one used above is due to Sir W. R. HAMILTON, and a brief explanation of its significance may not be out of place. If $u\,(a_1, b_1, c_1)$ and $v\,(a_2, b_2, c_2)$ are two vectors, the combination

$$u \cdot v = a_1 a_2 + b_1 b_2 + c_1 c_2$$

is called the scalar product of the two vectors, and has, according to GIBBS (*Vector Analysis*, edited by E. B. Wilson, New York, 1909), the notation given. The scalar product of a vector by itself is called the square of the vector, and is denoted by u^2. The vector

$$u \times v = (b_1 c_2 - c_1 b_2, \quad c_1 a_2 - a_1 c_2, \quad a_1 b_2 - b_1 a_2)$$

is called the vector product of v by u. If k is a scalar, *i. e.* a single number or function, as opposed to a vector or a vector field, then

$$u\,k = (a_1 k, \ a_2 k, \ a_3 k)$$

is called the product of the scalar k by the vector u. We now introduce the symbolic vector, or *vector operator*

$$\nabla = \left(\frac{\partial}{\partial x}, \ \frac{\partial}{\partial y}, \ \frac{\partial}{\partial z} \right).$$

This has no meaning when standing alone, but if combined with vectors or scalars, the operations indicated being carried out as if the three symbols were numbers, and these then interpreted as symbols of differentiation of the next following quantity, the resulting combinations have definite meanings. Thus

$$\nabla U = \left(\frac{\partial U}{\partial x}, \ \frac{\partial U}{\partial y}, \ \frac{\partial U}{\partial z} \right) = \text{grad } U,$$

$$\nabla \cdot V = \left(\frac{\partial X}{\partial x} + \frac{\partial Y}{\partial y} + \frac{\partial Z}{\partial z} \right) = \text{div } V = \text{div } (X, Y, Z),$$

$$\nabla \times V = \left(\frac{\partial Z}{\partial y} - \frac{\partial Y}{\partial z}, \ \frac{\partial X}{\partial z} - \frac{\partial Z}{\partial x}, \ \frac{\partial Y}{\partial x} - \frac{\partial X}{\partial y} \right)$$
$$= \text{curl } V,$$
$$= \text{curl } (X, Y, Z),$$

$$(\nabla U)^2 = \left(\frac{\partial U}{\partial x} \right)^2 + \left(\frac{\partial U}{\partial y} \right)^2 + \left(\frac{\partial U}{\partial z} \right)^2,$$

$$\nabla^2 U = \frac{\partial^2 U}{\partial x^2} + \frac{\partial^2 U}{\partial y^2} + \frac{\partial^2 U}{\partial z^2}.$$

Theorem II. *The potentials of all the distributions studied satisfy Laplace's differential equation at all points of free space.*

The significance of this fact is, that in many cases, the determination of a differential equation satisfied by a function which is sought, is the first step in finding that function. The main object of this and the next chapter may be described as the determination of auxiliary conditions, which, with the differential equation, determine the potential.

2. Developments of Potentials in Series.

Valuable information on the properties of Newtonian potentials may be inferred from developments in series of certain types. In addition, series frequently offer the best bases for computation in applications.

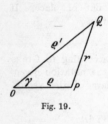

Fig. 19.

We seek first to develop a given potential as a power series in the distance of the variable point $P(\varrho, \varphi, \vartheta)$ from the origin of coördinates, which we take at a point O of free space. We take first the potential of a unit particle at $Q(\varrho', \varphi', \vartheta')$, not the origin (fig. 19). Then, in terms of the given spherical coördinates of P and Q, the distance r between them is given by

$$(2) \quad \begin{aligned} r^2 &= (\varrho \cos \varphi \sin \vartheta - \varrho' \cos \varphi' \sin \vartheta')^2 + (\varrho \sin \varphi \sin \vartheta - \varrho' \sin \varphi' \sin \vartheta')^2 \\ &\qquad + (\varrho \cos \vartheta - \varrho' \cos \vartheta')^2 \\ &= \varrho^2 - 2 \varrho \varrho' \cos \gamma + \varrho'^2, \end{aligned}$$

$$\cos \gamma = \cos \vartheta \cos \vartheta' + \sin \vartheta \sin \vartheta' \cos(\varphi - \varphi'),$$

γ being the angle between the rays OP and OQ. The potential at P of a unit particle at Q is

$$(3) \quad \frac{1}{r} = \frac{1}{\varrho'} \frac{1}{\sqrt{1 - 2 \dfrac{\varrho}{\varrho'} \cos \gamma + \dfrac{\varrho^2}{\varrho'^2}}} = \frac{1}{\varrho' \sqrt{1 - 2 u \mu + \mu^2}},$$

where we have set $\dfrac{\varrho}{\varrho'} = \mu$ and $\cos \gamma = u$.

Our task is now to develop $\dfrac{1}{r}$ as a power series in μ. By the binomial theorem, valid for $|z| < 1$,

$$(1-z)^{-\frac{1}{2}} = \alpha_0 + \alpha_1 z + \alpha_2 z^2 + \alpha_3 z^3 + \cdots, \quad \alpha_n = \frac{1 \cdot 3 \ldots (2n-1)}{2 \cdot 4 \ldots (2n)}, \quad \alpha_0 = 1.$$

Hence, if $|2 u \mu - \mu^2| < 1$,

$$(4) \quad \frac{1}{\sqrt{1 - 2 u \mu + \mu^2}} = \alpha_0 + \alpha_1 (2 u \mu - \mu^2) + \alpha_2 (2 u \mu - \mu^2)^2 + \cdots.$$

This is not a power series in μ, but it may be made into one by expanding the binomials in the separate terms and collecting like powers of μ, a process which is justified provided $|\mu| < \sqrt{2} - 1$[1]. The coefficients of the powers of μ will now be polynomials in u, and we write the result

(5) $$\frac{1}{\sqrt{1 - 2u\mu + \mu^2}} = P_0(u) + P_1(u)\mu + P_2(u)\mu^2 + \cdots,$$

where

$$P_0(u) = 1, \quad P_1(u) = u, \quad P_2(u) = \frac{3}{2}\left(u^2 - \frac{1}{3}\right), \quad \ldots.$$

Exercise.

Continue the above list of the coefficients as far as $P_6(u)$. Show generally that $P_n(u)$ may be written

$$P_n(u) = \sum_{k=0}^{[n/2]} \frac{1 \cdot 3 \ldots (2n - 2k - 1)}{2^k \cdot k! \,(n - 2k)!} \cdot (-1)^k u^{n-2k}$$

$$= \frac{1 \cdot 3 \ldots (2n - 1)}{n!}\left[u^n - \frac{n(n-1)}{(2n-1) \cdot 2} u^{n-2}\right.$$

$$\left. + \frac{n(n-1)(n-2)(n-3)}{(2n-1)(2n-3) \cdot 2 \cdot 4} u^{n-4} - \cdots\right].$$

3. Legendre Polynomials.

The coefficients $P_n(u)$ are of such frequent use, not only in potential theory, but in other branches of analysis, that we shall be warranted in devoting a separate section to them. They are called *Legendre polynomials*[2].

We observe first that $P_n(u)$ is of degree n, and that only alternate powers of u occur in it, so that *the Legendre polynomials of even degree are even functions of u, and those of odd degree are odd functions of u.*

Recursion Formulas. The series obtained by differentiating termwise a power series converges at all interior points of the region in which the power series converges, and represents the derivative of the function represented by the given series[3]. Hence, for $|\mu| < \sqrt{2} - 1$,

---

[1] The possibility of this rearrangement is most easily established by means of a theorem in the theory of analytic functions of a complex variable (See Chapter XII, § 6). The series (4) is a series of polynomials, and therefore of functions which are everywhere analytic, and it is uniformly convergent as to both u and μ if u is real and $-1 \leq u \leq 1$, and $|\mu| \leq \mu_1 < \sqrt{2} - 1$. The rearrangement may also be justified by elementary methods by first showing it possible for a dominating series, obtained from (4) by replacing u and μ by their absolute values, and the minus signs by plus signs. It is then easy to infer the possibility for the series (4).

[2] LEGENDRE, *Sur l'attraction des sphéroides*, Mémoires présentés à l'Académie par diverses Savans, Vol. X, Paris, 1785, p. 419. See also HEINE, *Theorie der Kugelfunktionen*, Berlin (1878) Vol. I, p. 2.

[3] Chapter XII, § 6, Exercise. The fact can also be verified by elementary methods, using the theorem that a series may be differentiated termwise, provided the result is a uniformly convergent series.

(6) $\dfrac{u - \mu}{(1 - 2 u \mu + \mu^2)^{\frac{3}{2}}} = P_1(u) + 2 P_2(u)\,\mu + 3 P_3(u)\,\mu^2 + \cdots .$

Comparing this series with (5), we see that

$$\frac{u - \mu}{\sqrt{1 - 2 u \mu + \mu^2}} = (u - \mu)\,[P_0(u) + P_1(u)\mu + \cdots]$$
$$= (1 - 2 u \mu + \mu^2)\,[P_1(u) + 2 P_2(u)\mu + \cdots].$$

The comparison of the coefficients of μ^n in the two sides of this equation, written as power series, yields, after simplification, the recursion formula

(7) $(n + 1)\,P_{n+1}(u) - (2 n + 1)\,u P_n(u) + n\,P_{n-1}(u) = 0.$

Exercises.

1. Show that

$P_n(1) = 1, \quad P_n(-1) = (-1)^n, \quad P_{2n-1}(0) = 0, \quad P_{2n}(0) = (-1)^n\,\alpha_n.$

2. Show that $P_n(u) = 0$ has n distinct roots in the open interval $(-1, 1)$, and that they are separated by the roots of $P_{n-1}(u)$.

Formulas for the Derivatives of Legendre Polynomials, and the Differential Equation which they Satisfy. Just as $\dfrac{1}{\sqrt{1 - 2 u \mu + \mu^2}}$ was developed in a power series in μ, we may develop the derivative of this function with respect to u:

(8) $\dfrac{\mu}{(1 - 2 u \mu + \mu^2)^{\frac{3}{2}}} = P_0'(u) + P_1'(u)\,\mu + P_2'(u)\,\mu^2 + \cdots ,$

the coefficients being polynomials in u, not as yet shown to be the derivatives of the corresponding Legendre polynomials, the series being uniformly convergent for $-1 \leqq u \leqq 1,\ |\mu| \leqq \mu_1 < \sqrt{2} - 1$. But such a series may be integrated termwise with respect to u between any two points of the closed interval $(-1, 1)$, and we find

$$\int_0^u \frac{\mu\,du}{(1 - 2 u \mu + \mu^2)^{\frac{3}{2}}} = \frac{1}{\sqrt{1 - 2 u \mu + \mu^2}} - \frac{1 \cdot}{\sqrt{1 + \mu^2}} = \sum_0^\infty \left[\int_0^u P_n'(u)\,du\right]\mu^n$$

$$= \sum_0^\infty [P_n(u) - P_n(0)]\,\mu^n.$$

Comparing the coefficients of μ^n in the two power series, we find

$$\int_0^u P_n'(u)\,du = P_n(u) - P_n(0),$$

and on differentiating both sides of this equation, we find that $P_n'(u)$ is indeed the derivative of $P_n(u)$. If we now compare the developments

(5) and (8), we find

$$(u - \mu)\,[P_0'(u) + P_1'(u)\,\mu + \cdots] = \mu\,[P_1(u) + 2\,P_2(u)\,\mu + \cdots]\,,$$

and from this we infer that

$$(9) \qquad\qquad u\,P_n'(u) - P_{n-1}'(u) = n\,P_n(u)\,.$$

As a first consequence of this relation, we may derive a differential equation satisfied by the Legendre polynomials. We eliminate between the equations (7) and (9), and equations derived from them, the polynomials other then $P_n(u)$ and its derivatives. Differentiating (7), we find

$$(n + 1)\,P_{n+1}'(u) - (2\,n + 1)\,P_n(u) - (2\,n + 1)\,u\,P_n'(u) + n\,P_{n-1}'(u) = 0\,.$$

Eliminating $P_{n-1}'(u)$ by means of (9), we have, with n in place of $n + 1$,

$$(10) \qquad\qquad P_n'(u) - u\,P_{n-1}'(u) = n\,P_{n-1}(u)\,.$$

Again eliminating $P_{n-1}'(u)$ by means of (9), we have

$$\cdot\,(1 - u^2)\,P_n'(u) + n\,u\,P_n(u) = n\,P_{n-1}(u)\,.$$

Differentiating this relation and once more eliminating $P_{n-1}'(u)$, we have the *homogeneous linear differential equation of the second order satisfied by the Legendre polynomials*:

$$(11) \qquad\qquad \frac{d}{du}\,[(1 - u^2)\,P_n'(u)] + n\,(n + 1)\,P_n(u) = 0\,.$$

Exercise.

3. Determine $P_n(u)$, except for a constant factor, on the assumption that it is a polynomial of degree n satisfying the above differential equation.

If from (10) we eliminate the term $u\,P_{n-1}'(u)$ by means of the equation obtained from (9) by replacing n by $n - 1$, we obtain the formula

$$P_n'(u) = (2\,n - 1)\,P_{n-1}(u) + P_{n-2}'(u)\,.$$

If we write the equations obtained from this by replacing n successively by $n - 2,\, n - 4,\, \ldots$, and add them all, we arrive at the following development of $P_n'(u)$ in terms of Legendre polynomials:

$$\begin{aligned}
(12) \qquad P_n'(u) = {}& (2\,n - 1)\,P_{n-1}(u) + (2\,n - 5)\,P_{n-3}(u) \\
& + (2\,n - 9)\,P_{n-5}(u) + \cdots,
\end{aligned}$$

the sum breaking off with the last term in which the index of the polynomial is positive or zero.

Expression for the Legendre polynomials as Trigonometric Polynomials. Making use of the formula of EULER for the cosine, we write

$$u = \cos\gamma = \frac{e^{i\gamma} + e^{-i\gamma}}{2}\,,$$

and with this value of u,

$$\frac{1}{\sqrt{1 - 2u\mu + \mu^2}} = \frac{1}{\sqrt{(1 - e^{i\gamma}\mu)(1 - e^{-i\gamma}\mu)}} = (1 - e^{i\gamma}\mu)^{-\frac{1}{2}}(1 - e^{-i\gamma}\mu)^{-\frac{1}{2}}$$

$$= (\alpha_0 + \alpha_1 e^{i\gamma}\mu + \alpha_2 e^{2i\gamma}\mu^2 + \cdots)(\alpha_0 + \alpha_1 e^{-i\gamma}\mu + \alpha_2 e^{-2i\gamma}\mu^2 + \cdots),$$

the series converging for all real γ if $|\mu| < 1$. These series may be multiplied termwise, and the product arranged as a power series in μ. Thus we have a second development of the function in (5):

$$\frac{1}{\sqrt{1 - 2u\mu + \mu^2}} = \alpha_0^2 + (\alpha_1\alpha_0 e^{i\gamma} + \alpha_0\alpha_1 e^{-i\gamma})\mu$$

$$+ (\alpha_2\alpha_0 e^{2i\gamma} + \alpha_1^2 + \alpha_0\alpha_2 e^{-2i\gamma})\mu^2 + \cdots$$

$$= \alpha_0^2 + 2\alpha_0\alpha_1 \cos\gamma\,\mu + (2\alpha_0\alpha_2 \cos 2\gamma + \alpha_1^2)\mu^2 + \cdots.$$

Comparing the coefficients of μ^n in the two, we have the desired expression for $P_n(u)$ as a trigonometric polynomial:

(13) $$P_n(u) = 2\alpha_0\alpha_n \cos n\gamma + 2\alpha_1\alpha_{n-1}\cos(n-2)\gamma$$

$$+ 2\alpha_2\alpha_{n-2}\cos(n-4)\gamma + \cdots.$$

the last term being

$$\alpha_{\frac{n}{2}}, \quad n \text{ even},$$

$$2\alpha_{\frac{n-1}{2}}\alpha_{\frac{n+1}{2}}\cos\gamma, \quad n \text{ odd}.$$

As the coefficients on the right are all positive, and as the separate terms attain their maxima for $\gamma = 0$, it follows that $|P_n(u)|$ attains its maximum value for real γ, $i.\,e.$ for real u in the interval $(-1, 1)$, for $u = 1$. This value has been found in Exercise 1 to be 1. It may also be found by setting $u = 1$ in (5). Thus, *the maximum of the absolute value of $P_n(u)$ for real u in the interval $(-1, 1)$ is 1, and this value is attained for $u = 1$.*

We see thus that the series (5) is convergent and equals the given function, not only for $|\mu| < \sqrt{2} - 1$, but for all $|\mu| < 1$.

Exercise.

4. Show by means of (12) that the maximum of $|P_n'(u)|$ for real u in $(-1, 1)$ is attained for $u = 1$, and is $\dfrac{n(n+1)}{2}$.

The maximum value of $|P_n(u)|$ for real or imaginary u, $|u| \leq 1$, is evidently attained for $u = i$, for then the terms of the polynomial as given in the exercise on page 125 attain their maximum absolute values, and except for the common factor i^n, are all real positive quantities. This maximum value is $\dfrac{P_n(i)}{i^n}$. It will be useful to have a simple upper bound for this maximum. Returning to equation (5), valid for $|u| \leq 1$,

$|\mu| < \sqrt{2} - 1$, we have

$$\frac{1}{\sqrt{1 - 2\,i\,\mu + \mu^2}} = P_0(i) + P_1(i)\,\mu + P_2(i)\,\mu^2 + \cdots$$

$$= \left[1 - i\,(1 + \sqrt{2})\,\mu\right]^{-\frac{1}{2}} \left[1 - i\,(1 - \sqrt{2})\,\mu\right]^{-\frac{1}{2}},$$

and the coefficient of μ^n in the expansion of this product cannot exceed in absolute value the coefficient of μ^n in the expansion of

$$\left[1 - (1 + \sqrt{2})\,\mu\right]^{-\frac{1}{2}} \left[1 - (1 + \sqrt{2})\,\mu\right]^{-\frac{1}{2}} = \left[1 - (1 + \sqrt{2})\,\mu\right]^{-1}.$$

It follows that for $|u| \leqq 1$,

(14) $$|P_n(u)| \leqq (1 + \sqrt{2})^n.$$

Exercise.

5. Show that the maximum m_n of $|P_n(u)|$ for $|u| \leqq 1$ satisfies the recursion formula, or difference equation:

$$m_{n+1} = \frac{2\,n+1}{n+1}\,m_n + \frac{n}{n+1}\,m_{n-1}; \quad m_0 = m_1 = 1.$$

Orthogonality. Just as it is sometimes desirable to express a given function as a Fourier series, so it is also sometimes desirable to express a given function as a series in Legendre polynomials. It is clear that any polynomial can be expressed as a terminating series of Legendre polynomials. For the equation giving $P_n(x)$ as a polynomial in x can be solved for x^n, so that x^n is a constant times a Legendre polynomial plus a polynomial of lower degree. Since this holds for each n, the lower powers of x can be eliminated, and x^n expressed as a terminating series of Legendre polynomials, with constant coefficients. Hence any polynomial can be so expressed by means of the formulas thus obtained. The equation (12) gives an example of a polynomial developed in terms of Legendre polynomials.

Functions which are entirely arbitrary, except for certain conditions of the nature of continuity, can be expressed, on the interval $(-1, 1)$, as convergent infinite series of Legendre polynomials with constant coefficients. We shall not attempt here to develop these conditions[1], but shall confine ourselves to showing how the series may be determined when the development is possible.

The simple method by which the coefficients of a Fourier series are determined is based on the fact that the functions

$$1, \ \cos x, \ \sin x, \ \cos 2\,x, \ \sin 2\,x, \ \ldots$$

have the property that the integral of the product of any two of them,

---

[1] See, however, the end of § 4 Chapter X. See also STONE, *Developments in Legendre Polynomials*, Annals of Mathematics, 2^d Ser., Vol. 27 (1926), pp. 315—329.

over the interval $(0,2\pi)$, is 0. A similiar situation is present in the case of the Legendre polynomials, for the interval $(-1,1)$. In fact,

$$(15) \qquad \int_{-1}^{1} P_m(u) P_n(u) \, du = 0, \qquad m \neq n.$$

Because of this property two different Legendre polynomials are said to be *orthogonal* on the interval $(-1,1)$, and the system of all Legendre polynomials is called an *orthogonal set* of functions on this interval. The above set of sines and cosines is an orthogonal set on the interval $(0,2\pi)$.

The stated property of the Legendre polynomials can be derived from the differential equation (11). If this be multiplied by $P_m(u)$, and integrated from -1 to 1 with respect to u, the result is

$$\int_{-1}^{1} P_m(u) \frac{d}{du} \big[(1-u^2) P_n'(u)\big] \, du + n(n+1) \int_{-1}^{1} P_m(u) P_n(u) \, du = 0.$$

In the first term, we employ integration by parts, and as the integrated term vanishes, we have

$$-\int_{-1}^{1} (1-u^2) P_m'(u) P_n'(u) \, du + n(n+1) \int_{-1}^{1} P_m(u) P_n(u) \, du = 0.$$

If we subtract from this equation that obtained from it by interchanging m and n, we have

$$\big[n(n+1) - m(m+1)\big] \int_{-1}^{1} P_m(u) P_n(u) \, du = 0.$$

From this the property of orthogonality (15) follows.

This orthogonality characterizes, among polynomials, those of Legendre. That is, apart from a non-vanishing constant factor in each, *the only system of polynomials containing one of each degree* (the 0th degree included), *orthogonal on the interval* $(-1,1)$, *is the set of Legendre polynomials.* It is not difficult to verify this directly, but we shall give a proof from which will emerge a new and useful expression for the Legendre polynomials.

Let $f(x)$ denote a polynomial of degree n which is orthogonal to a polynomial of each degree from 0 to $n-1$ inclusive. Then, since $f(x)$ is orthogonal to a constant, it is orthogonal to 1, and since it is orthogonal to 1 and to a linear function, it is orthogonal to x, and so, by induction, to x^2, x^3, ... x^{n-1}. Hence $f(x)$ is orthogonal to every polynomial of degree less than n. In particular

$$\int_{-1}^{1} f(x) (1-x)^r \, dx = 0, \qquad r = 0, 1, 2, \ldots, n-1.$$

We now integrate by parts, using as the integral of $f(x)$ that from -1 to x:

$$[\int_{-1}^{x} f(x)\,dx](1-x)^r\Big|_{-1}^{1} + r\int_{-1}^{1}\int_{-1}^{x} f(x)\,dx\,(1-x)^{r-1}\,dx = 0.$$

The first term vanishes for $r > 0$, and we see that the integral of $f(x)$ satisfies a set of orthogonality relations

$$\int_{-1}^{1}[\int_{-1}^{x} f(x)\,dx](1-x)^{r-1}\,dx = 0, \qquad r = 1, 2, \ldots, n-1.$$

If the process of integration by parts be repeated, we see that the functions

$$f(x), \quad \int_{-1}^{x} f(x)\,dx, \quad \int_{-1}^{x}\int_{-1}^{x} f(x)\,dx\,dx, \quad \int_{-1}^{x}\int_{-1}^{x}\ldots\int_{-1}^{x} f(x)\,dx\,dx\ldots dx,$$

the last integral being $(n-1)$-fold, are all orthogonal to 1. In other words, the n-fold integral

$$F(x) = \int_{-1}^{x}\int_{-1}^{x}\ldots\int_{-1}^{x} f(x)\,dx\,dx\ldots dx,$$

together with its first $n-1$ derivatives, vanishes for $x = 1$. But this function and its first $n-1$ derivatives obviously vanish for $x = -1$. Thus $F(x)$, a polynomial of degree $2n$, has an n-fold root at -1 and an n-fold root at 1, and is therefore of the form

$$F(x) = c\,(x^2 - 1)^n.$$

It is thus uniquely determined save for a constant factor, and therefore, so also is its derivative of nth order

$$f(x) = c\,\frac{d^n}{dx^n}(x^2 - 1)^n.$$

This is what we set out to prove. As $P_n(x)$ has the properties postulated for $f(x)$, $f(x)$ must be proportional to this Legendre polynomial.

Let us now determine the constant of proportionality so that $f(x)$ shall be $P_n(x)$. The coefficient of x^n in the above expression is

$$2n\,(2n-1)\,(2n-2)\ldots(n+1)\,c = \frac{(2n)!}{n!}\,c,$$

whereas the coefficient of x^n in $P_n(x)$ is, by the Exercise on page 125,

$$\frac{1 \cdot 3 \cdot 5 \ldots (2n-1)}{n!} = \frac{(2n)!}{2^n\,(n!)^2}.$$

The two will be equal if $c = \dfrac{1}{2^n\,n!}$. We thus arrive at the formula of RODRIGUES

$$P_n(x) = \frac{1}{2^n\,n!}\,\frac{d^n}{dx^n}(x^2 - 1)^n.$$

132   Properties of Newtonian Potentials at Points of Free Space.

Exercises.

6. Show by means of the formula of Rodrigues that $P_n(x)$ has n real distinct roots in the open interval $(-1, 1)$.

7. Assuming the formula of Rodrigues, derive the equation (15). Derive also the recursion formula (7) and the differential equation (11).

8. Derive the result

$$(16) \qquad \int_{-1}^{1} P_n^2(u)\, du = \frac{2}{2n+1},$$

first from Rodrigues' formula, and secondly, by deriving and then using the formula

$$\int_{-1}^{1} \frac{dx}{\sqrt{1-2x\lambda+\lambda^2}\,\sqrt{1-2x\mu+\mu^2}} = \frac{1}{\sqrt{\lambda\mu}} \log \frac{1+\sqrt{\lambda\mu}}{1-\sqrt{\lambda\mu}}.$$

Note that the second method gives also the relations of orthogonality (15).

We are now in a position to determine the coefficients in the development of a given function in a series of Legendre polynomials, on the assumption that the series converges uniformly. If we are to have

$$f(x) = c_0 P_0(x) + c_1 P_1(x) + c_2 P_2(x) + \ldots,$$

multiplication by $P_r(x)$ and integration from -1 to 1 with respect to x gives

$$\int_{-1}^{1} f(x) P_r(x)\, dx = c_r \int_{-1}^{1} P_r^2(x)\, dx = c_r \frac{2}{2r+1},$$

so that the coefficients must be given by

$$(17) \qquad c_r = \frac{2r+1}{2} \int_{-1}^{1} f(x) P_r(x)\, dx$$

if the function is developable in a uniformly convergent series.

Exercises.

9. Show that if $f(x) = x^n$,

$$c_r = (2r+1) \frac{n(n-1) \ldots (n-r+2)}{(n+r+1)(n+r-1) \ldots (n-r+3)}$$

if $n-r$ is even, and not negative; otherwise, $c_r = 0$. Show, accordingly, that

$$x^n = \frac{n!}{1 \cdot 3 \cdot 5 \ldots (2n+1)} \left[(2n+1) P_n + (2n-3) \frac{2n+1}{2} P_{n-2} \right.$$

$$\left. + (2n-7) \frac{(2n+1)(2n-1)}{2 \cdot 4} P_{n-4} + \ldots \right].$$

10. Show that $\int\limits_0^1 P_n(x)\,dx = 0$ if n is positive and even, and equal to

$$\frac{(-1)^{\frac{n-1}{2}}}{n+1}\frac{(n-2)(n-4)\ldots 1}{(n-1)(n-3)\ldots 2}$$

if n is odd. Hence show that if the function

$$f(x)=0,\quad -1\leqq x\leqq 0,\quad f(x)=1,\quad 0<x\leqq 1,$$

has a development in series of Legendre polynomials which can be integrated termwise after multiplication by any polynomial, that development must be

$$f(x)=\frac{1}{2}P_0(x)+\frac{3}{4}\alpha_0 P_1(x)-\frac{7}{8}\alpha_1 P_3(x)+\frac{11}{12}\alpha_2 P_5(x)-\cdots$$
$$+(-1)^k\frac{4k+3}{4k+4}\alpha_k P_{2k+1}(x)+\cdots.$$

Note that the value of the series at the point of discontinuity of $f(x)$ is the arithmetic mean of the limits of $f(x)$ as x approaches the point from either side.

11. Show that if the function

$$f(x)=0,\quad -1\leqq x\leqq 0,\quad f(x)=x,\quad 0\leqq x\leqq 1,$$

has a uniformly convergent development, this development must be

$$f(x)=\frac{1}{4}P_0(x)+\frac{1}{2}P_1(x)+\frac{5}{4}\frac{\alpha_0}{4}P_2(x)-\frac{9}{8}\frac{\alpha_1}{6}P_4(x)+\cdots$$
$$+(-1)^{k-1}\frac{4k+1}{4k}\frac{\alpha_{k-1}}{2k+2}P_{2k}(x)+\cdots.$$

12. Show that the above development is uniformly convergent, by showing that it is absolutely convergent for $x=1$.

13. Show that if the series

$$S(x)=c_0 P_0(x)+c_1 P_1(x)+c_2 P_2(x)+\cdots,\quad c_r=\frac{2r+1}{2}\int\limits_{-1}^1 f(x)P_r(x)\,dx,$$

is uniformly convergent, $f(x)-S(x)$ is orthogonal to all the Legendre polynomials.

As it can be shown that a continuous function not identically 0 on the interval $(-1,1)$ cannot be orthogonal on that interval to every polynomial, this exercise contains the key to the proof that developments in series of Legendre polynomials actually represent the functions developed, under suitable conditions of the character of continuity.

14. Show that for real a and b,

$$\int\limits_0^{2\pi}\frac{d\varphi}{a-ib\cos\varphi}=\int\limits_0^{2\pi}\frac{a+ib\cos\varphi}{a^2+b^2\cos^2\varphi}=\frac{2\pi}{\sqrt{a^2+b^2}},$$

and hence derive Laplace's integral formula for the Legendre polynomials,

$$P_n(u)=\frac{1}{\pi}\int\limits_0^{\pi}[u+i\sqrt{1-u^2}\cos\varphi]^n\,d\varphi.$$

15. Show by Schwarz' inequality that

$$\int_{-1}^{1} |P_n(x)| \, dx \leq \frac{2}{\sqrt{2n+1}}.$$

Show that if $f(x)$ is continuous with its first derivative, and has a piecewise continuous second derivative in $(-1, 1)$,

$$c_r = \frac{2r+1}{2r(r+1)} \int_{-1}^{1} \frac{d}{dx} [(1-x^2) f'(x)] P_r(x) \, dx,$$

and hence that the development in series of Legendre polynomials of $f(x)$ is uniformly convergent.

16. Show that if $f(x)$ is continuous on $(-1, 1)$, that polynomial $p(x)$ of degree n is the best approximation to $f(x)$ in the sense of least squares, *i. e.* such that

$$\int_{-1}^{1} [f(x) - p(x)]^2 \, dx = \text{minimum},$$

which is given by

$$p(x) = c_0 P_0(x) + c_1 P_1(x) + \cdots + c_n P_n(x),$$

where the coefficients are given by (17).

GAUSS showed how the Legendre polynomials lend themselves in a peculiarly efficient way to the approximate computation of integrals. If $x_1, x_2 \ldots x_n$ are the roots of $P_n(x)$, there exists a set of points on the interval $(-1, 1)$, dividing it into sub-intervals, $A_1, A_2, \ldots A_n$, each containing the corresponding x_i, such that

$$\sum_{1}^{n} f(x_i) A_i$$

is a close approximation to

$$\int_{-1}^{1} f(x) \, dx.$$

In fact, there is no polynomial $p(x)$ of degree not greater than $2n-1$ such that

$$\int_{-1}^{1} p(x) \, dx$$

gives a better approximation[1].

---

[1] GAUSS: *Methodus nova integralium valores per approximationem inveniendi.* Comment. soc. reg. Gottingensis rec. Vol. III, 1816; *Werke*, Vol. III, pp. 163-196. HEINE: *Handbuch der Kugelfunktionen*, Vol. II, Part. I. A brief exposition is to be found in RIEMANN-WEBER: *Differential- und Integralgleichungen der Mechanik und Physik*, Braunschweig 1925, Vol. I, pp. 315—318.

For further study of Legendre polynomials, the reader may consult BYERLY: *Fourier Series and Spherical Harmonics*, Boston, 1902; WHITTAKER and WATSON: *A Course of Modern Analysis*, 4th Ed., Cambridge, 1927; and the books of HEINE and RIEMANN-WEBER, mentioned above.

4. Analytic Character of Newtonian Potentials.

The formulas (3) and (5) give us the development of the potential of a particle of unit mass as a power series in ϱ :

$$(18) \qquad \frac{1}{r} = P_0(u)\frac{1}{\varrho'} + P_1(u)\frac{\varrho}{\varrho'^2} + P_2(u)\frac{\varrho^2}{\varrho'^3} + \cdots,$$

valid for $\frac{\varrho}{\varrho'} < \sqrt{2} - 1$. But the series continues to converge for $-1 \leqq u \leqq 1$, $\frac{\varrho}{\varrho'} < 1$, and to represent the same analytic function $\frac{1}{r}$ of ϱ for such values of the variable (see page 128).

We note first that this series is a series of homogeneous polynomials, in x, y, and z of ascending degree. Consider, for instance,

$$H_n = P_n(u)\frac{\varrho^n}{\varrho'^{n+1}}, \quad u = \cos\gamma = \frac{\xi x + \eta y + \zeta z}{\varrho'\varrho}.$$

$P_n(u)$ contains only the powers u^n, u^{n-2}, u^{n-4},... of u, and hence the radical ϱ only in the powers ϱ^{-n}, ϱ^{-n+2}, ϱ^{-n+4},.... Hence H_n contains this radical only with exponents 0, 2, 4, ..., none greater than n. This function is therefore rational and integral in x, y, z. It is further homogeneous of degree n, since u is homogeneous and of degree 0 in x, y, z.

Let us now show that $\frac{1}{r}$, the potential of a unit particle at Q, is analytic at points other than Q. A function $F(x, y, z)$ is said to be *analytic* at (a, b, c), provided it can be developed in a power series

$$\sum a_{ijk}(x-a)^i(y-b)^j(z-c)^k, \quad i = 0, 1, 2, \ldots, \quad j = 0, 1, 2, \ldots,$$
$$k = 0, 1, 2, \ldots,$$

which converges in a neighborhood of the point (a, b, c). No definite order of the terms is specified, so that it follows for power series in more than one variable that convergence is synonymous with absolute convergence[1].

In considering the potential $\frac{1}{r}$, we may take the point (a, b, c) as origin. The series (18) is a series of homogeneous polynomials in x, y, z,

$$\frac{1}{r} = H_0(x,y,z) + H_1(x,y,z) + H_2(x,y,z) + \cdots,$$

and if the parentheses about the groups of terms of the same degree be dropped, and the separate terms of the homogeneous polynomials be regarded as separate terms of the series, it becomes a power series in x, y, z

$$(19) \qquad \sum a_{ijk} x^i y^j z^k.$$

---

[1] See, for instance, KNOPP: *Theorie und Anwendung der unendlichen Reihen.* Berlin, 1922, pp. 132—133.

If we show that in some neighborhood of the origin this series converges and represents $\frac{1}{r}$, we shall have completed the proof that the potential $\frac{1}{r}$ is analytic at the origin, that is, at any point other than Q.

We may do this by setting up a *dominant series* for the series (18). A dominant series for a given series is one with positive terms, greater than or equal to the absolute values of the corresponding terms of the given series. Suppose that in (18) we replace u by

$$\bar{u} = \frac{|\xi||x|+|\eta||y|+|\zeta||z|}{\varrho'\varrho},$$

and then replace all minus signs in the Legendre polynomials by plus signs. The effect will be to give us a series of homogeneous polynomials in $|x|$, $|y|$, $|z|$, which, when the parentheses are dropped, becomes a dominant series (we are assuming that x, y, z, ξ, η, ζ are real) for (19):

(20) $$\sum A_{ijk}|x|^i|y|^j|z|^k.$$

Let us consider the convergence of the dominant series. Before the dropping of parentheses, it may be written

(21) $$P_0(i\bar{u})\frac{1}{\varrho'} + \frac{1}{i}P_1(i\bar{u})\frac{\varrho}{\varrho'^2} + \frac{1}{i^2}P_2(i\bar{u})\frac{\varrho^2}{\varrho'^3} + \cdots.$$

The powers of i here enter only apparently, for they may be factored out, and it is understood that this is done. Now in a series of positive terms, parentheses may be introduced or dropped at pleasure, for the sum of the first n terms, S_n in the series with parentheses, and s_n in the series without, are both increasing functions of n, and any S_n is less than some s_n, any s_n is less than some S_n, and hence both series converge, or else both diverge. Hence the dominant series (20) will converge if (21) does. Now $|\bar{u}|$ is not greater than 1, since $|\bar{u}|$ is the cosine of the angle between the directions $(|x|, |y|, |z|)$ and $(|\xi|, |\eta|, |\zeta|)$. Hence $|i\bar{u}| \leqq 1$, and so by equation (14),

$$\left|\frac{1}{i^n}P_n(i\bar{u})\right| \leqq (1+\sqrt{2})^n.$$

Thus (21) converges for $(1+\sqrt{2})\frac{\varrho}{\varrho'} < 1$, that is for $\varrho < (\sqrt{2}-1)\varrho'$. The dominating series (20) then converges, as we have seen, in the same neighborhood of the origin.

This, of course, means that (19) converges in the same neighborhood. But more, it converges to $\frac{1}{r}$. For since (21) and (20) converge to the same limit, we can chose N so that for any n and n' greater than N, the difference between the first n terms of (21) and the first n' terms of (20) is less than any assigned positive quantity ε. This difference consists in a certain set of terms of (20), and so dominates the corresponding difference in (18) and (19). Accordingly the last two series must converge to the same limit. This completes the proof that the potential $\frac{1}{r}$ is analytic.

Parenthetical Remarks on Power Series in Several Variables. Before proceeding to extend the above result to the usual continuous distributions of matter, we state several properties of power series of which we shall have need, with brief indications as to the proofs. In the first place,

If $F(x, y, z) = \sum a_{ijk} x^i y^j z^k$ converges for $x = x_0$, $y = y_0$, $z = z_0$, it converges uniformly for $|x| \leqq \lambda |x_0|$, $|y| \leqq \lambda |y_0|$, $|z| \leqq \lambda |z_0|$, where λ is any fixed positive proper fraction.

For, since a necessary condition that a series converge is that its terms approach 0, there is a number B such that

$$\left| a_{ijk} x_0^i y_0^j z_0^k \right| \leqq B, \quad i.\ e.\ \left| a_{ijk} \right| \leqq \frac{B}{|x_0|^i |y_0|^j |z_0|^k} .$$

Hence the series $F(x, y, z)$ is dominated by

$$\sum B \left| \frac{x}{x_0} \right|^i \left| \frac{y}{y_0} \right|^j \left| \frac{z}{z_0} \right|^k ,$$

and this, in turn, by $\sum B \lambda^{i+j+k}$. That the last series is convergent is most easily seen by regarding it as the result of multiplying by itself, three times, the geometric series for $\frac{1}{(1-\lambda)}$, for such a process is permitted in the case of convergent series with positive terms. Thus since the given series is dominated by a convergent series with constant terms, its convergence must be uniform.

On the same hypothesis, any given partial derivative of $F(x, y, z)$ is obtained by differentiating the series termwise. The resulting series converges uniformly for $|x| \leqq \lambda |x_0|$, $|y| \leqq \lambda |y_0|$, $|z| \leqq \lambda |z_0|$.

Consider first the derivative of $F(x, y, z)$ with respect to x. The result of termwise differentiation of the series is

$$\sum i\, a_{ijk} x^{i-1} y^j z^k .$$

This is dominated by the series obtained by expanding

$$B \left[\frac{d}{d\lambda} (1-\lambda)^{-1} \right] (1-\lambda)^{-1} (1-\lambda)^{-1}, \quad \text{or} \quad B (1-\lambda)^{-4},$$

and as this is convergent, the series obtained by differentiating termwise that for $F(x, y, z)$ is uniformly convergent in the region stated. It may therefore be integrated termwise, and we find in this way that it represents the derivative of $F(x, y, z)$.

The same is true for the derivatives with respect to y and z. By the same argument, the derivatives of these series may be found by termwise differentiation, the resulting series converging uniformly for $|x| \leqq \lambda^2 |x_0|$, $|y| \leqq \lambda^2 |y_0|$, $|z| \leqq \lambda^2 |z_0|$, and so on, the series for the derivatives of order n converging in a region given by the inequalities obtained by replacing λ^2 by λ^n. But as λ is any positive number less than 1, λ^n may be replaced by λ.

If, on the same hypotheses, $F(x, y, z) = 0$ *throughout any neighborhood of the origin, the coefficients of the power series all vanish.*

For in this neighborhood, or the portion of it in the cuboid $|x| \leqq \lambda |x_0|$, $|y| \leqq \lambda |y_0|$, $|z| \leqq \lambda |z_0|$, any given derived series must converge to 0. Hence, as

$$a_{ijk} = \frac{1}{i!\, j!\, k!} \left[\frac{\partial^{i+j+k}}{\partial x^i \partial y^j \partial z^k} F(x, y, z) \right]_{\substack{x=0 \\ y=0 \\ z=0}},$$

it follows that $a_{ijk} = 0$.

The Potentials of the Usual Distributions are Analytic at the Points of Free Space. Let us now consider a distribution of continuous density $\varkappa$, occupying a volume V. Let the origin O be taken at a point of free space, and let a denote the distance from O to the nearest point of V. In the series (19) for $\frac{1}{r}$, the coefficients a_{ijk} are functions of ξ, η, ζ, but the first n terms of that series are less in absolute value than a certain number of terms of the series (21), which, in turn, is dominated by

$$\sum (1 + \sqrt{2})^n \frac{\varrho^n}{a^{n+1}},$$

since $\varrho' \geqq a$. If $\varrho \leqq \lambda(1 - \sqrt{2})\, a$, $0 < \lambda < 1$, this series is dominated by the convergent series with constant terms

$$\sum \frac{1}{a} \lambda^n,$$

so that with the variables thus restricted, (19) is convergent *uniformly as to all its variables.*

The conditions on the variables are obviously met for $Q\,(\xi, \eta, \zeta)$ in V and $P\,(x, y, z)$ in the cube c: $|x| \leqq \cdot 2a$, $|y| \leqq \cdot 2a$, $|z| \leqq \cdot 2a$. The series (19) remains uniformly convergent in all its variables upon multiplication by $\varkappa = \varkappa\,(\xi, \eta, \zeta)$, and hence

$$U = \iiint_V \varkappa \frac{1}{r}\, dV = \sum \left[\iiint_V \varkappa\, a_{ijk}\, dV \right] x^i\, y^j\, z^k,$$

the series being uniformly convergent in c. Thus the potential is analytic at the origin, that is, at any point of free space.

The same treatment holds for a surface distribution. When it comes to double distributions, we note that

$$\frac{\partial}{\partial \xi} \frac{1}{r} = \frac{x - \xi}{r^3} = (x - \xi) \left[\sum a_{ijk} x^i y^j z^k \right]^3$$

and that in the region c, where the series is dominated by a convergent series with terms independent of the variables, the product on the right may be expanded and written as a single power series, uniformly convergent for Q in V and P in c. The same situation holds with respect to the linear combination of the partial derivatives with respect to ξ, η, ζ, with continuous coefficients l, m, n:

$$\frac{\partial}{\partial \nu} \frac{1}{r} = \left(\frac{\partial}{\partial \xi} \frac{1}{r} \right) l + \left(\frac{\partial}{\partial \eta} \frac{1}{r} \right) m + \left(\frac{\partial}{\partial \zeta} \frac{1}{r} \right) n$$

and the same process as before shows that the potential of a double distribution is analytic at the points of free space. Finally we remark that the potential of a distribution with piecewise continuous density is a sum of those with continuous densities. We thus have established

Theorem III. *The Newtonian potentials of particles and of the usual distributions of matter are analytic at the points of free space.*

The same, as a consequence, is true of the derivatives of the potentials, of all orders.

5. Spherical Harmonics.

We have seen that the development (18) for $\frac{1}{r}$ is equivalent to a development in terms of homogeneous polynomials

$$(22) \qquad \frac{1}{r} = H_0(x, y, z) + H_1(x, y, z) + H_2(x, y, z) + \cdots.$$

These polynomials are solutions of Laplace's equation. For, if the parentheses are omitted from the groups of terms of the same degree, we obtain a power series which is differentiable termwise in a neighborhood of the origin, and since the introduction of parentheses is always permitted, it follows that at least in the same region, the series of homogeneous polynomials is differentiable termwise. Hence, since $\frac{1}{r}$ satisfies Laplace's equation,

$$0 = \nabla^2 H_0(x, y, z) + \nabla^2 H_1(x, y, z) + \nabla^2 H_2(x, y, z) + \cdots.$$

Since a power series cannot converge to 0 in a region containing the origin in its interior unless all its coefficients vanish, it follows that all the terms of the above series vanish, and thus

$$\nabla^2 H_n(x, y, z) = 0.$$

A solution of Laplace's equation is called a *harmonic function*. As the polynomials $H_n(x, y, z)$ are peculiarly adapted to the treatment of problems connected with the sphere, they are called *spherical harmonics*. We shall understand by this term any homogeneous polynomial which satisfies Laplace's equation[1].

Let us examine the spherical harmonics given by (22). The first few terms are

$$\frac{1}{r} = \frac{1}{\varrho'} + \frac{1}{\varrho'^3} \left[\xi x + \eta y + \zeta z \right] + \frac{1}{2\,\varrho'^5} \left[\xi^2(2x^2 - y^2 - z^2) + \eta^2(2y^2 - z^2 - x^2) \right.$$
$$+ \zeta^2(2z^2 - x^2 - y^2) + 6\eta\zeta\, yz + 6\zeta\xi\, zx$$
$$\left. + 6\xi\eta\, xy \right] + \cdots.$$

The spherical harmonics thus depend on the parameters ξ, η, ζ. They remain spherical harmonics if the powers of ϱ' are dropped, and as the resulting polynomials satisfy Laplace's equation for all values of the parameters, it follows that the coefficients of the separate powers and products of these letters are also spherical harmonics. We thus can make a list of spherical harmonics of the first few orders:

0th order, 1,

1st order, x, y, z,

2d order, $2x^2 - y^2 - z^2$, $2y^2 - z^2 - x^2$, $2z^2 - x^2 - y^2$,

yz , zx , xy .

Those of the second order are not independent, for any one of those in the first line is the negative of the sum of the other two. The number of independent spherical harmonics of order n is $2n + 1$, that is, there exists a set of $2n + 1$ spherical harmonics of order n, such that any other spherical harmonic of the same order is a linear homogeneous combination of them, with constant coefficients. We leave the proof to the reader in exercises.

Exercises.

1. Write a list of spherical harmonics of the third order obtained by finding the coefficients of the polynomial $\varrho'^7 H_3 (x, y, z)$ in ξ, η, ζ. Show that seven of them can be picked out in terms of which all the others can be expressed.

2. Writing

$$H_n (x, y, z) = a_n + a_{n-1} z + a_{n-2} z^2 + a_{n-3} z^3 + \cdots + a_0 z^n,$$

where a_r is a homogeneous polynomial of degree r in x and y, show that a necessary and sufficient condition that this be a spherical harmonic is that it have the form

$$H_n (x, y, z) = a_n + a_{n-1} z - \frac{\nabla^2 a_n}{2!} z^2 - \frac{\nabla^2 a_{n-1}}{3!} z^3 + \frac{\nabla^2 (\nabla^2 a_n)}{4!} z^4$$
$$+ \frac{\nabla^2 (\nabla^2 a_{n-1})}{5!} z^5 - \cdots,$$

---

[1] The term spherical harmonic is often applied to a broader class of functions, namely, to any homogeneous solution of Laplace's equation.

where a_{n-1} and a_n, are arbitrary. Thus prove the statement of the text that there are $2n+1$ independent spherical harmonics of order n, in terms of which all spherical harmonics of that order can be linearly expressed.

3. Show how an independent set of $2n+1$ spherical harmonics of order n can be determined, and apply it to the case $n=3$.

4. Using Euler's relation for a homogeneous function of degree n

$$x\frac{\partial}{\partial x}H_n + y\frac{\partial}{\partial y}H_n + z\frac{\partial}{\partial z}H_n = nH_n,$$

show that if H_n is a spherical harmonic of order n, then $\dfrac{H_n}{\varrho^{2n+1}}$ is a solution of Laplace's equation for $\varrho \neq 0$.

5. A spherical harmonic of order n can be expressed in the form

$$H_n(x, y, z) = \varrho^n S_n(\varphi, \vartheta).$$

$S_n(\varphi, \vartheta)$ is called a *surface spherical harmonic* of order n. Taking from Chapter VII, page 183, the expression for Laplace's equation in spherical coördinates, show that this surface spherical harmonic must satisfy the differential equation

$$\sin\vartheta\frac{\partial}{\partial\vartheta}\left(\sin\vartheta\frac{\partial S_n}{\partial\vartheta}\right) + \frac{\partial^2 S_n}{\partial\varphi^2} + n(n+1)\sin^2\vartheta\, S_n = 0.$$

Note that the Legendre polynomial $P_n(u)$ is a surface spherical harmonic of order n, and that if in (2) we put $\vartheta' = 0$, $u = \cos\vartheta$, and $P_n(u)$ is independent of φ. Thus, assuming that $S_n(\varphi, \vartheta)$ is independent of φ, and making the substitution $\cos\vartheta = u$, find again the differential equation (11) satisfied by the Legendre polynomials.

6. Developments in Series of Spherical Harmonics.

In (18), we have the development of the potential of a particle in a series of spherical harmonics. Let us now consider the potential of a distribution of continuous density $\varkappa$ occupying a volume V, and let the origin O be taken at any point of free space. Let a denote the distance from O of the nearest boundary point of V. Then, with $Q(\xi, \eta, \zeta)$ in V and $P(x, y, z)$ in the sphere $\varrho \leq \lambda a$, $0 < \lambda < 1$, the series (18) is dominated by the geometric series for $(1-\lambda)^{-1}$, and thus is uniformly convergent in all its variables. Hence we may multiply by $\varkappa$ and integrate. We find

$$U = \iiint_V \varkappa\frac{1}{r}\,dV = H_0(x, y, z) + H_1(x, y, z) + H_2(x, y, z)\ldots,$$

where $H_n(x, y, z)$ is the spherical harmonic of degree n

$$H_n(x, y, z) = \iiint_V \varkappa P_n(u)\frac{\varrho^n}{\varrho'^{n+1}}\,dV = \varrho^n\iiint_V \varkappa\frac{P_n(u)}{\varrho'^{n-1}}\sin\vartheta'\,d\varrho'\,d\varphi'\,d\vartheta'.$$

where $u = \cos\gamma$ has the value given in equation (2).

Thus this potential is developable in a series of spherical harmonics, convergent at any interior point of the sphere about the origin through the nearest point of the distribution, and uniformly convergent in any smaller concentric sphere. The same is clearly true of surface distributions, and in the cases in which the densities are piecewise continuous.

When it comes to double distributions, we need to consider for a moment the potential of a doublet, or magnetic particle. We have

$$\frac{\partial}{\partial \xi} \frac{1}{r} = - \frac{\partial}{\partial x} \frac{1}{r} = \sum_{1}^{\infty} - \frac{1}{\varrho'^{n+1}} \frac{\partial [P_n (u) \varrho^n]}{\partial x},$$

the termwise differentiation being permitted, at least in a sufficiently small neighborhood of the origin. For the derivative, we have

$$\frac{\partial}{\partial x} P_n (u) \varrho^n = P'_n (u) \frac{\partial u}{\partial x} \varrho^n + P_n (u) n \varrho^{n-2} x,$$

or, making use of the expression for u in terms of cartesian coördinates, and the relation (9),

$$\frac{\partial}{\partial x} P_n (u) \varrho^n = \left[P'_n (u) \frac{\varrho \xi}{\varrho'} - P'_{n-1} (u) x \right] \varrho^{n-2}.$$

Hence

$$\frac{\partial}{\partial \xi} \frac{1}{r} = \sum_{1}^{\infty} \left[P'_{n-1} (u) x - P'_n (u) \frac{\varrho \xi}{\varrho'} \right] \frac{\varrho^{n-2}}{\varrho'^{n+1}}.$$

It will be noticed that the general term of this series is a homogeneous polynomial in x, y, z, and it may be proved to be harmonic just as were the separate terms in the development of $\frac{1}{r}$. The series is dominated, as may be seen by referring to Exercise 4 (p. 128) by

$$\sum_{0}^{\infty} \frac{1}{\varrho'^2} \left[\frac{n (n-1)}{2} + \frac{n (n+1)}{2} \right] \frac{\varrho^{n-1}}{\varrho'^{n-1}},$$

since $|\xi| \leqq \varrho'$ and $|x| \leqq \varrho$. If Q is in V, and P in the sphere $\varrho \leqq \lambda a$, this series is in turn dominated by the series

$$\sum_{0}^{\infty} \frac{1}{\varrho'^2} n^2 \lambda^{n-1},$$

which the ratio test shows to be convergent. Thus the potential of the doublet can be expanded in a series of spherical harmonics convergent in the sphere about the origin of radius λa, uniformly as to the coördinates of both P and Q. The rest of the treatment follows that for the volume distribution.

Theorem IV. *The potential of any of the usual distributions is developable in a series of spherical harmonics, convergent at any interior point of the sphere about the origin* (which may be taken at any point of free space), *through the nearest point of the distribution, and uniformly convergent in any concentric smaller sphere.*

7. Developments Valid at Great Distances.

We may also develop the potential of a particle as a series in negative powers of ϱ. All we need do is interchange P and Q, or, since u is symmetric, ϱ and ϱ' in (18). We have

$$\frac{1}{r} = P_0(u)\frac{1}{\varrho} + P_1(u)\frac{\varrho'}{\varrho^2} + P_2(u)\frac{\varrho'^2}{\varrho^3} + \cdots.$$

If a is the distance from the origin of the most distant point of a given distribution, say in a volume V, so that when Q is in V, $\varrho' \leqq a$, then this series is uniformly convergent in all six variables when P is outside the sphere $\varrho = \lambda a$, $\lambda > 1$. It may be multiplied by a continuous, or piece-wise continuous density and integrated termwise over V, and thus gives an expansion of the potential U of the volume distribution, valid at all points outside any sphere containing the whole distribution, and uniformly convergent if that sphere contains the distribution in its interior. The term arising from $\dfrac{P_n(u)\,\varrho'^n}{\varrho^{n+1}}$ is seen to become a homogeneous polynomial of degree n in x, y, z on multiplication by ϱ^{2n+1}. The other types of distribution may be treated in a similar way, and we arrive at the result

Theorem V. *The potential of any of the usual distributions is developable in a series of which the general term is a spherical harmonic of order n divided by ϱ^{2n+1}. This series is convergent outside any sphere about the origin and containing the distribution, and uniformly convergent outside such a sphere if it contains the distribution in its interior. The same is true of the partial derivatives of first order of these potentials.*

The last statement of the theorem can be verified by the process used in considering the development of the potential of a double distribution. In the case of the derivative of the potential of a double distribution, another differentiation will be necessary, but the treatment of this case presents no new difficulties. Later we shall see that the theorem is true for derivatives of the potential of any order[1].

Exercises.

1. A homogeneous cube of side $2a$ and center at the origin, has its sides parallel to the coördinate axes. Show that its potential has the development:

$$U = \frac{M}{\varrho} + \frac{7\,M a}{60\,\varrho^9}\,[3\,\varrho^4 - 5\,(x^4 + y^4 + z^4)] + \cdots.$$

Show that at distances from the center exceeding the length of the diagonal of the cube, the second term is less than 0.2 per cent of the first. Show that the potential is less than that of a sphere of equal mass and the same center, at distant points on the axes, and more on the diagonals. Does this seem reasonable?

---

[1] This follows from Chapter VIII (p. 211), the fact that the derivative of a harmonic function is harmonic, and from Chapter X, § 2. See also Exercise 4, at the end of Chapter VIII, page 228.

2. Given a distribution whose density is nowhere negative, show that if the origin of coördinates is taken at the center of mass, the development in falling powers of the distance lacks the terms of order -1 in x, y, z, and if, in addition, the axes are taken along the principle axes of inertia of the distribution, the initial terms of the development are

$$U = \frac{M}{\varrho} + \frac{(B + C - 2A)\, x^2 + (C + A - 2B)\, y^2 + (A + B - 2C)\, z^2}{2\,\varrho^5} + \cdots,$$

where A, B, C are the moments of inertia about the axes.

3. Show that if the development of the potential of a distribution be broken off,

$$U = \frac{M}{\varrho} + \frac{H_1\,(x,\,y,\,z)}{\varrho^3} + \cdots + \frac{H_n\,(x,\,y,\,z)}{\varrho^{2n+1}} + R_n ,$$

the remainder R_n is subject to the inequality

$$|R_n| \leq \frac{\dfrac{M}{b}\left(\dfrac{a}{b}\right)^{n+1}}{1 - \dfrac{a}{b}} ,$$

where a is the radius of a sphere about the origin containing all the masses, and b is the radius of a larger concentric sphere, to the exterior of which $P\,(x,\,y,\,z)$ is confined.

4. Show that at distances from the center of mass of a body, greater than ten times the radius of a sphere about the center of mass and containing the body, the equipotential surfaces vary in distance from the center of mass by less than 1.2 per cent. Show that the equipotentials of bounded distributions of positive mass approach spheres as they recede from the distribution.

8. Behavior of Newtonian Potentials at Great Distances.

We have seen that at great distances, developments hold for the potential of bounded distributions,

$$U = \frac{M}{\varrho} + \frac{H_1\,(a,\,y,\,z)}{\varrho^3} + \cdots, \qquad \frac{\partial U}{\partial x} = -\frac{M\,x}{\varrho^3} + \frac{H_2\,(x,\,y,\,z)}{\varrho^5} + \cdots,$$

the termwise differentation being permitted because the resulting series is uniformly convergent. Similar expressions exist for the other partial derivatives of the first order. From these we derive the important properties of the usual potentials at great distances:

Theorem V. *If U is the potential of any bounded distribution of one of the usual types, then at a great distance ϱ from any fixed point, the quantities*

$$\varrho U, \qquad \varrho^2 \frac{\partial U}{\partial x}, \qquad \varrho^2 \frac{\partial U}{\partial y}, \qquad \varrho^2 \frac{\partial U}{\partial z}$$

are all bounded. As $P\,(x,\,y,\,z)$ recedes to infinity in any direction, ϱU approaches the total mass of the distribution.

The limits of the quantities

$$\varrho^2 \frac{\partial U}{\partial x}, \quad \varrho^2 \frac{\partial U}{\partial y}, \quad \varrho^2 \frac{\partial U}{\partial z}$$

as ϱ becomes inifinite do not exist, in general. If, however, the direction in which P recedes to infinity is restricted, say so as to approach a limiting direction with direction cosines l, m, n, then these quantities approach limits

$$-M l, \quad -M m, \quad -M n,$$

respectively. In other words, the force becomes more and more nearly that due to a particle, situated at a fixed point, and having as mass that of the distribution. We have used this as a check in the exercises of Chapter I, assuming it at that point as reasonable.

In the development of the potential of a double distribution, valid for great distances, it turns out that the term in $\frac{1}{\varrho}$ is lacking. To say that the total mass of a double distribution is 0 is entirely reasonable, in view of its possible interpretation as the limit of two equal and opposite distributions on parallel surfaces, as these surfaces approach coincidence. This holds whether the total moment vanishes or not. It is to be noted that this circumstance of a vanishing total mass does not impair Theorem V; it enables us to make supplementary statements. In this case the four quantities there given approach the limit 0.

Exercises on the Logarithmic Potential.

1. Show that the partial derivatives of order n of the logarithmic potential of a particle

$$U = \log \frac{1}{r}$$

are homogeneous polynomials in x, y, ξ, and η, of degree n, divided by ϱ^{2n}. Show also that the potentials of the usual distributions satisfy Laplace's equation in two dimensions

$$V^2 U = \frac{\partial^2 U}{\partial x^2} + \frac{\partial^2 U}{\partial y^2}.$$

2. Show that

$$\log \frac{1}{r} = \log \frac{1}{\varrho'} + \cos (\varphi - \varphi') \frac{\varrho}{\varrho'} + \frac{1}{2} \cos 2 (\varphi - \varphi') \frac{\varrho^2}{\varrho'^2}$$

$$+ \frac{1}{3} \cos 3 (\varphi - \varphi') \frac{\varrho^3}{\varrho'^3} + \cdots,$$

and that the terms of this series are homogeneous polynomials in x and y which satisfy Laplace's equation.

3. Derive developments in terms of homogeneous polynomials satisfying Laplace's equation, and in terms of such polynomials divided by appropriate powers of ϱ, for the potentials of the usual logarithmic distributions.

4. Show that there are only two independent homogeneous polynomials of each order $(n > 1)$ which satisfy Laplace's equation, and that these may be taken as the

real and imaginary parts of $(x + iy)^n$. Show also that they are the numerators in certain derivatives of the logarithmic potential of a unit particle at the origin, when these are expressed as homogeneous polynomials divided by the proper powers of ϱ. Explain why only two of the $n + 1$ derivatives of order n are independent.

5. Show that if U is the logarithmic potential of one of the usual distributions, contained in a bounded portion of the plane, and of total mass M,

$$U - M \log \frac{1}{\varrho}$$

approaches 0 as ϱ becomes infinite, in fact, that ϱ times this difference is bounded for large ϱ. Show also that

$$\varrho \frac{\partial U}{\partial x}, \ \varrho \frac{\partial U}{\partial y}$$

are bounded for large ϱ. Make sharper statements for the case where $M = 0$.

Chapter VI.

Properties of Newtonian Potentials at Points Occupied by Masses.

1. Character of the Problem.

We continue our study of the properties of Newtonian potentials, now in the neighborhood of points of the distributions of matter. Our object is to find relations between the potential and the density, for the purpose indicated at the beginning of the last chapter. As it is only in the neighborhood of a point of a distribution that the density at that point makes itself felt in a preponderating way, we must of necessity investigate the behavior of the potentials at such points.

As the integrands of the integrals become infinite at such points, the study presents some difficulties, and it will probably be wise for the reader to use the present chapter in a manner similar to Chapter IV. He should by all means be acquainted with the results, a number of which have been verified in particular cases in the exercises of Chapters I, and III. He will do well to review the exercises in question in order that he may see the results in the light of illustrations of general principles. Some acquaintance with a few typical proofs, say the earlier ones, is also desirable. Otherwise, a detailed study of the chapter should be left until after the later material has shown the need of the present developments. It will then be found more interesting and more readily understandable.

2. Lemmas on Improper Integrals.

We shall confine ourselves, in this chapter, to regular surfaces and regions, and, in general, to densities which are piecewise continuous.

We have already met with improper integrals, in Chapter I, § 9 (p. 17) and in Chapter IV, § 11 (p. 119). At present it will serve if we restrict ourselves to integrands $f(Q)$ which become infinite only at a single point P of the region V of integration. In any region in V which does not contain the point P, we shall suppose that $f(Q)$ is piecewise continuous in the coördinates ξ, η, ζ of Q. It is not an essential restriction to assume that P is an interior point of V, for as we have seen, we may extend V, defining $f(Q)$ as 0 in the region added. We recall the definition of convergence:

the integral
$$I = \iiint\limits_V f(Q)\, dV$$

is said to be convergent, or to exist, provided

$$\lim_{\delta \to 0} \iiint\limits_{V-v} f(Q)\, dV$$

exists, where v is a variable regular region subject to the sole restrictions that it shall have P in its interior, and that its maximum chord shall not exceed δ. The value of the convergent integral is defined to be this limit.

If the integral I is convergent, the definition of convergence, applied to the first and last term, shows the following equation to be valid

$$\iiint\limits_V f(Q)\, dV - \iiint\limits_{V-v} f(Q)\, dV = \iiint\limits_v f(Q)\, dV,$$

where v is thought of, for the moment, as fixed. The equation once established, we may allow the maximum chord of v to approach 0. The left hand member of the equation then approaches 0, and we have

Lemma I. *If I is convergent, the integral*

$$\iiint\limits_v f(Q)\, dV$$

approaches 0 *with the maximum chord of v.*

We recall also the Cauchy test for convergence (p. 18). An inconvenience inherent in the application of that test is the very general character of the regions v that must be considered. We shall therefore find useful the criterion given by

Lemma II. *If there is a function $g(Q)$ such that $|f(Q)| \leqq g(Q)$, and such that*

$$\iiint\limits_V g(Q)\, dV$$

is convergent, then I is convergent.

This test obviates the necessity of considering general regions v, for the reason that if

$$\iiint\limits_{V-v} g(Q)\, dV$$

approaches a limit when v is a sphere about P, it will approach the same limit for the most general regular region v containing P in its interior, as the maximum chord of v approaches 0. This we shall show in a moment.

To prove the lemma, let v and v' denote any two regions having P as an interior point, with maximum chord less than δ. Let σ be a sphere about P of radius 2δ. Then

$$\left| \iiint_{V-v} f(Q)\,dV - \iiint_{V-v} f(Q)\,dV \right| = \left| \iiint_{\sigma-v'} f(Q)\,dV - \iiint_{\sigma-v} f(Q)\,dV \right|$$

$$\leqq \iiint_{\sigma-v} g(Q)\,dV + \iiint_{\sigma-v} g(Q)\,dV \leqq 2 \iiint_{\sigma} g(Q)\,dV.$$

The last integral is convergent, by hypothesis, and so approaches 0 with δ, by Lemma I. The Cauchy test then shows that I is convergent.

We now justify the remark made with respect to the convergence of the integral over $g(Q)$ for special regions. Let $\sigma_1, \sigma_2, \sigma_3, \ldots$ be a sequence of spheres about P, with radii approaching 0. Let

$$G_i = \iiint_{V-\sigma_i} g(Q)\,dV.$$

Then, by hypothesis, the monotone increasing sequence $G_1, G_2, G_3, \ldots$ approaches a limit. But the integral

$$G = \iiint_{V-v} g(Q)\,dV$$

lies, for small enough maximum chord of v, between a term of this sequence, as far advanced as we please, and some following term, and hence G approaches the same limit as the sequence, as the maximum chord of v approaches 0.

Remarks. All that has been said for triple integrals holds for double integrals with the mere substitution of two dimensional for three dimensional regions of integration. Furthermore, we may apply the results to integrands $f(Q)$ becoming infinite at two points P and P' by simply dividing the region of integration—say by a small sphere about one of these points—into two, one containing each point, and understanding that the improper integral over the whole region is the sum of the improper integrals over the two parts. This simply amounts to extending the definition of improper integral to the case of two infinities of the integrand. We shall have need of this remark in considering derivatives of potentials.

Lemma III. (a) *The integral*

$$\iiint_{V} \frac{dV}{r^\beta}, \qquad 0 < \beta < 3$$

is convergent, and for all regular regions V of the same volume, it is greatest when V is a sphere about P.

(b) *The integral*

$$\iint\limits_{S} \frac{dS}{r^{\beta}}, \qquad 0 < \beta < 2,$$

where S is a regular region of the plane, is convergent, and for all regions S of the same area, it is greatest when S is a circle about P.

That the integrals are convergent is easily proved by means of spherical and polar coördinates, respectively. In the integrals over regions with the infinities cut out, the integrands are continuous, and the multiple integrals are then equal to the iterated integrals with respect to these coördinates. But it is found that the iterated integrals are not improper, and the convergence is readily established (see Chapter I, page 18).

Suppose now that V is not a sphere about P. Then there will be points of V, outside the sphere Σ of equal volume about P, and also points in Σ not in V

The set v of points in V which are not interior to Σ may not constitute a region at all. For instance, the regular surface bounding V may touch, from within, arcs of an infinite number of parallel circles on the sphere. However, the integral of a continuous function f over such a set is easily defined. Let C denote a cube containing v. We define a function F, $F = f$ at the points of v, and $F = 0$ elsewhere in C. Then, by definition,

$$\iiint\limits_{v} f\, dV = \iiint\limits_{C} F\, dV.$$

It is true that F is discontinuous in C, but not at any interior points of v. The boundary of v lies entirely in the boundaries of Σ and V, and it is easy to show that a regular surface element can be enclosed in the interior of a region of arbitrarily small volume. It follows that the above integral exists. If f becomes infinite at a point P of v, the improper integral is defined in the usual way.

With these preliminaries, we see that

$$\iiint\limits_{\Sigma} \frac{dV}{r^{\beta}} - \iiint\limits_{V} \frac{dV}{r^{\beta}} = \iiint\limits_{\sigma} \frac{dV}{r^{\beta}} - \iiint\limits_{v} \frac{dV}{r^{\beta}},$$

where σ is the set of points of Σ not interior to V. But

$$\frac{1}{r^{\beta}} \geqq \frac{1}{a^{\beta}} \text{ in } \sigma, \qquad \frac{1}{r^{\beta}} \leqq \frac{1}{a^{\beta}} \text{ in } v,$$

a being the radius of Σ, and the inequalities holding at interior points. Hence the integral over Σ exceeds the integral over V if either σ or v

contains interior points, since the volumes (that is, the integrals of the function $f = 1$) of σ and v are equal. If neither σ or v have interior points, it follows at once that V coincides with Σ. Part (a) of the lemma is thus established, and similar reasoning establishes part (b).

Some equations and inequalities are of such frequent occurence in what follows that we add them as

Lemma IV.

(a) $2\,|\,ab\,| \leqq a^2 + b^2,\quad a,\,b$ real.

(b) $\dfrac{1}{r} - \dfrac{1}{r_0} = \dfrac{r_0^2 - r^2}{r r_0 (r + r_0)}$,

(c) $\dfrac{1}{r^3} - \dfrac{1}{r_0^3} = \left(\dfrac{1}{r} - \dfrac{1}{r_0}\right)\left(\dfrac{1}{r^2} + \dfrac{1}{r r_0} + \dfrac{1}{r_0^2}\right),\quad \dfrac{1}{r^5} - \dfrac{1}{r_0^5} = \left(\dfrac{1}{r} - \dfrac{1}{r_0}\right)\sum_1^4 \dfrac{1}{r^{4-i}\,r_0^i}.$

The inequality is the familiar consequence of $(a - b)^2 \geqq 0$, and the equations are obvious algebraic identities.

3. The Potentials of Volume Distributions.

We consider the potential U of a distribution of piecewise continuous density $\varkappa$, throughout a regular region V; also a typical component of the force:

$$U = \iiint_V \frac{\varkappa}{r}\,dV, \quad Z = \iiint_V \varkappa \frac{\zeta - z}{r^3}\,dV.$$

As $|\,\varkappa\,|$ is bounded, and as $|\,\zeta - z\,| \leqq r$, we see by Lemmas II and III that these integrals converge for all P in V. Thus the potential and force are defined everywhere.

We next show that these functions are everywhere continuous. The reasoning is typical of that to be used repeatedly in this chapter. We confine ourselves to the points of V, for we already know that the integrals are continuous everywhere else. Let P_0 be a point of V; as remarked, we may assume that it is interior. Then $U = U_1 + U_2$, where

$$U_1(P) = \iiint_\sigma \frac{\varkappa}{r}\,dV, \quad U_2(P) = \iiint_{V-\sigma} \frac{\varkappa}{r}\,dV,$$

where σ is a sphere about P_0. Now, given any $\varepsilon > 0$, we may take σ so small that

$$|\,U_1(P)\,| < \frac{\varepsilon}{3},$$

independently of the position of P, because of Lemmas III and I. For such σ,

$$|\,U_1(P) - U_1(P_0)\,| < \frac{2}{3}\,\varepsilon.$$

Then, with σ fixed, there is a neighborhood of P_0 such that when P is in it, and Q is in $V - \sigma$,

$$\left| \frac{1}{r} - \frac{1}{r_0} \right| < \frac{\varepsilon}{3 \, BV},$$

where r and r_0 are the distances $\overline{PQ}$ and $\overline{P_0Q}$, B is a bound for $|\varkappa|$, and V is the volume of the region V. Then, with P in this neighborhood,

$$|U_2(P) - U_2(P_0)| \leqq \iiint\limits_{V-\sigma} |\varkappa| \left| \frac{1}{r} - \frac{1}{r_0} \right| dV < \frac{\varepsilon}{3}.$$

Combining the inequalities for $U_1(P)$ and $U_2(P)$, we have

$$|U(P) - U(P_0)| < \varepsilon.$$

Thus U is continuous at P_0, and hence throughout space.

Characteristic of the reasoning is the breaking up of the region of integration into two, such that the integral over the first vanishes with the maximum chord of the region, *uniformly as to P*, and that in the second region, the integrand is a bounded density times a continuous function of all the coördinates of P and Q. The same argument holds for the function Z of P. Thus we have

Theorem I. *The potential U, and the components X, Y, Z of the force, due to a volume distribution of piecewise continuous density in the bounded volume V, exist at the points of V, and are continuous throughout space.*

But it is not evident without further study that the force components are, at points of the distribution, the corresponding derivatives of the potential, for the usual criterion for the possibility of differentiating under the sign of integration does not apply to improper integrals. Nevertheless, the relationship subsists (we are considering the gravitational field — in electrical or magnetic fields the force is the negative of the gradient of the potential).

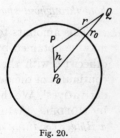

Fig. 20.

To show this, let us take the origin of coördinates at P_0, and let P have the coördinates $(0, 0, h)$ (fig. 20). We consider the function

$$\frac{U(P) - U(P_0)}{h} - Z(P_0) = \iiint\limits_{V} \varkappa \left[\frac{1}{h} \left(\frac{1}{r} - \frac{1}{r_0} \right) - \frac{\zeta}{r_0^3} \right] dV$$

$$= \iiint\limits_{V} \varkappa \left[\frac{2\zeta - h}{rr_0(r + r_0)} - \frac{\zeta}{r_0^3} \right] dV, \quad (h \neq 0).$$

Here we have employed Lemma IV (b) and the values $r_0^2 = \xi^2 + \eta^2 + \zeta^2$, $r^2 = \xi^2 + \eta^2 + (\zeta - h)^2$.

This integral is convergent, by Lemmas II and III, since $|\zeta| \leqq r_0$, and $|2\zeta - h| \leqq |\zeta| + |\zeta - h| \leqq r_0 + r$. It converges, and vanishes, for $h = 0$. If it is a continuous function of h, the difference quotient on the left approaches the limit $Z(P_0)$ as h approaches 0, that is, the derivative of the potential exists and equals Z. The problem is reduced, then, to showing the integral continuous.

If P is confined to the interior of a small sphere σ about P_0, the integrand is a bounded density times a function which is continuous in all the variables, when the integral is extended over the portion of V outside the sphere. The integral over this portion is therefore continuous in P, thus restricted. It remains to show that the integral over the sphere can be made arbitrarily small by restricting the radius of the sphere, uniformly as to P. But the integral is dominated by (*i.e.* is less in absolute value than)

$$B \iiint_\sigma \left(\frac{1}{r r_0} + \frac{1}{r_0^2} \right) dV \leqq \frac{B}{2} \iiint_\sigma \left[\frac{1}{r^2} + \frac{3}{r_0^2} \right] dV \leqq 2B \iiint_\sigma \frac{dV}{r_0^2},$$

by Lemmas IV (a) and III. As the last integral is convergent, it approaches 0 with the radius of σ, by Lemma I. This completes the proof. We have, therefore

Theorem II. *The potential U of the volume distribution of Theorem I is everywhere differentiable, and the equations*

$$X = \frac{\partial U}{\partial x}, \quad Y = \frac{\partial U}{\partial y}, \quad Z = \frac{\partial U}{\partial z},$$

hold throughout space.

This amounts to saying that the derivatives of the first order of U may be obtained by differentiating under the sign of integration. It is otherwise with the derivatives of the second order. In fact, the mere continuity of the density does not suffice to insure the existence of these derivatives[1]. We therefore impose on the density a condition introduced by HÖLDER[2]. A function $f(Q)$ of the coördinates of Q is said to· *satisfy a Hölder condition at P* if there are three positive constants, c, A and α, such that

$$|f(Q) - f(P)| \leqq A r^\alpha, \quad r = \overline{PQ},$$

for all points Q for which $r \leqq c$. If there is a region R in which $f(Q)$ satisfies a Hölder condition at every point, *with the same c, A and α,* $f(Q)$ is said to satisfy a *uniform* Hölder condition, or to satisfy a Hölder condition uniformly, in R.

---

[1] Here is an illustration of the necessity of the investigations of this chapter, for this situation would not have emerged in a study of the examples of Chapters I and III, where the densities are all analytic.

[2] *Beiträge zur Potentialtheorie*, Dissertation, Stuttgart, 1882.

Exercises.

1. Show that the function defined by

$$f(\xi) = \frac{1}{\log(1/|\xi|)}, \qquad \xi \neq 0, \qquad f(0) = 0,$$

is continuous at the origin, but does not satisfy a Hölder condition at that point. Devise a function which satisfies a Hölder condition at a point, but is not differentiable at that point. Thus a Hölder condition is stronger than continuity, but weaker than differentiability if $\alpha < 1$.

2. We know that a function of x, continuous in a closed interval, is uniformly continuous in that interval. Show that a similar theorem does not hold with respect to a Hölder condition, by an examination of the function defined in the closed interval $(0,1)$ as follows:

$$f(x) = \frac{1}{n} + \left[\frac{1}{n(n-1)}\right]^{\frac{n-1}{n}} \left(x - \frac{1}{n}\right)^{\frac{1}{n}}, \qquad \frac{1}{n} \leq x \leq \frac{1}{n-1}, \qquad n = 2, 3, 4, \ldots,$$

$$f(0) = 0.$$

We may now study the partial derivatives of U of the second order, at interior points of V. Let P_0 be such a point, and let Σ be a sphere about P_0, lying in V. Then $U = U_1 + U_2$, where U_1 is the potential of the masses within Σ, and U_2 the potential of the remaining masses. As P_0 is an exterior point for U_2, this potential has continuous derivatives of all orders at P_0 and is harmonic there. Thus the problem is reduced to one in which V is a sphere.

If the density of the sphere is constant, we have the following value of Z from Chapter I, § 9 (p. 19):

$$Z = -\frac{4}{3}\pi \varkappa z,$$

valid at interior points. As Z is the derivative of U with respect to z, by theorem II, we see that at interior points all six of the partial derivatives of U of second order exist and are continuous, and that in particular,

$$\frac{\partial^2 U}{\partial x^2} = \frac{\partial^2 U}{\partial y^2} = \frac{\partial^2 U}{\partial z^2} = -\frac{4}{3}\pi\varkappa, \quad \text{and} \quad \nabla^2 U = -4\pi\varkappa.$$

If we now write $\varkappa(Q) = [\varkappa(Q) - \varkappa(P_0)] + \varkappa(P_0)$, we see that the potential of a sphere whose density is continuous at P_0 is the sum of the potentials of a sphere whose density vanishes at P_0 and of a sphere with constant density, equal to that at P_0, of the given sphere. We are thus reduced to a consideration of the case in which the density vanishes at P_0. We now suppose that $\varkappa$ satisfies a Hölder condition at P_0. Assuming that the radius of the sphere Σ is less than c, this means that

$$|\varkappa| \leq A r_0^{\alpha}, \qquad r_0 = \overline{P_0 Q}.$$

Under these circumstances, differentiation under the sign of integration is still possible. In fact,

$$J = \left[\iiint\limits_{\Sigma} \varkappa \frac{\partial^2}{\partial z^2}\left(\frac{1}{r}\right) dV\right]_{P_0} = \iiint\limits_{\Sigma} \varkappa \left[\frac{3\zeta^2}{r_0^5} - \frac{1}{r_0^3}\right] dV,$$

where we have taken the origin at P_0, is a convergent integral, by
Lemma III, since $|\zeta| \leq r_0$, and $|\varkappa| \leq A r_0^\alpha$. If P is the point $(0, 0, h)$,
then

$$\frac{Z(P) - Z(P_0)}{h} - J = I,$$

for $h \neq 0$, where

$$I = \iiint\limits_{\Sigma} \varkappa \left[\frac{1}{h}\left(\frac{\zeta - h}{r^3} - \frac{\zeta}{r_0^3}\right) - \frac{3\zeta^2}{r_0^5} + \frac{1}{r_0^3}\right] dV.$$

The integral I is convergent as can be seen by the reasoning applied to J.
We wish to show that I tends to 0 with h. But to do this, we must eliminate h from the denominator. Now

$$\frac{1}{h}\left(\frac{\zeta - h}{r^3} - \frac{\zeta}{r_0^3}\right) = -\frac{1}{r^3} + \frac{\zeta}{h}\left(\frac{1}{r^3} - \frac{1}{r_0^3}\right),$$

and so, using Lemma III (c) and (b), and the values $r_0^2 = \xi^2 + \eta^2 + \zeta^2$,
$r^2 = \xi^2 + \eta^2 + (\zeta - h)^2$, we see that

$$I = \iiint\limits_{\Sigma} \varkappa \left[-\frac{1}{r^3} + \frac{\zeta(2\zeta - h)}{r r_0(r + r_0)}\left(\frac{1}{r^2} + \frac{1}{r r_0} + \frac{1}{r_0^2}\right) - \frac{3\zeta^2}{r_0^5} + \frac{1}{r_0^3}\right] dV.$$

This integral has a meaning for $h = 0$, in fact it is 0, for the integrand
then reduces to 0. If we can show that I is continuous in P at P_0, we
shall know that it approaches 0 as h approaches 0, and it will follow that
the derivative of Z with respect to z exists at P_0 and equals J.

To show that I is continuous at P_0 we follow the usual reasoning.
The integrand is continuous in $\Sigma - \sigma$, apart from the piecewise continuous density, where σ is a small sphere about P_0, provided P is interior
to σ. Hence I will be continuous if the integral over σ can be made
arbitrarily small by sufficiently restricting the radius of σ, independently
of the position of P. This we now show to be possible. Let us call I_σ
the integral over σ.

Now there are two infinities of the integrand of I_σ, one due to the
denominators containing r_0 and the other due to the denominators containing r as a factor. The first are rendered innocuous by the fact that
$|\varkappa| \leq A r_0^\alpha$. It is the term in $\frac{1}{r^3}$ which is troublesome. We must undertake further transformations. We have

$$\left| -\frac{1}{r^3} + \frac{\zeta(2\zeta - h)}{rr_0(r + r_0)}\frac{1}{r^2} \right| = \left| \frac{2\zeta^2 - \zeta h - r_0^2 - rr_0}{r^3 r_0(r + r_0)} \right|$$

$$= \left| \frac{\zeta(\zeta - h) - \xi^2 - \eta^2}{r^3 r_0(r + r_0)} - \frac{1}{r^2(r + r_0)} \right| \leqq \frac{2}{r^2 r_0},$$

since

$$|\zeta| \leqq r_0, \quad |\zeta - h| \leqq r, \quad \xi^2 + \eta^2 \leqq r^2, \quad r + r_0 \geqq r_0.$$

For the remaining terms in the bracket in the integrand, we have

$$\left| \frac{\zeta(2\zeta - h)}{rr_0(r + r_0)}\left(\frac{1}{rr_0} + \frac{1}{r_0^2}\right) - \frac{3\zeta^2}{r_0^5} + \frac{1}{r_0^3} \right| \leqq \frac{1}{r^2 r_0} + \frac{1}{rr_0^2} + \frac{4}{r_0^3}.$$

Hence the integrand of I_σ is dominated by

$$A B r_0^\alpha \left[\frac{4}{r_0^3} + \frac{1}{rr_0^2} + \frac{3}{r^2 r_0} \right] < 4 A B \left[\frac{1}{r_0^{3-\alpha}} + \frac{1}{r_0^{2-\alpha} r} + \frac{1}{r_0^{1-\alpha} r^2} \right].$$

We have a right to assume $\alpha < 1$, for a Hölder condition with one exponent always implies one with a smaller positive exponent. Then in the part of σ in which $r_0 \leqq r$, the last written function is only increased by replacing r by r_0. That is, it is less than $\frac{12 A B}{r_0^{3-\alpha}}$. In the rest of σ it is less than $\frac{12 A B}{r^{3-\alpha}}$ Then $|I_\sigma|$ is certainly less than the sum of the integrals of these two functions taken over the whole of σ, and since, by Lemma III, the first of these integrals is the greater, we have

$$|I_\sigma| < 24 A B \iiint_\sigma \frac{dV}{r_0^{3-\alpha}}.$$

As this integral is convergent, and independent of P, it follows by Lemma I that I_σ vanishes with the radius of σ, uniformly as to P. Thus I is continuous, and the existence of the derivative is proved. Further

$$\frac{\partial Z}{\partial z} = \frac{\partial^2 U}{\partial z^2} = J.$$

In the same way the existence of the other partial derivatives of U of the second order at P_0 can be proved. In particular, we have for the *Laplacian, $V^2 U$, of U*, the value obtained by interchanging x, y, z in J, and adding the results,

$$V^2 U = \iiint_\Sigma \varkappa \left[\frac{3(\xi^2 + \eta^2 + \zeta^2)}{r_0^5} - \frac{3}{r_0^3} \right] dV = 0.$$

This is for the potential with a density satisfying a Hölder condition and vanishing at P_0. If we add to the distribution one of constant density throughout the sphere, we have the result holding for a distribution with continuous density in a sphere, and satisfying a Hölder condition at P_0: *the derivatives exist, and*

$$V^2 U = -4\pi \varkappa(P_0).$$

Finally, if we add the potentials of distributions outside the sphere, nothing is contributed to the Laplacian, and the same equation holds. This differential equation, which contains Laplace's as a special case, is known as *Poisson's equation*[1]. We sum up the results on the derivatives of second order in

Theorem III. *Let U be the potential of a distribution with piecewise continuous density $\varkappa$ in a regular region V. Then at any interior point P_0 of V, at which $\varkappa$ satisfies a Hölder condition, the derivatives of second order of U exist and satisfy Poissons' equation*

$$\nabla^2 U = - 4\pi\varkappa.$$

The theorem leaves unmentioned the situation at boundary points of V. But here, in general, the derivatives of second order will not exist. It is clear that they cannot all be continuous, for as we pass from an exterior to an interior point through the boundary where $\varkappa$ is not 0, $\nabla^2 U$ experiences a break of $- 4\pi\varkappa$.

Poisson's equation enables us to find the density when we know the potential.

Exercises.

3. Show that a continuous function of x, which has derivatives in an interval including the origin except at the origin, cannot have a derivative at the origin unless the limits of the derivatives to either side are the same at the origin. Hence show that there are cases in which the second derivatives of the potential of a volume distribution do not exist at boundary points.

4. Show that a condition lighter than a Hölder condition is sufficient for the existence of the second derivative with respect to z of the potential of a volume distribution, namely the following. Denote by $\bar{\varkappa}$ the average of the values of $\varkappa$ on the circle through Q whose axis is the parallel to the z-axis through P_0, *i.e.* with the axes employed above,

$$\bar{\varkappa} = \frac{1}{2\pi} \int_0^{2\pi} \varkappa \, (r_0 \sin\vartheta' \cos\varphi, \; r_0 \sin\vartheta' \sin\varphi, \; r_0 \cos\vartheta') \, d\varphi, \qquad Q = (r_0, \, \vartheta', \, \varphi').$$

Then it is sufficient that $\bar{\varkappa}$ satisfy a Hölder condition at P_0. Verify also that the lighter condition is sufficient: there exists a continuous function $\delta(r)$, defined on some interval $0 < r \leq a$, such that $|\bar{\varkappa}| \leq \delta(r_0)$, that $\dfrac{\delta(r)}{r}$ never increases with r, and that

$$\int_0^a \frac{\delta(r)}{r} \, dr$$

is convergent.

---

[1] POISSON, *Remarques sur une équation qui se présente dans la théorie de l'attraction des sphéroïdes.* Nouveau Bulletin de la Société philomathique de Paris, Vol. III (1813), pp. 388—392. See also BACHARACH, *Geschichte der Potentialtheorie*, Göttingen, 1883, pp. 6—13.

4. Lemmas on Surfaces.

We shall limit ourselves to distributions on regular surface elements S, which are subject to the further restriction that the function $z = f(x, y)$, (x, y) in R, giving the standard representation (see p. 105), *shall have continuous partial derivatives of the second order in R*. These are bounded in absolute value by some constant M.

The results attained will hold for regular closed surfaces which are sufficiently smooth, because the lines breaking such surfaces up into regular elements may be drawn in a variety of ways, so as to avoid any given point of the surface under investigation. Since potentials are analytic in free space, it makes no difference what the character of the surface is except in the neighborhood of the point under investigation. Thus we may conclude that our results subsist for any regular surface, provided we keep away from the edges. Certain results subsist here also, like the continuity of the potentials of surface distributions. But in the enunciation of the results we shall suppose that we are dealing with an interior point of the surface.

It will be convenient to have a notation for the point of the surface S in whose neighborhood we are investigating the potential; let it be p. We shall find it convenient to use a system of axes in which the (ξ, η)-plane is tangent to S at p, this point being taken as origin. If we wish then to study how the potential changes as p moves on S, it will be necessary to think of the axes as changing with p. Certain inequalities derived will then hold *uniformly as to p*, when they can be expressed in terms of constants which are independent of the position of p, at least in a certain portion of S.

One such inequality we derive at once, and it will illustrate the idea. We have seen in Chapter IV, Theorems IV and VII (pages 101, 108) that S can be broken up into a finite number of regions of triangular form, for each of which a standard representation is possible with any orientation of the axes in which the ζ-axis makes an angle greater than 70^0 with no normal to the portion of S in question. Moreover, these pieces can be so taken that the normals vary in direction on each by less than 15^0. If p is a point of such an element, and the axes are taken in the tangent and normal position at p, the normals over the element in which p lies as well as over the adjacent elements, will deviate in direction from the ζ-axis by less than 30^0, so that we shall have a standard representation with this position of the axes which certainly holds in a neighborhood of p. In fact, if c denotes the minimum distance between any two non-adjacent triangular elements of S, such a neighborhood of p in which the standard representation holds, will include all of S within a distance c of p. And c will be independent of the position of p. *Thus the standard* *representation with the tangent-normal system of axes exists, uniformly as to p.*

More than this, the function $\zeta = \varphi\,(\xi,\,\eta)$ giving the standard representation of the portion S_1 of S within a sphere of radius c about p will have partial derivatives of the second order which are bounded in absolute value by a constant M, independent of the position of p. This is most easily seen by using the system of direction cosines relating the $(x,\,y,\,z)$-axes, in terms of which the defining standard representation of S is given, with the $(\xi,\,\eta,\,\zeta)$-axes in the tangent normal position at p. We may assume that both systems are right hand ones, and that they have the same origin, p. Then

$$\xi = l_1 x + m_1 y + n_1 f\,(x,\,y),$$
$$\eta = l_2 x + m_2 y + n_2 f\,(x,\,y),$$
$$\zeta = l_3 x + m_3 y + n_3 f\,(x,\,y).$$

We know that when $(\xi,\,\eta)$ is in the projection of S on the $(\xi,\,\eta)$-plane, these equations have a unique single-valued continuously differentiable solution $\zeta = \varphi\,(\xi,\,\eta)$, by Chapter IV, Theorem VII, (p. 108). And it is shown in the works on the Calculus[1] that the derivatives of φ are computed by the ordinary rules for implicit functions. Keeping in mind that in the determinant of the direction cosines, any element is equal to its cofactor, we find

$$\frac{\partial^2 \zeta}{\partial \xi^2} = - \frac{(m_2 + n_2 f_y)^2\, f_{xx} - 2\,(m_2 + n_2 f_y)\,(l_2 + n_2 f_x)\, f_{xy} + (l_2 + n_2 f_x)^2\, f_{yy}}{(l_3 f_x + m_3 f_y - n_3)^3}.$$

As f_x, f_y are continuous in the closed region R, they are bounded in absolute value, say by N, and the derivatives of f of the second order are bounded by M_1. As to the denominator, it is the cube of the cosine of the angle between the normal to S_1 and the ζ-axis, multiplied by $\sqrt{1 + f_x^2 + f_y^2}$ and as this angle never exceeds 30^0, the denominator is never less in absolute value than $\left(\dfrac{\sqrt 3}{2}\right)^3$. Hence

$$\left|\frac{\partial^2 \zeta}{\partial \xi^2}\right| \leqq 4\,(1 + N)\,M_1 \left(\frac{2}{\sqrt 3}\right)^3,$$

a quantity independent of p, which we call M. Exactly the same considerations apply to the other two derivatives of ζ of second order, the same constant M being available.

We may now enunciate

Lemma V. *If S_1 be the portion of S in a sphere of radius c about p, and if $\zeta = \varphi\,(\xi,\,\eta)$ is the equation of S_1 referred to axes tangent and normal to S at p, then*

$$|\,\zeta\,| \leqq M\,(\xi^2 + \eta^2),$$

for all points of S_1, where M is independent of p.

---

[1] See, for instance, OSGOOD, *Advanced Calculus*, Chapter V, especially § 9.

We have merely to expand the function $\zeta = \varphi\,(\xi,\,\eta)$ in a Taylor series about the origin, with remainder, remembering that the linear terms vanish because of the position of the axes:

$$\zeta = \tfrac{1}{2}\big[\overline{\varphi_{\xi\xi}}\,\xi^2 + 2\,\overline{\varphi_{\xi\eta}}\,\xi\eta + \overline{\varphi_{\eta\eta}}\,\eta^2\big].$$

Hence, using the bound M for the derivatives, and Lemma IV (a), we have

$$|\,\zeta\,| \leqq M\,(\xi^2 + \eta^2)$$

and the required inequality is established.

The density, $\sigma = \sigma\,(q)$, of a surface distribution on S at a point q may be regarded as a function of ξ and η, namely the coördinates of the projection of q on the $(\xi,\,\eta)$-plane. Let γ denote the angle between the normal at q and the ζ-axis, *i. e.* the normal at p. We then have

Lemma VI. *If σ satisfies a Hölder condition at p, the function $\sigma \sec \gamma$ also satisfies a Hölder condition at p. If σ satisfies a uniform Hölder condition on a portion of S, then $\sigma \sec \gamma$ satisfies a Hölder condition, uniformly as to p.*

As $\sec \gamma$, that is, $\sqrt{1 + \varphi_\xi^2 + \varphi_\eta^2}$, has bounded derivatives at points of S in the sphere of radius c about p, it satisfies a Hölder condition at p with exponent $\alpha = 1$. Let c be less than one, and less than the smaller of the two values, one of which assures the standard representation of the portion S_1 of S within a sphere of radius c about p, and the other of which assures the inequality of the Hölder condition. Then, since $\gamma = 0$ at p,

$$|\,\sigma\,(q) \sec \gamma - \sigma\,(p) \sec 0\,| = |\,[\sigma\,(q) - \sigma\,(p)]\sec \gamma + \sigma\,(p)\,[\sec \gamma - \sec 0]\,|$$
$$\leqq \sec 30^\circ A\,r^\alpha + \max |\,\sigma\,|\,A'r, \quad r = \overline{pq}.$$

If β is the smaller of the two numbers α and 1, then since $r \leqq 1$, $r^\beta \geqq r^\alpha$, $r^\beta \geqq r$, and

$$|\,\sigma\,(q) \sec \gamma - \sigma\,(p) \sec 0\,| \leqq A''r^\beta \quad \text{for } r \leqq c.$$

Thus the Hölder condition obtains. Moreover, in any region in which the Hölder condition on σ is uniform, all the constants involved are independent of the position of p. Thus the lemma is established.

Remark. In the inequality for the Hölder condition, we may replace r by its projection r' on the $(\xi,\,\eta)$-plane if we wish. As

$$r^2 = \xi^2 + \eta^2 + \zeta^2 = r'^2 + \zeta^2 \leqq r'^2\,(1 + M^2 r'^2) \leqq r'^2\,(1 + M^2 c^2),$$

we should only have to replace A'' by the constant

$$A''\,(1 + M^2 c^2)^{\beta/2}.$$

5. The Potentials of Surface Distributions.

Let S denote a surface subject to the restrictions of the last section, and let the density be piecewise continuous on S; that is, let it be a piecewise continuous function of the coördinates x and y of the projection of q on the (x, y)-plane of the standard representation of S, in the region R. We consider the potential

$$U = \iint_S \frac{\sigma}{r^3}\, dS = \iint_{S'} \sigma \sec \gamma \frac{1}{r^3}\, dS',$$

where S' is the projection of S on the (x, y)-plane of the standard representation of S as a whole. As the distance r between $P\,(x, y, z)$ and the variable point $q\,(\xi, \eta, \zeta)$ of S is never less than its projection r' on the (x, y)-plane, we see at once that the integral for U is convergent, by the Lemmas II and III (b). And by reasoning similar to that applied to the volume distributions, we see that U is continuous. This holds for boundary points of R as well as for interior points, for we may extend the region S', defining σ as 0 at the points annexed. Thus we have

Theorem IV. *The potential U of the given surface distribution exists at the points of S, and is continuous throughout space.*

Tangential derivatives. In investigating the derivatives of U, we shall make use of the tangent-normal system of axes. Restricting ourselves to a portion of S contained in a sphere of radius c about one of its points p, we have for any tangent-normal position of the axes, a single representation for the whole of this piece. As the potential of the rest of S is analytic in a neighborhood of p, we may neglect it, and assume once and for all that the whole of S is given by a function $\zeta = \varphi\,(\xi, \eta)$ having the properties derived in the last section, for axes tangent and normal to S at any of its points.

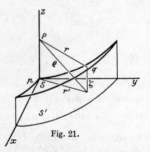

Fig. 21.

We first investigate the derivatives of U taken in any fixed direction parallel to the tangent plane at p, an interior point of S. We choose the x-axis in this direction, and the y-axis in a perpendicular tangent direction (fig. 21). Let P be a point of the z-axis. Then, for $z \neq 0$.

$$\frac{\partial U}{\partial x} = \iint_S \sigma \frac{\xi}{r^3}\, dS = \iint_{S'} \sigma \sec \gamma \frac{\xi}{r^3}\, dS',$$

$$r^2 = \xi^2 + \eta^2 + (\zeta - z)^2 = r'^2 + (\zeta - z)^2,$$

r' being the projection of r on the (x, y)-plane. We are interested in the existence of a limit for this derivative as z approaches 0.

In the first place, the mere continuity of σ is insufficient to insure the existence of such a limit.(see the Exercise, below). We shall therefore impose upon σ a Hölder condition. We shall show that the limit then exists, following the method used in § 3 to prove the continuity of certain integrals. Let σ' be a small circle in the (x, y)-plane about p. If we write

$$\frac{\partial U}{\partial x} = I + J, \quad I = \iint_{\sigma'} \sigma \sec \gamma \frac{\xi}{r^3} dS', \quad J = \iint_{S'-\sigma'} \sigma \sec \gamma \frac{\xi}{r^3} dS',$$

then for any fixed σ', J is continuous, and if $\varepsilon > 0$ be given, there will be a δ such that for $0 < |z_1| < \delta$, $0 < |z_2| < \delta$. $|J(z_2) - J(z_1)| < \frac{\varepsilon}{3}$. Consequently, if we can show that σ' can be taken so small that $|I| < \frac{\varepsilon}{3}$, independently of z, it will follow that for $0 < |z_1| < \delta$, $0 < |z_2| < \delta$,

$$\left| \left(\frac{\partial U}{\partial x} \right)_{z_1} - \left(\frac{\partial U}{\partial x} \right)_{z_2} \right| < \varepsilon.$$

This is the Cauchy condition for the existence of a limit.

To prove the desired property of I, we write $I = I_1 + I_2$, where

$$I_1 = \sigma(p) \iint_{\sigma'} \frac{\xi}{r^3} dS', \quad I_2 = \iint_{\sigma'} [\sigma(q) \sec \gamma - \sigma(p)] \frac{\xi}{r^3} dS'.$$

The first we compare with

$$\sigma(p) \iint_{\sigma'} \frac{\xi}{\varrho^3} dS', \quad \varrho^2 = \xi^2 + \eta^2 + z^2 = r'^2 + z^2.$$

This is 0, since the integrand has equal and opposite values at (ξ, η) and $(-\xi, \eta)$. Hence

$$I_1 = \sigma(p) \iint_{\sigma'} \xi \left(\frac{1}{r^3} - \frac{1}{\varrho^3} \right) dS' = \sigma(p) \iint_{\sigma'} \frac{\xi \zeta (2z - \zeta)}{r \varrho (r + \varrho)} \left[\frac{1}{r^2} + \frac{1}{r \varrho} + \frac{1}{\varrho^2} \right] dS'.$$

And so, since $|\xi| \leq r'$, $|\zeta| \leq M r'^2$, by Lemma V, $|2z - \zeta| \leq r + \varrho$, $r \geq r'$, $\varrho \geq r'$,

$$|I_1| \leq \max |\sigma| \iint_{\sigma'} \frac{dS'}{r'}.$$

This integral is convergent, and so vanishes with σ', by Lemmas III (b) and I.

As to I_2, Lemma VI enables us to write at once

$$|I_2| \leq A \iint_{\sigma'} \frac{dS'}{r'^{2-\alpha}},$$

and this also approaches 0 with the radius of σ'. The existence of the limit of the tangential derivative of U is thus assured. Moreover, a review of the steps will show that if a uniform Hölder condition obtains for the density on a certain portion of S, closed, and containing no boundary points of S, the inequalities obtained can be made independent of the position of p. We thus arrive at

Theorem V. *If the density σ of the surface distribution on S satisfies a Hölder condition at p, the derivative of U at P, in the direction of any tangent to S at p, approaches a limit as P, approaches p along the normal. If the Hölder condition holds uniformly over a closed portion of S which contains no boundary points of S, the limits of such derivatives are approached uniformly as to p on such a portion.*

Exercise.

Let S denote the surface of a plane circular lamina, in the (x, y)-plane, the origin being at the center. At $P(0, 0, z)$,

$$\frac{\partial U}{\partial x} = \iint_S \sigma \frac{\xi}{r^3} dS' = \iint_S \sigma \frac{r' \cos \varphi}{r^3} r' dr' d\varphi .$$

For σ, let us take a product $\sigma = f(r') \cos \varphi$, where $f(r')$ is never negative. Then, as $r^2 = r'^2 + z^2$ is independent of φ, we can carry out the integration with respect to φ, and we find

$$\frac{\partial U}{\partial x} \geqq \pi \int_{\frac{a}{2^m}}^{a} \frac{f(r') r'^2 dr'}{(r'^2 + z^2)^{3/2}} = \pi \sum_{n=1}^{m} \int_{\frac{a}{2^n}}^{\frac{a}{2^{n-1}}} \frac{f(r') r'^2 dr'}{(r'^2 + z^2)^{3/2}} ,$$

if a is the radius of the lamina. Show that if $f(r')$ is continuous and approaches 0 at the origin, but exceeds $\frac{1}{n}$ in the interval $\left(\frac{a}{2^{n+1}}, \frac{a}{2^n} \right)$, the above sum can·be made arbitrarily great by taking m large enough and $|z|$ small enough. Thus, continuity of the density is not enough to insure the existence of a limit for the tangential derivative.

Normal Derivatives. The study of the normal derivatives is simpler. At first, in addition to the piecewise continuity of σ, we shall assume simply that σ is continuous at p. With the same position of the axes (fig. 21), and P on the normal through p, we have, for $z \neq 0$,

$$\frac{\partial U}{\partial z} = \iint_S \sigma \frac{\zeta - z}{r^3} dS = \iint_{S'} \sigma \sec \gamma \frac{\zeta - z}{r^3} dS' .$$

Consider, as a basis of comparison, the potential U' of the plane lamina, occupying the area S' of the projection of S, with density $\sigma \sec \gamma$:

$$\frac{\partial U'}{\partial z} = - \iint_{S'} \sigma \sec \gamma \frac{z}{\varrho^3} dS' = I_1 + I_2, \quad \varrho^2 = \xi^2 + \eta^2 + z^2,$$

where

$$I_1 = - \iint_{\sigma'} \sigma \sec \gamma \frac{z}{\varrho^3} dS', \quad I_2 = - \iint_{S'-\sigma'} \sigma \sec \gamma \frac{z}{\varrho^3} dS',$$

σ' being a small circle about the origin. For fixed σ', I_2 is continuous in z, uniformly as to p, and vanishes for $z = 0$. I_1 can be written, using a mean value of $\sigma \sec \gamma$,

$$I_1 = - \iint_{\Omega} \sigma \sec \gamma \, d\Omega = - \overline{\sigma \sec \gamma} \, \Omega,$$

Ω being the solid angle subtended at $P(0, 0, z)$ by the surface of the circle σ', counted as positive if $z > 0$, and negative if $z < 0$. The limit of Ω, as z approaches 0 from above is 2π, and as z approaches 0 from below, is -2π. If $\varepsilon > 0$ is given, we restrict σ' so that for q in σ',

$$|\sigma(q) \sec \gamma - \sigma(p)| < \frac{\varepsilon}{6\pi},$$

and then, with σ' fixed, we select $\delta > 0$ so that for $0 < z < \delta$,

$$|\Omega - 2\pi| < \frac{\varepsilon}{3 \max |\sigma(q) \sec \gamma|}.$$

Then

$$|I_1 + 2\pi\sigma(p)| = |\overline{\sigma \sec \gamma} \, \Omega - 2\pi\sigma(p)|$$

$$= \overline{\sigma(q) \sec \gamma} \, (\Omega - 2\pi) + 2\pi [\overline{\sigma(q) \sec \gamma} - \sigma(p)] < \frac{2}{3}\varepsilon.$$

If we further restrict $|z|$, if necessary, so that I_2 differs from its limit, 0, by less than $\frac{\varepsilon}{3}$, we see that

$$\left| \frac{\partial U'}{\partial z} + 2\pi\sigma(p) \right| < \varepsilon.$$

Thus the derivative of U' with respect to z approaches the limit $-2\pi\sigma(p)$ as P approaches p along the positive z-axis. Similarly, it approaches $+2\pi\sigma(p)$ as P approaches p along the negative z-axis. It is readily verified that the approach is uniform with respect to p in any closed portion of S, including none of the boundary points, in which σ is continuous.

We now return to the potential U of the curved lamina, and consider the difference

$$\frac{\partial U}{\partial z} - \frac{\partial U'}{\partial z} = \iint_{S'} \sigma \sec \gamma \left[\frac{\zeta - z}{r^3} + \frac{z}{\varrho^3} \right] dS'$$

$$= \iint_{S'} \sigma \sec \gamma \left[\frac{\zeta}{r^3} - z \left(\frac{1}{r^3} - \frac{1}{\varrho^3} \right) \right] dS'.$$

According to the usual reasoning, this integral is continuous at $z = 0$, if the integral extended over a small circle σ' about p vanishes with σ', uniformly as to P. But this can be shown just as was the similar fact with respect to an integral arising in connection with the tangential derivatives.

Thus the difference of the derivatives of U and U' coincides with an integral which is continuous in z. The value of this integral for $z = 0$ is

$$\iint\limits_{S'} \sigma \sec \gamma \, \frac{\zeta}{r^3} \, dS' = \iint\limits_{S} \sigma \frac{\zeta}{r^3} \, dS = \iint\limits_{S} \sigma \left(\frac{\partial}{\partial z} \frac{1}{r} \right)_p dS \,,$$

which integral is obviously convergent, since $\left| \dfrac{\zeta}{r^3} \right| \leqq \dfrac{M}{r'}$. Hence we have for the limits of $\dfrac{\partial U'}{\partial z}$ as z approaches 0 from above and below respectively,

$$\left(\frac{\partial U}{\partial z} \right)_+ + 2\pi\sigma(p) = \left(\frac{\partial U}{\partial z} \right)_- - 2\pi\sigma(p) = \iint\limits_{S} \sigma \left(\frac{\partial}{\partial z} \frac{1}{r} \right)_p dS \,.$$

The limits are approached uniformly as to p for any closed interior portion of S on which σ is continuous. We now express the results in terms free from any system of axes. Let n denote the direction of the normal to S, in the sense agreed upon as positive. By the derivative of $\dfrac{1}{r}$ with respect to n, we mean the derivative at a point of S, in the direction of the positive normal, the coördinates x, y, z of P being the variables.

Theorem VI. *If the density σ of the distribution on S is continuous at p, the normal derivative of the potential U approaches limits as P approaches p along the normal to S at p from either side. These limits are*

$$\frac{\partial U}{\partial n_+} = -2\pi\sigma(p) + \iint\limits_{S} \sigma \frac{\partial}{\partial n} \frac{1}{r} \, dS \,,$$

$$\frac{\partial U}{\partial n_-} = +2\pi\sigma(p) + \iint\limits_{S} \sigma \frac{\partial}{\partial n} \frac{1}{r} \, dS \,.$$

These limits are approached uniformly as to p on any closed portion of S, containing no boundary points of S, on which the density is continuous.

Subtracting the second limit from the first, we have

$$\frac{\partial U}{\partial n_+} - \frac{\partial U}{\partial n_-} = -4\pi\sigma \,.$$

The significance of this equation is that it enables us to determine the density when we know the potential, or even if we know only the normal derivatives of the potential, or the normal components of the force.

Derivatives in any Direction. Since the derivative of U in any fixed direction is a homogeneous linear function of the derivatives in the direction of two tangents and a normal, it follows that any such derivative approaches a limit along the normal at a point p where the density satisfies a Hölder condition. And more, that if S_1 is a closed part of S not containing boundary points of S, on which the density satisfies a uniform Hölder condition, the derivative on U in a fixed direction approaches its limits uniformly along normals at all points of S_1. We shall now prove

Theorem VII. *Let σ satisfy a Hölder condition uniformly on S. Let V be a closed region of space partly bounded by S, but containing no boundary points of S, and such that a point P can approach S from only one side while remaining in V. Then the potential U of the distribution of density σ on S is continuously differentiable in V.*

We recall that this means (see p. 113) that if any one of the partial derivatives of U, say

$$F(P) = \frac{\partial U}{\partial x},$$

is defined on S in terms of its limiting values, then $F(P)$ is continuous in the closed region V. Now we have seen in the previous chapter that $F(P)$ is continuous at all points of free space, and such are all points of V except those on S. So it only remains to verify[1] that $F(P)$ is continuous at each point p of S.

We observe first that there is a sphere σ_1 about p, such that the points of V within σ_1 are simply covered by the normals to S at points near p. This fact is a consequence of the theorem on implicit functions[2]. Let X, Y, Z, be the coördinates of a point P of V, referred to axes tangent and normal to S at p. The equations of the normal at the point (ξ, η, ζ) of S are

$$\frac{x - \xi}{-\varphi_\xi} = \frac{y - \eta}{-\varphi_\eta} = \frac{z - \varphi(\xi, \eta)}{1},$$

where $\zeta = \varphi(\xi, \eta)$ is the equation of S referred to those axes. The normal will pass through (X, Y, Z) provided

$$(1) \qquad \begin{aligned} X &= \xi - \varphi_\xi (Z - \varphi), \\ Y &= \eta - \varphi_\eta (Z - \varphi). \end{aligned}$$

We wish to know that these equations have exactly one solution (ξ, η) for each set of values of X, Y, Z, at least in some neighborhood of the origin. Now they have the solution $(0, 0)$ when $X = Y = Z = 0$, and

---

[1] Such verification is needed. The mere fact that a function, continuous in an open region bounded by a surface S, approaches continuous limiting values along normals, does not guarantee that the function is continuous at points of S. A simple example illustrating this situation in two dimensions is given by $F(P) = \dfrac{2xy}{(x^2 + y^2)}$. The important element in the present case is that the approach along the normals is uniform.

[2] See Osgood, *Lehrbuch der Funktionentheorie*, Chap. II, § 5.

because $\varphi(\xi, \eta)$ has continuous partial derivatives of the second order, the functional determinant

$$\begin{vmatrix} \dfrac{\partial X}{\partial \xi}, & \dfrac{\partial Y}{\partial \xi} \\[2ex] \dfrac{\partial X}{\partial \eta}, & \dfrac{\partial Y}{\partial \eta} \end{vmatrix} = \begin{vmatrix} 1 - \varphi_{\xi\xi}(Z - \varphi) + \varphi_\xi^2, & -\varphi_{\xi\eta}(Z - \varphi) + \varphi_\xi \varphi_\eta \\[2ex] -\varphi_{\xi\eta}(Z - \varphi) + \varphi_\xi \varphi_\eta, & 1 - \varphi_{\eta\eta}(Z - \varphi) + \varphi_\eta^2 \end{vmatrix}$$

is continuous in the neighborhood of p, and reduces to 1 when all the variables vanish. Thus the hypotheses of the theorem on implicit functions are satisfied, and there is a neighborhood N_1 and a neighborhood N_2 of the origin such that when (X, Y, Z) is in N_1, there is one and only one solution (ξ, η) of the equations (1) in the neighborhood N_2. Any sphere σ_1 about p and lying in N_1 will serve our purpose.

Now let σ_1 be diminished, if necessary, so that the difference between the value of $F(P)$ at any point P of V in σ_1 differs from its limit at the foot of the normal through P by less than $\frac{\varepsilon}{3}$. This is possible because of the uniformity of the approach of $F(P)$ to its limiting values along normals to S. About a point of the normal at p we construct a sphere σ_2, interior to V and to σ_1, such that within it, $F(P)$ varies by less than $\frac{\varepsilon}{3}$. It follows that within the region covered by the normals to S, corresponding to the neighborhood N_2, and meeting σ_2, $F(P)$ differs from $F(p)$ by less than ε. As the reasoning holds for any $\varepsilon > 0$, $F(P)$ is continuous at p, as was to be proved.

6. The Potentials of Double Distributions.

We consider surfaces S subject to the conditions imposed in § 4, and moments μ which are piecewise continuous. We study the potential of the double distribution

$$U = \iint_S \mu \frac{\partial}{\partial \nu} \frac{1}{r} dS = \iint_{S'} \mu \sec \gamma \frac{\partial}{\partial \nu} \frac{1}{r} dS',$$

S' being the projection of S on the (ξ, η)-plane. Here, if $\cos \alpha$, $\cos \beta$, $\cos \gamma$ are the direction cosines of the normal to S at $q(\xi, \eta, \zeta)$, the normal derivative means

$$\frac{\partial}{\partial \nu} \frac{1}{r} = \left(\frac{\partial}{\partial \xi} \frac{1}{r}\right) \cos \alpha + \left(\frac{\partial}{\partial \eta} \frac{1}{r}\right) \cos \beta + \left(\frac{\partial}{\partial \zeta} \frac{1}{r}\right) \cos \gamma,$$

and as

$$\frac{\cos \alpha}{\varphi_\xi} = \frac{\cos \beta}{\varphi_\eta} = \frac{\cos \gamma}{-1},$$

this may be written

(2) $$\frac{\partial}{\partial \nu} \frac{1}{r} = \frac{(z - \zeta) - (x - \xi) \varphi_\xi - (y - \eta) \varphi_\eta}{r^3} \cos \gamma.$$

We notice first that U has a meaning when P is a point of S. For, taking $x = y = z = 0$,

$$U = - \iint\limits_{S'} \mu \, \frac{\zeta - \varphi_\xi \xi - \varphi_\eta \eta}{r^3} \, dS'.$$

If we apply the law of the mean for functions of two variables to the numerator of the integrand, remembering that φ_ξ and φ_η vanish at the origin, and that $\varphi_{\xi\xi}$, $\varphi_{\xi\eta}$, $\varphi_{\eta\eta}$ are bounded in absolute value by M, we find that the numerator is bounded in absolute value by $M\,(\xi^2 + \eta^2)$ $= M r'^2$. The integral is therefore convergent, by Lemmas II and III (b). The potential U is defined on S by the integral which represents it elsewhere, this integral, although improper, being convergent.

However, U, thus defined, is discontinuous at the points of S, experiencing a finite break there — unless the density happens to vanish at the point of S considered. The problem can at once be reduced to the problem of simple distributions. For, the derivatives of $\frac{1}{r}$ with respect to ξ, η, ζ being the negatives of those with respect to x, y, z, U may be written

$$(3) \qquad U = - \iint\limits_S \mu \cos\alpha \, \frac{\partial}{\partial x} \frac{1}{r} \, dS - \iint\limits_S \mu \cos\beta \, \frac{\partial}{\partial y} \frac{1}{r} \, dS$$
$$- \iint\limits_S \mu \cos\gamma \, \frac{\partial}{\partial z} \frac{1}{r} \, dS,$$

so that U is the negative of the sum of two tangential derivatives of surface distributions and one normal derivative of a surface distribution, with densities

$$\mu \cos\alpha, \qquad \mu \cos\beta, \qquad \mu \cos\gamma.$$

Since $\varphi\,(\xi, \eta)$ has continuous derivatives of the second order, the cosines satisfy Hölder conditions with exponent 1. The first two reduce to 0 at p, and so, μ being bounded, their products by μ also satisfy Hölder conditions at p. If μ is continuous at p, $\mu \cos\gamma$ is continuous at p, and this is sufficient in the case of the normal derivative for a limiting value. Hence we see that U approaches a limit as P approaches p along the normal to S at p if the moment is continuous there, from either side. The first two integrals are continuous. The limiting values of the third, on the other hand, are its value at p less $2\pi\mu\,(p) \cos\gamma$, and plus $2\pi\mu\,(p) \cos\gamma$, according as the approach is from the positive or negative side of S, by Theorem VI. But as $\cos\gamma = 1$ at p, this gives us the following result:

Theorem VIII. *As P approaches a point p of S along the normal to S at p, from either side, the moment μ being continuous at p, the potential U of the double distribution on S approaches limits, given by*

$$U_+ = 2\pi\mu\,(p) + U_0, \qquad U_- = - 2\pi\mu\,(p) + U_0.$$

On any closed portion of S containing no boundary points of S, on which μ is continuous, these limits are approached uniformly.

The last follows from the fact that the inequalities controlling the approach can be chosen independently of the position of p on the portion of S in question. It is a matter of mere detail to pick these up, and verify the fact.

If we subtract the limiting values of U, we have

$$U_+ - U_- = 4\pi\mu.$$

Thus, knowing the limiting values of the potential, we are enabled to determine the moment.

We may apply the same reasoning as that used in the proof of Theorem VII to establish

Theorem IX. *Let μ be continuous on S. Let V be a closed region of space partly bounded by S, but containing no boundary points of S, and such that a point P can approach S from only one side, while remaining in V. Then the potential U of the double distribution of moment μ on S is continuous in the closed region V, when defined on S by means of its limiting values.*

Normal Derivatives. For the existence of limits for the derivatives of the potential of a double distribution, more than continuity of the moment is required. We shall here confine ourselves to a study of the normal derivatives, which are the most important in potential theory, and derive two results concerning them.

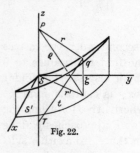
Fig. 22.

The first requires only the continuity of the moment, and although it does not assert the existence of a limit for a normal derivative, it asserts the existence of a limit for the difference of the normal derivatives on opposite sides of S. Taking the axes in the usual tangent-normal position at p, we form the difference of the derivative of U with respect to z at the point $P(0, 0, z)$ and at the point $T(0, 0, -z)$ (fig. 22). The distance qP we denote as usual by r, and the distance qT we shall denote by t, so that

$$r^2 = \xi^2 + \eta^2 + (\zeta - z)^2 = r'^2 + (\zeta - z)^2, \qquad t^2 = r'^2 + (\zeta + z)^2.$$

The difference of the derivatives is then

$$D = \iint\limits_{S'} \mu \left[\frac{\partial}{\partial z} \left(\frac{\partial}{\partial \nu} \frac{1}{r} \right) \right]_{-z}^{z} \sec\gamma \, dS',$$

or, using the value (2) for the normal derivative, and carrying out the steps indicated,

$$D = \iint\limits_{S'} \mu \left[\frac{1}{t^3} - \frac{1}{r^3} - 3\left(\frac{1}{t^5} - \frac{1}{r^5}\right)(z^2 + \zeta(\zeta - \xi\varphi_\xi - \eta\varphi_\eta)) \right.$$
$$\left. - 3\left(\frac{1}{t^5} + \frac{1}{r^5}\right)(2\zeta - \xi\varphi_\xi - \eta\varphi_\eta)\, z \right] dS'.$$

Let us now reduce the moment at p to 0 by the subtraction of the potential of the double distribution on S with constant moment, namely the value of μ at p. This potential is a constant times the solid angle subtended at P by S, and as we saw in Exercise 4, § 7, Chapter III (p. 69), may be regarded as analytic at interior points of S if we permit it to be many valued. In this case, the branches will differ by constants, and so the derivatives will be continuous. Hence the subtraction of such a potential will not affect the limit, as z approaches 0, of the difference D.

We notice also that if the integral giving D were extended over $S' - \sigma'$, where σ' is a small circle about p, it would vanish in the limit as z approached 0. Thus without affecting the limit of D we may assume that μ vanishes at p, and that the field of integration is an arbitrarily small circle about p. It follows that if the integral D', with the same integrand as D, but extended over a circle σ' of radius a, tends to 0 with a, uniformly as to z, the limit of D, as z approaches 0, will be 0. We now prove that this is the case. We write

$$D' = I_1 - 3I_2 - 3I_3 - 3I_4,$$

$$I_1 = \iint\limits_{\sigma'} \mu A_1\, dS', \quad I_2 = \iint\limits_{\sigma'} \mu A_2\, dS', \quad I_3 = \iint\limits_{\sigma'} \mu A_3\, dS',$$

$$I_4 = \iint\limits_{\sigma'} \mu A_4\, dS',$$

$$A_1 = \frac{1}{t^3} - \frac{1}{r^3}, \quad A_2 = \left(\frac{1}{t^5} - \frac{1}{r^5}\right)z^2, \quad A_3 = \left(\frac{1}{t^5} - \frac{1}{r^5}\right)\zeta(\zeta - \xi\varphi_\xi - \eta\varphi_\eta),$$

$$A_4 = \left(\frac{1}{t^5} + \frac{1}{r^5}\right)(2\zeta - \xi\varphi_\xi - \eta\varphi_\eta)\, z.$$

The end will be attained if we show that the integrals I_i approach 0 with a, uniformly as to z.

This may be done by the introduction of the distance ϱ from P to the projection (ξ, η) of q,

$$\varrho^2 = r'^2 + z^2.$$

Then

$$\left| \frac{r}{\varrho} - 1 \right| \leq \frac{r'^2}{r'^2 + z^2} M \, |2z - \zeta|,$$

and if $-\delta \leq z \leq \delta$, δ and a can be chosen so small that uniformly as to z in this interval, the quantity on the right is less, say, than $\frac{1}{2}$. Then $r > \frac{\varrho}{2}$ and similarly $t > \frac{\varrho}{2}$.

We now attack I_1, using Lemma IV (c) and (b), and the law of the mean.

$$I_1 = \bar{\mu} \iint_{\sigma'} A_1 \, dS' = \bar{\mu} \iint_{\sigma'} \frac{-4\zeta z}{rt\,(r+t)} \left(\frac{1}{r^2} + \frac{1}{rt} + \frac{1}{t^2} \right) dS'.$$

Hence, since $|\zeta| \leqq M r'^2$, $r > \frac{\varrho}{2}$, $t > \frac{\varrho}{2}$,

$$|I_1| \leqq \left| \bar{\mu}\, 192\, M \iint_{\sigma'} \frac{r'^2 z}{\varrho^5} \, dS' \right| = \left| \bar{\mu}\, 384\, M \pi \int_0^a \frac{r'^3 z}{(r'^2 + z^2)^{\frac{5}{2}}} \, dr' \right|.$$

The integral is not greater in absolute value than $\frac{2}{3}$, for any z, as may be seen by using the substitution $r' = z \tan \lambda$. Hence, since $\bar{\mu}$ approaches 0 with a, it follows that I_1 does also, uniformly as to z.

The remaining three integrals can be treated similarly. All are bounded quantities times $\bar{\mu}$. Thus, $\lim D = 0$. We formulate the result in

Theorem X. *If U is the potential of a double distribution on S with piecewise continuous moment μ, and if the moment is continuous at the point p of S, then the difference between the derivatives of U in the direction of the positive normal to S at p, at two points of this normal equally distant from p, approaches 0, as the points approach p. In particular, if the derivative approaches 0 from one side, it does also from the other.*

Our second result on normal derivatives assures us that their limits exist on S, but under the more stringent hypothesis that the moment has continuous second derivatives with respect to ξ and η in a neighborhood of p, where ξ and η are the coördinates of a variable point q of S with respect to a tangent-normal system of axes at p. We shall establish this by a method illustrating a different means of attack on the properties of potentials in the neighborhood of masses.

We construct a right circular cylinder with the normal to S at p as axis, and with radius small enough so that the portion of S near p within the cylinder is included in the region on which μ has continuous derivatives of second order. Let V be the portion of space within this cylinder, on the positive side of S, and otherwise bounded by a plane normal to the elements of the cylinder. If the radius of the cylinder is small enough, and the bounding plane is suitably chosen, V will be a regular region, and we may apply the divergence theorem to it. We change the variables in the divergence theorem to ξ, η, ζ, and apply it to the functions

$$X = \mu \frac{\partial}{\partial \xi} \frac{1}{r}, \qquad Y = \mu \frac{\partial}{\partial \eta} \frac{1}{r}, \qquad Z = \mu \frac{\partial}{\partial \zeta} \frac{1}{r},$$

the letters x, y, z entering r being regarded as fixed. The function μ is regarded as defined in V by means of its values on S, and the convention that it shall be independent of ζ. It then has continuous partial derivatives of the second order in the closed region V. If $P(x, y, z)$ is in V, $\frac{1}{r}$ becomes infinite in V, and it is necessary to cut it out from the field of integration. We surround P by a small sphere σ, with center at P. The divergence theorem then gives, since $\frac{1}{r}$ satisfies Laplace's equation in $V - v$,

$$\iiint\limits_{V-v} \left[\frac{\partial \mu}{\partial \xi} \frac{\partial}{\partial \xi} \frac{1}{r} + \frac{\partial \mu}{\partial \eta} \frac{\partial}{\partial \eta} \frac{1}{r} + \frac{\partial \mu}{\partial \zeta} \frac{\partial}{\partial \zeta} \frac{1}{r} \right] dV$$

$$= \iint\limits_{S} \mu \frac{\partial}{\partial \nu} \frac{1}{r} dS + \iint\limits_{\sigma} \mu \frac{\partial}{\partial \nu} \frac{1}{r} dS,$$

where v denotes the region within σ, and $\bar{S}$ is the surface bounding V. Let us investigate the integral over σ. As the normal is understood to be directed outward from the region of integration, it is here into the sphere σ, *i. e.* toward the point P from which r is measured. Hence the normal derivative is the negative of the derivative with respect to r, and so is $\frac{1}{r^2}$. Accordingly

$$\iint\limits_{\sigma} \mu \frac{\partial}{\partial \nu} \frac{1}{r} dS = \bar{\mu} \iint\limits_{\Omega} d\Omega = 4\pi \bar{\mu}.$$

Suppose we now let σ shrink to the point P. The volume integral is convergent, for since the derivatives of $\frac{1}{r}$ with respect to ξ, η, ζ, are the negatives of the derivatives with respect to x, y, z, the volume integral is the sum of three components of force due to volume distributions with continuous densities. Hence, as $\bar{\mu}$ approaches $\mu(P)$, we have

$$\iiint\limits_{V} \left[\frac{\partial \mu}{\partial \xi} \frac{\partial}{\partial \xi} \frac{1}{r} + \frac{\partial \mu}{\partial \eta} \frac{\partial}{\partial \eta} \frac{1}{r} + \frac{\partial \mu}{\partial \zeta} \frac{\partial}{\partial \zeta} \frac{1}{r} \right] dV = \iint\limits_{S} \mu \frac{\partial}{\partial \nu} \frac{1}{r} dS + 4\pi \mu(P).$$

If we follow the same procedure with

$$X = \frac{\partial \mu}{\partial \xi} \cdot \frac{1}{r}, \qquad Y = \frac{\partial \mu}{\partial \eta} \cdot \frac{1}{r}, \qquad Z = \frac{\partial \mu}{\partial \zeta} \cdot \frac{1}{r},$$

the integral over σ vanishes in the limit, and we have

$$\iiint\limits_{V} (\nabla^2 \mu) \frac{1}{r} dV + \iiint\limits_{V} \left[\frac{\partial \mu}{\partial \xi} \frac{\partial}{\partial \xi} \frac{1}{r} + \frac{\partial \mu}{\partial \eta} \frac{\partial}{\partial \eta} \frac{1}{r} + \frac{\partial \mu}{\partial \zeta} \frac{\partial}{\partial \zeta} \frac{1}{r} \right] dV$$

$$= \iint\limits_{S} \frac{\partial \mu}{\partial \nu} \frac{1}{r} dS.$$

Subtracting this identity from the preceding, we have

$$(4) \quad -\iiint_V (\nabla^2 \mu) \frac{1}{r} \, dV = \iint_S \mu \frac{\partial}{\partial \nu} \frac{1}{r} \, dS - \iint_S \frac{\partial \mu}{\partial \nu} \frac{1}{r} \, dS + 4\pi \mu (P).$$

The volume integral is the potential of a volume distribution with continuous density. It therefore has continuous derivatives throughout
space. The second integral on the right is the potential of a surface distribution with differentiable density, and so, by Theorem VII, has continuous derivatives in V, except possibly where S cuts the cylinder, and
certainly at all points of V near p. The last term on the right is continuously differentiable throughout V. The first term on the right is
the potential U of the double distribution we are studying, plus the
potential of a double distribution on the rest of the surface bounding
V, which is analytic near p, minus that due to the rest of S, also
analytic near p.

Hence U coincides with a sum of functions all of which are continuously differentiable in a portion of V near p. As p may be any interior point
of S, we may enunciate the following theorem, which includes the result
we desired to establish.

Theorem XI. *If the moment μ of the double distribution on S has con-*
tinuous partial derivatives of second order on S, then in any region V,
partially bounded by S, but containing no boundary points of S, and such
that a point P of V can approach S only from one side while remaining
in V, the partial derivatives of the potential U of the distribution, when
defined on the boundary of V by their limiting values, are continuous in
the closed region V.

Exercise.

Show that if P is exterior to V, the term $- 4\pi \mu (P)$ in formula (4) must be replaced by 0, and if P is an interior point of the portion of S bounding V, it must be
replaced by $- 2\pi \mu (P)$. Hence find again, on the hypothesis that μ has continuous
derivatives of second order, the results stated in Theorem VIII.

7. The Discontinuities of Logarithmic Potentials.

The treatment of logarithmic potentials can be carried out along
lines parallel to the treatment employed for Newtonian potentials, and
is in many respects simpler. However, their behavior can also be inferred directly from the behavior of Newtonian potentials. We proceed
to substantiate this remark.

We first show for the usual continuous logarithmic distributions
what we have already seen to be the case for the logarithmic particle,
namely that they are limiting cases of Newtonian potentials of distributions, on or within finite sections of cylindrical surfaces, as these
sections become infinitely long in both directions.

Let us examine the case of a volume distribution of density $\varkappa = \varkappa\,(\xi,\,\eta)$, in a cylinder with elements parallel to the z-axis, whose trace on the $(x,\,y)$-plane is a regular plane region A. Let the cylinder be cut off by the planes $z = -\,\beta_1,\ z = \beta_2$. We are interested in the existence and character of the limiting potential

$$U = \lim\left\{\iiint \frac{\varkappa}{r}\,dV + C\right\} = \lim_{\substack{\beta_1 \to \infty \\ \beta_2 \to \infty}}\left\{\iint_A\left[\int_{-\beta_1}^{\beta_2}\frac{\varkappa}{r}\,d\zeta\right]dS + C\right\},$$

where C is independent of the coördinates of the attracted particle at $P\,(x,\,y,\,0)$, though it will have to depend on β_1 and β_2 if the limit is to exist. We carry out first the integration with respect to ζ. There is no difficulty in showing that the triple integral may be thus evaluated as an iterated integral, even when P is interior to A. If r' represents the projection of r on the $(x,\,y)$-plane, that is, the distance from $(\xi,\,\eta)$ to $(x,\,y)$,

$$\int_{-\beta_1}^{\beta_2}\frac{\varkappa}{r}\,d\zeta = \varkappa\int_{-\beta_1}^{\beta_2}\frac{d\zeta}{\sqrt{r'^2 + \zeta^2}} = \varkappa\log\frac{\beta_2 + \sqrt{\beta_2^2 + r'^2}}{-\,\beta_1 + \sqrt{\beta_1^2 + r'^2}}.$$

We must determine C so that the limit in the expression for U exists. Let c denote the value of the last integral when $r' = 1$. This is in harmony with the convention made for logarithmic potentials (p. 63). Then

$$c = \varkappa\log\frac{\beta_2 + \sqrt{\beta_2^2 + 1}}{-\,\beta_1 + \sqrt{\beta_1^2 + 1}},$$

$$\int_{-\beta_1}^{\beta_2}\frac{\varkappa}{r}\,d\zeta = \varkappa\log\left[\frac{\beta_2 + \sqrt{\beta_2^2 + r'^2}}{\beta_2 + \sqrt{\beta_2^2 + 1}}\cdot\frac{-\,\beta_1 + \sqrt{\beta_1^2 + 1}}{-\,\beta_1 + \sqrt{\beta_1^2 + r'^2}}\right] + c,$$

and if C is taken as $-\,c$ times the area of A,

$$U = \lim_{\substack{\beta_1 \to \infty \\ \beta_2 \to \infty}}\iint_A \varkappa\log\left[\frac{\beta_2 + \sqrt{\beta_2^2 + r'^2}}{\beta_2 + \sqrt{\beta_2^2 + 1}}\cdot\frac{-\,\beta_1 + \sqrt{\beta_1^2 + 1}}{-\,\beta_1 + \sqrt{\beta_1^2 + r'^2}}\right]dS$$

$$= \lim_{\substack{\beta_1 \to \infty \\ \beta_2 \to \infty}}\iint_A \varkappa\log\left[\frac{1 + \sqrt{1 + \left(\frac{r'}{\beta_2}\right)^2}}{1 + \sqrt{1 + \left(\frac{1}{\beta_2}\right)^2}}\cdot\frac{1 + \sqrt{1 + \left(\frac{r'}{\beta_1}\right)^2}}{1 + \sqrt{1 + \left(\frac{1}{\beta_1}\right)^2}}\cdot\frac{1}{r'^2}\right]dS,$$

where we have multiplied and divided the second factor in the logarithm by its conjugate. Now if P is confined to a bounded region, all the radicals in this expression approach 1 uniformly, and it follows that the logarithm approaches $\log\frac{1}{r'^2}$ uniformly, and that the limit of the integral is the integral of the limit:

$$U = \iint_A 2\,\varkappa\log\frac{1}{r'}\,dS.$$

Thus the logarithmic potential of a distribution over an area is indeed a limiting case of a Newtonian potential, and a similar discussion will establish the corresponding facts for simple and double logarithmic distributions on curves.

We remark that if the above potential is thought of as that of a logarithmic spread of surface density σ, then $\sigma = 2\varkappa$, and a similar situation exists with respect to distributions on curves. *The amount of matter attracting according to the law of the inverse first power, in any area of the (x, y)-plane, is always to be understood as the amount of matter in a cylinder of height 2 whose trace is the given area, when the logarithmic potential is interpreted as a Newtonian potential, or as a limiting case of a Newtonian potential.*

The second question we have to consider, is whether—to keep to the case of the volume potential—the potential of the portion of the infinite distribution outside the planes $z = -a$ and $z = a$, is continuous, together with its derivatives, in the (x, y)-plane. It is readily computed to be

$$U' = \iint\limits_A 2\varkappa \log \frac{1}{a + \sqrt{a^2 + r'^2}} \, dS.$$

The integrand is clearly continuous in ξ, η, x, y, in any region which keeps these variables bounded and in which $\varkappa$ is continuous. Therefore U' is continuous in x and y in any bounded region. As for the derivatives with respect to x and y of the integrand, they will be found to be expressible as rational functions of $x, y, \xi,$ and η, and $\sqrt{a^2 + r'^2}$, whose denominators are products of powers of $\sqrt{a^2 + r'^2}$ and of $(a + \sqrt{a^2 + r'^2})$. Hence the derivatives of the integrand also are uniformly continuous when the variables are bounded, and it is the same with the derivatives of U'.

Thus the logarithmic potentials are equal to the Newtonian potentials due to bounded sections of the corresponding infinite cylindrical distributions, increased by continuous functions with continuous derivatives of all orders.

As an example, the potential of the volume distribution we have considered, bounded by two parallel planes, satisfies at interior points, Poisson's equation

$$\nabla^2 U = -4\pi\varkappa.$$

If U be regarded as the logarithmic potential

$$U = \iint\limits_A \sigma \log \frac{1}{r'} \, dS$$

of a surface distribution on the plane region A, then

$$\nabla^2 U = -2\pi\sigma.$$

Exercises.

1. Make a table of the properties, near the masses, of the logarithmic potentials

$$U = \iint_A \sigma \log \frac{1}{r'} \, dS, \qquad U = \int_c \lambda \log \frac{1}{r'} \, ds, \qquad U = \int_c \mu \frac{\partial}{\partial \nu} \log \frac{1}{r'} \, ds,$$

corresponding to those derived for Newtonian potentials in the present chapter.

2. Derive a few of these properties by the methods used in the chapter.

For further information on the discontinuities of Newtonian potentials at points of the masses, the reader should consult above all the article of E. SCHMIDT, in *Mathematische Abhandlungen* H. A. SCHWARZ *gewidmet*, Berlin, 1914. The treatment given in POINCARÉ's *Potentiel Newtonien*, Paris, 1899, may also be studied with profit. Further works on the subject may be found through the bibliographical indications at the end of the present volume.

Chapter VII.

Potentials as Solutions of Laplace's Equation; Electrostatics.

1. Electrostatics in Homogeneous Media.

The fundamental law of electrostatics was discovered by COULOUMB[1], and states that *the force between two small charged bodies is proportional in magnitude to the product of the charges and inversely proportional to the square of their distance apart*,

$$F = c \frac{e_1 e_2}{r^2},$$

the force being one of repulsion or attraction according as the charges are of the same or opposite kinds.

The constant of proportionality depends on the units employed. The unit of charge is usually so chosen in electrostatics that $c = 1$. In determining this unit, however, it is found that the medium present has an effect. Thus if the unit were determined in air at atmospheric pressure, the value of c would be found to rise by a fraction of one percent as the pressure was reduced toward 0. It is understood then, that the unit charge is such that two of them, a unit distance apart, repel with a unit force in vacuo. We shall consider in § 9 the effect of the medium or *dielectric* in which the charges are located. For the present we shall regard the space in which the charged bodies are placed as devoid of other matter. This will serve as a good approximation to actuality when

---

[1] Histoire et mémoires de l'Académie royale de sciences, Paris, 1785, pp. 569—577.

the charges are situated in air, with all different dielectric media at a considerable distance from the charges compared with their distances from each other.

Couloumb's law then agrees with Newton's law, except for a reversal of the sense of the force. We shall have electrostatic potentials of the same form as the gravitational potentials. The reversal of sense in the force will be accounted for by agreeing that the force shall be the *negative* of the gradient of the potential (see Chapter III, p. 53).

Conductors. Materials differ in the resistance they offer to the motion of charges placed on them. A charge on a *non-conductor*, such as a piece of glass, will not change in distribution perceptibly, even when subjected to electric forces. On the other hand, charges on conductors, among which are metals, move under any changes in the field of force in which the conductors are placed. A *conductor* may be defined as a body, a charge on which cannot be in equilibrium, if there is any electric force at any point of the body. The charge will be so distributed as to produce a field exactly neutralizing that in which the conductor is placed.

If the conductor was initially uncharged, it nevertheless appears to possess charges when introduced into a field of force. This is accounted for by the assumption that the conductor originally had equal and opposite charges, distributed with equal and opposite densities, so that they produced no effect. The production of a field of force in the conductor, by changing its position to one where there are forces, or by bringing charges into the neighborhood of the conductor, separates these charges, and produces the distribution which annihilates the field in the conductor in the manner indicated. The charges which appear because of the field are called *induced* charges, and their total amount is 0. If the conductor was originally charged, the induced charges are superposed, and the total charge remains unchanged by the addition of the induced charges. Since there is no force in a conductor when equilibrium is established, Gauss' theorem (p. 43) indicates that there are no charges in the interior. This is born out experimentally. We recapitulate:

In an electrostatic field, the potential is constant throughout each conductor, and there are no charges in the interiors of the conductors. There will, in general, be induced charges on the surfaces of the conductors. The total charge on each conductor is independent of the inducing field.

2. The Electrostatic Problem for a Spherical Conductor.

So far, potential theory has appeared in the light of the theory of certain distributions of matter acting in accordance with Newton's law, the distributions being given. The last two chapters were concerned with a derivation of properties needed for a change of point of view, and from now on, the potential theory will take on more the aspect of the theory of Laplace's equation.

In order to determine the electrostatic distribution of a given charge on a spherical conductor, new methods are not needed. At the same time, we approach the question from the new point of view, since in other problems, we cannot, as a rule, know the distribution from simple considerations of symmetry, or on the basis of knowledge already gained of distributions which satisfy all the requirements. The spherical conductor will thus illustrate a general problem of electrostatics.

We formulate the problem as follows. We have a sphere of radius a, whose center we take as origin of coördinates. We first determine the potential and then the density of a charge E in equilibrium on the sphere, from the following data:

a) $U = $ const, $\quad 0 \leqq \varrho \leqq a$, $\quad V^2 U = 0$, $\quad a < \varrho$;

b) U is everywhere continuous;

c) the derivatives of the first order of U are everywhere continuous, except for $\varrho = a$; here they satisfy the equation

$$\frac{\partial U}{\partial n_+} - \frac{\partial U}{\partial n_-} = -4 \pi \sigma,$$

σ being the surface density of the distribution;

d) $\varrho U \to E$ as ϱ becomes infinite.

We shall seek a solution of this problem on the assumption that U is a function of ϱ only. It will appear later (p. 218, Ex. 1) that the solution is unique. Either by substituting $U = U(\varrho)$ in Laplace's equation, or by borrowing the form of that equation in spherical coördinates from § 3, we find that it takes the form

$$V^2 U = \frac{1}{\varrho^2} \frac{d}{d\varrho} \varrho^2 \frac{dU}{d\varrho} = 0.$$

We find, accordingly, from (a), that

$$\varrho^2 \frac{dU}{d\varrho} = c_1, \qquad U = -\frac{c_1}{\varrho} + c_2, \quad \text{for} \quad \varrho > a.$$

The condition (d) then shows that $c_2 = 0$ and $c_1 = -E$. Accordingly, from (b) and (a),

$$U = \frac{E}{\varrho}, \qquad a \leqq \varrho,$$

$$U = \frac{E}{a}, \qquad \varrho \leqq a.$$

This gives the potential. The density is determined by (c). This gives

$$-\frac{E}{a^2} - 0 = -4 \pi \sigma, \quad \text{or} \quad \sigma = \frac{E}{4 \pi a^2}.$$

The density is thus constant. As a check, we notice that its integral over the surface of the sphere gives the total charge.

Exercises.

1. Determine, as a solution of Laplace's equation with suitable auxiliary conditions, the potential of a double distribution on the surface of a sphere. Assume that the potential is a function of the distance from the center only, and that the total moment is a given quantity M.

2. Determine, by the method of this section, the potential of a hollow sphere of radii a and b, of constant density $\varkappa$. Compare the results with Exercise 11, § 3, Chapter III (p. 57).

3. General Coördinates.

For the treatment of special problems, suitable coördinate systems are well nigh indispensable. The fact that the surface of the sphere, in the last section, is given by setting ϱ equal to a constant, was a great help. We shall be justified if we devote some attention to coördinate systems in general, with the main object of finding a means of expressing $\nabla^2 U$ in terms of any given coördinates in a simple manner.

Unless the reader is already somewhat familiar with the subject, he may find it helpful to illustrate for himself the following developments in the case of spherical coördinates, of which the simplest analytic description is given by the equations

$$(1) \qquad x = \varrho \sin \varphi \cos \vartheta, \qquad y = \varrho \sin \varphi \sin \vartheta, \qquad z = \varrho \cos \vartheta.$$

In an analogous way we define a system of coördinates in general by the equations

$$(2) \qquad x = f(q_1, q_2, q_3), \qquad y = g(q_1, q_2, q_3), \qquad z = h(q_1, q_2, q_3).$$

We shall suppose that the functions f, g, h are continuously differentiable for any values of the variables considered, and that they are solvable for q_1, q_2, q_3:

$$q_1 = q_1(x, y, z), \qquad q_2 = q_2(x, y, z), \qquad q_3 = q_3(x, y, z).$$

Then to a point (x, y, z) of space, or of a region of space where the necessary conditions are fulfilled, there corresponds a set of values of q_1, q_2, q_3, and to a set of values of q_1, q_2, q_3, there corresponds a point (x, y, z) of space.

A geometric picture of the system of coördinates q_1, q_2, q_3 is possible (fig. 23). Suppose we regard q_3 as constant, and allow q_1 and q_2 to vary. Then the equations (2) are the parametric equations of a surface, which we shall call a q_3-surface. To different values of q_3 correspond different surfaces. We thus have a family of q_3-surfaces, to each of which is attached a value of q_3. Similarly, we have a family of q_1-surfaces, and a family of q_2-surfaces. When values are assigned to q_1, q_2, and q_3, these values pick out surfaces, one from each family, and their intersection gives the point whose coördinates are (q_1, q_2, q_3). On the other hand, if a point is given, the three surfaces on which it lies, one from each family, determine the values of the three coördinates. Of course this is based on the assumption that the surfaces are well behaved, and intersect properly. Thus, if at a point, the surfaces, one from each family through that point, intersected in a curve through that point, the point would not be determined by the coördinates. Such inconveniences cannot arise if the curves in which the pairs of surfaces intersect meet at angles which are the faces of a trihedral angle which is not flat, *i. e.* if the functional determinant

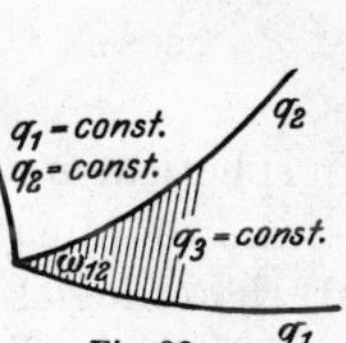

$$
(3) \qquad \frac{\partial (x,\, y,\, z)}{\partial (q_1,\, q_2,\, q_3)} = \begin{vmatrix} \dfrac{\partial x}{\partial q_1}, & \dfrac{\partial y}{\partial q_1}, & \dfrac{\partial z}{\partial q_1} \\[2ex] \dfrac{\partial x}{\partial q_2}, & \dfrac{\partial y}{\partial q_2}, & \dfrac{\partial z}{\partial q_2} \\[2ex] \dfrac{\partial x}{\partial q_3}, & \dfrac{\partial y}{\partial q_3}, & \dfrac{\partial z}{\partial q_3} \end{vmatrix},
$$

Fig. 23.

is not 0, for its rows are direction ratios of these three curves. We assume that it is not 0; this amounts to the condition already mentioned, that the equations (2) be solvable for q_1, q_2, q_3.

The curves given by (2) when q_2 and q_3 are held constant, that is, the intersections of q_2-surfaces and q_3-surfaces, are curves along which q_1 alone varies. We call them q_1-curves. Similarly, we have q_2-curves and q_3-curves. If q_1, q_2, q_3 are functions of a single variable t, the equations (2) give us the parametric equations of a curve. We shall find useful, expressions for the differentials of x, y, z and of the length of arc s of such a curve. The first follow at once from (2):

$$
dx = \frac{\partial x}{\partial q_1}dq_1 + \frac{\partial x}{\partial q_2}dq_2 + \frac{\partial x}{\partial q_3}dq_3,
$$

$$
(4) \qquad dy = \frac{\partial y}{\partial q_1}dq_1 + \frac{\partial y}{\partial q_2}dq_2 + \frac{\partial y}{\partial q_3}dq_3,
$$

$$
dz = \frac{\partial z}{\partial q_1}dq_1 + \frac{\partial z}{\partial q_2}dq_2 + \frac{\partial z}{\partial q_3}dq_3,
$$

The square of the differential of arc is the sum of the squares of these:

$$
(5) \qquad ds^2 = Q_1\, dq_1^2 + Q_2\, dq_2^2 + Q_3\, dq_3^2
$$
$$
+ 2Q_{23}\, dq_2\, dq_3 + 2Q_{31}\, dq_3\, dq_1 + 2Q_{12}\, dq_1\, dq_2,
$$

where

$$
Q_i = \left(\frac{\partial x}{\partial q_i}\right)^2 + \left(\frac{\partial y}{\partial q_i}\right)^2 + \left(\frac{\partial z}{\partial q_i}\right)^2, \quad Q_{ij} = \frac{\partial x}{\partial q_i}\frac{\partial x}{\partial q_j} + \frac{\partial y}{\partial q_i}\frac{\partial y}{\partial q_j} + \frac{\partial z}{\partial q_i}\frac{\partial z}{\partial q_j}.
$$

None of the quantities Q_1, Q_2, Q_3 vanish, for then one of the rows of the functional determinant (3) would consist of vanishing elements, and the determinant would vanish.

From (5) we obtain the differentials of arc of the coördinate curves, measured in the sense of increasing values of the coördinates, by allowing one alone to vary at a time:

$$
(6) \qquad ds_1 = \sqrt{Q_1}\, dq_1, \quad ds_2 = \sqrt{Q_2}\, dq_2, \quad ds_3 = \sqrt{Q_3}\, dq_3.
$$

From (4) we find the direction cosines of these curves:

$$(7) \quad \frac{\frac{\partial x}{\partial q_1}}{\sqrt{Q_1}}, \frac{\frac{\partial y}{\partial q_1}}{\sqrt{Q_1}}, \frac{\frac{\partial z}{\partial q_1}}{\sqrt{Q_1}}; \quad \frac{\frac{\partial x}{\partial q_2}}{\sqrt{Q_2}}, \frac{\frac{\partial y}{\partial q_2}}{\sqrt{Q_2}}, \frac{\frac{\partial z}{\partial q_2}}{\sqrt{Q_2}}; \quad \frac{\frac{\partial x}{\partial q_3}}{\sqrt{Q_3}}, \frac{\frac{\partial y}{\partial q_3}}{\sqrt{Q_3}}, \frac{\frac{\partial z}{\partial q_3}}{\sqrt{Q_3}},$$

and from these, we find the cosines of the angles ω_{23}, ω_{31}, ω_{12}, between the pairs of coördinates lines:

$$\cos \omega_{23} = \frac{Q_{23}}{\sqrt{Q_2 Q_3}}, \quad \cos \omega_{31} = \frac{Q_{31}}{\sqrt{Q_3 Q_1}}, \quad \cos \omega_{12} = \frac{Q_{12}}{\sqrt{Q_1 Q_2}}.$$

In spherical and cylindrical coördinates, these quantities vanish — that is, the coördinate curves, and hence also the coördinate surfaces, meet at right angles (except at points where the functional determinant vanishes). Such systems of coördinates are called *orthogonal systems*, and from now on, we shall confine ourselves to orthogonal systems. Accordingly, we shall have $Q_{23} = Q_{31} = Q_{12} = 0$.

Exercises.

1. Determine the points at which the functional determinant (3) is 0, in the case of spherical coördinates, and note that (*a*) at such points the coördinate surfaces cannot be said to meet at right angles, and (*b*) that such points do not uniquely determine the coördinates, even under the restriction of the usual inequalities $0 \leq \vartheta \leq \pi$, $0 \leq \varphi < 2\pi$.

2. Show that the condition for orthogonality can also be expressed in the form

$$\frac{\partial q_i}{\partial x} \frac{\partial q_j}{\partial x} + \frac{\partial q_i}{\partial y} \frac{\partial q_j}{\partial y} + \frac{\partial q_i}{\partial z} \frac{\partial q_j}{\partial z} = 0, \quad i \neq j.$$

There are two quantities which we now wish to know in terms of Q_1, Q_2, and Q_3. The first of these is the absolute value of the functional determinant (3). If we square that determinant according to Laplace's rule[1] we find

$$\left| \frac{\partial (x, y, z)}{\partial (q_1, q_2, q_3)} \right|^2 = \begin{vmatrix} Q_1, & Q_{12}, & Q_{31} \\ Q_{12}, & Q_2, & Q_{23} \\ Q_{31}, & Q_{23}, & Q_3 \end{vmatrix},$$

and hence, since our system is orthogonal,

$$(8) \quad \left| \frac{\partial (x, y, z)}{\partial (q_1, q_2, q_3)} \right| = \sqrt{Q_1 Q_2 Q_3}.$$

The second quantity for which an expression in terms of Q_1, Q_2, and Q_3 is desired is

$$D_{12} = \sqrt{\left[\frac{\partial (y, z)}{\partial (q_1, q_2)} \right]^2 + \left[\frac{\partial (z, x)}{\partial (q_1, q_2)} \right]^2 + \left[\frac{\partial (x, y)}{\partial (q_1, q_2)} \right]^2}.$$

---

[1] See, for instance Bôcher's *Introduction to Higher Algebra*, Chap. II, § 9.

This we transform by the readily verified algebraic identity

$$\begin{vmatrix} b, c \\ \beta, \gamma \end{vmatrix}^2 + \begin{vmatrix} c, a \\ \gamma, \alpha \end{vmatrix}^2 + \begin{vmatrix} a, b \\ \alpha, \beta \end{vmatrix}^2 = (a^2 + b^2 + c^2)(\alpha^2 + \beta^2 + \gamma^2)$$
$$- (a\alpha + b\beta + c\gamma)^2,$$

with the result

$$(9) \qquad D_{12} = \sqrt{Q_1 Q_2 - Q_{12}^2} = \sqrt{Q_1 Q_2}.$$

Expressions for Gradient, Divergence, Curl and Laplacian in General Coördinates. In general systems of coördinates it is usually convenient to express a vector at a point in terms of its components in the directions of the coördinate lines at that point. We have seen that the gradient of a scalar function is a vector which is independent of any system of axes. If we allow the (x, y, z)-axes to have the directions of the coördinate curves at P, for the moment, we have for the gradient of U at P,

$$\left(\frac{\partial U}{\partial x}, \frac{\partial U}{\partial y}, \frac{\partial U}{\partial z} \right) = \left(\frac{\partial U}{\partial s_1}, \frac{\partial U}{\partial s_2}, \frac{\partial U}{\partial s_3} \right),$$

or, using the expressions (6),

$$(10) \qquad \text{grad } U = \nabla U = \left(\frac{1}{\sqrt{Q_1}} \frac{\partial U}{\partial q_1}, \frac{1}{\sqrt{Q_2}} \frac{\partial U}{\partial q_2}, \frac{1}{\sqrt{Q_3}} \frac{\partial U}{\partial q_3} \right),$$

the components being along the coördinate lines.

The quantities Q_1, Q_2, Q_3 are given, in the expressions following (5), in terms of q_1, q_2, q_3. It is often convenient to have them in terms of x, y and z. This can now be accomplished by means of the above expression for the gradient. In fact, if we set $U = q_1$ in (10), we have

$$\nabla q_1 = \left(\frac{1}{\sqrt{Q_1}}, 0, 0 \right).$$

Thus $\dfrac{1}{\sqrt{Q_1}}$ appears as the magnitude $|\nabla q_1|$ of the gradient of q_1, whose value is

$$|\nabla q_1| = \sqrt{\left(\frac{\partial q_1}{\partial x} \right)^2 + \left(\frac{\partial q_1}{\partial y} \right)^2 + \left(\frac{\partial q_1}{\partial z} \right)^2}.$$

Thus, if we know the coördinates q_i in terms of x, y, z, the desired expressions are

$$(11) \qquad Q_1 = \frac{1}{(\nabla q_1)^2}, \qquad Q_2 = \frac{1}{(\nabla q_2)^2}, \qquad Q_3 = \frac{1}{(\nabla q_3)^2}.$$

We next seek the expression for the divergence of a given vector field. Let W (W_1, W_2, W_3) denote a vector field, specified in terms of its components in the direction of the coördinate curves. We may find an expression for the divergence of this field by the method of Exercise 5, § 5, Chapter II (p. 39). That is, we start from the definition

$$\text{div } W = \lim \frac{\iint\limits_{S} W_n \, dS}{V}$$

where V is the volume of a regular region R containing the fixed point P, the divergence at which is defined; S is its bounding surface, and the limit is to be taken as the maximum chord of R approaches 0. By the use of the divergence theorem it can be shown that in case the field is continuously differentiable in a neighborhood of P the limit exists, and actually gives the divergence (see p. 39, especially Exercise 5). Under these circumstances we may take for the regions employed, any convenient shape. We shall suppose that R is bounded by a pair of coördinate surfaces from each of the three families: $q_1 = a_1$, $q_1 = a_1 + \Delta a_1$, $q_2 = a_2$, $q_2 = a_2 + \Delta a_2$, $q_3 = a_3$, $q_3 = a_3 + \Delta a_3$. We now evaluate the above limit. First we have to compute the surface integral. To do this, we shall need to know the area ΔS of an element of the q_3-surface, bounded by q_1-curves and q_2-curves. For this we have the formula from the Calculus[1]

$$\Delta S = \int_{q_2}^{q_2+\Delta q_2} \int_{q_1}^{q_1+\Delta q_1} D_{12}\, dq_1\, dq_2 ,$$

where D_{12} is the expression for which we found the value (9). The result of employing the law of the mean in this integral is the expression

$$\Delta S = \sqrt{\overline{Q_1 Q_2}}\, \Delta q_1\, \Delta q_2 ,$$

which will form the basis for the surface integrals in the computation of the divergence. Similarly, the expression for the volume of R is

$$\Delta V = \sqrt{\overline{Q_1 Q_2 Q_3}}\, \Delta q_1\, \Delta q_2\, \Delta q_3 .$$

Consider now the integral of the normal component of the field over the face $q_3 = a_3$ of the region R. Since $W_n = -W_3$, this is the negative of

$$\iint W_3\, dS = \lim \sum W_3\, \Delta S = \lim \sum W_3 \sqrt{\overline{Q_1 Q_2}}\, \Delta q_1\, \Delta q_2$$

$$= \int_{a_1}^{a_1+\Delta a_1} \int_{a_2}^{a_2+\Delta a_2} W_3 \sqrt{Q_1 Q_2}\, dq_1\, dq_2 .$$

If we form the same integral for $q_3 = a_3 + \Delta a_3$, and subtract the above from it, we shall have the integral of the normal component of the field over two opposite faces of the region:

$$\int_{a_2}^{a_2+\Delta a_2} \int_{a_1}^{a_1+\Delta a_1} \left\{ \left[W_3 \sqrt{Q_1 Q_2}\right]_{q_3 = a_3 + \Delta a_3} - \left[W_3 \sqrt{Q_1 Q_2}\right]_{q_3 = a_3} \right\} dq_1\, dq_2$$

$$= \left\{ \left[W_3 \sqrt{Q_1 Q_2}\right]_{\substack{q_1 = q_1' \\ q_2 = q_2' \\ q_3 = a_3 + \Delta a_3}} - \left[W_3 \sqrt{Q_1 Q_2}\right]_{\substack{q_1 = q_1' \\ q_2 = q_2' \\ q_3 = a_3}} \right\} \Delta a_1\, \Delta a_2 ,$$

---

[1] Osgood, *Advanced Calculus*, p. 66, (7) and p. 269, Ex. 3.

where we have employed the law of the mean for integrals. Using also the law of the mean for differences, we reduce this to

$$\frac{\partial}{\partial q_3}\Big[W_3\sqrt{\overline{Q_1\,\overline{Q}_2}}\Big]\Delta a_1\,\Delta a_2\,\Delta a_3,$$

in which the variables q_1, q_2, q_3 have mean values corresponding to some point in R.

If we now add the corresponding expressions for the other pairs of faces in the q_2-surfaces and the q_3-surfaces, divide by the expression $\Delta V = \sqrt{\overline{Q_1}\,\overline{Q}_2\,\overline{Q}_3}\,\Delta a_1\,\Delta a_2\,\Delta a_3$ obtained above, for the volume of R, and pass to the limit as Δa_1, Δa_2, Δa_3 approach 0, we find

$$(12) \qquad \operatorname{div} \boldsymbol{W} = \nabla \cdot \boldsymbol{W}$$

$$= \frac{1}{\sqrt{Q_1 Q_2 Q_3}}\Big[\frac{\partial}{\partial q_1}\sqrt{Q_2 Q_3}\,W_1 + \frac{\partial}{\partial q_2}\sqrt{Q_3 Q_1}\,W_2 + \frac{\partial}{\partial q_3}\sqrt{Q_1 Q_2}\,W_3\Big].$$

It is true that for this expression all that is required of $\boldsymbol{W}$ is the existence of its derivatives of first order. We have supposed that they are continuous. But the existence of the derivatives of Q_1, Q_2, Q_3 is also implied, and this means a requirement not explicitly made. We shall assume that the derivatives involved exist and are continuous. Usually the coördinate systems employed are those in which the functions Q_1, Q_2, Q_3 are analytic in their arguments.

We are now able to find easily the expression for the Laplacian of U in terms of general coördinates. As it is the divergence of the gradient of U, we have at once, from (10) and (12),

$$(13) \qquad \nabla^2 U = \frac{1}{\sqrt{Q_1 Q_2 Q_3}}\Big[\frac{\partial}{\partial q_1}\Big(\sqrt{\frac{Q_2 Q_3}{Q_1}}\frac{\partial U}{\partial q_1}\Big) + \frac{\partial}{\partial q_2}\Big(\sqrt{\frac{Q_3 Q_1}{Q_2}}\frac{\partial U}{\partial q_2}\Big)$$
$$+ \frac{\partial}{\partial q_3}\Big(\sqrt{\frac{Q_1 Q_2}{Q_3}}\frac{\partial U}{\partial q_3}\Big)\Big].$$

As an application, let us find the Laplacian of U in spherical coördinates. We identify q_1 with ϱ, q_2 with φ, q_3 with ϑ. The square of the differential of arc can be found by geometric considerations, or from the equations (4) and (5), and is

$$ds^2 = d\varrho^2 + \varrho^2 \sin^2\vartheta\, d\varphi^2 + \varrho^2 d\vartheta^2,$$

so that

$$Q_1 = 1, \qquad Q_2 = \varrho^2 \sin^2\vartheta, \qquad Q_3 = \varrho^2.$$

We have, accordingly, by (13),

$$(14) \quad \nabla^2 U = \frac{1}{\varrho^2 \sin\vartheta}\Big[\frac{\partial}{\partial \varrho}\Big(\varrho^2 \sin\vartheta\,\frac{\partial U}{\partial \varrho}\Big) + \frac{\partial}{\partial \varphi}\Big(\frac{1}{\sin\vartheta}\frac{\partial U}{\partial \varphi}\Big) + \frac{\partial}{\partial \vartheta}\Big(\sin\vartheta\,\frac{\partial U}{\partial \vartheta}\Big)\Big]$$

$$= \frac{1}{\varrho^2}\frac{\partial}{\partial \varrho}\Big(\varrho^2 \frac{\partial U}{\partial \varrho}\Big) + \frac{1}{\varrho^2 \sin^2\vartheta}\frac{\partial^2 U}{\partial \varphi^2} + \frac{1}{\varrho^2 \sin\vartheta}\frac{\partial}{\partial \vartheta}\Big(\sin\vartheta\,\frac{\partial U}{\partial \vartheta}\Big).$$

Exercises.

3. Express the Laplacian of U in terms of cylindrical coördinates, ϱ, φ, z:

$$x = \varrho \cos \varphi, \quad y = \varrho \sin \varphi, \quad z = z.$$

4. Check, by the formula (12), the expression for the divergence in spherical coördinates obtained in Exercise 6, § 5, Chapter II (p. 39).

5. *Ring Coördinates.* The equations

$$x = r \cos \varphi, \quad y = r \sin \varphi, \quad z = \frac{\sin \mu}{\cosh \lambda + \cos \mu}, \quad \text{where} \quad r = \frac{\sinh \lambda}{\cosh \lambda + \cos \mu},$$

define x, y, z as functions of λ, μ, φ. Show that the φ-surfaces are meridian planes through the z-axis, that the λ-surfaces are the toruses whose meridian sections are the circles

$$x^2 + z^2 - 2 x \coth \lambda + 1 = 0,$$

and that the μ-surfaces are the spheres whose meridian sections are the circles

$$x^2 + z^2 + 2 z \tan \mu - 1 = 0.$$

Show that the system is orthogonal, except at points where the functional determinant (3) vanishes, and find these points. Finally, show that

$$d s^2 = r^2 \left[\frac{d \lambda^2 + d \mu^2}{\sinh^2 \lambda} + d \varphi^2 \right],$$

and, accordingly, that

$$\nabla^2 U = \frac{\sinh^2 \lambda}{r^3} \left[\frac{\partial}{\partial \lambda} \left(r \frac{\partial U}{\partial \lambda} \right) + \frac{\partial}{\partial \mu} \left(r \frac{\partial U}{\partial \mu} \right) + \frac{r}{\sinh^2 \lambda} \frac{\partial^2 U}{\partial \varphi^2} \right].$$

4. Ellipsoidal Coördinates.

As an illustration of coördinate systems, we choose ellipsoidal coördinates. We shall then make use of them in the discussion of the conductor problem for an ellipsoid. We start with a basic ellipsoid,

$$(15) \qquad \frac{x^2}{a^2} + \frac{y^2}{b^2} + \frac{z^2}{c^2} = 1, \quad c^2 < b^2 < a^2,$$

and form the functions

$$f(s) = \frac{x^2}{a^2 + s} + \frac{y^2}{b^2 + s} + \frac{z^2}{c^2 + s} - 1,$$

$$\varphi(s) = (a^2 + s)(b^2 + s)(c^2 + s).$$

The equation $f(s) = 0$, when s has any fixed value not a root of $\varphi(s)$, represents a central quadric surface, and for various values of s, a family of such surfaces. The sections of these surfaces by each of the coördinate planes are conic sections with the same foci, and the family of surfaces is called a *confocal family*. When s is very large and positive, the surface is a large ellipsoid of nearly spherical form. As s decreases, the ellipsoid shrinks, the difference in its axes becoming more pronounced. For $s = 0$, the ellipsoid reduces to the basic ellipsoid (15). The surface continues to be an ellipsoid as long as $s > -c^2$. As s approaches

$- c^2$, the semi-axes of the ellipsoid approach $\sqrt{a^2 - c^2}$, $\sqrt{b^2 - c^2}$, 0, that is, the ellipsoid approaches the flat elliptical surface

$$(16) \qquad \frac{x^2}{a^2 - c^2} + \frac{y^2}{b^2 - c^2} \leqq 1, \qquad z = 0,$$

having swept out all the rest of space.

When s becomes slightly less than $- c^2$, the quadric surface becomes a hyperboloid of one sheet, at first very close to the portion of the (x, y)-plane outside the elliptic surface (16). As s goes from $- c^2$ to $- b^2$, this hyperboloid expands, sweeping out all the rest of space except for the points of its limiting form, which is a portion of the (x, z)-plane bounded by a hyperbola, namely

$$(17) \qquad \frac{x^2}{a^2 - b^2} - \frac{z^2}{b^2 - c^2} \leqq 1, \qquad y = 0,$$

As s decreases from $-b^2$ to $-a^2$, the surface passes from the complementary portion of the (x, z)-plane, as a hyperboloid of two sheets, to a limiting form which is the entire (y, z)-plane, having swept through the whole of space except for the points of its limiting positions.

Thus for any point (x, y, z) not in a coördinate plane, and, in limiting forms, for points in these planes, there is an ellipsoid of the family, a hyperboloid of one sheet of the family, and a hyperboloid of two sheets of the family, which pass through the point. It looks as if we might have here three systems of surfaces which could function as coördinate surfaces, one of which is the basic ellipsoid. This is indeed the case. The values of s giving the members of the confocal system are the roots of the cubic

$$f(s)\,\varphi(s) = 0.$$

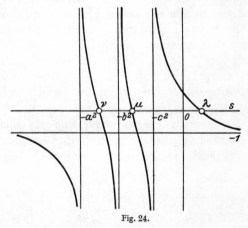

Fig. 24.

We have just had geometric evidence that this equation has three real roots, λ, μ, and ν, distributed as follows

$$(18) \qquad - a^2 \leqq \nu \leqq - b^2 \leqq \mu \leqq - c^2 \leqq \lambda.$$

The fact admits an immediate verification by considering the variation of the function $f(s)$ as s ranges from $- \infty$ to $+ \infty$ (fig. 24). The equation $f(s)\,\varphi(s) = 0$ has the same roots as $f(s) = 0$, except that the infinities of $f(s)$ may be additional roots of the first equation. These occur at the end-points of the intervals (18), and as the roots of $f(s)\,\varphi(s) = 0$

vary continuously with x, y, z, we see thus that this equation has, in fact, the roots distributed as stated.

We thus find that the system of confocal quadrics may be regarded as a system of λ-surfaces, which are ellipsoids, a system of μ-surfaces, which are hyperboloids of one sheet, and a system of ν-surfaces, which are hyperboloids of two sheets, and we may take λ, μ, ν as a system of coördinates. A point in space, except possibly for certain points in the coördinate planes, determines uniquely a set of values of λ, μ, ν. Let us see if, conversely, a set of values of λ, μ, ν, in the intervals (18), determines a point in space. Expressing the determining cubic in factored form, we have, since the coefficient of s^3 is -1,

$$(19) \qquad f(s)\,\varphi(s) = x^2\,(b^2 + s)\,(c^2 + s) + y^2\,(c^2 + s)\,(a^2 + s)$$
$$+ z^2\,(a^2 + s)\,(b^2 + s) - \dot{\varphi}(s) \equiv - (s - \lambda)\,(s - \mu)\,(s - \nu).$$

From this, we find by putting $s = -a^2$, $-b^2$, $-c^2$, successively,

$$(20) \qquad x^2 = \frac{(a^2 + \lambda)\,(a^2 + \mu)\,(a^2 + \nu)}{(a^2 - b^2)\,(a^2 - c^2)}, \qquad y^2 = - \frac{(b^2 + \lambda)\,(b^2 + \mu)\,(b^2 + \nu)}{(a^2 - b^2)\,(b^2 - c^2)},$$
$$z^2 = \frac{(c^2 + \lambda)\,(c^2 + \mu)\,(c^2 + \nu)}{(a^2 - c^2)\,(b^2 - c^2)}.$$

Each set of values of λ, μ, ν determines thus, not one, but eight points, symmetrically situated with respect to the (x, y, z)-planes. This difficulty can be avoided by an introduction of new coördinates, like those given by the equations $q_1^2 = a^2 + \lambda$, $q_2^2 = b^2 + \mu$, $q_3^2 = c_2 + \nu$, with the understanding that q_1 shall have the same sign as x, etc., or also by the introduction of elliptic functions. However, we shall not do this at this point, for our application will deal only with functions which are symmetric in the (x, y, z) planes, and it will not be necessary to distinguish between symmetric points.

The coördinates λ, μ, ν are known as *ellipsoidal* coördinates. We shall now show that the system is orthogonal. The components of the gradient of λ are its partial derivatives with respect to x, y and z. We find these by differentiating the equation defining λ, $f(\lambda) = 0$:

$$f'(\lambda)\,\frac{\partial \lambda}{\partial x} + \frac{2\,x}{a^2 + \lambda} = 0,$$

where

$$f'(\lambda) = - \frac{x^2}{(a^2 + \lambda)^2} - \frac{y^2}{(b^2 + \lambda)^2} - \frac{z^2}{(c^2 + \lambda)^2}.$$

Accordingly,

$$(21) \quad \nabla\lambda = \left(- \frac{2\,x}{(a^2 + \lambda)\,f'(\lambda)}, \quad - \frac{2\,y}{(b^2 + \lambda)\,f'(\lambda)}, \quad - \frac{2\,z}{(c^2 + \lambda)\,f'(\lambda)} \right),$$

$\nabla\mu$ and $\nabla\nu$ being found by substituting μ and ν for λ. The condition for the orthogonality of the λ-surfaces and the μ-surfaces, is, in accordance with Exercise 2, § 3 (p. 180),

$$\frac{x^2}{(a^2 + \lambda)(a^2 + \mu)} + \frac{y^2}{(b^2 + \lambda)(b^2 + \mu)} + \frac{z^2}{(c^2 + \lambda)(c^2 + \mu)} = 0,$$

from which we have dropped the factor $\frac{4}{f'(\lambda)\,f'(\mu)}$. This factor is certainly different from 0 at all points off the coördinate planes. We omit a consideration of the orthogonality at points of these planes, though it does not break down at all of them. We see that the above condition is fulfilled at other points by subtracting the equations $f(\lambda) = 0$, $f(\mu) = 0$, defining λ and μ:

$$(\lambda - \mu)\left[\frac{x^2}{(a^2 + \lambda)(a^2 + \mu)} + \frac{y^2}{(b^2 + \lambda)(b^2 + \mu)} + \frac{z^2}{(c^2 + \lambda)(c^2 + \mu)}\right] = 0.$$

Thus, if λ and μ are distinct, the condition for orthogonality is fulfilled, and $\lambda = \mu$ is only possible on a coördinate plane, in fact, on the *boundaries* of the limiting areas (16) and (17). One shows similarly that the other sets of surfaces are orthogonal.

Our object is now to find Laplace's equation in ellipsoidal coördinates. It is all a question of the quadratic form (5) for ds^2. We use the expressions (11). By (21),

$$(\nabla\lambda)^2 = \frac{4}{f'^2(\lambda)}\left[\frac{x^2}{(a^2 + \lambda)^2} + \frac{y^2}{(b^2 + \lambda)^2} + \frac{z^2}{(c^2 + \lambda)^2}\right] = -\frac{4}{f'(\lambda)},$$

$(\nabla\mu)^2$ and $(\nabla\nu)^2$ being found by the substitution of μ and ν for λ. But we should like to have these coefficients expressed in terms of λ, μ, ν alone. This can be done by differentiating the identity (19) with respect to s and substituting λ, μ, ν, for s, successively. We find

$$f'(s)\,\varphi(s) + f(s)\,\varphi'(s)$$
$$= -(s - \lambda)(s - \mu) - (s - \lambda)(s - \nu) - (s - \mu)(s - \nu),$$

$$f'(\lambda) = -\frac{(\lambda - \mu)(\lambda - \nu)}{\varphi(\lambda)}, \qquad f'(\mu) = +\frac{(\lambda - \mu)(\mu - \nu)}{\varphi(\mu)},$$

$$f'(\nu) = -\frac{(\lambda - \nu)(\mu - \nu)}{\varphi(\nu)}.$$

With these values the quadratic form becomes

$$(22) \quad ds^2 = (\lambda - \mu)(\lambda - \nu)\left(\frac{d\lambda}{2\sqrt{\varphi(\lambda)}}\right)^2 + (\lambda - \mu)(\mu - \nu)\left(\frac{d\mu}{2\sqrt{-\varphi(\mu)}}\right)^2$$
$$+ (\lambda - \nu)(\mu - \nu)\left(\frac{d\nu}{2\sqrt{\varphi(\nu)}}\right)^2.$$

A simplification suggests itself, namely the introduction of new coördinates defined by the differential equations

$$(23) \quad d\xi = \frac{d\lambda}{\pm 2\sqrt{\varphi(\lambda)}}, \qquad d\eta = \frac{d\mu}{\pm 2\sqrt{-\varphi(\mu)}}, \qquad d\zeta = \frac{d\nu}{\pm 2\sqrt{\varphi(\nu)}}.$$

The differential of arc is then given by

(24) $ds^2 = (\lambda - \mu)(\lambda - \nu)\, d\xi^2 + (\lambda - \mu)(\mu - \nu)\, d\eta^2 + (\lambda - \nu)(\mu - \nu)\, d\zeta^2.$

Such a change of coördinates does not affect the system of coördinate surfaces, since each of the coördinates is a function of but one of the old. We shall employ the following solutions of the differential equations (23):

(25) $\xi = \dfrac{1}{2}\displaystyle\int_{\lambda}^{\infty} \dfrac{ds}{\sqrt{\varphi(s)}}, \qquad \eta = \dfrac{1}{2}\displaystyle\int_{-b^2}^{\mu} \dfrac{ds}{\sqrt{-\varphi(s)}}, \qquad \zeta = \dfrac{1}{2}\displaystyle\int_{-c^2}^{\nu} \dfrac{ds}{\sqrt{\varphi(s)}}.$

By (8), the absolute value of the functional determinant (3) is

$$(\lambda - \mu)(\lambda - \nu)(\mu - \nu),$$

and this vanishes only on the ellipse (16) or the hyperbola (17), where the equality sign is used in those relations.

The Laplacian of U is given by

(26) $\nabla^2 U = \dfrac{1}{(\lambda - \mu)(\lambda - \nu)(\mu - \nu)}\left[(\mu - \nu)\dfrac{\partial^2 U}{\partial \xi^2} + (\lambda - \nu)\dfrac{\partial^2 U}{\partial \eta^2}\right.$

$$\left. + (\lambda - \mu)\dfrac{\partial^2 U}{\partial \zeta^2}\right].$

Exercise.

Develop the notion of general coördinates in the plane. Develop elliptic coördinates.

5. The Conductor Problem for the Ellipsoid.

For the solution of the problem of finding the distribution of a charge in equilibrium on an ellipsoidal conductor[1], we have the conditions, analogous to those for the spherical conductor,

a) $U = \text{const}, \qquad \lambda \leqq 0,$

                      $\nabla^2 U = 0, \qquad\quad 0 < \lambda;$

b) U is everywhere continuous;

c) the derivatives of the first order of U are continuous everywhere except for $\lambda = 0$, where they satisfy the equation

$$\frac{\partial U}{\partial n_+} - \frac{\partial U}{\partial n_-} = -4\pi\sigma;$$

d) $\varrho U \to E$ as ϱ becomes infinite, $\varrho^2 = x^2 + y^2 + z^2.$

---

[1] For historical indications with respect to the potentials of ellipsoidal surface distributions and of solid ellipsoids, see the Encyklopädie der Mathematischen Wissenschaften, II A 7b, BURKHARDT-MEYER, § 15.

Let us see if there is a solution of Laplace's equation depending only on λ. If there is, it will reduce to a constant on the surface of the ellipsoid, as it should. If U depends only on λ, or, what amounts to the same thing, only on ξ, the expression (26) shows that it must satisfy the equation

$$\frac{d^2 U}{d\xi^2} = 0, \quad \text{whence} \quad U = A\xi + B.$$

The constants are now determined by (d). Comparing the coefficients of s in the identity (19), we find

$$\lambda + \mu + \nu = \varrho^2 - (a^2 + b^2 + c^2).$$

As μ and ν are bounded, λ becomes infinite with ϱ, and $\lim \dfrac{\lambda}{\varrho^2} = 1$. Moreover,

$$(c^2 + s)^3 < \varphi(s) < (a^2 + s)^3,$$

and hence

$$\frac{1}{2}\int\limits_{\lambda}^{\infty} \frac{ds}{(a^2 + s)^{\frac{3}{2}}} < \xi < \frac{1}{2}\int\limits_{\lambda}^{\infty} \frac{ds}{(c^2 + s)^{\frac{3}{2}}}, \quad i.\,e. \quad \frac{1}{\sqrt{a^2 + \lambda}} < \xi < \frac{1}{\sqrt{c^2 + \lambda}}.$$

It follows that $\lim \sqrt{\lambda}\,\xi = 1$, and hence that $\lim \varrho\xi = 1$. Hence

$$\lim \varrho\, U = \lim \frac{1}{\xi} U = \lim \left(A + \frac{B}{\xi}\right).$$

If this limit is to exist and equal E, we must have $A = E$ and $B = 0$. Thus

(27)

$$U = E\xi = \frac{E}{2}\int\limits_{\lambda}^{\infty} \frac{ds}{\sqrt{\varphi(s)}}, \quad 0 \leqq \lambda,$$

$$U = \frac{E}{2}\int\limits_{0}^{\infty} \frac{ds}{\sqrt{\varphi(s)}}, \quad \lambda \leqq 0,$$

the second formula resulting from condition (b) and the fact (a) that $U = \text{const.}$ in the interior of the ellipsoid.

We have thus found a function which satisfies all the stated conditions in the interior of each octant. But U is obviously continuous and continuously differentiable in λ, and λ is a continuous and continuously differentiable function of x, y, z, for a root of an algebraic equation, whose leading coefficient is constant, is a continuous function of the coefficients, and is continuously differentiable in any region in which it does not coincide with another root. But the points at which roots of the equation $f(s)\,\varphi(s) = 0$ coincide are on the bounding curves of (16) and (17). Thus U is continuous, with its derivatives of first order, also on the coördinate planes, except on these curves. We shall see (Theorem VI, Chapter X) that solutions of Laplace's equation on two sides of a smooth surface, on which the solutions and their normal derivatives agree, form a single function satisfying Laplace's equation both near and *on* the surface. The doubtful curves are then cared for by Theorem XIII, Chapter X. Thus the values of U in the various octants form a single function, which really meets the conditions of the problem.

It remains to determine the density. As U is constant in the interior of the conductor, condition (c) becomes

$$\frac{\partial U}{\partial n_+} = -4\pi\sigma, \quad \text{or} \quad \sigma = -\frac{1}{4\pi}\frac{\partial U}{\partial n_+} = \frac{E}{8\pi}\frac{1}{\sqrt{\varphi(\lambda)}}\frac{\partial\lambda}{\partial n_+},$$

as is seen by the rule for differentiating an integral with respect to a limit of integration. The outward normal points in the direction of the λ-curve, so that by (22)

$$dn^2 = \frac{(\lambda-\mu)(\lambda-\nu)}{4\varphi(\lambda)}d\lambda^2, \quad \text{and hence} \quad \frac{\partial\lambda}{\partial n} = 2\sqrt{\frac{\varphi(\lambda)}{(\lambda-\mu)(\lambda-\nu)}},$$

If we put this value, for $\lambda = 0$, in the expression for σ just obtained, we find the result

(28) $$\sigma = \frac{E}{4\pi\sqrt{\mu\nu}}.$$

The problem is completely solved, if we are content with a formula! But here curiosity should be encouraged rather than the reverse, and discontent is in order. How does the charge distribute itself? The product $\mu\nu$ is the value, for $\lambda = 0$, of one of the symmetric functions of the roots of the equation determining the ellipsoidal coördinates. Let us find its value in terms of the coefficients. We compare the coefficients of s in the identy (19):

$$-(\mu\nu + \nu\lambda + \lambda\mu)$$
$$= x^2(b^2 + c^2) + y^2(c^2 + a^2) + z^2(a^2 + b^2) - (b^2c^2 + c^2a^2 + a^2b^2)$$
$$= a^2b^2c^2\left[\frac{x^2}{a^2}\left(\frac{1}{b^2}+\frac{1}{c^2}\right) + \frac{y^2}{b^2}\left(\frac{1}{c^2}+\frac{1}{a^2}\right) + \frac{z^2}{c^2}\left(\frac{1}{a^2}+\frac{1}{b^2}\right) - \left(\frac{1}{a^2}+\frac{1}{b^2}+\frac{1}{c^2}\right)\right]$$
$$= a^2b^2c^2\left[\left(\frac{1}{a^2}+\frac{1}{b^2}+\frac{1}{c^2}\right)\left(\frac{x^2}{a^2}+\frac{y^2}{b^2}+\frac{z^2}{c^2}-1\right) - \left(\frac{x^2}{a^4}+\frac{y^2}{b^4}+\frac{z^2}{c^4}\right)\right].$$

Hence, on the surface of the ellipsoid $\lambda = 0$, ·

$$\mu\nu = a^2b^2c^2\left(\frac{x^2}{a^4}+\frac{y^2}{b^4}+\frac{z^2}{c^4}\right).$$

The equation of the plane tangent to the ellipsoid at (x, y, z), is

$$(X-x)\frac{x}{a^2} + (Y-y)\frac{y}{b^2} + (Z-z)\frac{z}{c^2} = 0,$$

and the distance of this plane from the center is

$$p = \frac{\frac{x^2}{a^2}+\frac{y^2}{b^2}+\frac{z^2}{c^2}}{\sqrt{\frac{x^2}{a^4}+\frac{y^2}{b^4}+\frac{z^2}{c^4}}}, \quad \text{whence} \quad \sqrt{\frac{x^2}{a^4}+\frac{y^2}{b^4}+\frac{z^2}{c^4}} = \frac{1}{p}.$$

Collecting the results, we reduce (28) to

$$(29) \qquad \sigma = \frac{E}{4\pi abc}\, p,$$

or, *the density of the charge at any point of the ellipsoid is proportional to the distance from the center of the tangent plane at that point.*

Since the tangent planes to two similar and similarly placed ellipsoids have, at the points where they are pierced by any ray from their center, distances from the center which are in the constant ratio of the dimensions of the ellipsoids, we may also picture the distribution of the charge as follows. Imagine a slightly larger similar and similarly placed ellipsoid, and think of the space between the two ellipsoids filled with homogeneous material of total mass E. The thickness of this layer of material gives an approximate idea of the density, for the distance between tangent planes at corresponding points differs from the distance between the ellipsoids, measured perpendicularly to one of them at the point in question, by an infinitesimal of higher order. If now the outer ellipsoid shrinks down on the inner one, always remaining similar to it, and the material between them remaining homogeneously distributed, we shall have in the limit a distribution of the material which has the density of the charge in equilibrium on the conductor.

It will be observed that the density is greatest at the ends of the longest diameter, and least at the ends of the shortest diameter. This illustrates the tendency of a static charge to heap up at the points of greatest curvature[1].

Exercises.

1. Check the result (29) by integrating the density over the surface of the ellipsoid.

2. On the assumption that the density varies continuously with the form of the ellipsoid, show that the density of a static charge on a circular lamina of radius a at a distance ϱ from the center is given by

$$= \frac{E}{4\pi a} \cdot \frac{1}{\sqrt{a^2 - \varrho^2}}.$$

3. Find the potential of the above lamina at points of its axis (a) by specializing the result (27), and (b) by finding the integral of the density times the reciprocal of the distance. Reconcile the two results. Beware an error which introduces a factor $\frac{1}{2}$!

4. Show that if the ellipsoid is a prolate spheroid, and we pass to the limit as the equatorial radius approaches 0, the limiting distribution is that of a material straight line segment of constant linear density. Thus find again the result on the equipotential surfaces of Exercise 1, page 56.

---

[1] In fact, the density of charge on the ellipsoid is proportional to the fourth root of the total curvature of the surface.

6. The Potential of the Solid Homogeneous Ellipsoid.

Let us now consider a solid homogeneous ellipsoid (15), of density $\varkappa$. By Exercise 3 (p. 39) the volume cut out from this ellipsoid by a conical surface with vertex at the center and cutting out an element $\varDelta S$ from the surface is

$$\varDelta V = \frac{1}{3} \iint_{\varDelta S} r \cos (n,\, r)\, dS = \frac{1}{3} \iint_{\varDelta S} p\, dS,$$

where p is the perpendicular from the center to the plane tangent to the ellipsoid at the variable point of integration. The volume cut out by the same cone from a similar and similarly placed ellipsoid, whose dimensions are u_1 times those of the basic ellipsoid, is u_1^3 times the above quantity, or

$$\varDelta V = \frac{u_1^3}{3} \iint_{\varDelta S_0} p_0\, dS_0,$$

where we have introduced a subscript in order to emphasize the fact that the integration is over the surface of the basic ellipsoid. The volume cut out by the same cone from the region between two homothetic ellipsoids $u = u_1$, $u = u_2$ is

$$\varDelta V = \frac{u_2^3 - u_1^3}{3} \iint_{\varDelta S_0} p_0\, dS_0 = \bar{u}^2 \bar{p}_0\, \varDelta u\, \varDelta S_0,$$

where we have used the laws of the mean for differences and for integrals. We should like, however, to have this element of volume expressed in terms of the values of the functions involved at a point within the element of volume. We notice that for points on the same ray from the center, the values of p, for two ellipsoids, are proportional to the dimensions of the ellipsoids, so that on the ellipsoid $u = \bar{u}$, $p = \bar{u} p_0$. Also, for the element of surface of this ellipsoid, we have, $\varDelta S = \bar{u}^2 \varDelta S_0$. Hence

$$\varDelta V = \frac{1}{\bar{u}} \bar{p}\, \varDelta S \varDelta u.$$

Armed with this implement, we may now find the potential of a solid ellipsoid, or, more generally, of the body bounded by two homothetic ellipsoids, $u = u_1$, $u = u_2$. We have, for the latter

$$(30) \quad U = \lim \sum \frac{\varkappa\, \varDelta V}{r} = \varkappa \lim \sum \frac{\bar{p}\, \varDelta S\, \varDelta u}{\bar{u}\, r} = \varkappa \int_{u_1}^{u_2} \frac{1}{u} \iint_{S} \frac{p\, dS}{r}\, d u.$$

We notice first that the inner integral is the potential of a charge in equilibrium on the surface of the ellipsoid $u = u$, since the density of such a charge is proportional to p. Hence the inner integral is constant within the inner limiting ellipsoid; that is, it is independent of x, y and z, and is a function of u alone. Hence U is itself constant inside the inner ellipsoid $u = u_1$, and we find again Newton's theorem (Chapter I, p. 22), to the effect that *an ellipsoidal homoeoid exercises no attraction at points in its interior*. In fact, we might have found the law of distribution of a static charge on an ellipsoidal conductor by means of Newton's theorem, but we should still have had left the problem of determining the potential.

Let us now revert to the solid ellipsoid, writing accordingly, in (30), $u_1 = 0$, $u_2 = 1$. The inner integral is the potential of a spread of density p on the ellipsoid $u = u$ of semi-axes ua, ub, uc. It is therefore, by (29), the potential of a spread of total charge $4\pi abc u^3$. This potential, as given by (27) is

$$(31) \qquad U_u = 2\pi abc u^3 \int_{\lambda(u)}^{\infty} \frac{ds}{\sqrt{\varphi(u, s)}},$$

where

$$\varphi(u, s) = (a^2 u^2 + s)(b^2 u^2 + s)(c^2 u^2 + s),$$

and where $\lambda(u)$ is the greatest root of the equation

$$f(u, \lambda) = \frac{x^2}{a^2 u^2 + \lambda} + \frac{y^2}{b^2 u^2 + \lambda} + \frac{z^2}{c^2 u^2 + \lambda} - 1 = 0.$$

Thus the potential U of the solid ellipsoid, at an exterior point, given by (30), becomes

$$U_e = 2\pi abc \varkappa \int_0^1 u^2 \int_{\lambda(u)}^{\infty} \frac{ds}{\sqrt{\varphi(u, s)}} du.$$

This expression can be reduced to a simple integral. We introduce first a new variable of integration in the inner integral, by the substitution $s = u^2 t$:

$$U_e = 2\pi abc \varkappa \int_0^1 u \int_v^{\infty} \frac{dt}{\sqrt{\varphi(t)}} du, \qquad v = \frac{\lambda(u)}{u^2}.$$

We next employ integration by parts in the outer integral:

$$\int_0^1 u \int_v^{\infty} \frac{dt}{\sqrt{\varphi(t)}} du = \left[\frac{u^2}{2} \int_v^{\infty} \frac{dt}{\sqrt{\varphi(t)}}\right]_0^1 + \frac{1}{2} \int_0^1 u^2 \frac{1}{\sqrt{\varphi(v)}} \frac{dv}{du} du.$$

As v is the greatest root of the equation

$$(32) \qquad \frac{x^2}{a^2 + v} + \frac{y^2}{b^2 + v} + \frac{z^2}{c^2 + v} = u^2,$$

it always decreases as u increases, and hence may be used as a variable of integration in place of u. For $u = 1$, $v = \lambda$, the greatest root of the equation $f(\lambda) = 0$, while as u approaches 0, v becomes infinite. Hence

$$U_e = \pi\, a b c\, \varkappa \left\{ \int_\lambda^\infty \frac{dt}{\sqrt{\varphi(t)}} - \int_\lambda^\infty \left[\frac{x^2}{a^2+v} + \frac{y^2}{b^2+v} + \frac{z^2}{c^2+v} \right] \frac{dv}{\sqrt{\varphi(v)}} \right\}.$$

or, finally

$$(33) \qquad U_e = \pi\, a b c\, \varkappa \int_\lambda^\infty \left[1 - \frac{x^2}{a^2+s} - \frac{y^2}{b^2+s} - \frac{z^2}{c^2+s} \right] \frac{ds}{\sqrt{\varphi(s)}}.$$

To find the potential at an interior point, let $u = u_0$ characterize the ellipsoid of the family of similar ellipsoids which passes through the point $P(x, y, z)$. We shall now have to break the integral (30),—always with $u_1 = 0$, $u_2 = 1$—into two, since for the ellipsoids $u < u_0$, P is an exterior point. For the first, we still use for the inner integral in (30) the value (31). For the second, we have merely, by (27), to replace the lower limit by 0. Accordingly we have

$$U_i = 2\pi\, a b c\, \varkappa \left[\int_0^{u_0} u \int_v^\infty \frac{dt}{\sqrt{\varphi(t)}} \, du + \int_{u_0}^1 u \int_0^\infty \frac{dt}{\sqrt{\varphi(t)}} \, du \right].$$

In the first integral, we carry out an integration by parts. In the second, the inner integral is a constant. We note that when $v = 0$, $u = u_0$, by (32), since $P(x, y, z)$ lies on the ellipsoid $u = u_0$. We have, then,

$$U_i = 2\pi\, a b c\, \varkappa \left[\frac{u^2}{2} \int_0^\infty \frac{dt}{\sqrt{\varphi(t)}} \Bigg|_0^{u_0} + \frac{1}{2} \int_0^{u_0} u^2 \frac{1}{\sqrt{\varphi(v)}} \frac{dv}{du} \, du + \frac{1-u_0^2}{2} \int_0^\infty \frac{dt}{\sqrt{\varphi(t)}} \right]$$

$$= \pi\, a b c\, \varkappa \left\{ u_0^2 \int_0^\infty \frac{dt}{\sqrt{\varphi(t)}} - \int_0^\infty \left[\frac{x^2}{a^2+v} + \frac{y^2}{b^2+v} + \frac{z^2}{c^2+v} \right] \frac{dv}{\sqrt{\varphi(t)}} \right.$$

$$\left. + (1-u_0^2) \int_0^\infty \frac{dt}{\sqrt{\varphi(t)}} \right\},$$

that is,

$$(34) \qquad U_i = \pi\, a b c\, \varkappa \int_0^\infty \left[1 - \frac{x^2}{a^2+s} - \frac{y^2}{b^2+s} - \frac{z^2}{c^2+s} \right] \frac{ds}{\sqrt{\varphi(s)}}.$$

Thus in the interior of the ellipsoid, the potential is a quadratic function of x, y and z:

$$(35) \qquad U_i = -A x^2 - B y^2 - C z^2 + D,$$

where

$$A = \pi\, a b c\, \varkappa \int_0^\infty \frac{ds}{(a^2+s)\sqrt{\varphi(s)}}, \qquad D = \pi\, a b c\, \varkappa \int_0^\infty \frac{ds}{\sqrt{\varphi(s)}},$$

B and C being obtained from A by interchanging b with a, and c with a, respectively.

Exercises.

1. Show that the constants A, B, C are the same for all similar ellipsoids of the same density. Hence infer Newton's theorem on the ellipsoidal homoeoid. Find the value of the potential at interior points in terms of a single integral.

2. Specialize the results obtained for the potential at exterior and interior points of a homogeneous ellipsoid to the case of the sphere.

3. Obtain from the potential the components of force at interior and exterior points of a homogeneous ellipsoid. Verify directly that the formulas (33) and (35) define a potential for which $V^2 U_e = 0$, $V^2 U_i = -2(A + B + C) = -4\pi\varkappa$. Verify that the potential and force are everywhere continuous, and that ϱU_e approaches the total mass as ϱ become infinite.

4. Show that in the interior of a homogeneous ellipsoid, the equipotentials are similar and similarly placed ellipsoids of more nearly spherical form than the given ellipsoid. Show by means of the developments of the preceding chapter that these equipotentials join on continuously, with continuously turning tangent planes, to the equipotentials outside the ellipsoid, but, as a rule, with breaks in the curvatures.

5. In finding the solution of the conductor problem, we saw that a family of confocal ellipsoids, $\lambda = $ const. would be equipotentials. Show that a necessary and sufficient condition that a family of surfaces $F(x, y, z) = C$, where $F(x, y, z)$ has continuous partial derivatives of the second order, may be equipotential surfaces of a Newtonian potential (solution of Laplace's equation) is that $\dfrac{V^2 F}{(\nabla F)^2}$ is a function $\varphi(F)$ of F only. Show that if this condition is fulfilled, the potential is

$$U = c_1 \int^F e^{-\int^t \varphi(t)\,dt}\,dt + c_2.$$

6. Specialize the formulas for the potential of a homogeneous ellipsoid to the cases of prolate and oblate spheroids, evaluating the integrals which occur. Answers, for the prolate spheroid,

$$U_e = \frac{6E}{f^2}\left[\frac{4x^2 - 2r^2 - f^2}{2f}\log\sqrt{\frac{s-f}{s+f}} + \frac{s^2(2x^2 - r^2) - 2f^2 x^2}{s(s^2 - f^2)}\right],$$

for the oblate spheroid,

$$U_e = \frac{6E}{f^2}\left[\frac{4z^2 - 2r^2 + f^2}{2f}\sin^{-1}\frac{f}{s} + \frac{s^2(r^2 - 2z^2) - f^2 r^2}{s^2\sqrt{s^2 - f^2}}\right],$$

where f is the distance between the foci of a meridian section, s the sum of the focal radii to P, x, or z, the distance of P from the equatorial plane, and r the distance from P to the axis. In both cases U_i is obtained from U_e by replacing s by $2a$, the maximum diameter of the ellipsoid.

Numerical Computation. The computation of the potential and of the forces due to the distributions considered above, involves, in general, the solution of cubics and the evaluation of certain elliptic integrals. The approximate solution of the cubics in numerical cases will give no difficulty, but the usual approximation methods for the integrals do not work well on account of the slow convergence of the integrals. They are probably best handled by reducing them to normal forms and having recourse to tables[1].

Exercises.

7. Writing the formula (33) in the form

$$U_e = \pi\, a b c\, \varkappa\, [D\,(\lambda) - A\,(\lambda)\, x^2 - B\,(\lambda)\, y^2 - C\,(\lambda)\, z^2],$$

and writing

$$\sqrt{a^2 + s} = \frac{\sqrt{a^2 - c^2}}{\sin \varphi}, \quad \sqrt{a^2 + \lambda} = \frac{\sqrt{a^2 - c^2}}{\sin \vartheta}, \quad 0 < \vartheta \leqq \frac{\pi}{2},$$

$$k = \sqrt{\frac{a^2 - b^2}{a^2 - c^2}}, \quad k' = \sqrt{1 - k^2} = \sqrt{\frac{b^2 - c^2}{a^2 - c^2}},$$

show that

$$A\,(\lambda) = \frac{2}{(a^2 - c^2)^{\frac{3}{2}}\, k^2}\, [F\,(k,\, \vartheta) - E\,(k,\, \vartheta)],$$

$$B\,(\lambda) = \frac{2}{(a^2 - c^2)^{\frac{3}{2}}\, k^2\, k'^2}\left[E\,(k,\, \vartheta) - k'^2\, F\,(k,\, \vartheta) - k^2\, \frac{\sin \vartheta \cos \vartheta}{\sqrt{1 - k^2 \sin^2 \vartheta}}\right],$$

$$C\,(\lambda) = \frac{2}{(a^2 - c^2)^{\frac{3}{2}}\, k'^2}\left[\frac{\sin \vartheta \sqrt{1 - k^2 \sin^2 \vartheta}}{\cos \vartheta} - E\,(k,\, \vartheta)\right],$$

$$D\,(\lambda) = \frac{2}{(a^2 - c^2)^{\frac{1}{2}}}\, F\,(k,\, \vartheta).$$

In the derivation of the above values for $B\,(\lambda)$ and $C\,(\lambda)$, reduction formulas are needed. These may be obtained by differentiating

$$\frac{\sin \varphi \cos \varphi}{\sqrt{1 - k^2 \sin^2 \varphi}} \quad \text{and} \quad \frac{\sin \varphi \sqrt{1 - k^2 \sin^2 \varphi}}{\cos \varphi}.$$

8. An ellipsoidal conductor of semi-axes 7, 5 and 1 carries a unit charge in equilibrium. Determine the potential on the ellipsoid, and at points on the axes distant 20 units from the center. Compare these values with those of the potential at the last three points due to a unit charge on a small spherical conductor with the same center. Give the results to at least three significant figures.

9. The same ellipsoid, instead of being charged, is filled with homogeneously distributed attracting matter, of total mass 1. Find the potential at the same three exterior points, and determine the coefficients of the quadratic expression giving the potential at interior points. Plot the section, by the plane containing the greatest and least diameters, of the material ellipsoid, and of several interior equipotential surfaces.

7. Remarks on the Analytic Continuation of Potentials.

Newtonian potentials are analytic at the points of free space. On the other hand, the potentials, or some of their derivatives, are discontinuous

---

[1] The definitions of the Legendre normal forms, and brief tables of their values may be found in B. O. Pierce, *A Short Table of Integrals*, Boston. A discussion of elliptic integrals may be found in the ninth chapter of Osgood's *Advanced Calculus*.

on surfaces bearing masses, or bounding regions containing masses. But if the surfaces and the densities are analytic, the potentials to either side of the surfaces, as we have seen in special cases, may be analytic, and may be continued analytically across the surfaces. This is not in contradiction with the results of the last chapter, it simply means that the functions representing the potentials, when so continued, cease to represent the potentials on the farther sides of the surfaces.

Take, for instance, the potential of a charge E on the surface of a spherical conductor of radius a. Inside the sphere, the potential has the constant value $\dfrac{E}{a}$. Outside, it is $\dfrac{E}{\varrho}$. The first is analytic throughout space. The second is analytic except at the origin. For $\varrho < a$, $\dfrac{E}{\varrho}$ no longer represents the potential of the charge on the given sphere. It does, however, represent the potential of the same charge on any smaller concentric sphere of radius b, as long as $\varrho > b$. This is an example of the fact that one and the same function may be the potential of different distributions in a region exterior to both. We shall see later (p. 222) that when, and only when, the potential is given throughout all of space, the distribution of masses producing that potential is uniquely determined.

The potential, at exterior points, of a charge in equilibrium on an ellipsoidal conductor can also be continued into the interior, when it will also be the potential of an equal charge in equilibrium on a smaller confocal ellipsoid at exterior points. In fact, this holds for $\lambda > -c^2$, and even in the limit, so that the same function can represent the potential of an elliptic lamina. Here the function ceases to be analytic on the edge of the lamina—but only on the edge. It can therefore be continued across the lamina. Here it ceases to be the potential of the lamina, because that potential must have a break in its normal derivative on the lamina. The function cannot therefore be single valued (see the exercise, to follow).

A potential, then, can be due to various distributions. We shall see that it can always be regarded as due to masses nearer to the attracted particle than those which first determine it. Whether the masses may be made more distant or not is usually a question to be decided in special cases[1].

---

[1] The formulas of the last chapter show that if a potential of a volume distribution can be continued analytically across an analytic bounding surface from either side, the density, if it satisfies a Hölder condition, must be analytic, and similar results hold for other distributions. Conversely, it can be shown that analytic densities on analytic surfaces always yield potentials which are analytically continuable across the surfaces, and similarly for volume distributions with analytic densities. For references, see the Enzyklopädie der Mathematischen Wissenschaften, II C 3, LICHTENSTEIN, p. 209.

Exercise.

Specialize the result (27) to the case of a charge on an oblate spheroid, and evaluate the integral. Show that

$$\lambda = \frac{(r_1 + r_2)^2}{2} - a^2,$$

where r_1 and r_2 are the extreme distances from P to the circumference of the limiting circular lamina. Thus obtain the result in the form

$$U_e = \frac{E}{a} \sin^{-1} \frac{2a}{r_1 + r_2},$$

the branch of the inverse sine being so determined that U_e vanishes at infinity. Thus show that U_e is continuable across the limiting lamina, and forms then a *two*-valued function of the position of P. Note that U_e is constant on a system of confocal spheroids, and that on the axis, it is equal to $\frac{E}{a}$ times the angle subtended at P by a radius of the limiting lamina.

8. Further Examples Leading to Solutions of Laplace's Equation.

Steady Flow of Heat in an Infinite Strip. Suppose we have a very long strip of homogeneous metal, so long that we may idealize it as infinitely long. Let its two edges be kept at the temperature 0, and let one end be kept at temperatures which are a given function of position along that end. Let the faces be insulated. What will be the distribution of temperatures in the strip when a steady state is realized?

Let the strip lie in the region of the (x, y)-plane

$$R: \quad 0 \leqq x \leqq \pi, y \geqq 0.$$

We have, then, for the temperature U, the conditions

$$\frac{\partial^2 U}{\partial x^2} + \frac{\partial^2 U}{\partial y^2} = 0 \text{ in } R,$$

$$U = 0 \text{ for } x = 0 \text{ and } x = \pi,$$

$$U = f(x) \text{ for } 0 \leqq x \leqq \pi \text{ and } y = 0,$$

$$U \text{ continuous and bounded.}$$

We follow a method used by DANIEL BERNOUILLI[1] in a discussion of the vibrating string, and called by EULER *Bernouilli's principle*. It consists in finding particular solutions of the differential equation, and building up the desired solution as a linear combination of the particular solutions with constant coefficients, a process here rendered feasible by the linear homogeneous character of Laplace's equation. For, because of this character, a constant times a solution is a solution, and a sum of solutions is a solution.

---

[1] *Novi Commentarii Academiae Scientiarum Imperialis Petropolitanae*, Vol. 19, (1775), p. 239.

The method of finding particular solutions consists in seeking to satisfy the differential equation by a product of functions, of which each depends on one variable only. The solution of the partial differential equation is then reduced to the solution of ordinary differential equations. Thus if X is a function of x only, and Y of y only, $U = XY$ will satisfy Laplace's equation provided

$$X'' Y + X Y'' = 0,$$

or

$$\frac{X''}{X} = - \frac{Y''}{Y}.$$

As the left hand member does not depend on y, and the right hand member does not depend on x, neither can depend on either. Hence both are equal to a constant, which we shall write $-c^2$. Then

$$X'' + c^2 X = 0, \qquad Y'' - c^2 Y = 0,$$

and we find, accordingly, four types of particular solutions:

$$U = XY = e^{cy} \cos cx, \; e^{-cy} \cos cx, \; e^{cy} \sin cx, \; e^{-cy} \sin cx.$$

The first and third are not bounded in R, and we therefore reject them. The first does not vanish for $x = 0$. But the fourth does. The fourth will also vanish for $x = \pi$, for all values of y, provided $\sin \pi c = 0$. This equation is satisfied for $c = 1, 2, 3, \ldots$. Thus we have an infinity of solutions of Laplace's equation, all satisfying all but the third of the conditions to be met.

The question is now, can we build up the desired solution, fulfilling the third condition, in the form

$$U = \sum_1^\infty b_n e^{-ny} \sin nx\,?$$

If so, and if the series converges for $y = 0$, the third condition demands that

$$f(x) = \sum_1^\infty b_n \sin nx \qquad\qquad 0 \leqq x \leqq \pi.$$

We are thus led to a problem in Fourier series, and if $f(x)$ can be expanded in a series of this type which converges at every point of the interval, it is not difficult to show that the above series for U satisfies the conditions of the problem. We shall not consider questions of convergence at present. For Fourier series, a discussion of this topic will be found in Chapter XII, § 9. For reasonably smooth functions, the convergence is assured.

Exercises.

1. Show that if in the above problem $f(x) = 1$, we are led to the solution

$$U = \frac{4}{\pi} \left[e^{-y} \sin x + \frac{1}{3} e^{-3y} \sin 3x + \frac{1}{5} e^{-5y} \sin 5x \ldots \right] = \frac{2}{\pi} \tan^{-1} \frac{\sin x}{\sinh y},$$

the inverse tangent lying in the interval $\left(0, \dfrac{\pi}{2}\right)$. Show that U satisfies the conditions of the problem, except at the corners, where they are contradictory. Draw the isothermals for small x and y.

2. Solve the problem of the text with the alteration that the edges $x = 0$ and $x = \pi$ are insulated instead of kept at the temperature 0.

3. Five of the faces of a homogeneous cube are kept at the temperature 0, while the sixth is kept at temperatures which are a given function of position on this face. Show how to determine the temperatures in the interior, assumed stationary.

If, instead of having finite breadth, the plate occupies the whole upper half of the (x, y)-plane, the method of series is not available. Instead of replacing c in a particular solution by a variable n taking on positive integral values, multiplying by a function of n and summing, we may, however, replace it by a variable α, taking on continuous values, multiply by a function of α, and integrate. In fact, we assume

$$U(x, y) = \int_0^\infty e^{-\alpha y}[A(\alpha) \cos \alpha x + B(\alpha) \sin \alpha x]\, d\alpha.$$

Waiving the justification of the steps, we now set $y = 0$. If U is to take on the assigned values $f(x)$ on the edge $y = 0$ of the plate, we should have

$$f(x) = \int_0^\infty [A(\alpha) \cos \alpha x + B(\alpha) \sin \alpha x]\, d\alpha.$$

The question then arises, can $A(\alpha)$ and $B(\alpha)$ be so chosen that an arbitrary function $f(x)$ is represented by this formula? The answer is contained in the following identity, known as Fourier's integral theorem[1]

$$f(x) = \frac{1}{\pi} \int_{-\infty}^{+\infty} f(\xi) \int_0^\infty \cos \alpha\, (x - \xi)\, d\alpha\, d\xi,$$

which is valid, and in which the order of integration can be inverted, provided $f(x)$ satisfies certain conditions of smoothness and of behavior at infinity. In fact, if these conditions are met, the choice

$$A(\alpha) = \frac{1}{\pi} \int_{-\infty}^\infty \cos \alpha \xi\, f(\xi)\, d\xi, \qquad B(\alpha) = \frac{1}{\pi} \int_{-\infty}^\infty \sin \alpha \xi\, f(\xi)\, d\xi$$

meets the requirements of the problem, and the solution is

$$U(x, y) = \frac{1}{\pi} \int_{-\infty}^\infty f(\xi) \int_0^\infty e^{-\alpha y} \cos \alpha\, (x - \xi)\, d\alpha\, d\xi.$$

---

[1] See, for instance, RIEMANN-WEBER, *Die Differential- und Integralgleichungen der Mechanik und Physik*, Vol. I, Chapter IV, § 3. Braunschweig 1925; CARSLAW, *Introduction to the Theory of Fourier's Series and Integrals*, Chapter X, London 1921.

Exercise.

Determine the stationary temperatures in a homogeneous isotropic plate occupying a half-plane, when a strip of length 2 of the edge is kept at the temperature 1, while the rest of the edge is kept at the temperature 0. Answer, $U(x, y) = \dfrac{\vartheta}{\pi}$, where ϑ is the angle subtended at the point (x, y) by the segment kept at the temperature 1.

Flow of Heat in a Circular Cylinder. To solve Laplace's equation in a way to get solutions adaptable to problems dealing with circular cylinders, we start with that equation in cylindrical coördinates

$$V^2 U = \frac{1}{\varrho} \frac{\partial}{\partial \varrho} \varrho \frac{\partial U}{\partial \varrho} + \frac{1}{\varrho^2} \frac{\partial^2 U}{\partial \varphi^2} + \frac{\partial^2 U}{\partial z^2} = 0,$$

and seek solutions of the form $R \Phi Z$. For such a solution

$$\frac{\dfrac{1}{\varrho} \dfrac{d}{d\varrho} \varrho \dfrac{dR}{d\varrho}}{R} + \frac{1}{\varrho^2} \frac{\dfrac{d^2\Phi}{d\varphi^2}}{\Phi} + \frac{\dfrac{d^2 Z}{dz^2}}{Z} = 0.$$

The last term depends on z only, and the first two are independent of z. Hence we must have

(36)
$$\begin{cases} \dfrac{d^2 Z}{dz^2} - c_1 Z = 0, \\[2mm] \dfrac{\dfrac{1}{\varrho} \dfrac{d}{d\varrho} \varrho \dfrac{dR}{d\varrho}}{R} + \dfrac{\dfrac{d^2\Phi}{d\varphi^2}}{\Phi} + c_1 \varrho^2 = 0. \end{cases}$$

The second equation leads, by similar reasoning, to

(37)
$$\frac{d^2\Phi}{d\varphi^2} - c_2 \Phi = 0,$$

(38)
$$\frac{1}{\varrho} \frac{d}{d\varrho} \varrho \frac{dR}{d\varrho} + (c_2 + c_1\varrho^2) R = 0.$$

If U is to be a one-valued function in the cylinder—which we assume to have the axis of the cylindrical coördinates as axis—, Φ must be a function of φ with period 2π. It follows that in (37), c_2 must have the form $c_2 = -n^2$, where n is an integer. Hence

$$\Phi = \cos n\varphi \quad \text{or} \quad \sin n\varphi.$$

The character of c_1 will depend on the given boundary conditions. We leave it undetermined for the present. It can be made to disappear from the equation (38) by introducing a new independent variable, $x = \sqrt{c_1}\varrho$. The equation then becomes

(39)
$$\frac{d^2 R}{dx^2} + \frac{1}{x} \frac{dR}{dx} + \left(1 - \frac{n^2}{x^2}\right) R = 0.$$

This is known as *Bessel's equation*, and its solutions, as *Bessel functions*[1].

By the power series method, a solution of this differential equation may be found:

$$(40) \quad R = J_n(x) = \sum_0^\infty \frac{(-1)^k \left(\frac{x}{2}\right)^{n+2k}}{k!\,(n+k)!}$$

$$= \frac{x^n}{2^n \cdot n!}\left[1 - \frac{x^2}{2\,(2\,n+2)} + \frac{x^4}{2\cdot 4\,(2\,n+2)\,(2\,n+4)} - \cdots\right].$$

The series is always convergent, and represents *Bessel's function of the first kind of order n.* No solution of the differential equation other than a constant times $J_n(x)$ remains finite at the origin.

When we know a particular solution of an ordinary homogeneous linear differential equation of the second order, we may reduce the problem of finding the general solution to a quadrature. Thus if we substitute in the differential equation

$$R = u J_n(x),$$

and integrate the resulting differential equation for u, we find

$$R = c J_n(x) \int \frac{d x}{x J_n^2(x)} + c' J_n(x).$$

The second term of this solution is the Bessel function of the first kind. The first term, with the constant of integration properly fixed, is *Bessel's function of the second kind of order n.*

If the problem is to find the stationary distribution of temperatures in an infinite homogeneous cylinder

$$\varrho \leqq a, \quad z \geqq 0,$$

the temperature being kept at 0 on the curved surface $\varrho = a$, and kept at values given by a function $f(\varrho)$ on the plane face $z = 0$ (where, for simplicity we have assumed these temperatures to depend only on ϱ), we should expect the internal temperatures to be independent of φ. Accordingly, we should take $n = 0$. Then we should have, as particular solutions

$$U = J_0(\sqrt{c_1}\,\varrho)\,e^{\sqrt{c_1}\,z} \quad \text{and} \quad U = J_0(\sqrt{c_1}\,\varrho)\,e^{-\sqrt{c_1}\,z}.$$

---

[1] Bessel, *Untersuchungen des Theils der planetarischen Störungen, welcher aus der Bewegung der Sonne entsteht*, Abhandlungen der Königlichen Akademie der Wissenschaften zu Berlin, mathematische Klasse, 1824, pp. 1—52. Special cases of Bessel functions had been considered by D. Bernouilli and by Euler. See Watson, *Treatise on the Theory of Bessel Functions*, Cambridge, 1922, Chapter I.

If the temperatures are to be bounded, the first of these must be rejected. Solutions involving Bessel functions of the second kind are also to be rejected, since they become infinite for $\varrho = 0$. Accordingly, we take the solution

$$U = J_0\left(\sqrt{c_1}\varrho\right) e^{-\sqrt{c_1}z},$$

and since the temperature is to be 0 on the wall $\varrho = a$, for all z, we must have

$$J_0\left(\sqrt{c_1}\,a\right) = 0.$$

Now $J_0(x)$ has only real positive roots, and of these it has an infinite number[1]). Let them be denoted, in order of increasing magnitude by $\alpha_1, \alpha_2, \alpha_3, \ldots$. The condition on the wall will then be satisfied if $\sqrt{c_1} = \frac{\alpha_n}{a}$, $n = 1, 2, 3, \ldots$. The problem is thus reduced to the examination of the question as to whether the desired solution can be built up of the particular solutions, that is, in the form

$$U = A_1 J_0\left(\alpha_1 \frac{\varrho}{a}\right) e^{-\frac{\alpha_1}{a}z} + A_2 J_0\left(\alpha_2 \frac{\varrho}{a}\right) e^{-\frac{\alpha_2}{a}z}$$

$$+ A_3 J_0\left(\alpha_3 \frac{\varrho}{a}\right) e^{-\frac{\alpha_3}{a}z} + \cdots.$$

If we are to satisfy the condition on the plane face of the cylinder, we must be able to develop the function

$$f(\varrho) = f(at) = F(t)$$

in a series of the form

$$F(t) = A_1 J_0(\alpha_1 t) + A_2 J_0(\alpha_2 t) + A_3 J_0(\alpha_3 t) + \cdots, \quad 0 \leqq t \leqq 1.$$

This is always possible for sufficiently smooth functions. Moreover, it can be shown that the functions

$$J_0(\alpha_i t)\sqrt{t} \quad \text{and} \quad J_0(\alpha_k t)\sqrt{t}, \quad i \neq k,$$

are orthogonal on the interval $(0, 1)$ and that

$$\int_0^1 J_0^2(\alpha_i t)\, t\, dt = \tfrac{1}{2} J_1^2(\alpha_i),$$

so that if the series is uniformly convergent the coefficients are given by

$$A_i = \frac{2}{J_1^2(\alpha_i)} \int_0^1 F(t)\, J_0(\alpha_i t)\, t\, dt.$$

---

[1] See RIEMANN-WEBER, l. c., Vol. I, p. 337.

Special Spherical Harmonics. The differential equation for surface spherical harmonics of order n, obtained by the method of substituting a product $U = \varrho^n S$ in Laplace's equation, is

$$\frac{\partial^2 S}{\partial \varphi^2} + \sin \vartheta \frac{\partial}{\partial \vartheta} \sin \vartheta \frac{\partial S}{\partial \vartheta} + n(n+1) \sin^2 \vartheta \, S = 0,$$

or, with the independent variable $u = \cos \vartheta$,

$$\frac{\partial^2 S}{\partial \varphi^2} + (1-u^2) \left[\frac{\partial}{\partial u} (1-u^2) \frac{\partial S}{\partial u} + n(n+1) S \right] = 0.$$

If we seek spherical harmonics which are products of functions each of one variable, $S = \Phi P$, we see at once that Φ must be of the form $\sin c\varphi$, $\cos c\varphi$, or an exponential function. The only cases in which S will be a one-valued function of position on the whole sphere are those in which Φ is $\cos m\varphi$ or $\sin m\varphi$, where m is an integer. Accordingly, we take

$$S = \cos m\varphi \, P(u), \quad \text{or} \quad S = \sin m\varphi \, P(u),$$

and the differential equation for $P(u)$ is

(41) $$\frac{d}{du}(1-u^2)\frac{dP}{du} + \left[n(n+1) - \frac{m^2}{1-u^2} \right] P = 0.$$

This is found to have the solution

$$P = (1-u^2)^{\frac{m}{2}} \frac{d^m}{du^m} P_n(u) = P_n^m(u),$$

where $P_n(u)$ is the Legendre polynomial of degree n, and $P_n^m(u)$ is the usual notation for this solution of the equation (41). It is obviously identically 0 for $m > n$, but not for $m \leq n$. Expressed in terms of ϑ, it is a polynomial of degree $n - m$ in $\cos \vartheta$, multiplied by $\sin{}^m \vartheta$. Giving to m the values $0, 1, 2, \ldots n$, we find the surface spherical harmonics of order n:

$$P_n(u),$$

$$P_n^1(u) \cos \varphi, \qquad P_n^1(u) \sin \varphi,$$
$$P_n^2(u) \cos 2\varphi, \qquad P_n^2(u) \sin 2\varphi,$$
$$\cdots \qquad\qquad \cdots$$
$$P_n^n(u) \cos n\varphi, \qquad P_n^n(u) \sin n\varphi,$$

These functions are clearly independent, and there are $2n + 1$ of them. They therefore comprise a complete list of surface spherical harmonics of degree n, in terms of which any other can be expressed as a linear homogeneous combination. They are orthogonal on the surface of the unit sphere—in fact the integral with respect to φ of the product of any two of them, from 0 to 2π is 0. Moreover, it can be shown that

$$\int_{-1}^{1} [P_n^n(u)]^2 \, du = \frac{2}{2n+1} \frac{(n+m)!}{(n-m)!}.$$

The above special surface spherical harmonics vanish on equally spaced meridians, and on parallel circles, dividing the surface of the sphere into curvilinear rectangles. They are sometimes called *Tesseral Harmonics*. These, and related functions in which n and m are not both integers are adapted for use in problems connected with regions bounded by spherical surfaces, meridian planes, and cones through parallel circles.

Lamé Functions. Laplace's equation in ellipsoidal coördinates may be written

$$(\mu - \nu) \sqrt{\varphi(\lambda)} \frac{\partial}{\partial \lambda} \sqrt{\varphi(\lambda)} \frac{\partial U}{\partial \lambda} + (\lambda - \nu) \sqrt{\varphi(-\mu)} \frac{\partial}{\partial \mu} \sqrt{\varphi(-\mu)} \frac{\partial U}{\partial \mu}$$

$$+ (\lambda - \mu) \sqrt{\varphi(\nu)} \frac{\partial}{\partial \nu} \sqrt{\varphi(\nu)} \frac{\partial U}{\partial \nu} = 0.$$

Assuming the product form $U = LMN$ for the solution, we find

$$(\mu - \nu) L^* + (\lambda - \nu) M^* + (\lambda - \mu) N^* = 0,$$

where L^*, M^*, N^* are functions of λ, μ, ν, alone, respectively. If we solve this equation for L^*, we see that L^* is linear in λ, with coefficients apparently depending on μ and ν. But as L^* is independent of these variables, we must have $L^* = a\lambda + b$, where a and b are constants. It is similar with M^* and N^*. It turns out that L, M, and N are all solutions, in different intervals, of the same differential equation

$$\sqrt{\varphi(s)} \frac{\partial}{\partial s} \sqrt{\varphi(s)} \frac{dL}{ds} + (as + b) L = 0,$$

belonging to the same values of the parameters a and b. The solutions of this differential equation are known as *Lamé functions*. They are suited to the treatment of problems connected with regions bounded by ellipsoids, or by parts of any surfaces belonging to a system of confocal quadrics.

It thus appears that each region gives rise to functions more or less characteristic of the region, and also to a problem of developing an arbitrary function as an infinite series in the characteristic functions with constant coefficients. The treatment of such questions cannot be taken up here, as it would take us too far from the study of the fundamental properties of Newtonian potentials. The above indications have merely the purpose of suggesting the methods that are available for the actual solution of problems connected with Laplace's equation, and for the attaining of numerical results; and at the same time they may give some idea of the extent to which analysis is enriched by a great variety of interesting functions, which are useful in treating the most diverse problems. The reader who wishes to pursue the subject farther will find ample material. From the standpoint of actual application to problems, without much concern as to questions of convergence, he will find stimulating and rich in material BYERLY's *Fourier Series* and *Spherical Harmonics*, Boston, 1902. He will also find interesting the chapters devoted to the subject in the book of RIEMANN-WEBER (l. c. footnote p. 200), and COURANT-HILBERT, *Methoden der Mathematischen Physik*, Berlin, 1924. A more extensive study of the properties of the various functions may be made with the help of WHITTAKER and WATSON, *A Course in Modern Analysis*, Cambridge, 1927; BÔCHER, *Die Reihenentwickelungen der Potentialtheorie*, Leipzig, 1894. See also CARSLAW (l. c. footnote p. 200). References to further material may be found in the *Encyklopädie der mathematischen Wissenschaften*, Vol. II, especially II, A. 10, *Kugelfunktionen* etc., A. WANGERIN; II, C, 11, *Allgemeine Reihenentwickelungen*, E. HILB u. O. SZÁSZ.

9. Electrostatics; Non-homogeneous Media.

We have considered briefly some problems in electrostatics in which it was assumed that there was but one medium present. Before taking up the coexistence of different dielectrics, let us consider the effect on the force due to a single unit point charge at O, of a homogeneous dielectric not a vacuum. The charges on the molecules of this dielectric, having a certain degree of mobility, will move under the influence of the force. We shall reason in a heuristic manner, our object being to make plausible the physical laws which we shall formulate. Their actual justification must rest on experiment.

Thinking of the molecules as like small conductors, we should expect the charges to move so as to reduce the potential within each to a constant. Throughout the small region occupied by this conductor, we may regard the potential $U' = \dfrac{1}{\varrho}$, of the unit charge at O, as linear. If the gradient of this linear function were increased, the potential within the conductor could be brought to a constant value again by multiplying the induced charges by the same constant, so that *the degree of electrification of the molecule is proportional to the inducing force*. The charge on the molecule being negative on the side toward O, positive on the side away from O, and of total amount 0, its effect at moderate distances away will be sensibly that of a doublet, with axis in the direction of the radius from O, and of moment proportional to the inverse square of the distance from O. The factor of proportionality k will depend on the character of the molecule.

Let us now consider the potential of a uniform distribution of these doublets throughout space. We shall ignore the effects of the molecules in inducing charges on each other, a reasonable procedure, in view of their distances apart in comparison with their dimensions. Also, we shall ignore their tendency to move under the force of the charge at O. The sum of their combined effects will be satisfactorily given by an integral. If there is an average of N molecules per unit of volume, the integral will be that giving the potential of a distribution of doublets of moment density $\frac{Nk}{\varrho'^2}$, where ϱ' is the distance of the point Q at which the doublet is situated, from O (fig. 19, p. 124). If r denote, as usual, the distance from Q to the point P (a distance ϱ from O) at which the potential is to be reckoned, the potential of the doublet will be (p. 66)

$$\frac{Nk}{\varrho'^2} \frac{\partial}{\partial \varrho'} \frac{1}{r},$$

so that we have, for the potential of the induced charges,

$$U'' = \iiint \frac{Nk}{\varrho'^2} \frac{\partial}{\partial \varrho'} \frac{1}{r} \, dV,$$

the integral being extended over the whole of space. We shall, however, for a later application, first evaluate it when extended over the region between two spheres about O of radii a and b, $a < b$:

$$U'' = Nk \int_0^\pi \int_0^{2\pi} \int_a^b \frac{1}{\varrho'^2} \frac{\partial}{\partial \varrho'} \frac{1}{r} \varrho'^2 \, d\varrho' \sin \vartheta \, d\varphi \, d\vartheta$$

$$= Nk \int_0^\pi \int_0^{2\pi} \left[\frac{1}{r}\right]_{\varrho'=a}^{\varrho'=b} \sin \vartheta \, d\varphi \, d\vartheta$$

$$= 4\pi Nk \left[\frac{1}{4\pi\varrho'^2} \int_0^\pi \int_0^{2\pi} \frac{1}{r} \varrho'^2 \sin \vartheta \, d\varphi \, d\vartheta\right]_{\varrho'=a}^{\varrho'=b}.$$

The quantity in brackets is the potential at P of a unit charge distributed uniformly on the sphere of radius ϱ' about O, and so is equal to $\frac{1}{\varrho}$, or to $\frac{1}{\varrho'}$, according as P is outside or inside the sphere. Accordingly we have the three cases,

$$U'' = 4\pi Nk \left[\frac{1}{b} - \frac{1}{a}\right] \quad \text{for} \quad \varrho < a < b,$$

(42) $$U'' = 4\pi Nk \left[\frac{1}{b} - \frac{1}{\varrho}\right] \quad \text{for} \quad a < \varrho < b,$$

$$U'' = 0 \quad \text{for} \quad a < b < \varrho.$$

In particular, if we extend the integration over the whole of space by allowing a to approach O and b to become infinite in the second expression, we find

(43) $$U'' = -4\pi Nk \frac{1}{\varrho}.$$

The constant Nk is always such that this potential is less in magnitude than the inducing potential $U' = \frac{1}{\varrho}$, so that *the effect of the surrounding dielectric is to diminish the total potential in a constant ratio.* We write

(44) $$U = U' + U'' = \frac{1}{\varepsilon r},$$

where

$$\varepsilon = \frac{1}{1 - 4\pi N k}$$

is known as the *dielectric constant*, or the *inductive capacity of the medium*. The formula would indicate that its value is never less than 1, and no substance has been found which is not in harmony with this result.

We remark that if the dielectric had been different outside a neighborhood at P, the effect on the potential would simply have been to add to it the potential of distant distributions of charges. We are thus led to the first of the physical assumptions with respect to the effects of dielectrics:

(I) The charges present in space produce an electric field of force $\boldsymbol{F}(X, Y, Z)$, which is conservative, and therefore has a potential U,

$$\boldsymbol{F} = -\operatorname{grad} U.$$

The potential of an isolated point charge e at Q differs from

$$\frac{e}{\varepsilon r}$$

by a function which has, at Q, the character of the potential of distant charges.

If the above potential of an isolated unit point charge be multiplied by a density and integrated over a volume or surface, we should have a gravitational potential with the same density divided by ε, except for the potential of distant charges, and so should be led to

(II) The potential of a distribution of volume density $\varkappa$ satisfies, at P, the differential equation

$$\nabla^2 U = -4\pi \frac{\varkappa(P)}{\varepsilon},$$

and the potential of a surface distribution of density σ is continuous, at points of the surface, together with its tangential derivatives, while its normal derivatives satisfy the equation

$$\frac{\partial U}{\partial n_+} - \frac{\partial U}{\partial n_-} = -4\pi \frac{\sigma}{\varepsilon}.$$

A surface separating a medium of dielectric constant ε_1 from one of dielectric constant ε_2 requires consideration, even if no inducing charges are on it. Here the induced doublets on one side of the surface have different moments from those on the other side, and there is accordingly an unbalanced induced charge on the surface. In order to obtain a suggestion as to the situation, let us consider the case of the field of a unit charge, at the center of a sphere of radius R separating two dielectrics. Employing the formulas (42), with Nk replaced by its value in terms of ε_1 inside the sphere, and in terms of ε_2 outside, and adding in the potential U' of the inducing charge, we find for the potential within and without the sphere, the values

$$U_i = \frac{1}{\varepsilon_1 \varrho} + \left(\frac{1}{\varepsilon_2} - \frac{1}{\varepsilon_1}\right)\frac{1}{R},$$

$$U_e = \frac{1}{\varepsilon_2 \varrho}.$$

We are thus led to the assumption:

(III) On a surface separating a medium with one dielectric constant from one with another dielectric constant, no inducing charges being on it, the potential is continuous, together with its tangential derivatives. The normal derivatives, however, are in general discontinuous, and

$$\varepsilon_2 \frac{\partial U}{\partial n_+} - \varepsilon_1 \frac{\partial U}{\partial n_-} = 0.$$

It has been customary to call the charges placed in the field, as opposed to those induced in the dielectric, the "true" charges, while the induced charges, as they become evident when there are breaks, or variations, in the inductive capacity ε, have been called the "free" charges. The densities $\varkappa'$ and σ' of the "free" charges are given, if inducing charges are at a distance, by

$$\nabla^2 U = -4\pi\varkappa' \quad \text{and} \quad \frac{\partial U}{\partial n_+} - \frac{\partial U}{\partial n_-} = -4\pi\sigma'.$$

In accordance with the modern electronic theory of the atom, however, these old terms are inappropriate, for the "free" charge is just as actual as the "true" charge. The above equations, as a matter of fact, give exactly the total charge present. It would be better to call this total charge the *true charge*, and to call the charges introduced by the experimenter, rather than those induced in the dielectric, the *free charges*, for they are free to move on the conductors on which they are placed, while the charges induced in the dielectric are bound, each to its molecule.

(IV) ϱU remains bounded as ϱ becomes infinite, ϱ being the distance from some fixed point.

We now consider briefly two cases in which two dielectric media are present. We have just found the potential of the field of a point charge at the center of a sphere separating two homogeneous dielectrics. We note that in the first dielectric, the effect of the second makes itself felt merely by the addition of a constant to the potential, while in the second dielectric, the situation is as if it alone filled space. The lines of force are exactly as they would be in empty space; only the magnitude of the force experiences a break on the surface separating the media.

The situation is different, however, if the dividing surface is other than a sphere about the inducing charge. Let us consider the field of a point charge at the origin, the dividing surface being the plane $x = a$. We seek the potential on the assumption that it is symmetric about the x-axis, so that we may confine ourselves to a meridian plane, say the (x, y)-plane. If we write, in this plane,

$$U = \frac{1}{\varepsilon_1 \, |x^2 + y^2|} + V,$$

V will satisfy Laplace's equation everywhere except on the plane $x = a$, by (II), will be continuous everywhere by (I) and (III), and, also by (III), will satisfy the equation

$$-\frac{a}{(a^2 + y^2)^{\frac{3}{2}}} + \varepsilon_1 \frac{\partial V}{\partial x}\Big|_1 = -\frac{\varepsilon_2}{\varepsilon_1} \frac{a}{(a^2 + y^2)^{\frac{3}{2}}} + \varepsilon_2 \frac{\partial V}{\partial x}\Big|_2.$$

We can satisfy the conditions on V by assuming that in the second medium it is the potential of a point charge at O, and in the first, of a point charge at the symmetric point $(2a, 0, 0)$:

$$V = \frac{A}{|(2a - x)^2 + y^2|}, \quad x \leqq a, \quad V = \frac{A}{|x^2 + y^2|}, \quad a \leqq x,$$

the coefficient A being the same in both cases so that the potential will be continuous. If we substitute these expressions for V in the previous equation, we find

$$A = -\frac{\varepsilon_1 - \varepsilon_2}{\varepsilon_1 (\varepsilon_1 + \varepsilon_2)}.$$

Hence the required potential is

$$U = \frac{1}{\varepsilon_1 \, |x^2 + y^2|}$$

$$+ \frac{\varepsilon_1 - \varepsilon_2}{\varepsilon_1 (\varepsilon_1 + \varepsilon_2)} \frac{1}{|(2a - x)^2 + y^2|},$$

$$x \leqq a,$$

$$U = \frac{2}{\varepsilon_1 + \varepsilon_2} \frac{1}{|x^2 + y^2|}, \qquad a \leqq x.$$

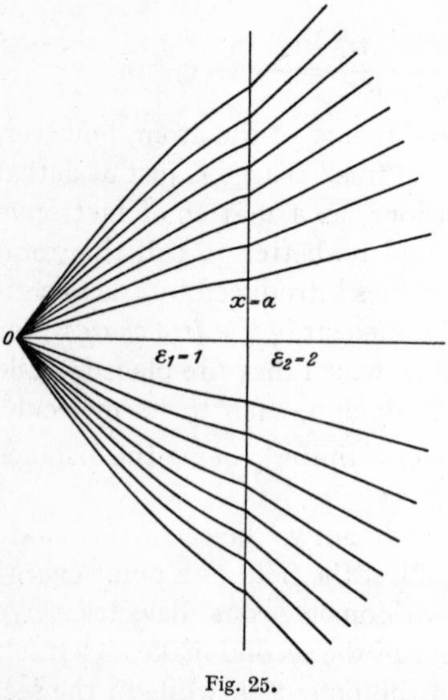

Comparing the situation with that in which the bounding surface was a sphere, we see that in the first medium the effect of the presence of the second amounts to more than the addition of a constant, whereas

Fig. 25.

in the second medium the first makes itself felt as if the dielectric constant of the second were replaced by the arithmetic mean of the two. The lines of force in the first medium are now the curved lines due to two Newtonian particles as discussed in the exercises of page 31. They experience a refraction on the boundary, becoming straight in the second medium (fig. 25).

This problem also gives a basis for illustrating the effect of a second medium at some distance away. We see that if either the dielectric constants are nearly equal, or the bounding surface is at a great distance, *a* large, the effect of the second medium is slight. This makes plausible the assumption made in the earlier sections of this chapter.

For further study of electrostatics, the reader may consult the appropriate chapters in ABRAHAM, *Theorie der Elektrizität*, Leipzig, 1918; JEANS, *Electricity and Magnetism*, Cambridge, 1925; MAXWELL, *A Treatise on Electricity and Magnetism*, Oxford, 1904; RIEMANN-WEBER, *Die Differential- und Integralgleichungen der Mechanik und Physik*, Braunschweig, 1925.

Chapter VIII.

Harmonic Functions.

1. Theorems of Uniqueness.

We have seen that Newtonian potentials are solutions of Laplace's equation at points free from masses. We shall soon learn that solutions of Laplace's equation are always Newtonian potentials, so that in studying the properties of such solutions, we are also studying the properties of Newtonian fields. We shall find that a surprising number of general properties follow from the mere fact that a function satisfies Laplace's equation, or is harmonic, as we shall say.

More definitely, a function $U(x, y, z)$ is said to be *harmonic at a point* $P(x, y, z)$ if its second derivatives exist and are continuous and satisfy Laplace's equation throughout some neighborhood of that point[1]. U is said to be *harmonic in a domain*, or open continuum, if it is harmonic at all the points of that domain. It is said to be *harmonic in a closed region*, that is, the set of points consisting of a domain with its boundary, if it is continuous in the region, and harmonic at all interior points of the region. If the domain or region is an infinite one, a supplementary condition will be imposed which will be given in § 3, p. 217. For the present, we confine ourselves to bounded regions. Functions will be assumed always to be one-valued unless the contrary is explicitly stated.

Since $V^2 U = 0$ is a homogeneous linear differential equation, it follows that if U_1 and U_2 are both harmonic in any of the above senses,

---

[1] The reader will do well to revert, in order to refresh his memory, to Chapter IV, where the notions of domain, region, neighborhood, etc. are defined.

$c_1 U_1 + c_2 U_2$ also is harmonic in the same sense, c_1 and c_2 being constants. It is the same for any finite sum. We shall consider infinite sums in Chapter X.

A potent instrument for the derivation of properties of harmonic functions is a set of identities following from the divergence theorem, and known as Green's theorems[1]. Let R denote a closed regular region of space, and let U and V be two functions defined in R, and continuous in R together with their partial derivatives of the first order. Moreover, let U have continuous derivatives of the second order in R. Then the divergence theorem holds for R with the field

$$X = V \frac{\partial U}{\partial x}, \qquad Y = V \frac{\partial U}{\partial y}, \qquad Z = V \frac{\partial U}{\partial z},$$

and it takes the form

$$(\text{I}) \qquad \iiint\limits_R V \nabla^2 U \, dV + \iiint\limits_R (\nabla U \cdot \nabla V) \, dV = \iint\limits_S V \frac{\partial U}{\partial n} \, dS,$$

where n means the outwardly directed normal to the surface S bounding R, and $\nabla U \cdot \nabla V$ means the scalar product of the gradients of U and V, that is,

$$\nabla U \cdot \nabla V = \frac{\partial U}{\partial x} \frac{\partial V}{\partial x} + \frac{\partial U}{\partial y} \frac{\partial V}{\partial y} + \frac{\partial U}{\partial z} \frac{\partial V}{\partial z}.$$

The equation (I) will be referred to as Green's first identity.

If U is harmonic and continuously differentiable[2] in R, (I) is applicable, and the first term vanishes. If we write $V = 1$, the identity becomes

$$(1) \qquad \iint\limits_S \frac{\partial U}{\partial n} \, dS = 0,$$

and we have

Theorem I. *The integral of the normal derivative of a function vanishes when extended over the boundary of any closed regular region in which the function is harmonic and continuously differentiable.*

Later (§ 7, Theorem XIII, p. 227) we shall see that a converse of this theorem is true, namely that if the integral when extended over the boundary of any closed regular region in a domain vanishes, the function is harmonic in that domain. We thus have a means of characterizing harmonic functions without supposing anything about its derivatives of second order.

---

[1] GEORGE GREEN, l. c. footnote page **38**.

[2] It will be noticed that the hypothesis that U is harmonic in R does not involve the supposition that its second derivatives are continuous in R, but only in the interior of R. However, the divergence theorem is applicable without further hypothesis, as is seen by § 11 of Chapter IV (p. 119).

We next identify V with U, still supposing U harmonic. Green's identity then becomes

(2) $$\iiint\limits_{R} (\nabla V)^2 \, dV = \iint\limits_{S} U \frac{\partial U}{\partial n} \, dS.$$

If U is the velocity potential of a flow of fluid of density 1, the left hand member of this equation represents twice the kinetic energy of that part of the fluid in R, and hence so does the right hand member. If the right hand member vanishes, the kinetic energy in R vanishes, and there should be no motion. The equation thus yields several theorems, which we proceed to formulate.

First, suppose $U = 0$ on S. Then, since by hypothesis $(\nabla U)^2$ is continuous in R, and never negative, it must vanish at all points of R. Hence

$$\frac{\partial U}{\partial x} = \frac{\partial U}{\partial y} = \frac{\partial U}{\partial z} = 0,$$

and U is constant in R. But $U = 0$ on S, and as it is continuous in the closed region, $U = 0$ throughout R. Thus follows

Theorem II. *If U is harmonic and continuously differentiable in a closed regular region R, and vanishes at all points of the boundary of R, it vanishes at all points of R.*

We deduce at once an important consequence. Let us suppose that U_1 and U_2 are both harmonic in R, and take on the same boundary values. Then their difference is harmonic in R and reduces to 0 on the boundary. Hence it vanishes throughout R. We may state the result as follows.

Theorem III. *A function, harmonic and continuously differentiable in a closed regular region R, is uniquely determined by its values on the boundary of R.*

The surface integral in (2) will also vanish if the normal derivative vanishes everywhere on S. Again we see that as a consequence, U will be constant in R, although we can no longer infer that it will vanish. Indeed the equation (2) is satisfied by any constant.

Theorem IV. *If U is one-valued, continuously differentiable and harmonic in the closed regular region R, and if its normal derivative vanishes at every point of the boundary of R, then U is constant in R. Also, a function, single valued and harmonic in R, is determined, save for an additive constant, by the values of its normal derivative on the boundary.*

Consider a fluid, flowing in a region consisting of a torus, with the potential $U = \tan^{-1} \frac{y}{x}$, where we take as z-axis the axis of the torus. The flow lines are easily seen to be circles with the z-axis as axis, and thus

there is no flow across the surface of the torus. That is, the normal derivative of U vanishes over the whole surface of R, and yet U is not
constant in R. Why is this not a contradiction of the last theorem?
The answer is that the potential is not one-valued, and it is for this
reason, in spite of a general statement at the outset that we should
consider only one-valued functions, unless the contrary was stated, that
the hypothesis that U shall be one-valued has been expressly introduced
in the theorem.

If U denotes the temperature of an isotropic homogeneous body
filling the region R, Theorem II shows that if the boundary of R is
kept at the constant temperature 0, there is no thermal equilibrium
possible unless the temperatures are everywhere 0 in the body. Theorem
IV shows that if the surface of R is thermally insulated, the only stationary temperatures possible occur when they are everywhere equal.

Suppose now that the body is neither thermally insulated nor has
its boundary kept at zero temperature, but that instead, it is immersed
in a medium of constant temperature U_0. Then heat will escape through
the surface at a rate proportional to the difference in temperature of the
body at the surface, and the surrounding medium, according to the law

(3) $$-\frac{\partial U}{\partial n} = h\,(U - U_0),$$

where h is an essentially positive quantity, usually constant, called the
surface conductivity. This is a physical law which is applicable when
there is no radiation of heat from the body. Under these circumstances
*a steady state of temperatures in the body is only possible when $U = U_0$
throughout the body.* For, under these circumstances the equation (2),
applied to the difference $U - U_0$ becomes

$$\iiint\limits_{R} [V\,(U - U_0)]^2\,dV + \iint\limits_{S} h\,(U - U_0)^2\,dS = 0.$$

The two terms on the left cannot either of them be negative, and hence
both must vanish. The integrals can only vanish, since the integrands
are continuous and never negative, when the integrands vanish. We
are thus led to

Theorem V. *Let U be harmonic and continuously differentiable in the
closed regular region R, and satisfy the condition on the boundary*

$$\frac{\partial U}{\partial n} + hU = g,$$

*where h and g are continuous functions of position on S, and h is never
negative. Then there is no different function satisfying the same conditions.*

Exercises.

1. Prove Theorem I by means of the fact that if the divergence of a field vanishes at every point of a regular region, the total divergence of the field for that region vanishes.

2. Show that in a closed vessel bounding a regular simply connected region, a steady irrotational flow of a fluid of density 1, other than rest, is impossible.

3. Prove that if $\varkappa$ is continuous in the closed, regular region R, and g is continuous on the boundary S of R, then there is not more than one function U, (a) continuous together with its partial derivatives of first order in R, (b) having continuous derivatives of the second order in the interior of R which satisfy Poisson's equation

$$\nabla^2 U = -4\pi\varkappa,$$

and (c) taking on the boundary values g. Give at least one more uniqueness theorem on Poisson's equation.

Remarks on Uniqueness Theorems. We have suggested, in the preceding theorems, rather than made an exhaustive study of, the possible theorems of uniqueness on harmonic functions. Suppose, for instance, that U vanishes on a part of S, while its normal derivative vanishes on the rest. Then U will be 0, and any harmonic function will be uniquely determined if the conditions imposed on it and any second function have as consequence that their difference is subjected to the boundary conditions on U. Generally speaking, we have a uniqueness theorem corresponding to any boundary conditions which make the surface integral in (2) vanish.

Every uniqueness theorem suggests an existence theorem. For instance, if continuous boundary values are given on S, there is not more than one harmonic function which takes them on. But is there one? As a matter of fact, corresponding to each of the uniqueness theorems given, there is a true existence theorem, and these existence theorems are among the most fascinating in the history of mathematics, and have been studied for a whole century. We shall revert to them in Chapter XI.

2. Relations on the Boundary between Pairs of Harmonic Functions.

Let us now suppose that both U and V are continuously differentiable in R and have continuous partial derivatives of the second order in R. We then have the identity (I), and in addition, the identity obtained by interchanging U and V. If the resulting equation is subtracted from (I), the result is Green's second identity,

$$\text{(II)} \qquad \iiint_R (U\nabla^2 V - V\nabla^2 U)\, dV = \iint_S \left(U\frac{\partial V}{\partial n} - V\frac{\partial U}{\partial n}\right) dS.$$

From this, we deduce at once

216   Harmonic Functions.

Theorem VI. *If U and V are harmonic and continuously differentiable in the closed regular region R, then*

$$\iint\limits_{S} \left(U \frac{\partial V}{\partial n} - V \frac{\partial U}{\partial n} \right) dS = 0,$$

S being the boundary of R.

We shall make much use, from time to time, of the identity (II) and the Theorem VI. In the present section, however, we shall confine ourselves to some simple applications of the theorem which are well adapted to use as exercises.

Exercises.

1. Show that Theorem VI remains valid if instead of assuming U and V harmonic, we assume that they are solutions of one and the same equation $\nabla^2 U = k U$, subject to suitable conditions of continuity.

2. Show that any two spherical harmonics of different orders are orthogonal on the surface of any sphere about the origin. Suggestion. Write $U = \varrho^n S_n (\varphi, \vartheta)$, $V = \varrho^m S_m (\varphi, \vartheta)$, and employ Theorem VI.

In particular, prove again the orthogonality of two Legendre polynomials of different degrees.

3. Show that the functions

$$U = (A \cos nx + B \sin nx) e^{ny}, \qquad V = (C \cos mx + D \sin mx) e^{my}$$

are harmonic in the region $0 \le x \le 2\pi$, $0 \le y \le 1$, $0 \le z \le 1$. Infer that if m and n are integers $m^2 \neq n^2$,

$$\int\limits_0^{2\pi} \cos mx \cos nx \, dx = \int\limits_0^{2\pi} \cos mx \sin nx \, dx = \int\limits_0^{2\pi} \sin mx \sin nx \, dx = 0.$$

4. If $U = u_1 (\lambda) u_2 (\mu, \nu)$ and $V = v_1 (\lambda) v_2 (\mu, \nu)$ are harmonic in the ellipsoid

$$\frac{x^2}{a^2} + \frac{y^2}{b^2} + \frac{z^2}{c^2} \le 1,$$

λ, μ, and ν being ellipsoidal coördinates based on this ellipsoid, then

$$\frac{U}{\sqrt[4]{(\lambda - \mu)(\lambda - \nu)}} \quad \text{and} \quad \frac{V}{\sqrt[4]{(\lambda - \mu)(\lambda - \nu)}}$$

are orthogonal on any ellipsoid $\lambda = \lambda_1 < 0$, confocal with the above, provided

$$u_1 (\lambda_1) \neq 0, \quad v_1 (\lambda_1) \neq 0, \quad u_1 (\lambda_1) v_1' (\lambda_1) - u_1' (\lambda_1) v_1 (\lambda_1) \neq 0.$$

3. Infinite Regions.

The divergence theorem, on which the results of the first two sections are based, is not valid for infinite regions without further hypotheses on the functions involved. It is, however, highly desirable to have similar theorems for functions which are harmonic outside a given bounded surface—for instance, in connection with problems on conductors.

Although we defined a regular region in Chapter IV, § 9 (p. 113) as a bounded region, let us now understand that at least when qualified by the word infinite, it may comprise unbounded regions. An infinite regular region would then be a region bounded by a regular surface (and hence a bounded surface), and containing all sufficiently distant points.

Let R be an infinite regular region, and Σ a sphere, containing the boundary of R in its interior. Then the divergence theorem holds[1] for the region R', consisting of the points of R within and on Σ:

$$\iiint\limits_{R'} \left(\frac{\partial X}{\partial x} + \frac{\partial Y}{\partial y} + \frac{\partial Z}{\partial z} \right) dV = \iint\limits_{S} (Xl + Ym + Zn)\, dS$$

$$+ \iint\limits_{\Sigma} (Xl + Ym + Zn)\, dS,$$

provided X, Y, Z satisfy the requirements of Chapter IV (p. 119). In order to extend the theorem to the whole of R, we let the radius ϱ of Σ, whose center we think of as fixed, become infinite. If then

(4) $\qquad\qquad \varrho^2 X, \ \varrho^2 Y, \ \varrho^2 Z \quad$ approach 0,

uniformly as to directions, as ϱ becomes infinite, the integral over Σ tends to 0, and we have the divergence theorem for R, the volume integral over R being defined as the limit *for spherical regions with fixed center*.

We shall now impose on the functions U and V of the opening sections, the additional conditions for infinite regions, that

$$\varrho U, \ \varrho^2 \frac{\partial U}{\partial x}, \ \varrho^2 \frac{\partial U}{\partial y}, \ \varrho^2 \frac{\partial U}{\partial z}; \ \varrho V, \ \varrho^2 \frac{\partial V}{\partial x}, \ \varrho^2 \frac{\partial V}{\partial y}, \ \varrho^2 \frac{\partial V}{\partial z},$$

shall be bounded in absolute value for all sufficiently large ϱ, where ϱ is the distance from any fixed point. Of functions satisfying this condition, we shall say that they are *regular at infinity*. This, it will be recalled, is the character of Newtonian potentials of bounded distributions. If M is a bound for the absolute value of the quantities listed above, then for the functions X, Y, Z of § 1 (p. 212), we have

$$\left| \varrho^2 X \right| = \left| \varrho V \varrho \frac{\partial U}{\partial x} \right| \leqq M \frac{M}{\varrho}, \quad \left| \varrho^2 Y \right| \leqq \frac{M^2}{\varrho}, \quad \left| \varrho^2 Z \right| \leqq \frac{M^2}{\varrho},$$

and the condition (4) is fulfilled. Under these circumstances, the identities (I) and (II) hold for infinite regular regions.

We shall from now on understand that when a function is said to be *harmonic in an infinite domain or region*, this includes the demand that it shall be regular at infinity.

---

[1] This will probably be seen most easily by use of the second extension principle (p. 113). R' may be approximated to by a regular region formed by cutting out from R' a small tube connecting a face of the boundary of R with Σ. The resulting region is bounded by a single regular surface.

Let us now see whether the theorems derived for finite regions hold for infinite regions. In the first place, $V = 1$ is not regular at infinity, so that Theorem I cannot be derived as it was for bounded regions. Indeed, it is not always true, as can be seen from the example $U = 1/r$. But if we apply Theorem I to the portion R' of R included within and on a regular surface Σ enclosing all of the boundary S of R, we obtain.

Theorem I'. *If R is a regular infinite region, and U is harmonic and continuously differentiable in R, the integral*

$$\iint_{\Sigma} \frac{\partial U}{\partial n}\, dS$$

has one and the same value when extended over the boundary of any finite regular region containing all the boundary of R in its interior.

In all the later theorems of § 1 and § 2, U and V are assumed to be harmonic, and so are regular at infinity if R is infinite. Hence these theorems hold also for infinite regions.

Exercises.

1. Apply Theorem II to prove the uniqueness of the potentials in the problems on static charges on conductors in the last chapter.

2. Show that if U is harmonic throughout all of space, it is identically 0. Suggestion: consider the limiting form of equation (2).

3. Show that if U and V are harmonic in the infinite region R, the volume integrals in (I) and (II) are convergent in the strict sense.

4. Any Harmonic Function is a Newtonian Potential.

We may now substantiate the statement made at the beginning of the chapter, to the effect that any harmonic continuously differentiable function is a Newtonian potential. This is done by means of Green's third identity. Let R be any regular region, bounded or infinite, and let $P(x, y, z)$ be any interior point. We take for V, in the identity (II) the function

$$V = \frac{1}{r},$$

where r is the distance from P to $Q(\xi, \eta, \zeta)$, ξ, η, ζ, being now taken as the variables of integration in that identity, in place of x, y, z. Since P is interior to R, the identity cannot be applied to the whole region R, so we surround P with a small sphere σ with P as center, and remove from R the interior of the sphere. For the resulting region R', we have, since $\frac{1}{r}$ is harmonic in R',

$$(5) \qquad -\iiint_{R'} \frac{1}{r}\, \nabla^2 U\, dV = \iint_{S} \left(U\, \frac{\partial}{\partial \nu}\, \frac{1}{r} - \frac{1}{r}\, \frac{\partial U}{\partial \nu} \right) dS$$

$$+ \iint_{\sigma} \left(U\, \frac{\partial}{\partial \nu}\, \frac{1}{r} - \frac{1}{r}\, \frac{\partial U}{\partial \nu} \right) dS.$$

Here ν denotes the normal to the boundary of R, pointing outward from R, so that on σ, it has the direction opposite to the radius r. Hence the last integral may be written

$$(6) \qquad \iint\limits_{\Omega} \Big(U \frac{1}{r^2} + \frac{1}{r} \frac{\partial U}{\partial r} \Big) r^2 \, d\Omega = \bar{U} \cdot 4\pi + \iint\limits_{\Omega} r \frac{\partial U}{\partial r} \, d\Omega ,$$

where U is a value of U at some point of σ, and the integration is with respect to the solid angle subtended at P by the element of σ. The limit of the integral over σ in (5), as the radius of σ approaches 0, is thus $4\pi U(P)$, and the volume integral on the left converges to the integral over R. We thus arrive at the third identity

$$(III) \quad U(P) = -\frac{1}{4\pi} \iiint\limits_{R} \frac{\nabla^2 U}{r} \, dV + \frac{1}{4\pi} \iint\limits_{S} \frac{\partial U}{\partial \nu} \frac{1}{r} \, dS - \frac{1}{4\pi} \iint\limits_{S} U \frac{\partial}{\partial \nu} \frac{1}{r} \, dS .$$

The hypotheses underlying this identity are that U and its partial derivatives of the first order are continuous in R, and that its partial derivatives of the second order are continuous in the interior of R, and that the volume integral is convergent if R is infinite. In this case we assume also that U is regular at infinity.

The first term on the right is the potential of a volume distribution of density $-\dfrac{\nabla^2 U}{4\pi}$, the second is the potential of a distribution on the boundary S of R, of density $\dfrac{\dfrac{\partial U}{\partial \nu}}{4\pi}$, while the third is the potential of a double distribution on S of moment $-\dfrac{U}{4\pi}$. Thus *not only do harmonic functions appear as Newtonian potentials, but so also do any functions with sufficient differentiability.* In particular, the identity (III) gives at once

Theorem VII. *A function, harmonic and continuously differentiable in a closed-regular region R may be represented as the sum of the potentials of a simple and of a double distribution on the boundary of R.*

If U is harmonic in any region, it is also harmonic and continuously differentiable in any region included in the first, and hence can be represented as the potential of spreads on the surface of the included region. Thus we have a more general aspect of the facts illustrated on page 197, that different distributions may, in restricted portions of space, have one and the same potential. If, however, two distributions are required to have the same potential throughout space, it can be proved that the two distributions must be essentially the same.

Before taking this up, however, we should notice a further consequence of Theorem VII. Let T be any domain, regular or not, and let U be harmonic in T. Then U is harmonic in any sphere lying entirely in

T, and is thus, in that sphere, the potential of Newtonian spreads on the surface. But we have seen in Chapter V, § 4 (p. 139), that such spreads are analytic at the points of free space, and hence in the interior of the sphere. As such a sphere can be described about any point of T, we have

Theorem VIII. *If U is harmonic in a domain, it is analytic at all the points of that domain.*

The extraordinary fact thus emerges that if a function has continuous derivatives of the second order in a domain, the circumstance that the sum of a certain three of these derivatives vanishes throughout the domain, has as consequence, not only the existence and continuity of the derivatives of all orders, but also that the function is analytic throughout the domain. This striking property of Laplace's equation, *that it has only analytic solutions*, is shared by a class of partial differential equations, namely those of elliptic type[1].

5. Uniqueness of the Distribution Producing a Potential.

Let U be continuous together with its derivatives of the first and second orders except on a finite number of regular surfaces S (open or closed) without common points. We suppose further that U and its derivatives of first and second orders at P, approach limits as P approaches any point P_0 of S, not on an edge, from either side of S. Moreover, we assume that U, together with its limiting values from one side near P_0, constitute a function which is continuous at all points of a neighborhood of P_0, on S and on the given side of S. This shall be true for either side, and also for the derivatives mentioned. We suppose that the second derivatives satisfy a Hölder condition at all points not on S, and finally that U is harmonic at all points outside a sufficiently large sphere Σ.

Formula III shows that in any regular region R containing none of the points of S, U is the potential of certain distributions. We now show that *U can be represented, at all points of space not on S, as the potential of one and the same distribution.*

In the first place, the integral

$$U_1 = -\frac{1}{4\pi} \iiint_{\Sigma} \frac{V^2 U}{r}\, d\dot{V}$$

is everywhere continuous, together with its derivatives of the first order, and has the same Laplacian as U. Hence $U - U_1$ is everywhere harmonic,

[1] See Encyklopädie der Mathematischen Wissenschaften, II C 12, LICHTENSTEIN, *Neuere Entwickelung der Theorie partieller Differentialgleichungen zweiter Ordnung vom elliptischen Typus*, pp. 1320—1324.

except on S, and has, with its derivatives of the first order, the same discontinuities as U.

If a positive sense be assigned to the normal to the regular surface elements of S, then

$$U_2 = - \frac{1}{4\pi} \iint_S \left(\frac{\partial U}{\partial \nu_+} - \frac{\partial U}{\partial \nu_-} \right) \frac{1}{r} \, dS$$

and

$$U_3 = \frac{1}{4\pi} \iint_S (U_+ - U_-) \frac{\partial}{\partial \nu} \frac{1}{r} \, dS$$

are harmonic except on S. Because of the hypotheses on U, it is not difficult to verify that the density and moment of these distributions admit derivatives of the first and second orders respectively, so that the results of Chapter V (Theorems IV, VI, VIII, XI) are applicable. Hence

$$U_{2+} - U_{2-} = 0, \qquad \frac{\partial U_2}{\partial n_+} - \frac{\partial U_2}{\partial n_-} = \frac{\partial U}{\partial n_+} - \frac{\partial U}{\partial n_-},$$

$$U_{3+} - U_{3-} = U_+ - U_-, \qquad \frac{\partial U_3}{\partial n_+} - \frac{\partial U_3}{\partial n_-} = 0,$$

at all interior points of S. Accordingly,

$$U - U_1 - U_2 - U_3$$

is harmonic except on S, and, together with its normal derivatives, has the same limiting values from either side at all interior points of S. If defined in terms of these limiting values, $U - U_1 - U_2 - U_3$ becomes harmonic at all interior points of S (Theorem VI, p. 261). On the edges of S, this function is bounded, and hence can be so defined there as to be harmonic everywhere (Theorem XIII, p. 271). It then vanishes identically, by Exercise 2, page 218 and U has the value

$$(7) \qquad U = - \frac{1}{4\pi} \iiint_{\Sigma} \frac{\nabla^2 U}{r} \, dV - \frac{1}{4\pi} \iint_S \left(\frac{\partial U}{\partial \nu_+} - \frac{\partial U}{\partial \nu_-} \right) \frac{1}{r} \, dS$$

$$+ \frac{1}{4\pi} \iint_S (U_+ - U_-) \frac{\partial}{\partial \nu} \frac{1}{r} \, dS$$

at all points of space not on S. It is thus at every point not on S the potential of a single set of Newtonian distributions, as stated.

However, we are by no means assured that no other distributions produce the same potential. In fact, if we changed the volume densities at the points of a finite number of regular surface elements, or the surface densities on a finite number of regular curves, the integrals would be unaffected, and a different distribution would produce the same potential. But to exhibit this possibility, we have had to admit discontinuous densities.

We shall now establish

Theorem IX. *No potential due to spreads in regular regions and on regular surfaces, finite in number, with continuous densities and moments, can be due to any other spreads of the same character.*

At the outset, it is clear that if two representations were possible, the spreads would have to be in the same regions and on the same surfaces. For if P were an interior point of one volume distribution, not on any spread of the second representation, the potential of the second spread would be harmonic at P, while that of the first would not. After subtracting the potential of the volume distribution, a similar argument applies to the surfaces.

Let $\varkappa$, σ, and μ denote the differences of the volume and surface densities respectively, of the two supposed representations, and of the moments of the double distributions. These functions are continuous, and they are densities and moments of a distribution producing a potential which vanishes everywhere, save possibly on the surfaces bearing spreads:

$$(8) \qquad 0 = \iiint\limits_V \frac{\varkappa}{r}\, dV + \iint\limits_S \frac{\sigma}{r}\, dS + \iint\limits_S \mu\, \frac{\partial}{\partial \nu} \frac{1}{r}\, dS.$$

Transposing the first two terms, we see that the double distribution is the sum of a surface and of a volume distribution with continuous densities. It is hence continuous, according to the results of Chapter VI, and so its moment is 0.

The last term is therefore absent from equation (8), and we see that the surface integral is the potential of volume distribution with continuous density. It therefore has derivatives of the first order which are everywhere continuous, and thus Gauss' theorem is applicable to the potential of the surface distribution. We apply it to the surface of a small sphere about any point of the distribution, and infer that the total mass within the sphere is 0. If the density were anywhere positive, we could find a sphere, cutting out from the surface bearing the distribution, a piece on which the density was positive, since the density is continuous, and the total mass within the sphere would not then vanish. Hence the surface density is 0. Then, applying Gauss' theorem to the potential of the volume distribution, we infer in the same way that its density is also everywhere 0, and the theorem is proved.

Exercises.

1. Show, by (III), that if U is harmonic throughout all of space, and regular at infinity it is identically 0.

2. In the last chapter, Exercise 2 (p. 191), we saw that a static charge on a circular lamina became infinite at the edge of the lamina. Theorem IX does not therefore show that but one distribution will produce the potential of the lamina. Prove that there is no other distribution, continuous at all interior points of the lamina and producing the same potential.

6. Further Consequences of Green's Third Identity.

The identity (III) gives us at once a new and more general proof of Gauss' theorem on the arithmetic mean. Let U be harmonic and continuously differentiable in R. Then

$$(9) \qquad U(P) = \frac{1}{4\pi} \iint\limits_{S} \frac{\partial U}{\partial \nu} \frac{1}{r} \, dS - \frac{1}{4\pi} \iint\limits_{S} U \frac{\partial}{\partial \nu} \frac{1}{r} \, dS.$$

If R is bounded by a sphere S, and P is at the center of the sphere, the first integral vanishes, by Theorem I, since r is constant on S. We have therefore

$$U(P) = \frac{1}{4\pi r^2} \iint\limits_{S} U \, dS.$$

This result is based on the assumption that U and its derivatives of the first order are continuous in the closed sphere. However, the derivatives do not appear here, and it is clear that we need make no assumptions as to their behavior on the boundary. In fact, the relation holds for any interior concentric sphere, and therefore, if U is continuous, it holds also in the limit, for the given sphere. Indeed, U may have certain discontinuities if the limit of the integral is the integral of the limit of U, properly understood. We content ourselves, however, with the following enunciation.

Gauss' Theorem of the Arithmetic Mean. *If U is harmonic in a sphere, the value of U at the center of the sphere is the arithmetic mean of its values on the surface.*

As a corollary, we deduce

Theorem X. *Let R denote a closed bounded region* (regular or not) *of space, and let U be harmonic, but not constant, in R. Then U attains its maximum and minimum values only on the boundary of R.*

That U actually takes on its extreme values is a consequence of its continuity in the closed region R (see Exercise 5, page 98). Let E denote the set of points at which $U = M$, the maximum of U. It cannot contain all interior points of R, for if it did U would be constant. Accordingly, if E contained any interior point of R, it would have a frontier point P_0 in the interior of R (see Exercise 4, page 94). There would then be a sphere about P_0, entirely in R, and passing through points not in E. That is, the values of U on the sphere would never exceed M, and at some points, be less than M. As $U(P_0) = M$, we should have a contradiction with Gauss' theorem. Hence E can contain no interior points of R, as was to be proved. The same argument applies to the minimum[1].

---

[1] This form of the proof of the theorem is due to Professor J. L. WALSH.

Exercises.

1. Show that if U is harmonic and not constant, in an infinite region with finite boundary, it either attains its extremes on the boundary, or attains one of them on the boundary and approaches the other at infinity.

2. Extend Theorem III as follows. Let R be any closed region, regular or not, with finite boundary, and let U be harmonic in R. Show that there is no different function, harmonic in R, with the same boundary values as U.

3. Given a single conductor in an infinite homogeneous medium, and a charge in equilibrium on the conductor, there being no other charges present, show that the density is everywhere of the same sign.

7. The Converse of Gauss' Theorem.

The property of harmonic functions given by Gauss' theorem is so simple and striking, that it is of interest to inquire what properties functions have which are, as we shall express it, their own arithmetic means on the surfaces of spheres. Let R be a closed region, and V a function which is continuous in R, and whose value at any interior point of the region is the arithmetic mean of its values on the surface of any sphere with that point as center, which lies entirely in R:

$$(10) \qquad V(P) = \frac{1}{4\pi r^2} \int_0^\pi \int_0^{2\pi} V(Q)\, r^2 \sin\vartheta\, d\varphi\, d\vartheta, \qquad r \leqq a,$$

where Q has the spherical coördinates (r, φ, ϑ) with P as origin, and a is the distance from P to the nearest boundary point of R.

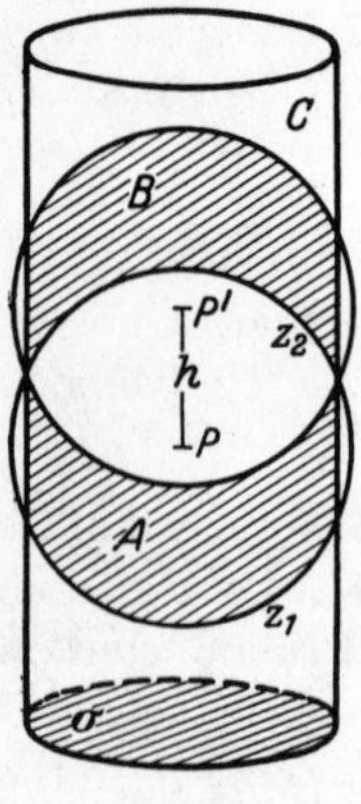

Fig. 26.

We first remark that V is also its own arithmetic mean over the volumes of spheres. For if we multiply both sides of equation (10) by r^2 and integrate with respect to r from 0 to r, we have, since $V(P)$ is independent of r,

$$V(P)\frac{r^3}{3} = \frac{1}{4\pi} \int_0^r \int_0^\pi \int_0^{2\pi} V(Q)\, r^2 \sin\vartheta\, d\varphi\, d\vartheta\, dr, \quad r \leqq a,$$

or,

$$(11) \qquad V(P) = \frac{3}{4\pi r^3} \iiint_\Sigma V(Q)\, dV,$$

where Σ is the sphere of radius r about P.

We now show that $V(P)$ has continuous derivatives at the interior points of R. Let P be any interior point of R, and let a denote a fixed number less than the distance from P to the nearest boundary point of R. Let us take P as origin, and the z-axis in the direction of the derivative to be studied (fig. 26). Let P' be the point $(0, 0, h)$, h being small enough so that P' also has a minimum distance greater than a from the boundary of R. Then

$$\frac{V(P')-V(P)}{h} = \frac{3}{4\pi a^3 h}\left[\iiint_{\Sigma'} V(Q)\,dV - \iiint_{\Sigma} V(Q)\,dV\right],$$

where Σ denotes the sphere of radius a about P, and Σ' the equal sphere about P'. For small enough h, these spheres intersect, so that the integrals over the common part destroy each other. Let C denote the cylinder through the intersection of the spheres, with axis parallel to the z-axis. The parts of the spheres outside C have a volume which is an infinitesimal in h of higher order (of the order of h^3), so that since V is bounded in R, because of its continuity, the integrals over these parts of the spheres are also infinitesimals of higher order. We may then write

$$(12) \quad \frac{V(P')-V(P)}{h} = \frac{3}{4\pi a^3 h}\left[\iiint_{B} V(Q)\,dV - \iiint_{A} V(Q)\,dV\right] + \psi_1(h),$$

where $\psi_1(h)$ vanishes with h, and A is the part of Σ in C but not in Σ', and B is the part of Σ' in C but not in Σ. We now express the volume integrals as iterated integrals with respect to z and the surface of the projection σ of A and B on the (x, y)-plane. Let $z_1(x, y)$ and $z_2(x, y)$ denote the values of z on the lower surfaces of A, and B, respectively. Then $z_1(x, y) + h$ and $z_2(x, y) + h$ are the values of z on the upper surfaces of A and B. The bracket in (12) can then be written

$$\iint_{\sigma}\left[\int_{z_2}^{z_2+h} V\,dz - \int_{z_1}^{z_1+h} V\,dz\right]d\sigma$$

$$= h\iint_{\sigma}[V(x, y, z_2 + \vartheta_2 h) - V(x, y, z_1 + \vartheta_1 h)]\,d\sigma,$$

$$(0 < \vartheta_1 < 1,\ 0 < \vartheta_2 < 1),$$

$$= h\iint_{\sigma}[V(x, y, z_2(x, y)) + V(x, y, z_1(x, y))]\,d\sigma + \psi_2(h)\,h$$

where we have first used the law of the mean, and secondly the fact that the values of V at points a distance h or less apart is a uniform infinitesimal in h, so that $\psi_2(h)$ vanishes with h. Thus

$$\frac{V(P')-V(P)}{h} = \frac{3}{4\pi a^3}\iint_{\sigma}[V(x, y, z_2) - V(x, y, z_1)]\,d\sigma + \psi_3(h).$$

If we now replace the field of integration σ by the surface of Σ, as in the derivation of the divergence theorem (page 87), we have

$$\frac{V(P')-V(P)}{h} = \frac{3}{4\pi a^3}\iint_{\Sigma_1} V\cos(n, z)\,dS + \psi_3(h).$$

Σ_1 being the portion of Σ within C. We may now pass to the limit as

h approaches 0. As the integrand is continuous, we see that the limit exists, and that

$$(13) \qquad \frac{\partial V}{\partial z} = \frac{3}{4\pi a^3} \iint\limits_{\Sigma} V \cos (n, z) \, dS.$$

The tedious reckoning is now done, and the rest is simple. Because of the continuity of V, this derivative is continuous, and because a can be any sufficiently small positive number, the result holds for any interior point of R.

If we now apply to (13) the divergence theorem, we find

$$(14) \qquad \frac{\partial V}{\partial z} = \frac{3}{4\pi a^3} \iiint\limits_{\Sigma} \frac{\partial V}{\partial z} \, dV,$$

the integral being over the region bounded by Σ. Hence *the derivatives of V of first order are also their own arithmetic means over the volumes of spheres in any region in the interior of R.*

The process can now be repeated as often as we like. Since any region interior to R is one of a nest of regions, each interior to the next, and the last interior to R (see page 317), we see that the partial derivatives, of any given order, of V exist and are continuous in any region interior to R.

In particular,

$$\frac{\partial^2 V}{\partial z^2} = \frac{3}{4\pi a^3} \iint\limits_{\Sigma} \frac{\partial V}{\partial z} \cos (n, z) \, dS,$$

and

$$\nabla^2 V = \frac{3}{4\pi a^3} \iint\limits_{\Sigma} \frac{\partial V}{\partial n} \, dS,$$

at all points a distance more than a from the boundary. It is easy to show that the last integral vanishes. In fact, if in (10) we cancel the constant factor r^2 inside and outside the integral, and differentiate the resulting equation with respect to r, this being possible because of the continuity of the derivatives of V, we have

$$0 = \int\limits_0^\pi \int\limits_0^{2\pi} \frac{\partial V}{\partial r} \sin \vartheta \, d\varphi \, d\vartheta,$$

which may also be written

$$\iint\limits_{\Sigma} \frac{\partial V}{\partial n} \, dS = 0.$$

Thus, at any interior point of R, V is harmonic, and we have the converse[1] of Gauss' theorem,

---

[1] Due to KOEBE, Sitzungsberichte der Berliner Mathematischen Gesellschaft, Jahrgang V (1906), pp. 39—42.

Theorem XI. *If V is continuous in the closed region R, and at every interior point of R has as value the arithmetic mean of its values on any sphere with center at that point and lying in R, then V is harmonic in R.*

This theorem will be of repeated use to us. As already suggested, it may serve as a basis for the definition of harmonic functions.

We shall now consider two consequences of the above developments. The first is with regard to the derivatives of a harmonic function. If we apply the equation (13) to the function

$$U = V - \frac{M + m}{2},$$

where M and m are the extremes of V in R, then $|U| \leqq \dfrac{(M - m)}{2}$ and

$$\left| \frac{\partial V}{\partial z} \right| = \left| \frac{\partial U}{\partial z} \right| \leqq \frac{3}{4 \pi a^3} \iint_{\Sigma} |U \cos (n, z)| \, dS$$

$$\leqq \frac{3}{4 \pi a^3} \frac{M - m}{2} \int_0^\pi \int_0^{2\pi} |\cos \vartheta| \, a^2 \sin \vartheta \, d\varphi \, d\vartheta = \frac{3}{4 a} (M - m).$$

Accordingly, we have derived

Theorem XII. *If a function is harmonic in a closed region R, the absolute values of its derivatives of first order at any interior point are not greater than three fourths the oscillation of the function on the boundary of R divided by the distance of the point from the boundary.*

A second consequence is a converse of Theorem I. We state it as

Theorem XIII[1]. *If U is continuous in a region R, and has continuous derivatives of the first order in the interior of R, and if the integral*

$$\iint_S \frac{\partial U}{\partial n} \, dS$$

vanishes when extended over the boundary of all regular regions interior to R, or even if only over all spheres, then U is harmonic in the interior of R.

This may be proved as follows. Let P be an interior point of R, and Σ a sphere, of radius r, about P, and lying in the interior of R. Then, by hypothesis,

$$0 = \iint_{\Sigma} \frac{\partial U}{\partial n} \, dS = \int_0^\pi \int_0^{2\pi} \frac{\partial U}{\partial r} \, r^2 \sin \vartheta \, d\varphi \, d\vartheta,$$

---

[1] This theorem, in space, and in the plane, respectively, was discovered independently by Koebe (footnote, p. 226) and by Bôcher, Proceedings of the American Academy of Arts and Sciences, Vol. **41** (1906). Koebe's treatment is also valid in the plane.

and so, as r is constant on Σ,

$$\int\limits_{0}^{\pi}\int\limits_{0}^{2\pi} \frac{\partial U}{\partial r} \sin \vartheta \, d\varphi \, d\vartheta = 0.$$

If we integrate this equation from 0 to r with respect to r, we have

$$\int\limits_{0}^{\pi}\int\limits_{0}^{2\pi} U(Q) \sin \vartheta \, d\varphi \, d\vartheta - 4\pi U(P) = 0,$$

the integral being taken over the sphere of radius r about P. But this equation is equivalent to

$$U(P) = \frac{1}{4\pi r^2} \iint\limits_{\Sigma} U(Q) \, dS.$$

This holds at first for spheres interior to R, but by continuity it holds for spheres in R. Thus the function U is its own arithmetic mean on the surfaces of spheres in R and so, by Theorem XI, is harmonic in R. The theorem is thus proved.

Exercises.

1. Show that if V is continuous in a region R, and is its own arithmetic mean throughout the volumes of spheres in R, it is also its own arithmetic mean on the surfaces of spheres in R. Hence show that if a function is bounded and integrable in R, and is its own arithmetic mean throughout the volumes of spheres in R, it is harmonic in the interior of R.

2. Prove Koebe's converse of Gauss' theorem as follows. Let V be continuous and its own arithmetic mean in R. Let Σ be any sphere in R, and U the function, harmonic in Σ, with the same boundary values on Σ as V. This function exists, by Chapter IX, § 4 (page 242). Consider $V - U$ in Σ.

3. Investigate the analogues of the developments of this section in one dimension.

4. Show, by means of Theorem XII, that a series of spherical harmonics, convergent in a sphere about the origin, may be differentiated termwise at any interior point of the sphere.

Chapter IX.

Electric Images; Green's Function.

1. Electric Images.

In the closing section of Chapter VII, we saw an example of a case in which a potential with certain requirements as to its normal derivatives on a plane could be represented on one side of the plane by the potential of a point charge on the opposite side of the plane. This is an example of the use of electric images.

In the present section, we shall confine ourselves to the case in which one homogeneous medium is supposed to fill space, the dielectric constant being 1. Let us suppose that we have a plane conducting lamina, so great in its dimensions that it may be considered infinite, and let us suppose that it is *grounded*, or *connected to earth*, which means that it may acquire whatever charges are necessary to enable it to remain at the potential 0. If then a point charge is brought into the neighborhood of the plane, it will induce charges on it, namely such as make the potential of point charge and charge on the plane together equal to 0 on the plane. How can we find the induced charge?

We shall presently have the necessary materials to show that on the far side of the plane, the potential, if bounded, must be everywhere 0. If that region had a finite boundary, this would follow from Theorem II, of the last chapter. But it has not, and we shall borrow the fact. Let us take the plane of the infinite lamina as the (y, z)-plane, with the x-axis through the point charge. Let this be of amount e, and situated at $P(a, 0, 0)$. If now we place a point charge $-e$ at the image of P in the lamina, thought of as a mirror, that is at the point $P'(-a, 0, 0)$, the potential of the two charges will be 0 on the lamina, and the problem is solved. For (supposing $a > 0$), the potential is

$$U = \frac{e}{\sqrt{(x-a)^2 + y^2 + z^2}} - \frac{e}{\sqrt{(x+a)^2 + y^2 + z^2}}, \qquad x \geqq 0,$$
$$U = 0. \qquad x \leqq 0.$$

The density of the charge on the lamina is

$$\sigma = -\frac{1}{4\pi}\left(\frac{\partial U}{\partial n_+} - \frac{\partial U}{\partial n_-}\right) = -\frac{e\,a}{2\pi\,(a^2 + \eta^2 + \zeta^2)^{\frac{3}{2}}},$$

as is readily verified. The total induced charge is found, by integrating the density over the infinite lamina, to be $-e$, that is, the total induced charge is equal and opposite to the inducing charge. We notice moreover, that the density of the charge varies inversely with the cube of the distance from the inducing charge.

Exercises.

1. Verify the correctness of the values given for the density and total amount of the induced charge given above.

2. Consider the conducting surface consisting of the half plane $z = 0$, $y \geqq 0$, and the half plane $y = 0$, $z \geqq 0$. Find the potential due to a charge e at $(0, b, c)$ $b > 0$, $c > 0$, and the induced charge on the conductor. Determine the density of electrification of the half planes, showing that they bear charges proportional to the angles between them and the coaxial plane through the point charge, and that the sum of the charges on the two planes is the negative of the inducing charge. Show that the density approaches 0 at the edge of the conductor.

3. Given a point source of fluid in the presence of an infinite plane barrier, determine the potential of the flow, assumed to be irrotational and solenoidal.

4. At what angle other than a right angle can two half-planes meet to form a conductor the charge induced on which by a point charge can be determined by the method of images?

5. A grounded conductor, occupying a bounded region, is in the presence of a point charge. Show that the density of the induced charge will never change sign.

6. The total charge on the above conductor will be less in magnitude than the inducing charge. But if the conductor is a closed hollow surface, and the inducing charge is in its interior, the induced charge will be equal in magnitude to the inducing charge. Prove these statements.

Infinite Series of Images. Suppose now that we have two parallel grounded conducting planes, and a point charge between them. Let axes be chosen so that the planes are $x = 0$ and $x = a$, while the charge is at $(c, 0, 0)$, $0 < c < a$. A charge $- e$ at $(2a - c, 0, 0)$ will reduce the potential to 0 at $x = a$. To reduce it to 0 on $x = 0$, we shall have to introduce corresponding charges of opposite sign at the points symmetric in the plane $x = 0$, *i. e.* a charge $- e$ at $(-c, 0, 0)$ and a charge e at $(- 2a + c, 0, 0)$. But the potential on $x = a$ is then not 0, so we introduce a pair of new charges symmetric to the last in the plane $x = a$, and so on. Since the charges are getting farther and farther from the planes, their influence gets less and less, and it seems that the process should converge. If we write the potential in the form

$$U = \sum_{-\infty}^{\infty} \frac{e}{\sqrt{(x - 2na - c)^2 + y^2 + z^2}} - \sum_{-\infty}^{\infty} \frac{e}{\sqrt{(x - 2na + c)^2 + y^2 + z^2}},$$

the series do not converge, for they have terms comparable with those of the harmonic series. But if we group the terms properly, say as in

$$U = \sum_{-\infty}^{\infty} e \left(\frac{1}{\sqrt{(x - 2na - c)^2 + y^2 + z^2}} - \frac{1}{\sqrt{(x - 2na + c)^2 + y^2 + z^2}} \right),$$

the resulting series has terms whose ratios to the corresponding terms of the series

$$\sum \frac{1}{n^2}$$

are bounded for sufficiently large n^2. It follows that when (x, y, z) is confined to any bounded region in which none of the charges are located, the second series for U is absolutely and uniformly convergent. It is not difficult to verify that this potential is 0 on the planes $x = 0$ and $x = a$. That the sum of the series is harmonic is easily shown by means of Theorem XI of the last chapter, for in any closed region in which the series is uniformly convergent, it may be integrated termwise.

The method of images is also available in the case of spherical conducting surfaces. We revert to this application later.

Exercises.

7. Show that the density of the induced distribution on the plane $x = 0$ is given by

$$\sigma = \frac{e}{4\pi} \sum_{-\infty}^{\infty} \left\{ \frac{2na - c}{[(2na - c)^2 + \varrho^2]^{\frac{3}{2}}} - \frac{2na + c}{[(2na + c)^2 + \varrho^2]^{\frac{3}{2}}} \right\}, \qquad \varrho^2 = \eta^2 + \zeta^2.$$

The density on the second plane may be obtained from this by replacing c by $a - c$. It is interesting and instructive to find the total charges on the two planes. They turn out to be proportional to the distances of the point charge from the planes, and in total amount $-e$. Referring to Exercise 6, we see that the situations here, and in the case of a single infinite plane, are as if the charge were enclosed in a hollow conducting surface, of finite extent.

8. Find the distribution of the charge induced on the walls of a cuboid by a point charge in its interior[1].

2. Inversion; Kelvin Transformations.

From the solution of certain problems in electrostatics, and indeed, in potential theory in general, we may infer the solution of others by means of a transformation of space known as *inversion in a sphere*. Two points are said to be *inverse* in a sphere, or with respect to a sphere, if they are on the same ray from the center, and if the radius of the sphere is a mean proportional between their distances from the center. If every point of space be thought of as transported to its inverse in the sphere, we have the transformation in question.

Let us now examine some of the properties of an inversion. Let us take the center of the sphere as origin of coördinates, and let a denote the radius of the sphere. If $P(x, y, z)$ and $P'(x', y', z')$ be any two points which are inverse in the sphere, at distances r and r', respectively, from the origin, we have for the equations of the transformation

(1) $$x = \frac{a^2}{r'^2} x', \qquad y = \frac{a^2}{r'^2} y', \qquad z = \frac{a^2}{r'^2} z', \qquad r r' = a^2.$$

The transformation is obviously its own inverse. The equation $A(x^2 + y^2 + z^2) + Bx + Cy + Dz + E = 0$ becomes $E(x'^2 + y'^2 + z'^2) + Ba^2 x' + Ca^2 y' + Da^2 z' + Aa^4 = 0$, so that the inversion carries all spheres or planes into spheres or planes. A necessary and sufficient condition that a sphere be transformed into itself is that it be orthogonal to the sphere of inversion, as may be seen by means of the theorem that the length of the tangent from a point P to a sphere is a mean proportional between the distances from P to the two points where any secant through P cuts the sphere. Any circle orthogonal to the sphere of inversion is the intersection of spheres which are orthogonal to the sphere of inversion, and so is transformed into itself. If l_1 is a line through P, there is a single circle C_1 through P, tangent to l_1 and orthogonal to

---

[1] See Appell, *Traité de Mécanique Rationelle*, T. III, Exercise 12, Chap. XXIX.

the sphere of inversion. If l_2 is a second line through P, there is a single circle C_2 with the corresponding properties. These circles are transformed into themselves by the inversion, and at their two intersections (for they must intersect again at the point inverse to P) they make the same angles. It follows that any angle is carried by the inversion into an equal angle, and the transformation is *conformal*[1].

Kelvin Transformations. Let us now consider the effect of an inversion on a harmonic function. We start by expressing the Laplacian of U in terms of x', y', z'. The differential of arc is given by

$$(2) \qquad ds^2 = \frac{a^4}{r'^4} ds'^2 = \frac{a^4}{r'^4} (dx'^2 + dy'^2 + dz'^2),$$

and accordingly,

$$\nabla^2 U = \frac{r'^6}{a^6} \left[\frac{\partial}{\partial x'} \left(\frac{a^2}{r'^2} \frac{\partial U}{\partial x'} \right) + \frac{\partial}{\partial y'} \left(\frac{a^2}{r'^2} \frac{\partial U}{\partial y'} \right) + \frac{\partial}{\partial z'} \left(\frac{a^2}{r'^2} \frac{\partial U}{\partial z'} \right) \right].$$

This may be given a different form. As

$$\frac{\partial}{\partial x'} \frac{a^2}{r'^2} \frac{\partial U}{\partial x'} = a^2 \left[\frac{1}{r'^2} \frac{\partial^2 U}{\partial x'^2} + 2 \frac{1}{r'} \left(\frac{\partial}{\partial x'} \frac{1}{r'} \right) \frac{\partial U}{\partial x'} \right]$$

$$= \frac{a^2}{r'} \left[\frac{\partial^2}{\partial x'^2} \left(\frac{1}{r'} U \right) - U \frac{\partial^2}{\partial x'^2} \frac{1}{r'} \right],$$

and as $\frac{1}{r'}$ is a harmonic function of x', y', z' (except at the origin), we have

$$(3) \qquad \nabla^2 U = \frac{r'^5}{a^5} \left[\frac{\partial^2}{\partial x'^2} \left(\frac{a}{r'} U \right) + \frac{\partial^2}{\partial y'^2} \left(\frac{a}{r'} U \right) + \frac{\partial^2}{\partial z'^2} \left(\frac{a}{r'} U \right) \right].$$

It follows that if $U(x, y, z)$ is a harmonic function of x, y and z in a domain T, then

$$V(x', y', z') = \frac{a}{r'} U \left(\frac{a^2 x'}{r'^2}, \frac{a^2 y'}{r'^2}, \frac{a^2 z'}{r'^2} \right)$$

is harmonic in x', y', and z' in the domain T' into which T is carried by the inversion.

This transformation of one harmonic function into another is known as a *Kelvin transformation*[2].

The Point Infinity. An inversion in a sphere is one-to-one except that the center of the sphere of inversion has no corresponding point. The neighborhood of the origin goes over into a set of points at a great

---

[1] It should be remarked that the transformation by inversion, though conformal, does not carry a trihedral angle into a congruent trihedral angle, but into the symmetric one. Thus a set of rays forming the positive axes of a right-hand system would go over into circular arcs whose tangents form the positive axes of a left-hand system.

[2] W. Thomson, Lord Kelvin, Journal de mathématiques pures et appliquées, Vol. 12 (1847), p. 256.

distance—into an infinite domain. If U is harmonic at the center of the sphere of inversion, or the center of inversion, as it is sometimes called, V will be regular at infinity, as is easily verified. On the other hand, if U is harmonic in an infinite domain, and therefore also regular at infinity, it may be expressed in terms of potentials of distributions on the surface of a sufficiently large sphere, by (III), page 219, and will thus be expressible in the form

$$U = \frac{H_0\,(x,\,y,\,z)}{r} + \frac{H_1\,(x,\,y,\,z)}{r^3} + \cdots,$$

where H_0, H_1, ... are homogeneous polynomials of the degrees given by the indices, as we saw in Chapter V (p. 143). Accordingly

$$V = \frac{H_0\,(x',\,y',\,z')}{a} + \frac{H_1\,(x',\,y',\,z')}{a^3} + \cdots,$$

is convergent inside the sphere about the origin inverse to any sphere outside of which the series for U is convergent. Of course the transformation does not define V at the origin, but we see that if it is defined there by this series which defines it at points nearby, it will be harmonic at the origin. Thus a function which is harmonic in an infinite domain goes over, by a Kelvin transformation, into a function which is harmonic in a neighborhood of the origin, if properly defined at that single point.

In order to be able to regard an inversion as one-to-one, we introduce an ideal point infinity, and say that the inversion carries the center of inversion into the point infinity, and the point infinity into the center of inversion. We should naturally say that the point infinity belongs to any infinite domain with finite boundary, and this demands an extension of the notion of interior point. We say that the point infinity is interior to a set of points provided there is a sphere such that every point outside the sphere belongs to the set. An unbounded set is a domain provided all its points are interior points, and provided any two of its points can be joined by a polygonal line of a finite number of sides, at most one of which is infinite in length, and all of whose points belong to the domain. The point infinity is a limit point of a set provided there are points of the set outside of every sphere. In short, we ascribe to the point infinity with respect to any set of points, exactly the properties which the center of inversion has with respect to the set into which the given set is transformed by an inversion.

Exercises.

1. If $H_n\,(x,\,y,\,z)$ is a spherical harmonic of order n, show that $\dfrac{H_n\,(x,\,y,\,z)}{r^{2n+1}}$ is harmonic throughout space except at the origin.

2. Show that an inversion in a sphere with center O and a Kelvin transformation carry the potential of a point charge e at a point $Q\,(\alpha,\,\beta,\,\gamma)$, not the point O,

into the potential of a charge at the point Q' $(\alpha', \beta', \gamma')$ inverse to Q. Show that the amount of the charge is changed in the ratio $OQ':a$, where a is the radius of the sphere of inversion $\left(e' = \dfrac{e\,\delta'}{a},\ \delta'^2 = \alpha'^2 + \beta'^2 + \gamma'^2\right)$.

3. Show that if v is a small volume about $Q\,(\alpha, \beta, \gamma)$, and v' the volume into which v is transformed by an inversion in a sphere about O, of radius a, then, to within an infinitesimal of higher order in the maximum chord of v, $v' = \dfrac{\delta'^6}{a^6}\,v$, where δ' is the distance from the origin O to some point of v'. Hence show that densities $\varkappa$ and $\varkappa'$, at corresponding points Q and Q', of volume distributions producing potentials U and V related by the corresponding Kelvin transformation, are related by the equation $\varkappa' = \left(\dfrac{a}{\delta'}\right)^5 \varkappa$. Determine a similar relation for surface distributions. Check by Poisson's equation and the equation (3), and by the equation relating surface densities with the break in the normal derivatives of the potential.

4. Show that two points symmetric in a plane are transformed by an inversion into two points inverse in the sphere corresponding by the inversion to the plane.

Induced Charge on a Sphere. Let us now see what we get by an inversion and a Kelvin transformation from the problem of the charge induced on a plane Π by a point charge e at P_1 not on Π. The potential U of the charge e and of the charge induced on Π, is, as we have seen, equal, on the side of Π on which P_1 lies, to the combined potential of

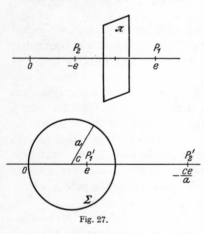

Fig. 27.

the charge e at P_1 and of a charge $-e$ at the point P_2 symmetric in Π; beyond Π, $U = 0$.

Let us now subject space to an inversion in a sphere with center O at a point of the ray from P_1 through P_2, beyond P_2, and let us subject U to the corresponding Kelvin transformation. The plane Π goes over into a sphere Σ through O, and P_1 and P_2 go over into two points P_1' and P_2' which are inverse with respect to Σ, by Exercise 4 (fig. 27). If a is the radius of Σ, and c the distance of P_1' from the center of Σ, the distance of P_2' from the center will be $\dfrac{a^2}{c}$. The distances of P_1' and P_2' from the center of inversion O will then be $a + c$ and $a + \dfrac{a^2}{c} = \dfrac{(a + c)\,a}{c}$, respectively. Thus, by Exercise 2, the Kelvin transformation carries U into a potential V, which, in the interior of Σ is the potential of charges at P_1' and P_2', of opposite signs, and whose magnitudes are proportional to the distances of these points from the center of inversion, *i. e.* in the ratio $c:a$. We have thus the desired result: *a charge e at a point a distance* *c from the center of a sphere, and a charge* $-\dfrac{ec}{a}$ *at the point inverse to the first in the sphere, produce together a potential which is 0 on the surface of the sphere.* This enables us to find the induced charge on a sphere caused by a point charge either within or without the sphere. We could find the density by means of Exercise 3, but we shall find it directly at a later point.

The problem of Exercise 2, § 1 enables us to find, by inverting in a sphere with center on one of the planes, the charge induced by a point charge on the surface, consisting of a hemisphere and the part of its diametral plane outside the sphere of which the hemisphere is part.

Exercise.

What will be the shape of the conductor if the center of inversion is not on one of the two planes? Enumerate a number of other cases in which induced charges on surfaces may be found by the method of images and inversions.

The Possibility of Further Transformations. It is natural to ask whether there are not further transformations of space, similar to inversions, and of functions, similar to Kelvin transformations, which enable us to pass from a function, harmonic in one set of variables, to a function harmonic in a second set. We have seen that Laplace's equation is invariant under a rigid motion of space, and hence harmonic functions remain harmonic functions under such a transformation of coördinates. The same is clearly true of a reflection in a plane, say the (y, z)-plane: $x' = -x$, $y' = y$, $z' = z$. The Laplacian of a function goes over into a constant multiple of itself under a homothetic transformation: $x' = ax$, $y' = ay$, $z' = az$, and such transformations leave harmonic functions harmonic. But these transformations, together with inversions and combinations of them, are all there are of the kind in question.

The transformations of space mentioned are the only conformal ones, as is proved in works on differential geometry[1]. But if we are to have any analytic transformation

$$x = f(x', y', z'), \qquad y = g(x', y', z'), \qquad z = h(x', y', z')$$

in which

$$V(x', y', z') = \varphi(x', y', z')\, U[f(x', y', z'), g(x', y', z'), h(x', y', z')]$$

is harmonic in $x'y'z'$ whenever U is harmonic in x, y, z, it can be shown that the transformation must be conformal.

The situation is different if we do not require the transformation to carry over *every* harmonic function into a harmonic function. Thus if we only require that it shall carry all harmonic functions independent of z into harmonic functions, there are transformations in which z is un-

---

[1] See, for instance, BLASCHKE, *Vorlesungen über Differentialgeometrie*, Berlin 1924, Bd. I, § 40.

changed, which carry such harmonic functions into harmonic functions,
namely all those in which f and g are the real and imaginary parts of an
analytic function of $x' + i y'$ (see Exercise 10, p. 363).

We may say, therefore, that in space, there are no new transformations of the character of Kelvin transformations, although in the plane,
there is a great variety of them.

3. Green's Function.

At the close of § 1 in the last chapter, the question of the existence
of certain harmonic functions was raised, among them, one which
we shall now formulate as that of the existence of a function, harmonic in a closed region R, and taking on preassigned continuous
boundary values. The problem of showing that such a function exists,
or of finding it when it exists, is known as the *Dirichlet problem*, or the
first boundary problem of potential theory. It is historically the oldest
problem of existence of potential theory. We are about to outline an
attack on this problem, and in the next section, carry it through in the
very simple but important case in which R is a sphere. We shall see
that there is a relation between this problem and the problem of the
charge induced on the surface of R by a point charge within R. The
guiding thought is simple. We first seek to express a harmonic function
in terms of its boundary values. We then see if the expression found continues to represent a harmonic function when the boundary values are
any given continuous function.

The natural point of departure is the formula (9) of the last chapter,

$$U(P) = -\frac{1}{4\pi} \iint\limits_{S} \left(U \frac{\partial}{\partial \nu} \frac{1}{r} - \frac{\partial U}{\partial \nu} \frac{1}{r} \right) dS,$$

valid if U is harmonic in the closed regular region R bounded by S.
This formula expresses U at any interior point of R in terms of its boundary values and those of its normal derivative. But we know that the
boundary values alone determine U, and it is natural to try to eliminate
the normal derivative. For this purpose we may take the relation of
Theorem VI of the last chapter:

$$0 = -\frac{1}{4\pi} \iint\limits_{S} \left(U \frac{\partial V}{\partial \nu} - \frac{\partial U}{\partial \nu} V \right) dS,$$

where V is any function harmonic in R. If, now, a harmonic function V
can be found, such that

$$\frac{1}{r} + V$$

vanishes at all points of S, the normal derivative of U will be eliminated by adding these two equations. Such a function V, however, is nothing other than the potential of the charge induced on a grounded sheet conductor with the form of the surface S, by a unit charge at P, and the function

$$G(Q,P) = \frac{1}{r} + V(Q,P)$$

is the value at Q of the potential of the inducing charge at P and the induced charge together. This function is known as *Green's function* for the region R and the *pole P*. In terms of Green's function we have

$$(4) \qquad U(P) = -\frac{1}{4\pi} \iint\limits_{S} U(Q)\frac{\partial}{\partial \nu} G(Q,P)\, dS,$$

where the differentiation and integration are with respect to the coördinates ξ, η, ζ, of Q. Thus if Green's function exists, and has continuous partial derivatives of the first order in any closed portion of R which does not contain P, any function $U(P)$, harmonic in R, admits the above representation[1].

Now suppose that instead of having under the integral sign the function $U(Q)$, representing the boundary values of a function known to be harmonic in R, we have an arbitrary continuous function of the position of Q on S. What then does the integral

$$(5) \qquad F(P) = -\frac{1}{4\pi} \iint\limits_{S} f(Q)\frac{\partial}{\partial \nu} G(Q,P)\, dS$$

represent? Granted (a) that Green's function exists, we have to show, if we wish to solve the Dirichlet problem in this way, (b) that $F(P)$ is harmonic in P, and (c) that it takes on the boundary values $f(P)$. Let us consider this programme for a moment.

First, to establish the existence of Green's function, we have to solve a special case of the Dirichlet problem, namely find a harmonic function taking on the same boundary values as $-\frac{1}{r}$. Moreover, we have to solve the problem for all positions of P in the interior of R. GREEN himself argued that such a function existed from the physical evidence. Of course the static charge on S exists! We have here an excellent example of the value and danger of intuitional reasoning. On the credit side is the fact that it led GREEN to a series of important discoveries, since well

---

[1] It is true that the derivation of the formula (4) is based on the assumption that U is continuously differentiable in R. But if harmonic in R, U will be continuously differentiable in any closed region interior to R, and by applying (4) to a suitably chosen interior region, we can, by a limit process, infer its validity for R without further hypothesis on the derivatives of U.

established. On the debit side is its unreliability, for there are, in fact, regions for which Green's function does *not* exist[1].

If Green's function has been shown to exist for R, we must then make sure that $F(P)$ is harmonic in R. We know that $G(Q, P)$ is harmonic in Q for fixed P, and we shall see presently that it is symmetric, and it will follow that it is harmonic in P. After that, it must be shown that the integral is harmonic in P. This done, we must show that $F(P)$ takes on the given boundary values.

Under proper limitations on R, the programme is a feasible one, and has been carried out in an elegant manner by LIAPOUNOFF[2]. We shall find it relatively easy in the case of the sphere, but for more general regions, simpler and farther reaching methods are now available.

The Symmetry of Green's Function[3]. The usual proofs of the symmetry of Green's function are based on Green's identity II, which demands some hypothesis on the derivatives of the function on the boundary. These, in general, do not exist. We may, however, proceed as follows.

Let R denote a closed bounded region, and let $G(Q, P)$ denote Green's function for R with pole P, supposed to exist. This supposition includes the demand that it be harmonic in R, except at P, and that it approach 0 at every boundary point, but includes no demand on the derivatives on the boundary. We note that the continuity is uniform in any region in R which omits a sphere about P, and hence that for any $\varepsilon > 0$, there is a $\delta > 0$, such that $G(Q, P) < \varepsilon$ at all points of R whose distance from the boundary is less than δ. Furthermore, in any closed region interior to R, the minimum of $G(Q, P)$ is positive, for otherwise we should have a contradiction of Gauss' theorem of the arithmetic mean.

Now let μ be any positive constant. The equipotential $G(Q, P) = \mu$ lies in the interior of R; it also lies in the closed subregion of R $\frac{\mu}{2} \leqq G(Q, P) \leqq 2\mu$. In this region the hypotheses of Theorem XIV, Chapter X (p. 276) are in force, and hence *in any neighborhood of any equipotential surface, there are non-singular equipotential surfaces*.

We next show that a non-singular equipotential surface $G(Q, P) = \mu'$ bounds a finite regular region. The interior points of such a region, namely those for which $G(Q, P) > \mu'$, evidently constitute an open set, since $G(Q, P)$ is continuous, except at P, which is clearly interior to the set. Secondly, any two interior points can be connected by a regular

---

[1] GREEN's introduction of the function which bears his name is in his *Essay*, l. c. footnote § 5, Chapter II, p. 38. An example of a region for which Green's function does not exist is given by LEBESGUE, *Sur des cas d'impossibilité du problème de Dirichlet*, Comptes Rendus de la Société Mathématique de France, 1913, p. 17. See Exercise 10, p. 334.

[2] *Sur quelques questions qui se ratachent au problème de Dirichlet*, Journal de mathématiques pures et appliquées, 5 Ser. Vol. IV, (1898).

[3] This topic may well be omitted on a first reading of the book.

curve lying in the interior. This will be proved if it can be shown that any interior point Q_0 can be so connected with P, for any two can then be connected by way of P.

Let T_0 denote the set of points of R' which can be connected with Q_0 by regular curves entirely in the interior of R'. If a boundary point Q_1 of T_0 were not a boundary point of R', there would be a sphere about it interior to R', and within this sphere there would be points of T_0. Thus Q_1 and all points near it could be joined by straight line segments to a point of T_0, and this, by a regular curve, to Q_0. Q_1 would then be an interior point of T_0, and not a boundary point. Thus $G(Q, P) = \mu'$ at every boundary point of T_0, so that if T_0 did not contain P, and $G(Q, P)$ were thus harmonic in T_0, it would be constant. As this is not the case, P lies in T_0, and so can be joined to Q_0 in the required way.

Finally, as the bounding surface S' of R' has no singular points, it may be represented in the neighborhood of any of its points by an equation $z = \varphi(x, y)$, if the axes are properly orientated, $\varphi(x, y)$ being analytic. It follows that the surface can be divided by regular curves into regular surface elements. These will be properly joined, and so R', being bounded by a regular surface, is a regular region.

Turning now to the symmetry of Green's function, we cut out from R' two small spheres σ and σ', about P and any second interior point P' of R', the spheres lying in the interior of R'. In the resulting region both $G(Q, P)$ and $G(Q, P')$ are continuously differentiable and harmonic. Hence II is applicable (see the footnote, p. 217), and we have

$$\iint_{S'} \left[G(Q, P) \frac{\partial G(Q, P')}{\partial \nu} - G(Q, P') \frac{\partial G(Q, P)}{\partial \nu} \right] dS$$

$$+ \iint_{\sigma' + \sigma} \left[G(Q, P) \frac{\partial G(Q, P')}{\partial \nu} - G(Q, P') \frac{\partial G(Q, P)}{\partial \nu} \right] dS = 0.$$

We now allow the radii of σ and σ' to approach 0. Near P', $G(Q, P)$ and its derivatives are continuous, whereas $G(Q, P')$ differs from $\frac{1}{r'}$ by a harmonic function $V(Q, P)$, r' being the distance $P'Q$. On σ' the normal ν points along the radius toward the center P'. Accordingly, the integral over σ' may be written

$$\iint_{\sigma'} G(Q, P) \, d\Omega + r'^2 \iint G(Q, P) \frac{\partial V(Q, P')}{\partial \nu} \, d\Omega$$

$$- r' \iint \frac{\partial G(Q, P)}{\partial \nu} \, d\Omega - r'^2 \iint V(Q, P') \frac{\partial G(Q, P)}{\partial \nu} \, d\Omega,$$

the integrations being with respect to the solid angle subtended at P'. As r' approaches 0, all but the first term approach 0, and this approaches $4\pi G(P', P)$. Similarly, the integral over σ approaches $-4\pi G(P, P')$.

The integral over S' is unaffected by this limit process. The resulting equation holds for all non-singular equipotential surfaces $G(Q, P) = \mu'$. But there are values of μ' as close to 0 as we please for which this surface is non-singular. Accordingly we may allow μ' to approach 0 through such values. The first term in the integral over S' has the value

$$\mu' \iint\limits_{S'} \frac{\partial G(Q, P')}{\partial \nu} dS = -4\pi\mu',$$

for $G(Q, P')$ is the sum of a function harmonic in R' and the potential of a unit particle in R'. As to the second term, $G(Q, P')$ is not constant on S', but as the other factor of the integrand is never positive, we may employ the law of the mean, and write this second term

$$4\pi G(\bar{Q}, P'),$$

where $\bar{Q}$ is some point on S'. As μ' approaches 0, the first term approaches 0, and as $\bar{Q}$ must become arbitrarily near to the boundary of R, where $G(Q, P')$ approaches 0 uniformly, the second term also approaches 0. In the limit then, there are but two terms left in the identity, and this, after a transposition and division by 4π, becomes

$$G(P', P) = G(P, P').$$

Here P and P' may be any two interior points of R, and thus the symmetry of Green's function is established.

Exercise.

1. Show that if $\sigma(P, Q)$ is the density at Q of the charge induced on S by a unit charge at P, the formula (4) may be written

$$U(P) = -\iint\limits_{S} U(Q)\sigma(Q, P) dS,$$

Referring to Exercise 6, p. 230, show that $U(P)$ is a weighted mean of its values on S, and hence lies between its extreme values on S. The above is the form in which GREEN wrote the formula (4).

4. Poisson's Integral.

We proceed now to set up Green's function for the sphere. Let a be the radius of the sphere, and let P be a point a distance ϱ from the center O. Then a unit charge at P will induce on the surface of the sphere, thought of as a grounded conducting surface, a distribution whose potential in the interior of the sphere is the same as that of a charge $\frac{-a}{\varrho}$ at the point P' inverse to P in the sphere, as we saw in § 2. Accordingly, if r and r' are the distances of P and P' from Q, Green's function for the sphere is

$$G(Q, P) = \frac{1}{r} - \frac{a}{\varrho}\cdot\frac{1}{r'} = \frac{1}{r} - \frac{\overline{OP'}}{a}\frac{1}{r'}.$$

Evidently Green's function is continuously differentiable in the coördinates of Q in any closed portion of the sphere omitting the point P, so that it may be used in the formula (4). This then becomes

$$(6) \qquad U(P) = -\frac{1}{4\pi} \iint_S U(Q) \frac{\partial}{\partial \nu}\left[\frac{1}{r} - \frac{a}{\varrho}\frac{1}{r'}\right] dS.$$

Let us express the integrand in terms of the coördinates $(\varrho, \varphi, \vartheta)$ of P and $(\varrho', \varphi', \vartheta')$ of Q. Since

$$r^2 = \varrho^2 + \varrho'^2 - 2\varrho\varrho'\cos\gamma, \quad \text{and} \quad r'^2 = \frac{a^4}{\varrho^2} + \varrho'^2 - 2\frac{a^2}{\varrho}\varrho'\cos\gamma,$$

where

$$\cos\gamma = \cos\vartheta\cos\vartheta' + \sin\vartheta\sin\vartheta'\cos(\varphi - \varphi'),$$

we have

$$\frac{\partial}{\partial\nu}\frac{1}{r} = \frac{\partial}{\partial\varrho'}\frac{1}{r}\bigg|_{\varrho'=a} = \frac{\varrho\cos\gamma - \varrho'}{r^3}\bigg|_{\varrho'=a} = \frac{\varrho\cos\gamma - a}{r^3},$$

$$\frac{\partial}{\partial\nu}\frac{1}{r'} = \frac{\frac{a^2}{\varrho}\cos\gamma - a}{r'^3} = \frac{\varrho^2}{a^2}\frac{a\cos\gamma - \varrho}{r^3},$$

where in the last step we have used the fact that $G(Q, P)$ vanishes when Q is on the surface of the sphere. With these values, the formula (6) becomes

$$(7) \quad U(\varrho, \varphi, \vartheta) = \frac{a^2 - \varrho^2}{4\pi a} \iint_S \frac{U(\varphi', \vartheta')\, dS}{r^3}, \quad r^2 = \varrho^2 + a^2 - 2a\varrho\cos\gamma.$$

As this formula involves no derivatives of U, it holds if U is harmonic in the interior of R and continuous in R, as may be seen by applying it to a smaller concentric sphere and passing to the limit as the radius of this sphere approaches a. It is known as *Poisson's integral*[1].

Let us now ask whether the boundary values can be any continuous function. Does

$$(8) \qquad V(\varrho, \varphi, \vartheta) = \frac{a^2 - \varrho^2}{4\pi a} \iint_S \frac{f(\varphi', \vartheta')\, dS}{r^3}$$

solve the Dirichlet problem for the sphere? We shall prove that it does.

First of all, we have the identity, for Q on S,

$$(9) \qquad \frac{a^2 - \varrho^2}{r^3} = -\frac{1}{r} + 2a\frac{a - \varrho\cos\gamma}{r^3} = -\frac{1}{r} - 2a\frac{\partial}{\partial\nu}\frac{1}{r},$$

which shows that V is the sum of the potentials of a simple and of a double distribution on S with continuous density and moment. Hence

---

[1] Journal de l'Ecole Polytechnique, Vol. 11 (1820), p. 422. See also the Encyklopädie der Mathematischen Wissenschaften, II, A 7b, *Potentialtheorie*, BURKHARDT u. MEYER, p. 489.

V is harmonic in all of space except on S, and in particular, within the sphere.

Secondly, as $P(\varrho, \varphi, \vartheta)$ approaches the point $Q_0(a, \varphi_0, \vartheta_0)$ of the surface of the sphere in any manner, $V(\varrho, \varphi, \vartheta)$ approaches $f(\varphi_0, \vartheta_0)$. To show this, we start with the remark that the formula (7) holds for the harmonic function 1, so that

$$(10) \qquad 1 = \frac{a^2 - \varrho^2}{4\pi a} \iint\limits_{S} \frac{dS}{r^3}.$$

Multiplying both sides of this equation by the constant $f(\varphi_0, \vartheta_0)$ and subtracting the resulting equation from (8), we have

$$V(\varrho, \varphi, \vartheta) - f(\varphi_0, \vartheta_0) = \frac{a^2 - \varrho^2}{4\pi a} \iint\limits_{S} \frac{[f(\varphi', \vartheta') - f(\varphi_0, \vartheta_0)]}{r^3} dS.$$

Now let σ denote a small cap of the sphere S with Q_0 as center, subtending at the center of the sphere a cone whose elements make an angle 2α with its axis. If $\varepsilon > 0$ is given, α can be chosen so small that on σ, $|f(\varphi', \vartheta') - f(\varphi_0, \vartheta_0)| < \frac{\varepsilon}{2}$. Then, making use of (10), we see that

$$\left| \frac{a^2 - \varrho^2}{4\pi a} \iint\limits_{\sigma} \frac{f(\varphi', \vartheta') - f(\varphi_0, \vartheta_0)}{r^3} dS \right| < \frac{\varepsilon}{2} \frac{a^2 - \varrho^2}{4\pi a} \iint\limits_{S} \frac{dS}{r^3} = \frac{\varepsilon}{2}.$$

But if we confine P to the interior of the cone coaxial with the one subtended by σ, and with the same vertex, but with half the angular opening, then when Q is on the portion $S - \sigma$ of S,

$$\cos\gamma \le \cos\alpha, \quad \text{and} \quad r^2 \ge \varrho^2 + a^2 - 2\varrho a \cos\alpha.$$

Let us call r_0 the minimum value of r thus limited. Then if M is a bound for $|f(\varphi, \vartheta)|$ on S,

$$\left| \frac{a^2 - \varrho^2}{4\pi a} \iint\limits_{S-\sigma} \frac{f(\varphi', \vartheta') - f(\varphi_0, \vartheta_0)}{r^3} dS \right| < \frac{a^2 - \varrho^2}{4\pi a} \frac{2M}{r_0^3} 4\pi a^2,$$

a quantity which can be made less than $\frac{\varepsilon}{2}$ by sufficiently restricting $a - \varrho$. Thus

$$|V(\varrho, \varphi, \vartheta) - f(\varphi_0, \vartheta_0)| < \varepsilon$$

in a region which contains all the points within and on the sphere which are within a certain distance of Q_0. So V is not only continuous on the boundary, but assumes the given boundary values. Accordingly, *the Dirichlet problem is solved for the sphere*. There is no real difference between the formulas (7) and (8) when $f(\varphi, \vartheta)$ is a continuous function.

Moreover, Poisson's integral also solves the Dirichlet problem for the infinite region exterior to the sphere. For, as we have seen, the integral is the sum of simple and double distributions on S. The first is continuous. For the second, we have the moment

$$\mu = -\frac{f(\varphi', \vartheta')}{2\pi},$$

as a glance at the formulas (8) and (9) shows. Accordingly the limits V_- and V_+ of V from within and from without S are connected by the relation

$$V_+ - V_- = 4\pi\mu = -2f(\varphi', \vartheta').$$

Hence, as we have shown that $V_- = f(\varphi', \vartheta')$, we know that $V_+ = -f(\varphi', \vartheta')$. If we change a sign in (8), and write it

(11) $$V(\varrho, \varphi, \vartheta) = \frac{\varrho^2 - a^2}{4\pi a} \iint\limits_S \frac{f(\varphi', \vartheta')\,dS}{r^3},$$

the function thus represented is harmonic outside the sphere (this implying also regularity at infinity), and assumes the boundary values $f(\varphi, \vartheta)$.

Remark. As a matter of fact, Poisson's integral represents a function harmonic everywhere except on S when $f(\varphi, \vartheta)$ is any integrable function. We shall have the materials for a proof of this fact in the next chapter. But in case $f(\varphi, \vartheta)$, while remaining integrable, has discontinuities, V can no longer approach this function at every boundary point. What we can say—for the above reasoning still applies to integrable bounded functions—is that V approaches $f(\varphi, \vartheta)$ at every boundary point where this function is continuous, and lies between the least upper and greatest lower bound of this function.

Exercises.

1. Show by elementary geometry that the function $G(Q, P)$, p. 240, vanishes when Q is on the surface of the sphere.

2. Verify that Green's function is symmetric, when R is a sphere.

3. Show that the density of the charge induced on the surface of a sphere by a point charge is inversely proportional to the cube of the distance from the point charge.

4. Set up Green's function for the region R consisting of all of space to one side of an infinite plane. Set up the equation corresponding to Poisson's integral for this region, and show that it can be given the form

$$V(P) = \frac{1}{2\pi} \iint\limits_S f(Q)\,d\Omega,$$

the integration being with respect to the solid angle subtended at P by an element of the plane S. Show that this formula solves the Dirichlet problem for the region R, on the understanding that instead of requiring that V shall be regular at infinity (which may not be consistent with its assuming the boundary values $f(P)$), we require that it shall be bounded in absolute value. Here $f(P)$ should be assumed to be continuous and bounded. Discuss the possibility of inferring the solution of the Dirichlet problem for the sphere from this by means of an inversion.

5. Show that if $f(Q)$ is piecewise continuous on the surface of a sphere S, there exists a function, harmonic in the interior of the sphere, and approaching $f(P)$ at every boundary point at which this function is continuous. Show that if Q_0 is an interior point of one of the regular arcs on which $f(Q)$ is discontinuous, the harmonic function will approach the arithmetic mean of the two limiting values of $f(Q)$ at Q_0, and determine the limiting value of the harmonic function if Q_0 is a point at which several arcs on which $f(Q)$ is discontinuous meet.

6. A homogeneous thermally isotropic sphere has its surface maintained at temperatures given by $U = \cos \vartheta$, ϑ being the co-latitude. Determine the temperatures in the interior of the sphere for a steady state.

7. Derive Gauss' theorem of the arithmetic mean from Poisson's integral.

8. Show that if U is harmonic at every proper point of space (not the point infinity) and is bounded, it is a constant.

9. Let R be a closed region bounded by a surface S with a definite normal at each point, and such that each point of S is on a sphere entirely in R. Let U be harmonic in R, no hypothesis being made on its first derivatives on the boundary, other than that the normal derivatives exist as one-sided limits and are 0. Show that U is constant in R, thus generalizing in one direction Theorem IV, Chapter VIII, p. 213. Suggestion. Apply Poisson's integral to U in the sphere through the boundary point at which U attains its maximum, on the assumption that the statement is not true.

A great deal has been written about Poisson's integral, and something on it will be found in nearly every book on Potential Theory (see the bibliographical notes, p. 377). In recent literature on the subject, the reader may be interested in the geometric treatment given by PERKINS, *An Intrinsic Treatment of Poisson's Integral*, American Journal of Mathematics, Vol. 50 (1928), pp. 389—414.

Poisson's integral in two dimensions has similar properties. An excellent treatment of it is to be found in BÔCHER'S *Introduction to the Theory of Fourier's Series*, Annals of Mathematics, 2^d Ser. Vol. VII (1906) pp. 91—99. Very general theorems on the subject are found in EVANS, *The Logarithmic Potential*, New York, 1927.

5. Other Existence Theorems.

We have spoken several times of existence theorems, and we have proved one, namely, that given a sphere and a function defined and continuous on the surface of the sphere, there exists a function continuous in the sphere and harmonic in its interior, which assumes the given boundary values. An existence theorem in mathematics has nothing to do with any metaphysical sense of the word "exist"; it is merely a statement that the conditions imposed on a function, number, or other mathematical concept, are not contradictory. The proof of an existence theorem usually consists in showing how the function, or other thing whose existence is asserted, can be actually produced or constructed. Indeed it has been maintained that a proof of existence must be of this nature. The solution of the Dirichlet problem for the sphere has established the existence of a harmonic function with given boundary values on a sphere by producing a formula which gives the harmonic function. The existence theorem corresponding to this for a general region is known as the *first fundamental existence theorem of potential theory*.

The Cauchy-Kowalevsky Existence Theorem. There are other existence theorems concerning harmonic functions. Applicable to all differential equations with analytic coefficients is the Cauchy-Kowalevsky theorem[1]. For Laplace's equation, its content may be formulated as follows. Let $P(x_0, y_0, z_0)$ be a point of space, and let S denote an arbitrary surface passing through P, analytic at P. By this we shall understand that for a proper orientation of the axes S has a representation $z = f(x, y)$, where $f(x, y)$ is developable in a power series in $x - x_0$, $y - y_0$, convergent in some neighborhood of the point (x_0, y_0). Let $\varphi_0(x, y)$ and $\varphi_1(x, y)$ denote two functions, analytic at (x_0, y_0). Then *there exists a three dimensional neighborhood N of P and a function $U(x, y, z)$ which is harmonic in N and which assumes on the portion of S in N the same values as the function $\varphi_0(x, y)$, and whose normal derivative assumes on the same portion of S the values $\varphi_1(x, y)$. There is only one such function.* Here a positive sense is supposed to have been assigned to the normal to S, in such a way that it varies continuously over S.

This theorem tells us that we may assign arbitrarily the value of a harmonic function *and* of its normal derivative on a surface element, provided all data are analytic. Thus it appears that essentially *two* arbitrary functions of position on a surface fix a harmonic function, whereas the first fundamental existence theorem indicates that one arbitrary function is sufficient. But in the latter case, this function is given over the *whole* of a closed surface, whereas in the former, the two functions are given only on an open piece of surface . The Cauchy-Kowalevsky theorem asserts the existence of a function harmonic on both sides of the surface on which values are assigned, as well as on the surface, but only in a neighborhood of a point. The first fundamental existence theorem asserts that even though the assigned boundary values be merely continuous, a function exists which is harmonic throughout the entire interior of the region on whose surface values are assigned, but not that it can be continued through the surface. The Cauchy-Kowalevsky theorem asserts the existence of a function in some neighborhood of a point (or *im Kleinen*, as it is expressed in German), the first fundamental existence theorem, throughout a given extended region (im Großen).

The Second Fundamental Existence Theorem. We have seen that if continuous boundary values are assigned, on the surface of a regular region, to the normal derivatives, not more than one function, apart

---

from an additive constant, harmonic in the region, can have normal derivatives with these values. Can the boundary values be any continuous function? Evidently not, in the case of finite regions at least, for Theorem I of the last chapter places a restriction on them. Suppose that this condition is fulfilled, that is, in the case of finite regions, that the integral over the surface of the assigned boundary values vanishes. The problem of finding a function, harmonic in the region, and having normal derivatives equal to the function given on the boundary is known as *Neumann's problem*, or the *second boundary value problem of potential theory*, and the theorem asserting the existence of a solution of this problem is known as the *second fundamental existence theorem of potential theory*.

In considering the Neumann problem, it is natural to ask whether there is not a function similar to Green's function which may here play the role which Green's did for the Dirichlet problem. We consider the case of a bounded region, and follow the analogy of the work of § 3. We wish to eliminate U from under the integral sign in

$$U(P) = \frac{1}{4\pi} \iint\limits_S \left[\frac{\partial U}{\partial \nu} \frac{1}{r} - U \frac{\partial}{\partial \nu} \frac{1}{r} \right] dS$$

by means of

$$0 = \frac{1}{4\pi} \iint\limits_S \left[\frac{\partial U}{\partial \nu} V - U \frac{\partial}{\partial \nu} V \right] dS,$$

in order that U may be expressed in terms of the boundary values of its normal derivative alone. This could be accomplished if we could find a function V, harmonic in R, and having a normal derivative which was the negative of that of $\frac{1}{r}$. But this is impossible, since, by Gauss' theorem on the integral of the normal derivative, the integral of the normal derivative of $\frac{1}{r}$ over S, the surface of R, is -4π, while if V is harmonic in R, the integral of its normal derivative over S is 0. We therefore demand that *the normal derivative of V shall differ from that of* $-\frac{1}{r}$ *by a constant*, and this will serve our purpose. Then the combined potential

$$G(Q, P) = \frac{1}{r} + V(Q, P),$$

if it exists, is known as *Green's function of the second kind for R*. In terms of this function, we obtain the following expression for $U(P)$ by adding the last two equations:

(12) $$U(P) = \frac{1}{4\pi} \iint\limits_S \frac{\partial U}{\partial \nu} G(Q, P) dS + \frac{c}{4\pi} \iint\limits_S U(Q) dS.$$

This gives U in terms of its normal derivatives except for an additive constant, which is all that could be expected, since U is determined by its normal derivatives only to within an additive constant. Further consideration of this formula is left for the following exercises, where it is assumed once and for all that $G(Q, P)$ exists and possesses the requisite continuity and differentiability.

Exercises.

1. Determine the value of the constant in the formula (12), and thus show that the last term is the mean of the values of $U(P)$ on S.

2. Show that $G(P, Q) = G(Q, P)$ for Green's function of the second kind.

3. Given a generalized function of Green

$$G(Q, P) = \frac{1}{r} + V(Q, P),$$

where $V(P, Q)$ is harmonic in R and subject to any boundary conditions which have as consequence that

$$\iint\limits_{S} \left[G(Q, P_1)\frac{\partial}{\partial\nu}G(Q, P_2) - G(Q, P_2)\frac{\partial}{\partial\nu}G(Q, P_1) \right] dS = 0,$$

show that $G(P, Q) = G(Q, P)$.

4. With the notation of § 4, show that

$$G(Q, P) = \frac{1}{r} + \frac{a}{\varrho\, r'} + \frac{1}{a}\log\frac{2\,a^2}{a^2 - \varrho\,\varrho'\cos\gamma + \varrho\,r'}$$

is Green's function of the second kind for the sphere, *i. e.* (*a*) that the second and third terms constitute a function $\Phi(\varrho', \varphi', \vartheta')$ harmonic in the sphere, and (*b*) that the normal derivative is constant on the surface of the sphere. Suggestion as to part (*a*). The direct reckoning showing that the third term is harmonic may be tedious. Remembering that P is fixed, it is easily verified that the third term is a linear function of the logarithm of the sum of the distance of Q from a fixed point (the inverse of P) and the projection of this distance on a fixed line. It is then simply a matter of verifying the fact that the logarithm of such a sum, referred in the simplest possible way to a suitable coördinate system, is harmonic, and of the examination of possible exceptional points.

5. Verify that the above function is symmetric in P and Q.

6. With the above function, show that (12) becomes

$$U(P) = \frac{1}{4\pi}\iint\limits_{S}\frac{\partial U}{\partial\nu}\left[\frac{2}{r} + \frac{1}{a}\log\frac{2\,a}{a - \varrho\cos\gamma + r}\right]dS + U(O),$$

O being the center of the sphere.

7. Show that the formula

$$V(\varrho, \varphi, \vartheta) = \frac{1}{4\pi}\iint\limits_{S} f(\varphi', \vartheta')\left[\frac{2}{r} + \frac{1}{a}\log\frac{2\,a}{a - \varrho\cos\gamma + r}\right]dS,$$

$f(\varphi, \vartheta)$ being any continuous function such that $\iint\limits_{S} f(\varphi', \vartheta')\,dS = 0$, solves the Neumann problem for the sphere.

8. Show how to solve the Neumann problem for the outside region bounded by a sphere. Show how the condition that the integral of $f(\varphi, \vartheta)$ shall vanish can be removed by the addition of a suitable multiple of $\frac{1}{\varrho}$ to a formula analogous to that of Exercise 6.

Exercises on the Logarithmic Potential.

9. Define harmonic functions in bounded domains of the plane, establish Green's identities for bounded regular plane regions, and develop the properties of functions harmonic in bounded domains.

10. Set up Laplace's equation in general coördinates in the plane, and discuss inversion in the plane. If, by an inversion, a bounded domain T goes over into a bounded domain T', and if $U(x, y)$ is harmonic in T, show that

$$V(x', y') = U\left(\frac{a^2 x'}{r'^2}, \quad \frac{a^2 y'}{r'^2}\right)$$

is harmonic in T'. Thus, in the plane, we have in place of a Kelvin transformation, a mere transformation by inversion, and this leaves a harmonic function harmonic.

In space, regularity at infinity has been so defined that a function, harmonic at infinity (and, by definition, this means also regular at infinity) goes over by a Kelvin transformation into a function harmonic at the center of inversion. We follow the same procedure in the plane and say that U is regular at infinity provided

a) U approaches a limit as ϱ becomes infinite in any way, ϱ being the distance from any fixed point, and

b) $\left|\varrho^2 \dfrac{\partial U}{\partial x}\right|$ and $\left|\varrho^2 \dfrac{\partial U}{\partial y}\right|$ remain bounded as ϱ becomes infinite.

11. Develop properties of functions harmonic in infinite domains of the plane. In particular show that

$$\int \frac{\partial U}{\partial n}\, ds = 0$$

when extended over any closed regular curve including the boundary of the infinite domain in which U is harmonic (see Theorem I', p. 218), and that if U is harmonic and not constant in the infinite region R, it attains its extremes on and only on the boundary of R (see Exercise 1, p. 224).

12. Define and discuss the properties of Green's function in two dimensions, and derive Poisson's integral in two dimensions.

13. Discuss Neumann's problem for the circle.

14. Study harmonic functions in one dimension, considering, in particular, Green's function.

Chapter X.

Sequences of Harmonic Functions.

1. Harnack's First Theorem on Convergence.

We have already found need of the fact that certain infinite series of harmonic functions converge to limiting functions which are harmonic. We are now in a position to study questions of this sort more systematically. Among the most useful is the following theorem due to HARNACK[1].

Theorem I. *Let R be any closed region of space, and let $U_1, U_2, U_3, \ldots$ be an infinite sequence of functions harmonic in R. If the sequence converges*

---

[1] *Grundlagen der Theorie des logarithmischen Potentials*, Leipzig, 1887, p. 66.

uniformly on the boundary S of R, it converges uniformly throughout R, and its limit U is harmonic in R. Furthermore, in any closed region R′, entirely interior to R, the sequence of derivatives

$$\left[\frac{\partial^{i+j+k}}{\partial x^i \, \partial y^j \, \partial z^k} U_n\right], \qquad n = 1, 2, 3, \ldots,$$

i, j, k being fixed, converges uniformly to the corresponding derivative of U.

First, the sequence converges uniformly in R. For the difference $(U_{n+p} - U_n)$ is harmonic in R, and so by Theorem **X**, Chapter VIII (p. 223), is either constant, or attains its extremes on S. Hence its absolute value is never greater in the interior of R than on S, and since the sequence converges uniformly on S, it must converge uniformly in R. Also, a uniformly convergent sequence of continuous functions has a continuous function as limit[1] and hence the limit U of the sequence is continuous in R.

Secondly, U is harmonic in the interior of R, by the converse of Gauss' theorem on the arithmetic mean (Theorem **XI**, Chapter VIII, p. 227). For each term of the sequence is its own arithmetic mean on spheres in R, and since a uniformly convergent sequence of continuous functions may be integrated termwise, that is, since the limit of the integral of U_n is the integral of the limit U, it follows that U also is its own arithmetic mean on spheres in R. Hence, by the theorem cited, U is harmonic in the interior of R, and as it is continuous in R, it is harmonic in R.

Finally, the sequence of derivatives converges uniformly to the corresponding derivative of U. Consider first the partial derivatives of the first order with respect to x. By Theorem **XII**, Chapter VIII (p. 227), if a is the minimum distance of any point of $R′$ from the boundary of R,

$$\left|\frac{\partial}{\partial x}(U_n - U)\right| \leqq \frac{4}{3}\frac{1}{a} \, 2 \max |U_n - U|,$$

the quantity on the left being taken at any point of $R′$, and that on the right being the maximum in R. Since the right hand member approaches 0 as n becomes infinite, the left hand member approaches 0 uniformly, and the convergence of the sequence of the derivatives to $\frac{\partial U}{\partial x}$ is established. To extend the result to a partial derivative of any order, we need only to apply the same reasoning to the successive derivatives, in a nest of regions, each interior to the preceding and all in R. This can always be done so that $R′$ will be the innermost region (see Chapter XI, § 14, p. 317).

---

[1] See, for instance, OSGOOD, *Funktionentheorie*, I, Chap. III, § 3.

Remarks. The theorem has been enunciated for sequences rather than for series, but there is no essential difference. For the convergence of an infinite series means nothing other than the convergence of the sequence whose terms are the sums of the first n terms of the series. And the convergence of a sequence S_1, S_2, S_3, ... can always be expressed as the convergence of the series

$$S_1 + (S_2 - S_1) + (S_3 - S_2) + \ldots.$$

But there are cases in which we have neither a sequence nor a series before us where the same principle as that expressed in the theorem is useful. Suppose, for instance, that it has been established that

$$\frac{\partial}{\partial \nu} G(Q, P)$$

is harmonic in the coördinates of P in a region R', interior to the region R for which $G(Q, P)$ is Green's function. Can we infer that the function given by Green's integral (equation (5), page 237) is harmonic in R'? Recalling the definition of integral, we note that any of the sums of which the integral is the limit, being a finite sum of functions which are harmonic in R', is also harmonic in R'. If these sums approach the integral uniformly in R', the reasoning used in the theorem shows that the limit is harmonic in R'. This can easily be shown to be the case in the present instance.

In order to express the extension of the theorem in a suitable way, let us remark that if δ is supposed given, the sum

$$\sum_k f(Q_k) \, \Delta S_k,$$

in which the maximum chord of the divisions ΔS_k of S is restricted to be not greater than δ, is a function of δ. It is infinitely many valued, to be sure, but its values are still determined by the value of δ, and its bounds are uniquely determined. If $f(Q_k)$ depends also on parameters, like the coördinates of a point P, the sum will also depend on these parameters. What are we to understand by the statement that a many-valued function is harmonic in R? We shall say that a function $U(P, \delta)$ is harmonic in R if to any of its values at any point P_0 of R there corresponds a one-valued function having the same value at P_0, whose value at any other point P of R is among those of $U(P, \delta)$ at P, and that this one-valued function is harmonic in R. Such a one-valued function we call a *branch* of $U(P, \delta)$. To say that $U(P, \delta)$ converges uniformly to a limit as δ approaches 0, shall mean that there is a one-valued function U such that $\varepsilon > 0$ being given, δ can be so restricted that

$$|U(P, \delta) - U| < \varepsilon$$

for all points P in the set of points for which the convergence is uniform, and for all branches of the many valued function $U(P, \delta)$.

With these preliminaries, we may state the theorem as follows: *let R be any closed region in space, and let U (P, δ) be continuous in R and harmonic in the interior of R. Then if U (P, δ) converges uniformly to a limit on the boundary of R, it converges uniformly throughout R to a one-valued function U, which is harmonic in R. Any given derivative of U(P, δ) converges uniformly in any closed region R′ interior to R to the corresponding derivative of U.* By a derivative of U (P, δ), if U (P, δ) is many valued, we mean the many valued function whose values at any point are those of the corresponding derivative of the branches of U (P, δ) at that point.

It follows that if $f (Q, P)$ is continuous in the coördinates of P and Q, when Q is on the boundary S of the regular region R, and P is in a region R' interior to R, and if $f(Q, P)$ is harmonic in P for P in R', for every fixed Q on S, then

$$F (P) = \iint_S f (Q, P)\, dS$$

is harmonic in R'.

2. Expansions in Spherical Harmonics.

We have seen that Newtonian potentials can be expanded in series of spherical harmonics, and that harmonic functions are Newtonian potentials. It follows that harmonic functions can be so expanded. We are now concerned with the determination of the expansion when the harmonic function is not given in terms of Newtonian distributions.

We take as point of departure, Poisson's integral

$$(1) \qquad U (\varrho, \varphi, \vartheta) = \frac{a^2 - \varrho^2}{4 \pi a} \iint_S \frac{U (a, \varphi', \vartheta')}{r^3}\, dS, \quad r^2 = \varrho^2 + a^2 - 2 a \varrho \cos \gamma$$

where S is the surface of the sphere of radius a about the origin, and where U is harmonic in the closed region bounded by S. We have seen equation (9), (p. 241) that

$$(2) \qquad \frac{a^2 - \varrho^2}{r^3} = - \frac{1}{r} - 2 a \frac{\partial}{\partial \nu} \frac{1}{r},$$

and that (equation (18), page 135)

$$(3) \qquad \frac{1}{r} = P_0 (u) \frac{1}{\varrho'} + P_1 (u) \frac{\varrho}{\varrho'^2} + P_2 (u) \frac{\varrho^2}{\varrho'^3} + \cdots, \quad u = \cos \gamma,$$

valid for $\varrho < \varrho'$. If we differentiate this series termwise with respect to ϱ', and set $\varrho' = a$, we have

$$(4) \qquad \frac{\partial}{\partial \nu} \frac{1}{r} = - P_0 (u) \frac{1}{a^2} - 2 P_1 (u) \frac{\varrho}{c^3} - 3 P_2 (u) \frac{\varrho^2}{a^4} \cdots.$$

Setting $\varrho' = a$ in (3) and using this and (4), we find for the function (2) the expression

$$\frac{a^2 - \varrho^2}{r^3} = \frac{1}{a}\left[P_0(u) + 3 P_1(u)\frac{\varrho}{a}\right.$$
$$\left. + 5 P_2(u)\frac{\varrho^2}{a^2} + \cdots + (2k+1)P_k(u)\frac{\varrho^k}{a^k} + \cdots\right],$$

the series being uniformly convergent for $\varrho \leqq \lambda a$, $0 < \lambda < 1$. This function may therefore be used in (1), and the integration carried out termwise, so that we have

$$(5) \quad U(\varrho, \varphi, \vartheta) = \sum_0^\infty (2k+1)\left[\frac{1}{4\pi a^2}\iint_S U(a, \varphi', \vartheta') P_k(u)\, dS\right]\frac{\varrho^k}{a^k}.$$

Since $\varrho^k P_k(u)$ is a spherical harmonic of order k, we have here a development of U in spherical harmonics, determined by the boundary values of U, the series being convergent for $\varrho < a$, and uniformly convergent in any region R' interior to the sphere. We shall discuss later the question of convergence on the sphere itself.

Let us apply this development to the spherical harmonic

$$H_n(\varrho, \varphi, \vartheta) = \varrho^n S_n(\varphi, \vartheta)$$

We find

$$\varrho^n S_n(\varphi, \vartheta) = \sum_0^\infty (2k+1)\left[\frac{1}{4\pi a^2}\iint_S a^n S_n(\varphi', \vartheta') P_k(u)\, dS\right]\frac{\varrho^k}{a^k}.$$

The coefficients of the powers of ϱ on both sides of this equation must be identical, and we conclude that

$$(6) \quad \begin{cases} \iint_S S_n(\varphi', \vartheta') P_k(u)\, dS = 0, \qquad k \neq n, \\[2mm] S_n(\varphi, \vartheta) = \frac{(2n+1)}{4\pi a^2}\iint_S S_n(\varphi', \vartheta') P_n(u)\, dS, \\[2mm] \text{or } \int_0^\pi\int_0^{2\pi} S_n(\varphi', \vartheta') P_n(\cos\gamma)\sin\vartheta'\, d\varphi'\, d\vartheta' = \frac{4\pi}{2n+1}S_n(\varphi, \vartheta). \end{cases}$$

The spherical harmonics $\varrho^k P_k(u)$ are often called *zonal harmonics*, as the surfaces on which they vanish divide the surface of the sphere into zones. If the factor ϱ^k be suppressed, we have what is known as a *surface zonal harmonic*. This is therefore another name for Legendre polynomials, although the term is often used in the wider sense of any solution of the differential equation (11) (page 127), for Legendre polynomials, whether n is integral or not. The ray (φ, ϑ) from which the angle γ is measured is called the *axis* of the zonal harmonic. The first equation (6) states for an apparently particular case, that *two spherical harmonics of different orders are orthogonal on the surface of the unit sphere*, a result found in Exercise 2, § 2, Chapter VIII, (p. 216). The last equation (6) states that *the integral over the unit sphere of the product of any spherical harmonic of order n by the surface zonal harmonic of the same order is the value of the spherical harmonic on the axis of the zonal harmonic, multiplied by* 4π *and divided by* $2n + 1$.

Thus, if U is harmonic in a neighborhood of the origin and hence has a uniformly convergent development in terms of spherical harmonics

$$U = S_0 + S_1 \varrho + S_2 \varrho^2 + \cdots,$$

the terms of this series may be obtained by multiplying both sides of the equation by $P_k(u)$ and integrating over the surface of a sphere lying in the region in which the development is uniformly convergent. The result is nothing other than the development (5), where a is the radius of this sphere. Of course in deriving the development (5) we did not need to know that the series converges for P on the sphere itself.

The development of a harmonic function in a series of spherical harmonics is a special case of developments of harmonic functions in given regions in series of polynomials characteristic of those regions[1].

Exercises.

1. Check the equations (6) for simple cases, for instance $S_0 = 1$, $S_1 = \cos\vartheta$, $S_2 = \cos 2\varphi \sin\vartheta$, with $P_0(u)$, $P_1(u)$, $P_2(u)$.

2. Derive Gauss' theorem on the arithmetic mean from (5).

3. Derive the expansion in terms of spherical harmonics divided by powers of ϱ, valid outside a sphere.

4. If U is harmonic in the region between two concentric spheres, show that it can be expanded in a series.

$$U = \sum_{-\infty}^{\infty} \varrho^k S_k(\varphi, \vartheta),$$

where $S_{-k}(\varphi, \vartheta)$ $(k > 0)$ is a surface spherical harmonic of order $k - 1$, the series being uniformly convergent in any region lying between the two spheres, and having no points in common with their surfaces. Show how the spherical harmonics of the development are to be determined.

5. Show that any function, harmonic in the region bounded by two concentric spheres is the sum of a function which is harmonic in the interior of the outer sphere, and a function which is harmonic outside the inner sphere.

6. Show that there are no two different developments in spherical harmonics of a harmonic function, the developments having the same origin.

7. Show that

$$\frac{1}{a^k} \iint_S U(a, \varphi', \vartheta') P_k(u) \sin\vartheta' \, d\varphi' \, d\vartheta'$$

is independent of a for all $a \leq a_1$, where a_1 is the radius of a sphere about the origin in which U is harmonic.

8. Show by means of the equation (6_2) that any surface spherical harmonic of degree n is a linear combination with constant coefficients of functions obtained by giving to the axis of the surface zonal harmonic $P_n(u)$ at most $2n + 1$ distinct directions.

---

[1] See J. L. WALSH, Proceedings of the National Academy of Sciences, Washington, Vol. XIII (1927), pp. 175—180.

9. Show that

$$I = \frac{1}{2\pi} \int\limits_0^{2\pi} P_k \left(\cos \vartheta \cos \vartheta' + \sin \vartheta \sin \vartheta' \cos \varphi'\right) d\varphi'$$

$$= P_k (\cos \vartheta) \, P_k (\cos \vartheta').$$

Suggestion. The integral is a polynomial of order k in $\cos \vartheta$, since the integral of any odd power of $\cos \varphi'$ is 0. Hence we may write

$$I = \sum_0^k c_r (\vartheta') \, P_r (\cos \vartheta),$$

and the problem is reduced to the determination of the coefficients $c_r (\vartheta')$.

3. Series of Zonal Harmonics.

Suppose that U is harmonic in the neighborhood of a point, which we take as origin, and that it is symmetric about some line through that point; in other words, if we take the axis of spherical coördinates along that line, U is independent of the longitude φ. Then the development (5) takes the form

$$U(\varrho, \vartheta) = \sum_0^\infty (2k+1) \left[\frac{1}{4\pi a^2} \iint\limits_S U(a, \vartheta') \, P_k (\cos \vartheta \cos \vartheta' \right.$$

$$\left. + \sin \vartheta \sin \vartheta' \cos (\varphi - \varphi')) \, dS \right] \frac{\varrho^k}{a^k}.$$

As U is independent of φ, we may set $\varphi = 0$ in the integrals, and carry out the integration with respect to φ', with the result (see Exercise 9, above):

$$U(\varrho, \vartheta) = \sum_0^\infty \frac{2k+1}{2} \left[\int\limits_0^\pi U(a, \vartheta') \, P_k (\cos \vartheta') \sin \vartheta' \, d\vartheta' \right] P_k (\cos \vartheta) \frac{\varrho^k}{a^k}.$$

Hence the function $U(\varrho, \vartheta)$, harmonic within the sphere of radius a about the origin, and continuous within and on the surface, is developable in a series of zonal harmonics,

$$(7) \qquad U(\varrho, \vartheta) = \sum_0^\infty c_k P_k (\cos \vartheta) \, \varrho^k,$$

$$c_k = \frac{2k+1}{2 a^k} \int\limits_{-1}^1 U(a, \cos^{-1} u) \, P_k (u) \, du,$$

uniformly convergent in any region interior to the sphere[1].

---

[1] Attention should be called to the distinction between this type of development and that considered in Chapter V, § 3, (page 129), and in Theorem III, Corollary, of the next section. Here it is a question of developing a harmonic function in a region of space; there it is a question of developing an arbitrary function of one variable — yet the developments leading to Theorem III really connect the two.

For $\vartheta = 0$, this series reduces to

$$U(\varrho, 0) = \sum_0^\infty c_k \varrho^k,$$

and the coefficients are seen to be simply those of the power series in ϱ for the values of U on the axis. We see thus that *a function, harmonic in a neighborhood of a point, and symmetric about an axis through that point, is uniquely determined by its values on the axis.* For the function $U(\varrho, 0)$ has a unique development as a power series, so that the coefficients are uniquely determined, and these in turn, uniquely determine U. With this theorem goes the corresponding existence theorem:

Theorem II. *Let $f(\varrho)$ be developable in a series of powers of ϱ, convergent for $\varrho < a$. Then there is one and only one function $U(\varrho, \vartheta)$, symmetric about the axis of ϑ, harmonic in the interior of the sphere about the origin of radius a, and reducing for $\vartheta = 0$ to $f(\varrho)$, and for $\vartheta = \pi$ to $f(-\varrho)$.*

We have just seen that there is not more than one such function. Let the development of $f(\varrho)$ be

$$f(\varrho) = \sum_0^\infty c_k \varrho^k.$$

As this series is convergent for $\varrho = \lambda a$, $0 < \lambda < 1$, it follows that its terms are bounded in absolute value for $\varrho = \lambda a$, say by the constant B, and accordingly that

$$|c_k| \leqq \frac{B}{(\lambda a)^k}.$$

Since the Legendre polynomials never exceed 1 in absolute value for $-1 \leqq u \leqq 1$, the series

$$U = \sum_0^\infty c_k P_k(u) \varrho^k$$

is dominated by the series

$$\sum_0^\infty B \frac{\varrho^k}{(\lambda a)^k},$$

and therefore converges uniformly for $\varrho \leqq \lambda^2 a$. Hence by Theorem I, it represents a function harmonic in the interior of the sphere of radius $\lambda^2 a$, and since λ is any positive number less than 1, this function is harmonic in the interior of the sphere of radius a. As the sum U has the requisite symmetry and reduces to $f(\varrho)$ for $\vartheta = 0$, and to $f(-\varrho)$ for $\vartheta = \pi$, the theorem is proved.

As an example of a development in zonal harmonics, let us take the potential of the circular wire, studied in § 4, Chapter III, (p. 58). The determination of the value of the potential at points of the axis is very simple, and was found in Exercise 2, page 56:

$$U(\varrho, 0) = \frac{M}{\sqrt{c^2 + \varrho^2}} = \frac{M}{c}\left[1 - \frac{1}{2}\frac{\varrho^2}{c^2} + \frac{1}{2}\frac{3}{4}\frac{\varrho^4}{c^4} - \frac{1}{2}\frac{3}{4}\frac{5}{6}\frac{\varrho^6}{c^6} + \cdots\right],$$

where M is the total mass and c the radius of the wire. Hence for $0 \leq \varrho < c$

$$U(\varrho, \vartheta) = \frac{M}{c} \left[P_0(\cos \vartheta) - \frac{1}{2} P_2(\cos \vartheta) \frac{\varrho^2}{c^2} + \frac{1}{2} \frac{3}{4} P_4(\cos \vartheta) \frac{\varrho^4}{c^4} - \cdots \right].$$

Similarly, it may be shown that for $\varrho > c$,

$$U(\varrho, \vartheta) = \frac{M}{\varrho} \left[P_0(\cos \vartheta) - \frac{1}{2} P_2(\cos \vartheta) \frac{c^2}{\varrho^2} + \frac{1}{2} \frac{3}{4} P_4(\cos \vartheta) \frac{c^4}{\varrho^4} - \cdots \right].$$

Exercises.

1. Check the result of Exercise 3, page 62, by means of one of the above series.

2. Obtain and establish the development of a function harmonic outside a given sphere in terms of zonal harmonics divided by proper powers of ϱ, the function being symmetric about an axis.

3. The surface of the northern hemisphere of a homogeneous isotropic sphere of radius 1 is kept at the constant temperature 1, while the surface of the southern hemisphere is kept at the constant temperature 0. Determine a series of zonal harmonics for the temperature at interior points, a steady state being postulated. Estimate the temperature at a distance 0.5 from the center on a radius making the angle 60^0 with the axis. Check the estimate by computation.

4. Find the potential of a hemispherical surface of constant density in the form of series in zonal harmonics, one valid for points outside the sphere and one valid inside. Partial answer,

$$U = \frac{M}{c} \left[P_0(\cos \vartheta) + \frac{1}{2} P_1(\cos \vartheta) \frac{\varrho}{c} - \frac{1}{2} \frac{1}{4} P_3(\cos \vartheta) \frac{\varrho^3}{c^3} + \cdots \right],$$

where M is the mass and c the radius of the hemisphere, the origin being at the center and the axis of ϑ pointing toward the pole of the hemisphere.

4. Convergence on the Surface of the Sphere.

Suppose that in the development (5) we write, under the integral sign, $f(\varphi', \vartheta')$ in place of the function $U(a, \vartheta', \varphi')$, and call the resulting series $V(\varrho, \varphi, \vartheta)$:

$$(8) \qquad V(\varrho, \varphi, \vartheta) = \sum_0^\infty (2k+1) \left[\frac{1}{4\pi a^2} \iint_S f(\varphi', \vartheta') P_k(u) \, dS \right] \frac{\varrho^k}{a^k}.$$

If $f(\varphi, \vartheta)$ is continuous, as we shall assume, the integrals are bounded in absolute value, so the series is uniformly convergent for $\varrho \leq \lambda a$, $0 < \lambda < 1$. As the terms are spherical harmonics, the series converges here to a harmonic function. Moreover, for $\varrho < a$, the series converges to the function given by (8), § 4, Chapter IX, that is, by Poisson's integral. So we know that the series converges at all interior points of the sphere to the harmonic function whose boundary values are $f(\varphi, \vartheta)$. However, it is often of importance to know that the series converges on the bounding surface S. We shall show that this is the case if $f(\varphi, \vartheta)$

is continuously differentiable on the unit sphere, or, what amounts to the same thing, that it has continuous partial derivatives of the first order with respect to φ and ϑ for two distinct positions of the axis from which ϑ is measured. The series converges under lighter conditions on $f(\varphi, \vartheta)$, but the hypothesis chosen yields a simpler proof.

The derivative of $f(\varphi, \vartheta)$ with respect to the arc s of any continuously turning curve, making an angle τ with the direction of increasing φ, the sense of increasing τ being initially toward the north pole, from which ϑ is measured, is given by the formula

$$\frac{df}{ds} = \frac{\partial f}{\partial \varphi} \frac{\cos \tau}{\sin \vartheta} - \frac{\partial f}{\partial \vartheta} \sin \tau.$$

From this we draw two inferences. Since such a representation holds for two distinct positions of the axis, we may, for any point of the sphere, choose that coördinate system for which ϑ and $\pi - \vartheta$ are not less than half the angular distance between the two positions of the axes, so that $\left| \frac{df}{ds} \right|$ *is uniformly bounded,* say by B. For $\left| \frac{\partial f}{\partial \varphi} \right|$ and $\left| \frac{\partial f}{\partial \vartheta} \right|$, being uniformly continuous on the sphere, are bounded. Secondly, the variable s may be identified with the length of arc along any meridian curve or parallel of latitude, so that $f(\varphi, \vartheta)$ has continuous derivatives of the first order with respect to the angles, with *any* orientation of the axes of coördinates.

Turning now to the proof of the convergence of the series (8), we denote by $s_n(\varphi, \vartheta)$ the sum of the terms of the series as far as the term in ϱ^n. Then by equation (12), page 127, we have, for $\varrho = a$,

$$s_n(\varphi, \vartheta) = \frac{1}{4\pi} \int_0^\pi \int_0^{2\pi} \sum_0^n (2k+1) f(\varphi', \vartheta') P_k(u) \sin \vartheta' \, d\varphi' \, d\vartheta'$$

$$= \frac{1}{4\pi} \int_{-1}^1 \int_0^{2\pi} f(\varphi', \vartheta') [P'_{n+1}(u) + P'_n(u)] \, d\varphi' \, du.$$

As all the terms of this equation can be interpreted as values of functions at points of the unit sphere, it is really independent of a coördinate system, and we are free to take what orientation of the axes we wish. Let us therefore take the polar axis through the point at which we wish to study the convergence. Then $u = \cos \gamma$ becomes $\cos \vartheta'$, and we may carry out the integration with respect to φ' by introducing the mean on parallel circles of $f(\varphi, \vartheta)$:

$$F(u) = \frac{1}{2\pi} \int_0^{2\pi} f(\varphi', \vartheta') \, d\varphi', \quad u = \cos \vartheta'.$$

The result is

(9) $$s_n(\varphi, 0) = \frac{1}{2} \int\limits_{-1}^{1} F(u)\,[P'_{n+1}(u) + P'_n(u)]\,du.$$

Since the derivatives of $f(\varphi', \vartheta')$ with respect to φ' and ϑ' are bounded in absolute value by B,

$$\left|\frac{dF(u)}{d\vartheta'}\right| = \frac{1}{2\pi}\left|\int\limits_{0}^{2\pi} \frac{\partial}{\partial\vartheta'}\, f(\varphi', \vartheta')\, d\varphi'\right| \leqq B,$$

and

(10) $$|F'(u)| = \left|\frac{dF(u)}{du}\right| = \left|\frac{\dfrac{dF(u)}{d\vartheta'}}{\dfrac{du}{d\vartheta'}}\right| \leqq \frac{B}{\sqrt{1-u^2}}.$$

Let us now carry out an integration by parts in (9), remembering that $P_{n+1}(-1)$ and $P_n(-1)$ are equal and opposite, and that $P_{n+1}(1) = P_n(1) = 1$, $F(1) = f(\varphi, 0)$:

$$s_n(\varphi, 0) = f(\varphi, 0) - \frac{1}{2}\int\limits_{-1}^{1} F'(u)\, P_{n+1}(u)\, du - \frac{1}{2}\int\limits_{-1}^{1} F'(u)\, P_n(u)\, du.$$

It is now not difficult to show that these integrals approach 0 as n becomes infinite. Take, for instance the second. Let $0 < \alpha < 1$. Then

$$\int\limits_{-1}^{1} F'(u)\, P_n(u)\, du \leqq \frac{B}{\sqrt{1-\alpha^2}}\int\limits_{-\alpha}^{a}|P_n(u)|\,du + B\int\limits_{-1}^{-a}\frac{du}{\sqrt{1-u^2}} + B\int\limits_{a}^{1}\frac{du}{\sqrt{1-u^2}}.$$

We apply Schwarz' inequality to the first term (see page 134, Exercise 15), and evaluate the last two integrals, with the result

$$\left|\int\limits_{-1}^{1} F'(u)\, P_n(u)\, du\right| \leqq \frac{2B}{\sqrt{1-\alpha^2}\sqrt{2n+1}} + 2B\cos^{-1}\alpha.$$

If $\varepsilon > 0$ is given, we choose $\alpha < 1$, so that the second term is less than $\frac{\varepsilon}{2}$, and then choose n so that the first term is less than $\frac{\varepsilon}{2}$. Thus, as stated, the integrals in the expression for $s_n(\varphi, 0)$ approach 0 as n becomes infinite, and it follows that $s_n(\varphi, 0)$ approaches the limit $f(\varphi, 0)$. Thus the series (8) does converge for $\varrho = a$, and to the value $f(\varphi, \vartheta)$. Moreover, the inequalities being independent of the position of the point where the convergence was studied, *the convergence is uniform.*

Incidentally, we may draw conclusions as to the expansion of functions in series of Legendre polynomials. Let $f(\varphi, \vartheta)$ be independent of φ. Writing $f(\varphi, \vartheta) = f(u)$, we assume that this function is continuously differentiable in $(-1, 1)$. The conditions of the theorem just established are then met, and the series (8) becomes a series of zonal harmonics, uniformly convergent for $\varrho = a$, and we have

$$f(u) = \sum_{0}^{\infty}{}' \left[\frac{2k+1}{2} \int_{-1}^{1} f(u')\, P_k(u')\, du' \right] P_k(u).$$

We formulate the results as follows.

Theorem III. *Let $f(\varphi, \vartheta)$ be continuously differentiable on the unit sphere. It is then developable in a uniformly convergent series of surface spherical harmonics.*

Corollary. *Any function $f(u)$, continuously differentiable in the closed interval $(-1, 1)$, is developable in that interval in a uniformly convergent series of Legendre polynomials in u.*

Exercise.

By means of Exercises 11 and 12 of § 3, Chapter V (p. 133) extended to the function $f(x) = 0$, $-1 \leq x \leq a$, $f(x) = x - a$, $a \leq x \leq 1$, generalize the above corollary to the case in which $f(u)$ is merely piecewise differentiable in $(-1, 1)$. Suggestion. Using integration by parts, and the formula following (11), page 127, we find

$$c_r = \frac{1}{2} \left[\frac{P_{r+2}(a)}{2r+3} - \left(\frac{1}{2r+3} + \frac{1}{2r-1} \right) P_r(a) + \frac{P_{r-2}(a)}{2r-1} \right].$$

Thus the series for $f(x)$ will converge uniformly if the series $\sum \frac{1}{n} |P_n(a)|$ converges. We obtain a bound for $|P_n(a)|$, $a^2 < 1$, from Laplace's formula, page 133. Replacing the integrand by its absolute value, and $\sqrt{1 - a^2}$ by k, we have

$$|P_n(a)| \leqq \frac{2}{\pi} \int_{0}^{\frac{\pi}{2}} (1 - k^2 \sin^2 \varphi)^{\frac{n}{2}}\, d\varphi < \frac{2}{\pi} \int_{0}^{\frac{\pi}{2}} \left[1 - \left(\frac{2k}{\pi} \varphi \right)^2 \right]^{\frac{n}{2}} d\varphi$$

$$< \frac{1}{k} \int_{0}^{\frac{\pi}{2}} \sin^{n+1} \varphi\, d\varphi \left(\varphi = \frac{\pi}{2k} \cos \vartheta \right).$$

5. The Continuation of Harmonic Functions.

In Chapter VII, § 5 (p. 189), we had need of a theorem enabling us to identify as a single harmonic function, functions defined in different parts of space. We shall now consider this problem, and the general question of extending the region of definition of a harmonic function.

Theorem IV. *If U is harmonic in a domain T, and if U vanishes at all the points of a domain T' in T, then U vanishes at all the points of T.*

Let T'' denote the set of all points of T in a neighborhood of each of which $U = 0$. Then T'' is an open set, containing T'. The theorem amounts to the statement that T'' coincides with T. Suppose this were not the case. Then T'' would have a frontier point P_0 in T (cf. Chapter IV,

§ 5, Exercise 4, p. 94). In any neighborhood of P_0 there would be points of T'', and thus about one of them, P_1, there would be a sphere σ containing P_0 and lying in T. Taking P_1 as origin, U would be developable in a series of spherical harmonics, convergent in this sphere. The spherical harmonics of this development could be determined by integration over a sphere of radius so small that U vanished identically on its surface, since P_1 was to be interior to T''. Thus the development (5) would show that U vanished throughout σ, and therefore throughout a neighborhood of P_0. Thus P_0 would be an interior point of T'', and not a frontier point, as assumed. It follows that T'' contains all the points of T, and the theorem is proved.

It follows that if a function is harmonic in a domain T, it is determined throughout T by its values in any domain T' whatever, in T. For if U_1 and U_2 are two functions, harmonic in T, and coinciding in T', their difference is 0 throughout T, by the theorem.

Theorem V. *If T_1 and T_2 are two domains with common points, and if U_1 is harmonic in T_1 and U_2 in T_2, these functions coinciding at the common points of T_1 and T_2, then they define a single function, harmonic in the domain T consisting of all points of T_1 and T_2.*

For since T_1 and T_2 have common points, and any such point P_0 is interior to both, there is a sphere about P_0 lying in both T_1 and T_2. Let its interior be denoted by T'. Then if U be defined as equal to U_1 in T_1 and to U_2 in T_2, it is uniquely determined in T_1 by its values in T', by Theorem IV, and similarly, it is uniquely determined in T_2. It is therefore harmonic throughout T, as was to be shown.

So far, we have been restricting ourselves to one-valued functions. But when it comes to continuations, this is not always possible. For we may have a chain of overlapping domains, the last of which overlaps the first, and a function harmonic in the first, and continuable in accordance with the above theorem throughout the chain, may fail to have the same values in the overlapping part of the last and first domains, when thought of as single-valued functions in each of these domains. For instance, let the interior of a torus, with z-axis as axis, be divided by meridian planes into a number of overlapping domains of the sort considered. Starting in one of them with the function $\tan^{-1}\left(\dfrac{y}{x}\right)$, we arrive, after a circuit of the domains, at sets of values differing by 2π. These values constitute branches of the many-valued function, and each branch can be continued in the same way. We arrive, in this case, at an infinitely many-valued function, any of whose branches is harmonic in any simply connected region in the torus. Since any of these branches is a harmonic continuation of any other, it is customary to speak of them all as constituting a single *many-valued harmonic function*. However, we shall continue to understand that we are speaking of one-valued functions unless the contrary is stated, although this does not mean that the one-valued function may not be a specified branch of a many-valued one, in a region in which a continuation to another branch is impossible.

We now establish the theorem on harmonic continuation which was needed in connection with the problem of a static charge on an ellipsoidal conductor:

Theorem VI. *Let T_1 and T_2 be two domains without common points, but whose boundaries contain a common isolated regular surface element E. Let U_1 be harmonic in T_1 and U_2 in T_2. If U_1 and U_2 and their partial derivatives of the first order have continuous limits on E, and if the limits of U_1 and U_2 and of their normal derivatives in the same sense coincide on E, then each is the harmonic continuation of the other*, that is, the two together form a single harmonic function in the domain T consisting of the points of T_1, T_2 and the interior points of E.

By saying that the boundaries contain a common *isolated* regular surface element E, we mean that about each interior point of E, there is a sphere within which the only boundary points of either T_1 or T_2 are points of E.

To prove the theorem, let P_0 be any interior point of E, and let σ denote a sphere about P_0, all of whose points are in T_1, T_2, or E. Let r_1 and r_2 be the regions consisting of the points in σ and T_1, and in σ and T_2, respectively, together with their boundary points. If now U is defined as equal to U_1 in r_1, and to U_2 in r_2, and if P is any interior point of r_1, the identity III of Chapter VIII, § 4, p. 219, becomes

$$U(P) = \frac{1}{4\pi} \iint\limits_{s_1} \frac{\partial U}{\partial \nu} \frac{1}{r} \, dS - \frac{1}{4\pi} \iint\limits_{s_1} U \frac{\partial}{\partial \nu} \frac{1}{r} \, dS,$$

s_1 being the surface bounding r_1.

Again, the identity II (page 215) is applicable to the region r_2, with the above U and with $V = \frac{1}{r}$, since r does not vanish in r_2:

$$0 = \frac{1}{4\pi} \iint\limits_{s_2} \frac{\partial U}{\partial \nu} \frac{1}{r} \, dS - \frac{1}{4\pi} \iint\limits_{s_2} U \frac{\partial}{\partial \nu} \frac{1}{r} \, dS,$$

s_2 being the surface bounding r_2. If these two equations are added, the integrals over the portion of E in σ destroy each other, since the normal derivatives are taken in opposite senses, and so, by the hypothesis on U_1 and U_2, are equal and opposite. The resulting equation is

$$U(P) = \frac{1}{4\pi} \iint\limits_{\sigma} \frac{\partial U}{\partial \nu} \frac{1}{r} \, dS - \frac{1}{4\pi} \iint\limits_{\sigma} U \frac{\partial}{\partial \nu} \frac{1}{r} \, dS.$$

Exactly the same formula determines U in r_2. But it gives U as harmonic throughout σ. Thus, by Theorem V, U, defined as U_1 in T_1, as U_2 in T_2, and as their common limit on E, is harmonic throughout T_1, T_2, and a neighborhood of P_0. But as P_0 is any interior point of E, this function is harmonic throughout T, as was to be proved.

As a corollary, we may state the following: *If U is harmonic in a closed region R, and if the boundary of R contains a regular surface element on which U and its normal derivative vanish, then U is identically 0 in R.* For, by the theorem, 0 is a harmonic continuation of U, and thus, by Theorem IV, U is 0 throughout the interior of R, and, being continuous in R, it is also 0 on the boundary of R.

Exercises.

1. Why is the above corollary not a consequence of the Cauchy-Kowalevsky existence theorem?

2. Let U be harmonic in a regular region R whose boundary contains a plane regular surface element, and let $U = 0$ at all points of this element. Show that U admits a harmonic continuation in the region symmetric to R in the plane. The same when U has any constant value on the plane surface element.

3. Show that if U is harmonic in a sphere, and vanishes at all those points of the surface of the sphere which are in a neighborhood of a point of the surface, it admits a harmonic extension throughout all of space exterior to the sphere.

4. Derive results similar to those of Exercises 2 and 3, where instead of it being assumed that U vanishes on a portion of the boundary, it is assumed that the normal derivative of U vanishes on that portion.

6. Harnack's Inequality and Second Convergence Theorem.

HARNACK has derived an inequality[1], of frequent usefulness, for harmonic functions which do not change signs. If U is harmonic in the sphere S, and is either never negative or never positive in S, we may take a mean value of $\frac{1}{r^3}$ from under the integral sign in Poisson's integral [Chapter IX, (7), p. 241], and write

$$U(P) = \frac{a^2 - \varrho^2}{4\pi a} \frac{1}{\bar{r}^3} \iint\limits_S U(Q)\, dS = \frac{a(a^2 - \varrho^2)}{\bar{r}^3} U(O),$$

where O is the center of the sphere, the last step being an application of Gauss' theorem. The extreme values of $\bar{r}$, if $\overline{OP} = \varrho$ is held fixed, are $a - \varrho$ and $a + \varrho$. Accordingly we have the *inequality of Harnack* for the case in which $U \geq 0$:

$$(11) \qquad \frac{a(a - \varrho)}{(a + \varrho)^2} U(O) \leq U(P) \leq \frac{a(a + \varrho)}{(a - \varrho)^2} U(O).$$

If $U \leq 0$, the inequality signs are reversed.

From this we derive a more general inequality. We keep to the case $U \geq 0$, as that in which $U \leq 0$ may be treated by a simple change of sign of U. We state the result in

---

[1] *Grundlagen der Theorie des logarithmischen Potentials*, Leipzig, 1887, p. 62.

Theorem VII. *Let U be harmonic and never negative in the domain T, and let R be a closed region in T. Let O be a point of R. Then there exist two positive constants, c and C, depending only on R and T, such that in R*

$$c\,U(O) \leqq U(P) \leqq C\,U(O).$$

To prove this, let $4a$ be the minimum distance from the points of R to the boundary of T. This quantity is positive, for otherwise R would have a point on the boundary of T, which is impossible since R is in T and all the points of T are interior points. Consider the set of domains consisting of the spheres of radius a with centers at the points of R. By the Heine-Borel theorem all the points of R are interior to a finite number of these spheres. We add one, if necessary, namely that with center O, and call the resulting system of a finite number of spheres Σ. Now U is harmonic and not negative in a sphere about O of radius $4a$, and hence, writing in Harnack's inequality $4a$ in place of a, and $2a$ in place of ϱ, we find that on, and therefore in, a sphere of radius $2a$ about O,

$$\frac{2}{9}\,U(O) \leqq U(P) \leqq 6\,U(O).$$

As every point of R is interior to a sphere of Σ, of radius a, it follows that there is a center of a sphere of Σ, other than O, in the sphere of radius $2a$ about O. Call this center P_1. U is harmonic and not negative in a sphere of radius $4a$ about P_1, and hence Harnack's inequality can be applied in this sphere. Since the value at the center is restricted by the last inequalities, we have, in a sphere of radius $2a$ about P_1,

$$\left(\frac{2}{9}\right)^2 U(O) \leqq U(P) \leqq 6^2\,U(O).$$

If n is the number of spheres in Σ, we can, in at most n steps, pass from the sphere about O to a sphere containing any point of R. It follows, by repeating the reasoning, that for any point in R,

$$\left(\frac{2}{9}\right)^n U(O) \leqq U(P) \leqq 6^n\,U(O),$$

so that the theorem is proved, with $c = \left(\dfrac{2}{9}\right)^n$ and $C = 6^n$.

As a corollary we have at once Harnack's second convergence theorem,

Theorem VIII. *Let $U_1(P)$, $U_2(P)$, $U_3(P)$, ... be an infinite sequence of functions, harmonic in a domain T, such that for every P in T, $U_n(P) \leqq U_{n+1}(P)$, $n = 1, 2, 3, \ldots$. Then if the sequence is bounded at a single point O of T, it converges uniformly in any closed region R in T to a function which is harmonic in T.*

A bounded monotone sequence is always convergent, so that the sequence $[U_i(O)]$ is convergent. Moreover, by Theorem VII, if P is in R (which may always be extended, if necessary, so as to contain O),

$$c\,[U_{n+p}(O) - U_n(O)] \leqq U_{n+p}(P) - U_n(P) \leqq C\,[U_{n+p}(O) - U_n(O)],$$

so that the convergence of the sequence at O carries with it the uniform convergence of the sequence throughout R. It follows from Theorem I that the limiting function is harmonic in R. But as R is any region in T, the limiting function is harmonic in T. The theorem is thus proved.

It is clear that the theorem may be applied to series of harmonic functions whose terms are not negative, and that a corresponding theorem holds for a harmonic function depending on a parameter, as the parameter approaches a limit, provided that at every point P of the domain in which the function is harmonic, the function is a never decreasing function of the parameter.

Exercise.

Let R be a closed region with the property that there is a number a, such that any point Q of the boundary of R lies on the surface of a sphere in R, of radius a. If U is harmonic, and never negative in the interior of R, show that there is a constant K, such that at any point P of R,

$$U \leqq \frac{K}{\delta^2},$$

where δ is the distance from P to the nearest boundary point of R.

7. Further Convergence Theorems.

Suppose we have an infinite set of functions f_1, f_2, f_3, $\ldots$, all continuous in a region R. Since R is closed, each function is uniformly continuous in R; that is, corresponding to any n and any $\varepsilon > 0$, there is a $\delta > 0$, such that for any two points of R whose distance apart does not exceed δ,

$$|f_n(P) - f_n(Q)| < \varepsilon.$$

Here, the number δ may have to be chosen smaller and smaller, for any given ε, as n increases. But if for any $\varepsilon > 0$ a δ can be chosen which is independent of n, so that one and the same inequality of the above type holds for all P and Q whose distance does not exceed δ, and for all n, then the functions are said to be *equicontinuous*, or *equally continuous* in R. This means that their continuity is uniform, not only with respect to the positions of P and Q in R, but also with respect to n. To illustrate in the simple case of a linear region, the functions

$$f_n(x) = \frac{2nx}{1 + n^2 x^2}, \quad n = 1, 2, 3, \ldots,$$

are not equicontinuous in an interval including $x = 0$. For $f_n(x)$ is

0 at $x = 0$, and 1 at $x = \dfrac{1}{n}$. Thus, no matter how small $\delta > 0$, there are functions of the set whose values at points in an interval of length δ differ by 1. On the other hand, the functions $f(x) = ax + b$, $0 \leqq b \leqq 1$, $0 \leqq a + b \leqq 1$, are equicontinuous. For since $|a| \leqq 1$, no function of the set varies by more than ε in an interval of length ε. The choice $\delta = \varepsilon$ will serve for the whole set.

We now prove the

Theorem of Ascoli[1]. *Any infinite sequence of functions which are equicontinuous and uniformly bounded in absolute value in a closed bounded region R, contains a sub-sequence which converges uniformly in R to a continuous limit.*

To prove this, we form first an infinite sequence of points in R, P_1, P_2, P_3, ..., the points of the sequence being everywhere dense in R. This means that in every sphere about any point of R, there are points of the sequence. Such a sequence may be formed in a variety of ways, for instance as follows. Assuming some cartesian coördinate system, we take first the points in R whose coördinates are all integers. These we arrange in "dictionary order", *i. e.* two points whose x-coördinates are different are placed in order of magnitude of these coördinates. Two points whose x-coördinates are the same, are placed in the order of magnitude of their y-coördinates, if these are different, otherwise in order of their z-coördinates. These points are then taken as $P_1, P_2, \ldots P_n$, n being the number of them, in the order in which we have arranged them. Next we add all new points of R whose coördinates are integral multiples of $\dfrac{1}{2}$, also arranged in dictionary order. After these, we add all new points whose coördinates are integral multiples of $\dfrac{1}{2^2}$, and so on. To find a point of this set in a sphere of radius a about any point of R, we merely need to determine what power of $\dfrac{1}{2}$ is less than a, and we are sure to find a point in the sphere among those of the set whose coördinates are integral multiples of that power of $\dfrac{1}{2}$.

Since the functions of the set are bounded in absolute value, their values at P_1 have at least one limit point, by the Bolzano-Weierstrass theorem. Then there is an infinite sequence culled from the sequence $f_1, f_2, f_3, \ldots$ which converge, at P_1, to such a limiting value. Let us call this sequence

$$f_{11}, \; f_{12}, \; f_{13}, \; \ldots.$$

In the same way, we can cull from this sequence, a second sub-sequence, which converges to a limit at P_2. Let it be denoted by

$$f_{21}, \; f_{22}, \; f_{23}, \; \ldots.$$

[1] Atti della R. Accademia dei Lincei, **18** memorie mat. (1883), pp. 521—586.

From this, we can cull again a sub-sequence converging to a limit at P_3. Let it be denoted by

$$f_{31}, f_{32}, f_{33}, \ldots.$$

And so on. We may thus obtain an infinite sequence of sequences, with the property that the nth sequence converges at $P_1, P_2, P_3, \ldots P_n$.

From these, we can now cull a sequence which converges at all the points of the set $P_1, P_2, P_3, \ldots$. We have only to use the *diagonal process*, and form the sequence

$$(12) \qquad f_{11}, f_{22}, f_{33}, \ldots f_{nn}, \ldots.$$

Since this sequence, at least from the nth term on, is contained in the sequence

$$f_{n1}, f_{n2}, f_{n3}, \ldots,$$

it converges at P_n, and all the points of the set with smaller index. As n can be any integer, the sequence (12) converges at all points P_i.

This sequence converges uniformly in R. For if any $\varepsilon > 0$ be given, there is a $\delta > 0$ such that

$$(13) \qquad |f_{nn}(P) - f_{nn}(Q)| < \frac{\varepsilon}{3}$$

for any two points P and Q of R whose distance apart does not exceed δ, for all n. This because the given sequence is equicontinuous. Now let m be such that $\frac{1}{2^m} < \delta$, and let n_1 be such that the finite set of points $P_1, P_2, P_3, \ldots P_{n_1}$ contains all the points of R, whose coördinates are integral multiples of $\frac{1}{2^m}$. Then there are points of this finite set S within a distance δ of every point of R. Finally, let N be such that for $n > N$, $p > 0$,

$$(14) \qquad |f_{n+p,\, n+p}(P_i) - f_{nn}(P_i)| < \frac{\varepsilon}{3}$$

for all the points P_i of the set S.

Then for any point P of R, there is a point $Q = P_i$ of the set S for which the inequality (13) is in force for $f_{n+p,\, n+p}(P)$ and for $f_{nn}(P)$. Writing the corresponding inequalities, and combining them with (14), we find

$$|f_{n+p,\, n+p}(P) - f_{nn}(P)| < \varepsilon,$$

an inequality which holds for all P in R. But this is the Cauchy condition for convergence, and as it is uniform throughout R, the sequence (12) converges uniformly in R. Since a uniformly convergent sequence of continuous functions has a continuous limit function, the theorem is proved.

Applying Ascoli's theorem to harmonic functions, we have the following result:

Theorem IX. *If U_1, U_2, U_3, ... is an infinite sequence of functions all harmonic in a bounded domain T, and uniformly bounded in T, then given any closed region R in T, there is an infinite sub-sequence taken from the given sequence which converges uniformly in R to a limit function harmonic in R.*

Let a be the minimum distance of the points of R from the boundary of T, and let B be a bound for the absolute values of the functions U_i in T. Then, by Theorem XII of Chapter VIII (p. 227), the directional derivatives of the functions U_i are bounded in absolute value, in R, by

$$\frac{3}{4a} 2B,$$

and the sequence of these functions is therefore equicontinuous in R. Hence, by the theorem of Ascoli, the sequence contains a sub-sequence which converges uniformly in R, and by Theorem I, the limiting function is harmonic in R. By taking further subsequences, we can show that the limiting function is harmonic in T. The condition that T be bounded may be removed by an inversion, if T has an exterior point.

Convergence in the Mean. A final theorem, which is sometimes useful, deals with convergence in the mean. A sequence of functions $f_1, f_2, f_3, \ldots,$ defined and integrable in a regular region R is said to *converge in the mean to a function f* provided the sequence

$$s_n = \iiint_R [f_n - f]^2 \, dV$$

converges to 0. That is, the error, in the sense of least squares, in substituting f_n for f, approaches 0 as n becomes infinite.

Exercises.

1. Show that there exist sequences which converge at every point of an interval, but do not converge in the mean in that interval, by an examination of the sequence

$$f_n(x) = n^2 x e^{-nx}, \qquad\qquad n = 1, 2, 3, \ldots$$

on the interval $(0,1)$.

2. Construct an example showing that there exist sequences of functions which converge in the mean in a region, but converge at no point of the region. Suggestion. Take the interval $(0,1)$, and construct a sequence of functions 0 everywhere on this interval, except that the nth function is 1 on a sub-interval whose length decreases as n increases. Do this in such a way as to bring out the required situation, and prove that your results are correct. The functions so constructed will be discontinuous, but the example can easily be modified so as to make the functions continuous.

If a sequence $f_1, f_2, f_3, \ldots$ converges in the mean to a function f, then, given $\varepsilon > 0$, there exists an N such that for any $n > N$, $m > N$,

$$\iiint_R [f_n - f]^2 \, dV < \frac{\varepsilon}{4}, \qquad\qquad \iiint_R [f_m - f]^2 \, dV < \frac{\varepsilon}{4},$$

so that by means of the easily verified inequality

$$|a - b|^2 \leqq 2[|a - c|^2 + |b - c|^2],$$

we see that

$$s_{m, n} = \iiint_R [f_m - f_n]^2 \, dV < \varepsilon.$$

It is therefore a necessary condition for convergence in the mean to a function, that, given any $\varepsilon > 0$, there is an N such that for $n > N$, $m > N$, $s_{m, n} < \varepsilon$. When this condition is fulfilled, the sequence is said to *converge in the mean* — quite apart from any question as to the existence of a limit function to which the sequence converges in the mean. As a matter of fact, it can be proved, under suitable assumptions, that such a limiting function exists, but we shall not concern ourselves with a general proof here[1]. In the case of harmonic functions, however, the existence of a limiting function is easily established.

Theorem X. *Let* $U_1, U_2, U_3, \ldots$ *be an infinite sequence of functions, harmonic in the closed region* R, *and convergent in the mean in* R. *Then the sequence converges uniformly, in any closed region* R' *interior to* R, *to a harmonic limiting function.*

Let P be any point of R', and a the minimum distance from the points of R' to the boundary of R. Let σ denote the sphere of radius a about P. Then as harmonic functions are their own arithmetic means throughout spheres in the regions in which they are harmonic (see page 224),

$$U_m(P) - U_n(P) = \frac{3}{4 \pi a^3} \iiint_\sigma [U_m(Q) - U_n(Q)] \, dV.$$

Accordingly, applying Schwarz' inequality, we find

$$[U_m(P) - U_n(P)]^2 \leqq \left(\frac{3}{4 \pi a^3}\right)^2 \iiint_\sigma [U_m(Q) - U_n(Q)]^2 \, dV \iiint_\sigma dV$$

$$\leqq \frac{3}{4 \pi a^3} \iiint_R [U_m(Q) - U_n(Q)]^2 \, dV.$$

The right hand member is independent of P, and by hypothesis, becomes arbitrarily small with $n > N$, $m > N$, for large N. Hence the sequence $U_1, U_2, U_3, \ldots$ is uniformly convergent in R'. The rest of the argument is now familiar.

8. Isolated Singularities of Harmonic Functions.

A singular point of a harmonic function U is a point at which U is not harmonic, but in every neighborhood of which there are points at

---

[1] See E. FISCHER, Comptes Rendus de l'Académie des Sciences de Paris, T. 144 (1907), pp. 1022—24; 1148—51.

which U is harmonic. Thus the surfaces bearing Newtonian distributions consist of singular points of the potentials of the distributions. We have devoted a chapter to the study of the behavior of harmonic functions in the neighborhood of such singular points. But we have done little with isolated singular points, such a point being one at which a function U is not harmonic although it is harmonic in the rest of a neighborhood of that point. The point at which a particle is situated is an isolated singular point for the potential of the particle, but this is not the only type of isolated singular point.

Let U have an isolated singular point, and let us take this point as origin of coördinates. If S_1 and S_2 are two spheres, both within the neighborhood in which U is harmonic except at the origin O, and with centers at O, the formula (9), page 223, applied to the region between S_1 and S_2, the latter having the larger radius, becomes

$$U(P) = \frac{1}{4\pi} \iint\limits_{S_2} \left[\frac{\partial U}{\partial \nu} \frac{1}{r} - U \frac{\partial}{\partial \nu} \frac{1}{r} \right] dS + \frac{1}{4\pi} \iint\limits_{S_1} \left[\frac{\partial U}{\partial \nu} \frac{1}{r} - U \frac{\partial}{\partial \nu} \frac{1}{r} \right] dS.$$

The first of the surface integrals is harmonic within S_2. The second, no matter how small S_1, is harmonic outside S_1, and can be expanded in a series of spherical harmonics divided by powers of ϱ, the series being convergent for any $\varrho > 0$, and uniformly so outside any sphere about O. Thus we may write the equation, valid except at O within the sphere S_2,

$$(15) \qquad U(P) = V(P) + \frac{c}{\varrho} + \frac{S_1(\varphi, \vartheta)}{\varrho^2} + \frac{S_2(\varphi, \vartheta)}{\varrho^3} + \cdots,$$

where $V(P)$ is harmonic within S_2.

Suppose first, that for some $\mu \geqq 0$, $|\varrho^\mu U(P)|$ is bounded in S_2. We change, in (15), φ and ϑ to φ' and ϑ', multiply by $\varrho^\mu P_n(u)$, where $u = \cos \gamma$, and integrate over the surface of the sphere of radius ϱ about O, within S_2:

$$\int\limits_0^\pi \int\limits_0^{2\pi} \varrho^\mu U(Q) P_n(u) \sin \vartheta' d\varphi' d\vartheta' = \varrho^\mu \int\limits_0^{2\pi} \int\limits_0^\pi V(Q) P_n(u) \sin \vartheta' d\varphi' d\vartheta'$$
$$+ \frac{4\pi}{2n+1} S_n(\varphi, \vartheta) \varrho^{\mu - n - 1},$$

by (6). The integral on the left is bounded, and so is the first term on the right. Then the last term must also be bounded. This means that if $\mu - n - 1 < 0$, $S_n(\varphi, \vartheta)$ must vanish identically. For otherwise, there would be a ray (φ_0, ϑ_0) on which it had a constant value not 0, and for points on this ray, ϱ could be taken so small as to make the last terms arbitrarily large. We therefore have the theorem:

Theorem XI. *Let the function U be harmonic in a neighborhood of O except at O itself. If there is a constant $\mu \geqq 0$, such that in some* *included neighborhood of $O \,|\, \varrho^\mu\, U\,(P)\,|$ is bounded, then in that neighborhood, except at O, U is given by a finite number of terms of the series* (15), *there being no terms for which* $n > \mu - 1$.

As a special case, we have the important

Corollary. An isolated singularity of a bounded harmonic function is removable[1].

If $\mu = 0$, there are no terms at all of the series after the function $V\,(P)$. Thus U coincides, except at O, with a function which is harmonic at O, and by a change in definition at this point, namely the definition which gives it the value $V\,(O)$, it becomes harmonic at O. A harmonic function is said to have a *removable* singularity at an isolated singular point if it can be made harmonic at the point by a change in its definition at that point alone.

It is evident that the corollary continues to hold if instead of requiring that U be bounded, we ask merely that $|\, \varrho^\mu\, U\,|$ be bounded, for some $\mu < 1$. But one does not often meet the need of it in the broader form.

Exercise.

1. If $G_1\,(P, Q)$ and $G_2\,(P, Q)$ are Green's functions for two regions, one in the other, show that $G_2\,(P, Q) - G_1\,(P, Q)$ may be so defined at the pole Q as to be harmonic in P in the smaller region.

Let us now assume that in some neighborhood of O, say a sphere of radius a, about O, U is harmonic except at O, and never negative. As $1 + P_n\,(u)$ is also never negative, we have, by (15) for all $0 < \varrho < a$,

$$\int\limits_0^\pi \int\limits_0^{2\pi} U\,(Q)\,[1 + P_n\,(u)]\sin\vartheta'\,d\varphi'\,d\vartheta' =$$

$$\int\limits_0^\pi \int\limits_0^{2\pi} V\,(\varrho, \varphi', \vartheta')\,[1 + P_n\,(u)]\sin\vartheta'\,d\varphi'\,d\vartheta' + 4\pi\left[\frac{c}{\varrho} + \frac{S_n\,(\varphi, \vartheta)}{(2\,n+1)\,\varrho^{n+1}}\right] \geqq 0.$$

We conclude from this that for $n > 1$, $S_n\,(\varphi, \vartheta) \equiv 0$. For since $S_n\,(\varphi, \vartheta)$, for $n > 1$, is orthogonal on the unit sphere to any constant, it must, unless identically 0, change signs. For the points of a ray on which $S_n\,(\varphi, \vartheta) < 0$, we could take ϱ so small that the term in $S_n\,(\varphi, \vartheta)$ in the last inequality, predominated over the preceding ones, and thus, because of its negative sign, we should have a contradiction of the inequality. By applying the same reasoning to $U\,(P) + C$ and to $C - U\,(P)$, we arrive at

Theorem XII. *If in the neighborhood of an isolated singular point, the function U is either bounded above, or bounded below, then in the neighborhood of that point, it is the sum of a function harmonic at that point and a function $\dfrac{c}{\varrho}$, where c is a constant, positive, negative or 0.*

---

[1] Due to H. A. SCHWARZ, Journal für reine und angewandte Mathematik, Vol. 74 (1872), p. 252.

Exercises.

2. From the equation

$$\int\limits_{0}^{\pi}\int\limits_{0}^{2\pi} [U(Q) - V(Q)]\, P_n(u)\, \sin \vartheta'\, d\varphi'\, d\vartheta' = \frac{4\pi}{2n+1}\, \frac{S_n(\varphi, \vartheta)}{\varrho^{n+1}},$$

the integral being over the sphere of radius ϱ about O, derive for the spherical harmonic $S_n(\varphi, \vartheta)$ in (15) the inequality

$$|S_n(\varphi, \vartheta)| \leqq \sqrt{\frac{2n+1}{2\pi}}\, \varrho^{n+1} \sqrt{\int\limits_{0}^{\pi}\int\limits_{0}^{2\pi} U^2 \sin \vartheta'\, d\varphi'\, d\vartheta' + \int\limits_{0}^{\pi}\int\limits_{0}^{2\pi} V^2 \sin \vartheta'\, d\varphi'\, d\vartheta'}.$$

From this draw the conclusions

a) if
$$\int\limits_{0}^{\pi}\int\limits_{0}^{2\pi} U^2 \sin \vartheta'\, d\varphi'\, d\vartheta'$$

is bounded, the singularity of U at O is removable,

b) if
$$\varrho^{\mu} \int\limits_{0}^{\pi}\int\limits_{0}^{2\pi} U^2 \sin \vartheta'\, d\varphi'\, d\vartheta'$$

is bounded, the series (15) contains no spherical harmonics of order greater than $\frac{(\mu - 2)}{2}$. In particular the singularity is removable if the above function is bounded for some $\mu < 2$. (EVANS).

3. To say that U becomes positively infinite at O means that given N, however large, there is a neighborhood of O at all points of which, except O, $U > N$. Show that if O is an isolated singularity of U at which U becomes positively infinite, then U must be of the form

$$U(P) = V(P) + \frac{c}{\varrho}.$$

4. Show that if O is an isolated singularity of U, and if U is neither bounded nor becomes positively infinite, nor negatively infinite, then in every neighborhood of O, U takes on any preassigned real value.

Isolated Singular Curves. We say that a curve is an isolated singular curve of a harmonic function U, provided U is harmonic at none of the points of the curve, but is harmonic in some neighborhood of every point of the curve, the curve excepted. We shall confine ourselves to a single theorem on isolated singular curves, needed in Chapter VIII, § 5 (p. 190).

Theorem XIII. *Let C denote a regular curve. If C is an isolated singular curve for the harmonic function U, and if U is bounded in some domain containing the curve, then the singularity of U on the curve is removable.*

Let V denote the potential of a distribution of unit linear density on C. We need as a lemma that V becomes positively infinite at every point of C. This is easily shown by means of the observation that the potential at P of a distribution of positive density is only decreased by a change of position of the masses to more distant points. Thus the value of V at P is greater than or equal to that of a straight wire lying in a ray from P, of the same length as C, whose nearest point to P is as the same distance as the nearest point of C. We find for the potential of the straight wire

$$\log\left(1 + \frac{l}{\varrho}\right),$$

where l is the length of the wire, and ϱ the distance from P to its nearest point. Hence V is uniformly greater than or equal to this function, when ϱ is the distance from P to the nearest point of C.

By the Heine-Borel theorem, there is a finite number of spheres with centers on C containing all the points of C in their interiors, which lie in the domain in which U is harmonic, except at the points of C, and in which U is bounded. If their radii are all decreased, so slightly that they still contain all points of C in their interiors, the points in all of them constitute a regular region R, on the surface S of which U is continuous. We now borrow from the next chapter the fact that the Dirichlet problem is solvable for R. Let U^* denote the function, harmonic in R, and assuming the same boundary values as U. Then $U - U^*$ is 0 on S, harmonic in the interior of R except on C, and bounded in absolute value, say by B. Now αV becomes infinite on C for any fixed α, $0 < \alpha < 1$. Hence the region R' consisting of the points of R for which αV is less than any given fixed constant K, however great, excludes all the points of C. Given any point P in R but not on C, let K be chosen, greater than B, and so that P is in R'. Then in R', the function

$$\alpha V - (U - U^*)$$

is continuous, and has only positive boundary values. It is harmonic in the interior of R', and hence is positive throughout R'. Hence at P,

$$(U - U^*) < \alpha V < \alpha \log\left(1 + \frac{l}{\varrho}\right).$$

Here ϱ is fixed, but α can be any number between 0 and 1. Hence $U - U^*$ is less at P than any positive number. By applying the same considerations to $U^* - U$, we see that this difference also is less than any positive number. Hence $U = U^*$ at any point of R not on C. If, therefore, we define U as equal to U^* on C, U becomes harmonic throughout R. This is what is meant by saying that the singularity of U on C is removable.

It is clear that the reasoning applies to any set of points which can be so spread with masses as to have a potential which becomes positively infinite at every point of the set. But the theorem as stated suffices for our purposes[1].

---

[1] A completely general result of this type will be found in Chapter XI, § 20.

Exercise.

Exercise.

Study the behavior of a harmonic function at infinity when this is an isolated singular point, by an inversion, or otherwise.

9. Equipotential Surfaces.

A question, for the discussion of which developments in spherical harmonics constitute the most suitable tool, is that of the character of equipotential surfaces, particularly in the neighborhood of a point of equilibrium of the field. At other points, the equipotential surfaces have exceedingly simple character, but at points of equilibrium the study of the character of these surfaces presents serious difficulties. The problem is rather one of geometric beauty than of physical importance, and perhaps for this reason, it has not been carried far. Yet from an analytic standpoint, it is one of the first applications of the theory of functions defined implicitly. We must content ourselves with some indications.

Let U be one-valued, harmonic, and not constant in a neighborhood of a point O, which we take as origin of coördinates. Suppose first that the gradient of U does not vanish at O. Then in the development in spherical harmonics,

$$(16) \qquad U - U_0 = H_1(x, y, z) + H_2(x, y, z) + \ldots,$$

$H_1(x, y, z)$ is not identically 0. If we choose the orientation of the axes so that the plane $H_1(x, y, z) = 0$ becomes the (x, y)-plane,

$$\frac{\partial U}{\partial z} \neq 0$$

at the origin. The equation $U = U_0$ has the solution $(0, 0, 0)$, and hence by the theorem on implicit functions, there is an analytic surface $z = f(x, y)$ which in a neighborhood of O is identical with the locus $U = U_0$ in that neighborhood. That is, *the equipotential surface $U = U_0$ in the neighborhood of a point at which $\nabla U \neq 0$, consists of a single analytic regular surface element.* Furthermore, this surface element divides the points in a neighborhood of O into two domains, in one of which $U > U_0$, and in the other $U < U_0$, since $\dfrac{\partial U}{\partial z} \neq 0$ near O.

The next question which arises is as to how frequently the exceptional points at which $\nabla U = 0$ occur. They may be isolated, as is the case with $U = x^2 + y^2 - 2z^2$. They may fill a line, as is the case with $U = xy$. They cannot fill any regular surface element E. For if C be any regular curve on E, whose length of arc, measured from a convenient point is s, we find from the vanishing of the gradient the fact that

$$\frac{\partial U}{\partial s} = 0,$$

and so, that U would be constant on E. Thus $U - U_0$ and its normal derivative would vanish on E, and hence, by the corollary to Theorem VI, this difference would vanish in any region in which it was harmonic. Thus U would be constant, contrary to our assumption.

Let us now suppose that $V U = 0$ at O. Then in the development (16), $H_1(x, y, z)$ will be lacking. Let $H_n(x, y, z)$ be the first term not identically 0. Then the locus defined by $H_n(x, y, z) = 0$ consists of a conical surface with vertex at O. The function $H_n(x, y, z)$ may have rational factors, in which case the locus will consist of several algebraic cones with vertex at O. Among these, there may, in case some factors are linear, be planes. But no factor will occur twice, for if it did, $H_n(x, y, z)$ and its gradient would vanish at the points where this factor vanished, and as the set of these points certainly contains a regular surface element, $H_n(x, y, z)$ would be identically 0. Thus $V H_n(x, y, z)$ vanishes at most on a finite number of the elements of the conical locus $H_n(x, y, z) = 0$. Let us call this locus C.

The points of the locus $U = U_0$, other than O, are given by

$$(17) \quad 0 = S_n(\varphi, \vartheta) + S_{n+1}(\varphi, \vartheta) \varrho + S_{n+2}(\varphi, \vartheta) \varrho^2 + \cdots = F(\varrho, \varphi, \vartheta),$$

where $S_n(\varphi, \vartheta) = \varrho^{-n} H_n(x, y, z)$, is not identically 0. Let P_0 be a point of the cone C, at which $V H_n(x, y, z)$ is not 0, and let us take for the (x, y)-plane the tangent plane to C at P_0, with the x-axis through P_0. The spherical coördinates of P_0 will be $\left(\varrho_0, 0, \frac{\pi}{2} \right)$. At P_0,

$$\frac{\partial}{\partial \vartheta} S_n(\varphi, \vartheta) \bigg|_0 = \frac{1}{\varrho^n} \frac{\partial}{\partial \vartheta} H_n \bigg|_0 = -\frac{1}{\varrho^{n-1}} \frac{\partial H_n}{\partial z} \bigg|_0,$$

and this is not 0, as we have seen in considering equipotentials at points where the gradient does not vanish. It follows that the equipotential (17) has a point near the generator of the cone C, $S_n(\varphi, \vartheta) = 0$, through P_0. For $S_n(0, \vartheta)$ has opposite signs for $\vartheta = \left(\frac{\pi}{2} \right) + \eta$ and $\vartheta = \left(\frac{\pi}{2} \right) - \eta$, for sufficiently small η, and on the rays $\left(0, \frac{\pi}{2} - \eta \right)$ and $\left(0, \frac{\pi}{2} + \eta \right)$, ϱ can be taken so small that the first term in (17) predominates over the rest, which form a uniformly convergent series even after division by ϱ. Thus for such a ϱ, $F\left(\varrho, 0, \frac{\pi}{2} - \eta \right)$ and $F\left(\varrho, 0, \frac{\pi}{2} + \eta \right)$ have opposite signs, and hence $F(\varrho, 0, \vartheta)$ must vanish for an intermediate value of ϑ. This holds for all sufficiently small ϱ; and for small enough ϱ, the derivative with respect to ϑ of $S_n(0, \vartheta)$ predominates over the derivative of the sum of the remaining terms, so that for small enough ϱ, there is a point P_1 of the equipotential, for which $\varphi = 0$, and at which

$$\frac{\partial}{\partial \vartheta} F(\varrho, 0, \vartheta) \neq 0.$$

Thus the conditions for the theorem on implicit functions are fulfilled, and the equipotential in the neighborhood of P_1 consists of the points of a surface element S, given by

$$\vartheta = f(\varrho, \varphi).$$

This surface can be continued, by the same theorem, for values of ϱ near 0, toward the origin to within any given distance of that point. The derivative of ϑ with respect to ϱ is given by the usual rule for the differentiation of implicit functions, and is seen, because $\frac{\partial S_n}{\partial \vartheta} \neq 0$ at $\left(0, \frac{\pi}{2}\right)$, to be uniformly bounded in absolute value, say by c, for all sufficiently small ϱ and φ. As ϑ lies, for small enough ϱ, between $\frac{\pi}{2} - \eta$ and $\frac{\pi}{2} + \eta$ for any positive η, it follows that the limit of ϑ as ϱ approaches 0, is $\frac{\pi}{2}$, and hence that

$$\left| \vartheta - \frac{\pi}{2} \right| \leq c\varrho.$$

Hence on S,

$$|z| = |\varrho \cos \vartheta| = \left| \varrho \sin \left(\frac{\pi}{2} - \vartheta \right) \right| \leq |\varrho \sin c\varrho|,$$

so that the distance from S to C for small φ is an infinitesimal of second order in ϱ. In this sense, the equipotential surface element S is tangent to the cone C. It is obvious that $F(\varrho, \varphi, \vartheta)$ does not vanish on any ray through O for which $S_n(\varphi, \vartheta) \neq 0$, for small enough ϱ, so that *the equipotential $U = U_0$, except within circular cones of arbitrarily small angular opening about the finite number of singular generators of the cone C, will, in the neighborhood of O, consist of a finite number of smooth surface elements tangent to the cone C.*

One consequence of this fact is that the equipotential surface, near one of its points where the gradient of U vanishes, cannot consist of a single regular surface element. For such an element can be tangent, in the above sense, only to a cone which is flat, that is, to a plane, and the cone C can be a plane only when $H_1(x, y, z)$ is not identically 0.

In general, the character of the equipotential surface near a point where the gradient vanishes, is thus closely related to the cone C. The general properties of algebraic cones given by the vanishing of a spherical harmonic do not appear to have been extensively studied. For $n = 2$, the cone is characterized by the fact that it has three generators each at right angles to the others.

Another case in which we can make a definite statement is that in which $H_n(x, y, z)$ is the product of linear factors, the planes corresponding to which all intersect in a single line. If this line be taken as z-axis, $H_n(x, y, z)$ will be independent of z, and if we substitute $H_n = \varrho^n S_n(\varphi)$

in Laplace's equation in cylindrical coördinates, we find

$$\frac{d^2 S_n}{d \varphi^2} + n^2 S_n = 0,$$

so that $S_n = A \sin (\varphi - \varphi_0)$. The cone C then degenerates into a set of equally spaced planes through a common line. If in addition U itself is independent of z, we know that the equipotential surface through O consists of n cylindrical surface elements in the neighborhood of the axis, each tangent to one of the planes of C.

But it would be a mistake to suppose that in general, U, the first not identically vanishing term in whose development in spherical harmonics about O, is of the character just considered, had an equipotential surface through O consisting of n separate sheets each tangent to one of the planes of C. An inspection of the equipotential

$$U = z^2 - x^2 - y^3 + 3 x^2 y = 0$$

is sufficient to show that this is not always the case[1].

Exercise on the Logarithmic Potential.

Study the character of the isolated singularities of harmonic functions in two dimensions.

There is a further result on equipotential surfaces which has already been of use to us (p. 238). It may be formulated as follows:

Theorem XIV. *Let R denote a closed bounded region, and let U be harmonic in a domain including R. Then the points of R at which the gradient ∇U vanishes lie on a* finite *number of equipotential surfaces $U = $ const.*

It is known[2] that about any point P_0 of R at which

$$\frac{\partial U}{\partial x} = 0, \qquad \frac{\partial U}{\partial y} = 0, \qquad \frac{\partial U}{\partial z} = 0,$$

there is a neighborhood, including all points with real or imaginary coördinates sufficiently near to P_0, such that all points of the neighborhood, at which these derivatives vanish simultaneously, consist either of the point P_0 alone, or of a finite number of manifolds. For our purposes,

---

[1] This example shows the inaccuracy of certain statements in MAXWELL's *Treatise on Electricity and Magnestism*, 3rd ed. Oxford (1904), p. 172. "If the point P is not on a line of equilibrium, the nodal line does not intersect itself." This and the assertion which follows are wrong. Rankine's theorem as there stated is also in need of change: "If n sheets of the same equipotential intersect each other, they make angles $\frac{\pi}{n}$." Consider, for instance, the example $U = z (x^3 - 3 x y^2)$.

[2] See OSGOOD, *Funktionentheorie*, Vol. II, Chap. II, § 17, p. 104; KELLOGG, *Singular Manifolds among those of an Analytic Family*, Bulletin of the American Mathematical Society, Vol. XXXV (1929).

the essential property of these manifolds is that any two points,

$$P_1 (x_1' + i x_1'', \ y_1' + i y_1'', \ z_1' + i z_1'')$$

and $\qquad P_2 (x_2' + i x_2'', \ y_2' + i y_2'', \ z_2' + i z_2''),$

of any one of them, can be connected by a continuous curve,

$$x = x'(t) + i x''(t), \quad y = y'(t) + i y''(t), \quad z = z'(t) + i z''(t),$$

whose coördinates have continuous derivatives with respect to t except possibly at a finite number of points, and which lies entirely in the manifold. On such a curve,

$$\frac{dU}{dt} = \frac{\partial U}{\partial x}\frac{dx}{dt} + \frac{\partial U}{\partial y}\frac{dy}{dt} + \frac{\partial U}{\partial z}\frac{dz}{dt} = 0,$$

and hence U has the same value at any two points of the manifold. As the number of manifolds is finite, we conclude that there is a complex neighborhood of P_0 in which all the points at which $\nabla U = 0$ lie on a finite number of equipotentials $U = c_1, \ U = c_2, \ldots, \ U = c_n$. The real points at which the gradient vanishes, being in the neighborhood in question, must also lie on these surfaces, and, since we are supposing U real, on those for which the constants c_i are real.

If E is the set of points of R at which $\nabla U = 0$, E is obviously a closed set, and each of its points lie in a neighborhood of the above character. Hence, by the Heine-Borel theorem, E lies in a finite number of such neighborhoods, and the number of the equipotential surfaces which contain all points in R at which $\nabla U = 0$ is thus finite, as we wished to prove.

Chapter XI.

Fundamental Existence Theorems.

1. Historical Introduction.

As we saw in § 3 of Chapter IX (p. 237), Green, in 1828, inferred the existence of the function which bears his name from the assumption that a static charge could always be induced on a closed grounded conducting surface by a point charge within the conductor, and that the combined potential of the two charges would vanish on the surface. From this, he inferred the possibility of solving the Dirichlet problem. Such considerations could not, however, be accepted as an existence proof. In 1840, Gauss[1] gave the following argument. Let S denote the boundary of the region for which the Dirichlet problem is to be solved.

---

[1] *Allgemeine Lehrsätze*, l. c., footnote, page 83.

Let a distribution of density σ and total mass M be placed on S, in such a way that any portion of S has a total positive mass on it. Let U denote the potential of this distribution, and f a continuous function of position on S. Then, GAUSS argued, there must be a distribution subject to the given restrictions, for which the integral

$$\iint_S (U - 2f)\, \sigma\, dS$$

is a minimum. It is then shown that for the minimizing distribution, $U - f$ must be constant on S. If in particular $f = 0$, U will be a positive constant on S, so that by adding to the potential U for any given f the proper multiple of the potential for $f = 0$, we obtain a potential whose boundary values are f. The serious difficulty with this proof is that it is not clear that there is a distribution, subject to the given conditions, which makes the integral a minimum. Indeed, it is not true without further restrictions. In fact, the Dirichlet problem is not always solvable, and no "proof" can be valid unless it places some restriction on the region.

Similarly, in 1847, Sir WILLIAM THOMSON, Lord KELVIN[1], attempted to found a proof on the least value of an integral. The same considerations were used by DIRICHLET[2] in lectures during the following decade. For reasons to be indicated presently, the method used is still of high importance.

One might be led to it as follows. We imagine the region R, for which the problem is to be solved, and the rest of space, filled with charges, and in addition, a spread on the bounding surface S. We suppose that the total potential is regular at infinity. The potential energy of these distributions is, according to § 11, Chapter III (p. 81),

$$E = \frac{1}{2} \iiint U \varkappa\, dV + \frac{1}{2} \iint_S U \sigma\, dS,$$

where U is the potential, $\varkappa$ the volume density, and σ the surface density. On the assumption that U is a sufficiently smooth function, we have

$$\varkappa = -\frac{\nabla^2 U}{4\pi}, \qquad \sigma = -\frac{1}{4\pi}\left[\frac{\partial U}{\partial n_+} - \frac{\partial U}{\partial n_-}\right].$$

If we put these values in the expression for the energy, and transform the integrals by means of Green's second identity, we find for E the

[1] Journal de mathématiques pures et appliquées, Vol. 12, p. 496; *Reprint of Papers on Electrostatics and Magnetism*, London, 1884.

[2] P. G. DIRICHLET, *Die im umgekehrten Verhältnis des Quadrates der Entfernung wirkenden Kräfte*, edited by F. GRUBE, Leipzig, 1876.

expression

$$E = \frac{1}{8\pi} \iiint (\nabla U)^2 \, dV = \frac{1}{8\pi} \iiint \left[\left(\frac{\partial U}{\partial x} \right)^2 + \left(\frac{\partial U}{\partial y} \right)^2 + \left(\frac{\partial U}{\partial z} \right)^2 \right] dV,$$

the integral being extended over the whole of space.

Now it is a principle of physics that equilibrium is characterized by the least potential energy consistent with the constraints, or conditions imposed on the system. Suppose that the condition imposed on U is that it shall have given values f on the boundary S of R. The charges can move under this condition, for we have seen that different spreads can have the same potential in restricted portions of space, say on S. But we know that equilibrium will not be attained as long as the region in which they can move contains charges. Thus equilibrium is characterized by the fact that U is harmonic in the interior of R, as well as outside S.

We are thus led to the following mathematical formulation of the problem. Consider the class of all functions U which have continuous derivatives of the second order in the interior and exterior domains T and T' bounded by S, which are continuous everywhere, and which assume on S the continuous values f. We seek that one of these functions which renders the *Dirichlet integral*

$$I = \iiint_R \left[\left(\frac{\partial U}{\partial x} \right)^2 + \left(\frac{\partial U}{\partial y} \right)^2 + \left(\frac{\partial U}{\partial z} \right)^2 \right] dV$$

a minimum. We have here extended the integral only over R, but it is clear that the integral over the whole of space cannot be a minimum unless that extended over R is a minimum. Since for real U, I cannot be negative, there must be a function U, subject to the given restrictions, for which the integral is least — so ran the argument, and this argument received the name of the *Dirichlet principle*. We shall criticize it presently.

But for the moment, let us suppose that a minimum does exist — and it does in many cases. What are the properties of the function u for which the integral is least? Let u' be any other function with the required properties. Then $h = u' - u$ has the required properties, except that it vanishes on S, and so $u + \eta h$, for any η, has all the required properties. Now

$$I(u + \eta h) = I(u) + 2\eta \iiint_R (\nabla u \cdot \nabla h) \, dV + \eta^2 I(h).$$

Since u gives to I its least value, it is impossible for $u + \eta h$ to give it a less value. It follows that

$$I(u, h) = \iiint_R (\nabla u \cdot \nabla h) \, dV = 0,$$

for if this were not so, η could be chosen so small a positive or negative number that the second term would predominate over the third, and so it would be possible to make the sum of these two terms negative. This is impossible since $I(u + \eta h)$ would then be less than $I(u)$. If now the equation $I(u, h) = 0$ be transformed by Green's second identity, we have, since $h = 0$ on S,

$$- \iiint_R h \, (\nabla^2 u) \, dV = 0 .$$

It follows that $\nabla^2 u = 0$ throughout R. For if $\nabla^2 u$ were positive at an interior point, since it is continuous, we could find a sphere within which it remained positive, and then choose for h a function 0 outside this sphere, positive inside, and having continuous derivatives of the second order, and thus such that the function $u + h$ had the required properties. For such a function h, the last integral could not vanish. Hence $\nabla^2 u = 0$, and u is harmonic. Thus the Dirichlet problem is solved in every case in which the Dirichlet integral has a minimum under the given conditions.

Now why does the Dirichlet integral not always have a minimum? The values which it has for all admissible functions U are infinite in number, and none of them is negative. It is true that they have a lower limit, that is, a number below which no values of I go, but to which they approximate arbitrarily closely. But this is not saying that there is a function u for which I takes on this lower limit. As an example of the fact that an integral may have a lower limit without a minimum, consider

$$\int_0^1 y^2 \, dx ,$$

where the functions y are subjected to the requirement that they are continuous on $(0, 1)$, and assume the values 0 and 1 at $x = 0$ and $x = 1$, respectively. Clearly the lower limit of the integral is 0, as may be seen by using the power curves, $y = x^n$. The integral then approaches 0 with $\frac{1}{n}$. Now if any continuous function y made the integral 0, it could not be different from 0 at any point of the interval, by a type of reasoning we have employed a number of times. Hence y could not take on the value 1 for $x = 1$.

This difficulty with the Dirichlet principle was felt by mathematicians at an early date. WEIERSTRASS was among the first to emphasize its unreliability, and in 1870 gave a conclusive example showing the principle in its current form to be false[1]. It therefore remained in disrepute for a number of years, until in 1899, HILBERT[2] showed how, *under proper*

---

[1] See the references in the Encyklopädie der mathematischen Wissenschaften, II A 7b, p. 494.

[2] Jahresbericht der Deutschen Mathematiker-Vereinigung, Bd. 8 (1900), p. 184.

conditions on the region, boundary values, and the functions U admitted, it could be proved to be reliable.

But in the mean time, the problem had not remained dormant. SCHWARZ[1] had made notable progress with the problem in two dimensions, where it is particularly important for its connection with the theory of functions of a complex variable. The next step of importance in three dimensions was due to NEUMANN[2], who used a method known as the *method of the arithmetic mean*.

By way of introduction, let us consider for the instant, a double distribution

$$W = \frac{1}{2\pi} \iint_S \mu \frac{\partial}{\partial \nu} \frac{1}{r} \, dS,$$

the moment now being denoted by $\frac{\mu}{2\pi}$. This notation brings simplifications with it. Thus, if we denote by W^-, W^0 and W^+ the limit of W from within the surface S as P approaches a point p of S, the value at p, and the limit as P approaches p from without S, we have

$$W^- = -\mu + W^0, \qquad W^+ = \mu + W^0.$$

Suppose that the surface is convex. Then, when W^0 is written in the form

$$W^0 = -\frac{1}{2\pi} \iint \mu \, d\Omega,$$

the integration being with respect to the solid angle subtended at p by the element of surface, we see that $-W^0$ is the arithmetic mean of the values of μ, transferred along radii, to the hemisphere of the unit sphere about p which lies to the side of the tangent plane at p on which S lies. Thus the extremes of $-W^0$ lie strictly between the extremes of μ, if this function is continuous, as we shall assume. *In other words, the values of the double distribution, on the surface, vary less, in this sense, than do those of μ.* We are here supposing that μ is not constant.

Now suppose we take a second double distribution, with μ replaced by $-W^0$. The negative of its value on S will vary still less. If the process is repeated, we have a succession of potentials whose moments are becoming more and more nearly constant. Perhaps from such potentials we may build up a function giving the solution of the Dirichlet problem. This is the underlying idea of the method. We form the sequence of

---

[1] See his collected works.

[2] Berichte über die Verhandlungen der Königlich Sächsischen Gesellschaft der Wissenschaften zu Leipzig, 1870, pp. 49—56, 264—321. Cf. also PICARD, *Traité d'Analyse*, 3rd ed. Paris 1922, Vol. I, pp. 226—233; Vol. II, pp. 41—45.

potentials, leaving μ for the moment undetermined,

$$(1) \qquad W_1 = -\frac{1}{2\pi} \iint_S \mu \frac{\partial}{\partial \nu} \frac{1}{r} dS, \qquad W_2 = -\frac{1}{2\pi} \iint_S W_1^0 \frac{\partial}{\partial \nu} \frac{1}{r} dS, \dots,$$

$$W_n = -\frac{1}{2\pi} \iint_S W_{n-1}^0 \frac{\partial}{\partial \nu} \frac{1}{r} dS, \dots.$$

For these, we have the limiting relations

$$
\begin{aligned}
(2) \qquad
&W_1^- = \mu && + W_1^0, & &W_1^+ = -\mu && + W_1^0, \\
&W_2^- = W_1^0 && + W_2^0, & &W_2^+ = -W_1^0 && + W_2^0, \\
&W_3^- = W_2^0 && + W_3^0, & &W_3^+ = -W_2^0 && + W_3^0, \\
&\cdots\cdots\cdots\cdots\cdots && & &\cdots\cdots\cdots\cdots\cdots \\
&W_n^- = W_{n-1}^0 && + W_n^0, & &W_n^+ = -W_{n-1}^0 && + W_n^0, \\
&\cdots\cdots\cdots\cdots\cdots && & &\cdots\cdots\cdots\cdots\cdots
\end{aligned}
$$

NEUMANN proved that if S is convex and is not composed of two conical surfaces, there exists a constant k, $0 < k < 1$, such that

$$\max W_n^0 - \min W_n^0 \leqq k \left(\max W_{n-1}^0 - \min W_{n-1}^0 \right), \quad \text{all } n,$$

and it is clear that

$$\min W_{n-1}^0 \leqq \min W_n^0 \leqq \max W_n^0 \leqq \max W_{n-1}^0.$$

From these inequalities, it follows that W_n^0 approaches a constant c, uniformly, as n becomes infinite.

We may now build up a solution of the Dirichlet problem. From the first column of (2) we form the sum

$$(W_1^- - W_2^-) + (W_3^- - W_4^-) + \cdots + (W_{2n-1}^- - W_{2n}^-) = \mu - W_{2n}^0.$$

We see from this that the series

$$\sum_1^\infty (W_{2n-1}^- - W_{2n}^-)$$

converges uniformly to the limit $\mu - c$.

Now the function W_1, μ being continuous, approaches continuous limits on S from within, and when defined in terms of these limits, constitutes a continuous function in the interior region bounded by S. It is similar with the outer region. Hence $W_1^0 = \frac{1}{2}(W_1^- + W_1^+)$ is continuous on S. Hence W_2 enjoys the same properties, and so on. All the functions W_i, when defined on S in terms of their limits from within, are harmonic in R. As the series

$$\sum_1^\infty (W_{2n-1} - W_{2n}),$$

whose terms are harmonic within R, and continuous in the closed region R, is uniformly convergent on the boundary, as we have just seen, it converges uniformly in R to a function harmonic in R, by Theorem I of the last chapter. This limiting function U takes on the boundary values $\mu - c$. Thus had we started with $\mu = f$, and determined the corresponding c, we should have in

$$U_i = c + \sum_{1}^{\infty} (W_{2n-1} - W_{2n}),$$

the solution of the Dirichlet problem for R.

Similarly, we find, taking $\mu = -f$, and determining the corresponding c, that with the terms defined on S by their limits from without,

$$U_e = -c + \sum_{1}^{\infty} W_n$$

gives us the solution of the Dirichlet problem for the external region R'; with the objection, however that it is not regular at infinity if $c \neq 0$. This difficulty comes from the fact that the solution is built up of double distributions, and not from any impossibility of the problem. We may obviate it as follows. Let P_0 be any point interior to R, and let r be the distance of P from P_0. If we solve, to within an additive constant, the Dirichlet problem for R' with the same boundary values as $\frac{1}{r}$, we find a function $-C + V$, where C is certainly not 0, and V is regular at infinity. Thus

$$\frac{1}{r} + C - V$$

is harmonic in R', and, apart from the term C, regular at infinity, and vanishes on S. Hence

$$U_e = -c + \sum_{1}^{\infty} W_n + \frac{c}{C}\left[\frac{1}{r} + C - V\right]$$

is regular at infinity, and so harmonic in the entire region R', and assumes the boundary values f on S.

Thus the method of NEUMANN, when the details have been attended to, delivers a real existence theorem. The restriction to convex surfaces, however, was felt to be an artifical one, inherent rather in the method than in the problem itself, and attempts were made, with success, to extend it. Much more far reaching results were attained by POINCARÉ[1] by the *méthode de balayage*, or method of sweeping out.

Instead of building up the solution from functions which are harmonic in R and do not take on the right boundary values, POINCARÉ

---

[1] Comptes Rendus de l'Académie des Sciences de Paris, T. 104 (1887), p. 44; American Journal of Mathematics, Vol. 12 (1890); p. 211; *Théorie du Potential Newtonien*, Paris, 1899, p. 260.

builds a succession of functions which are not harmonic in R, but do take on the right boundary values, the functions becoming more and more nearly harmonic. Briefly, the process is as follows. He shows first that if the problem can be solved when the boundary values are those of any polynomial in x, y, z, it can be solved for the boundary values of any function continuous in R.

The problem is then to solve the Dirichlet problem for the boundary values of a polynomial f. This polynomial is, in R, the potential of a distribution of density

$$\varkappa = - \frac{\nabla^2 f}{4\pi}$$

in R, plus certain surface potentials. An infinite succession of spheres is then formed, so that every interior point of R is interior to some sphere of the set. In the first sphere, f is replaced by the harmonic function with the same boundary values on the sphere, a thing which is possible because the solution of the Dirichlet problem for spheres is known. Call the function, thus defined in the first sphere, but equal to f elsewhere in R, W_1. W_1 is then replaced in the second sphere by the harmonic function with the same boundary values as W_1 on the sphere, and the new function, elsewhere equal to W_1, is called W_2. The process is called sweeping out, because in each sphere after such a process, the Laplacian becomes 0, so that there are no masses in the sphere. But the sweeping out may sweep masses into an intersecting sphere already clean. Accordingly, after the second sphere is swept out, the first is swept again, and so on, in the order $1, 2, 1, 2, 3, 1, 2, 3, 4, 1, 2, 3, 4, 5, \ldots$, so that each sphere is swept infinitely often. It is shown that the process gradually sweeps the masses toward the boundary, and that the sequence

$$W_1, \ W_2, \ W_3, \ \ldots,$$

always keeping the right boundary values, converges to a function which is harmonic within R. This is the idea of the method. We need not give further detail, for we shall revert to it again (p. 322).

The success of POINCARÉ was soon followed by other treatments of the problem, establishing even more general results. POINCARÉ showed that the Dirichlet problem was solvable for any region, such that for every point p of the boundary, there was a sphere through p containing no interior points of the region. In 1898 HILBERT reestablished the method of reasoning used by THOMSON and DIRICHLET; and the resulting type of argument has since been most useful, as it is applicable to a great variety of problems[1].

---

[1] This method of the calculus of variations was successfully employed by LEBESGUE in two dimensions to establish the possibility of solving the Dirichlet problem under very general conditions, *Sur le problème de Dirichlet*, Rendiconti

So far, it was generally believed that the Dirichlet problem was solvable for any region, and that limitations of generality were inherent in methods, rather than in the problem itself. It was ZAREMBA[1] who first pointed out that there were regions for which the problem was not possible. Suppose, for instance, that R consists of the domain interior to the unit sphere about O, with the point O alone excepted, plus the boundary of this domain, *i. e.* the surface of the sphere and the point O. If we assign to the surface of the sphere the boundary values 0, and to the point O the value 1, the Dirichlet problem is not solvable. For if there were a solution, it would have at O an isolated singularity in whose neighborhood it was bounded. That is, the singularity would be removable. After its removal the resulting function would be harmonic throughout the interior of the sphere, assuming continuously the boundary values 0. Such a function we know to be identically 0. Thus a function which fulfills the conditions imposed cannot exist.

In 1913, LEBESGUE gave an example of a still more striking case of the impossibility of the Dirichlet problem (see Exercise 10, p. 334). Suppose we take a sphere with a deformable surface, and at one of its points push in a very sharp spine. The region R, consisting of the points of the sphere thus deformed is one for which the Dirichlet problem is not always solvable, if the spine is sharp enough. We can see this in an intuitive way by thinking of the region as a heat conducting body. Let the portion of the surface near and including the spine be kept cold, at the temperature 0^0, and let the rest of the surface be kept warm, say at 100^0. Thermal equilibrium may be possible, but the temperatures from within will not approach 0 continuously at the point of the spine. There simply is insufficient surface in the neighborhood of the point to absorb heat fast enough to keep the temperatures near 0^0 at this point. These considerations can be made rigorous, and we have an exceptional point, by no means isolated, at which there is trouble for the Dirichlet problem. Recent investigations have been connected with the nature and possible distribution of these exceptional points.

The method of which we shall now give an account in detail is due to FREDHOLM[2], and is the method of integral equations. It is less general

---

del Circolo Matematico di Palermo. T. 24, 1907, pp. 371—402. See also ZAREMBA, *Atti del 4 Congresso Internazionale dei Mathematici* (1909), Vol. II, pp. 194—199; Bulletin de l'Académie des Sciences de Cracovie (1909), pp. 197—264; Acta Mathematica, Vol. XXXIV (1911), pp. 293—316; COURANT, *Über die Existenztheoreme der Potential- und Funktionentheorie*, Journal für reine und angewandte Mathematik, Bd. 144 (1914), pp. 190—211; COURANT has in a number of articles shown the great power of the method. See COURANT und HILBERT, *Die Methoden der mathematischen Physik*, Berlin, 1924.

[1] L. c. Acta Mathematica, p. 310.

[2] Öfversigt af Kongl. Svenska Vetenskaps-Akademiens Förhandlingar, Vol. 57 (1900), pp. 39—46.

than a number of other methods, but it has the great advantage of being able to deliver a number of existence theorems at the same time. Later we consider a more general method for the Dirichlet problem.

2. Formulation of the Dirichlet and Neumann Problems in Terms of Integral Equations.

Let R denote a finite region bounded by a surface S, subject to the condition that for any of its points p, there is a neighborhood, the portion of S within which, when referred to coördinate axes in which the (x, y)-plane is tangent to S at p, has a representation $z = f(x, y)$, this function having partial derivatives of the first two orders which are continuous. It is easily verified that the results of Chapter VI on the discontinuities of distributions on S hold at all points of S, when the appropriate conditions on density or moment are fulfilled.

We consider first the potential of a double distribution on S, which we write in the form

$$W(P) = \frac{1}{2\pi} \iint\limits_S \mu \frac{\partial}{\partial \nu} \frac{1}{r} \, dS.$$

This function is harmonic in the interior of R. If it is to solve the Dirichlet problem for the continuous boundary values $F(p)$ — we shall find it convenient to characterize points of the boundary of a region by small letters — we must have

$$W_-(p) = F(p) = -\mu(p) + \frac{1}{2\pi} \iint\limits_S \mu(q) \frac{\partial}{\partial \nu} \frac{1}{r} \, dS.$$

The double distribution is also harmonic in the infinite region R' bounded by S, and so regular at infinity. If it is to give the solution of the Dirichlet problem for R', we must have

$$W_+(p) = F(p) = +\mu(p) + \frac{1}{2\pi} \iint\limits_S \mu(q) \frac{\partial}{\partial \nu} \frac{1}{r} \, dS.$$

The two equations can be written as one, if we introduce a parameter:

(3) $$f(p) = \varphi(p) - \lambda \iint\limits_S \varphi(q) K(p, q) \, dS,$$

where

$$\varphi(p) = \mu(p), \qquad K(p, q) = \frac{1}{2\pi} \frac{\partial}{\partial \nu} \frac{1}{r}.$$

For $\lambda = 1$, $f(p) = -F(p)$, this equation reduces to the condition that W is the solution of the Dirichlet problem for the interior region R. For $\lambda = -1$, $f(p) = F(p)$, it reduces to the condition that W is the solution of the Dirichlet problem for the infinite region R'.

In the equation (1), the functions $f(p)$ and $K(p, q)$ are known. The function to be determined, $\varphi(p)$, occurs under the sign of a definite integral. It may seem, therefore, as if the individuality of $\varphi(p)$ were destroyed by the integration process, and as if the equation therefore could not be solved for φ(p). However, FREDHOLM noticed that the equation was the limiting form of a set of n linear algebraic equations in n unknowns, and this observation enabled him to solve it completely.

The equation (3) is called, following HILBERT, an *integral equation*. The function $K(p, q)$ is called the *kernel* of the integral equation.

To solve the Neumann problem for R and R', we use a simple distribution

$$V(P) = \frac{1}{2\pi} \iint\limits_S \sigma \frac{1}{r}\, dS.$$

We have seen that on the hypothesis that σ satisfies a uniform Hölder condition, V has continuous derivatives in the closed regions R and R', and that the limits of the normal derivatives are given by

$$\frac{\partial V}{\partial n_-} = \sigma(p) + \frac{1}{2\pi} \iint\limits_S \sigma(q) \frac{\partial}{\partial n} \frac{1}{r}\, dS, \quad \frac{\partial V}{\partial n_+} = -\sigma(p) + \frac{1}{2\pi} \iint\limits_S \sigma(q) \frac{\partial}{\partial n} \frac{1}{r}\, dS.$$

We have here integral equations of the same type as (3). For the double distribution, the kernel is $\frac{1}{2\pi}$ times the reciprocal of the distance $PQ = r$, first differentiated in the direction of the normal at the boundary point q, and then with P replaced by p. For the simple distribution, the kernel is $\frac{1}{2\pi}$ times the derivative of $\frac{1}{r}$ in the direction of the normal at p, with Q replaced by q. It is therefore simply the kernel $K(p, q)$ with arguments interchanged, that is it is $K(q, p)$. Hence, if we write

(4) $$f(p) = \psi(p) - \lambda \iint\limits_S \psi(q)\, K(q, p)\, dS,$$

a solution of this equation would give, for $\lambda = -1$, and $f(p)$ equal to the assigned values of the normal derivative, the solution of the Neumann problem for R. For $\lambda = 1$, and $f(p)$ equal to the negative of the assigned values for the normal derivative, it would give the solution of the Neumann problem for R'.

Thus two fundamental existence theorems are reduced to the solution of the two *associated integral equations* (3) and (4), this being the term applied to pairs of integral equations when the kernel of one is obtained from that of the other by the interchange of the arguments.

3. Solution of the Integral Equations for Small Values of the Parameter.

We shall first consider integral equations of the forms (3) and (4) in which $f(p)$ and $K(p, q)$ are continuous functions of the coördinates of p and q for all positions of these points on S. It will be seen that all that is said will hold for other regions of definition of these functions, for instance a linear interval, a region of the plane, or of space. Only, q is always to have the same region as p. In order to emphasize the independence of the theory of dimensions, and also in the interests of simplicity, we shall write a single integral sign, and replace dS by dq, q being the point whose coördinates are the variables of integration. Thus the equations to be studied become

(3) $$f(p) = \varphi(p) - \lambda \int \varphi(q) K(p, q) \, dq,$$

(4) $$f(p) = \psi(p) - \lambda \int \psi(q) K(q, p) \, dq,$$

We begin with the equation (3) and seek a solution by a method of successive approximations. We take any continuous function $\varphi_0(q)$, substitute it for $\varphi(q)$ under the integral sign, and solve for $\varphi(p)$, calling the resulting first approximation $\varphi_1(p)$:

$$\varphi_1(p) = f(p) + \lambda \int \varphi_0(q) K(p, q) \, dq.$$

From $\varphi_1(p)$ we determine similarly a second approximation

$$\varphi_2(p) = f(p) + \lambda \int \varphi_1(q) K(p, q) \, dq,$$

and so on. If we wish to express $\varphi_2(p)$ and later approximations in terms of $\varphi_0(p)$, we must, in order to avoid confusion, introduce a new variable point of integration, r, say, and write

$$\varphi_1(q) = f(q) + \lambda \int \varphi_0(r) K(q, r) \, dr.$$

Substituting this in the expression for the second approximation, we find

$$\varphi_2(p) = f(p) + \lambda \int f(q) K(p, q) \, dq$$
$$+ \lambda^2 \iint \varphi_0(r) K(q, r) K(p, q) \, dr \, dq.$$

Before going further, we remark that this sort of change in the notation for variables of integration will be met with repeatedly, and is inevitable. The reader should accustom himself to it promptly. We shall also find it convenient to introduce at once the *iterated kernels*:

(5) $$K_n(p, q) = \int K_{n-1}(p, r) K(r, q) \, dr, \qquad K_0(p, q) = K(p, q).$$

In terms of these, one finds at once for the nth approximation,

$$\varphi_n(p) = f(p) + \lambda \int f(q) K(p, q) \, dq + \lambda^2 \int f(q) K_1(p, q) \, dq + \cdots$$
$$+ \lambda^{n-1} \int f(q) K_{n-2}(p, q) \, dq + \lambda^n \int \varphi_0(q) K_{n-1}(p, q) \, dq.$$

It is now easy to show that this approximation converges, for small $|\lambda|$, to a solution of (3), as n becomes infinite. In fact, if K denotes the product of the maximum of $|K(p, q)|$ by the content (length, area, or volume) of S, and if L denotes the maximum of $|f(p)|$, the series

(6)
$$\varphi(p) = f(p) + \lambda \int f(q) K(p, q) dq + \cdots$$
$$+ \lambda^n \int f(q) K_{n-1}(p, q) dq + \cdots$$

is dominated by

$$L + L(\lambda K) + \cdots + L(\lambda K)^n + \cdots,$$

and so is absolutely and uniformly convergent as to p and λ for $|\lambda| \leq \lambda_1$, where $\lambda_1 K < 1$. That it satisfies the equation (3) may be verified by direct substitution.

Exercises.

1. Show that
$$K_n(p, q) = \int K(p, r) K_{n-1}(r, q) dr.$$

2. Solve the integral equation
$$f(s) = \varphi(s) - \lambda \int_0^1 \varphi(t) K(s, t) dt,$$

where
a) $K(s, t) = 1$, b) $K(s, t) = st$, c) $K(s, t) = s - t$.

Answers,

b) $\varphi(s) = f(s) + \dfrac{3}{3 - \lambda} s \displaystyle\int_0^1 f(t) t \, dt,$

c) $\varphi(s) = f(s) + \dfrac{12\lambda}{12 + \lambda^2} \displaystyle\int_0^1 f(t) \left\{ (s - t) - \lambda \left[st - \dfrac{1}{2}(s + t) + \dfrac{1}{3} \right] \right\} dt.$

4. The Resolvent.

The solution (6) can evidently be put into the form

$$\varphi(p) = f(p) + \lambda \int f(q) R(p, q; \lambda) dq,$$

where the function

(7)
$$R(p, q; \lambda) = K(p, q) + \lambda K_1(p, q) + \lambda^2 K_2(p, q) + \cdots$$

is the *resolvent* for the kernel $K(p, q)$. If the equation (7) is solved for $K(p, q)$, we have at once two fundamental equations for the resolvent:

(8)
$$K(p, q) = R(p, q; \lambda) - \lambda \int R(p, r; \lambda) K(r, q) dr,$$

(9)
$$K(p, q) = R(p, q; \lambda) - \lambda \int R(r, q; \lambda) K(p, r) dr.$$

These equations contain implicitly the key to the whole theory of the integral equations (3) and (4). We illustrate this statement by showing that for $|\lambda| \leq \lambda_1$, the equation (3) has but one continuous solution. Suppose, in fact, that $\varphi(p)$ is a continuous solution of (3). We replace, in this equation, p by r, multiply by $R(p, r; \lambda)$, and integrate with respect to r. We have, then, by (8),

$$\int f(r) R(p, r; \lambda) dr = \int \varphi(r) R(p, r; \lambda) dr$$
$$+ \int \varphi(q) K(p, q) dq - \int \varphi(q) R(p, q; \lambda) dq.$$

The first and last terms on the right cancel, and if we employ the resulting equation to eliminate from (3) the integral containing $\varphi(q)$, we have

$$(10) \qquad \varphi(p) = f(p) + \lambda \int f(q) R(p, q; \lambda) dq$$

as a necessary consequence of (3). The solution must therefore have this form, and so is uniquely determined. We have seen that this is a solution, but it may also be verified by substitution and use of the identity (9).

In the same way, we show that the equation (4) has one and but one continuous solution, namely

$$(11) \qquad \psi(p) = f(p) + \lambda \int f(q) R(q, p; \lambda) dq.$$

5. The Quotient Form for the Resolvent.

If we should now attempt to solve the Dirichlet problem by the above methods, we should find the same difficulty which limited the success of NEUMANN's attack, namely in the proof that the various series converge for $\lambda = 1$ or -1. FREDHOLM's great contribution consisted in large measure in the representation of the resolvent as the quotient of two always convergent power series in λ. This, it will be observed, is the case in Exercise 2 (p. 289), where the resolvent is the quotient of two polynomials.

FREDHOLM was led to this result by a consideration of a system of linear algebraic equations of which (3) is a limiting form. Although valuable as giving an insight into the nature of integral equations, we shall not take the space to develop this phase of the problem, but refer for it to works on integral equations[1]. The results are as follows. With the abridged notation

$$(12) \quad K\begin{pmatrix} p_1, p_2, \ldots, p_n \\ q_1, q_2, \ldots, q_n \end{pmatrix} = \begin{vmatrix} K(p_1, q_1), & K(p_1, q_2), & \ldots, & K(p_1, q_n) \\ K(p_2, q_1), & K(p_2, q_2), & \ldots, & K(p_2, q_n) \\ \cdot \cdot \cdot \cdot \cdot \cdot \cdot \cdot \cdot \cdot \cdot \cdot \cdot \cdot \cdot \cdot \\ K(p_n, q_1), & K(p_n, q_2), & \ldots, & K(p_n, q_n) \end{vmatrix},$$

---

[1] See, for instance, BÔCHER, *An Introduction to the Study of Integral Equations*, Cambridge Tracts, 1909, § 7; RIEMANN-WEBER, *Die Differential- und Integralgleichungen der mathematischen Physik*, Braunschweig, 1925, Vol. I, Chapter XII.

we form the two series

$$\delta(\lambda) = 1 - \delta_1 \lambda + \delta_2 \lambda^2 - \delta_3 \lambda^3 + \cdots,$$

(13)

$$\delta_n = \frac{1}{n!} \iint \cdots \int K \begin{pmatrix} r_1, r_2, \ldots, r_n \\ r_1, r_2, \ldots, r_n \end{pmatrix} dr_1 dr_2 \ldots dr_n;$$

$$N(p, q; \lambda) = K(p, q) - N_1(p, q) \lambda + N_2(p, q) \lambda^2 - \cdots,$$

(14)

$$N_n(p, q) = \frac{1}{n!} \iint \cdots \int K \begin{pmatrix} p, r_1, r_2, \ldots, r_n \\ q, r_1, r_2, \ldots, r_n \end{pmatrix} dr_1 dr_2 \cdots dr_n.$$

That these series are convergent for all values of λ follows from a theorem of HADAMARD[1] to the effect that the absolute value of a determinant of order n whose elements do not exceed K in absolute value is not greater than $K^n n^{n/2}$.

It is not difficult, though perhaps a little tedious, to verify that

$$(15) \qquad R(p, q; \lambda) = \frac{N(p, q; \lambda)}{\delta(\lambda)}$$

is the desired expression for the resolvent as the quotient of two always convergent power series. One substitutes this value of $R(p, q; \lambda)$ in the equation (7), multiplies by $\delta(\lambda)$, and compares the coefficients of the powers of λ.

Exercises.

1. Give the details of the proof of the convergence of the series (13) and (14), and verify the equation (15).

2. Show that if $K(p, q)$ is the sum of n products, each a function of p alone times a function of q alone, the series (13) and (14) become finite sums. Note that this is the case in Exercise 2, page 289.

In terms of the new functions, the identities (8) and (9) become

$$(16) \qquad \delta(\lambda) K(p, q) = N(p, q; \lambda) - \lambda \int N(p, r; \lambda) K(r, q) dr,$$

$$(17) \qquad \delta(\lambda) K(p, q) = N(p, q; \lambda) - \lambda \int N(r, q; \lambda) K(p, r) dr.$$

At first, we know that these equations are valid for all $|\lambda| \leq \lambda_1$. But they are equations between always convergent power series, and the fact they hold for all sufficiently small $|\lambda|$ guarantees that they hold for all λ.

If λ is not a root of the equation $\delta(\lambda) = 0$, the equations (16) and (17) may be divided by $\delta(\lambda)$, and then reduce to (8) and (9). These equations may then be used to solve the integral equations (3) and (4) just as before. We have therefore the result: *the equations (3) and (4), if λ is not a root of $\delta(\lambda) = 0$, have one and only one continuous solution each. These are given by the equations (10) and (11), respectively.*

---

[1] Bulletin des sciences mathématiques et astronomiques, 2nd ser., Vol. XVII (1923), p. 240. BÔCHER, l. c. § 8.

6. Linear Dependence; Orthogonal and Biorthogonal Sets of Functions.

The case in which λ is a root of $\delta(\lambda) = 0$ is of prime importance for our applications. We devote this section to a preparation for the study of this case.

Given a set of n functions, $\varphi_1(p), \dot{\varphi}_2(p), \ldots, \varphi_n(p)$, with a common region S of definition, we say that these functions are *linearly dependent* in S if there exist n constants, $c_1, c_2, \ldots, c_n$, not all 0, such that

$$c_1 \varphi_1(p) + c_2 \varphi_2(p) + \cdots + c_n \varphi_n(p) = 0$$

at all points of S. They are *linearly independent* if this is not the case. They are orthogonal on S if

$$\int \varphi_i(p) \varphi_j(p) \, dp = 0, \quad i \neq j, \ i,j = 1, 2, \ldots, n.$$

Exercises.

1. Show that

a) if one of the functions of a set is identically 0, the functions are linearly dependent,

b) if to a set of functions which are linearly dependent a new function is added, the functions of the augmented set are linearly dependent,

c) at least one function of a linearly dependent set can be expressed as a linear homogeneous combination of the others, with constant coefficients.

2. Show that a necessary and sufficient condition for the linear dependence of a set of continuous functions is the vanishing of the determinant of GRAM:

$$|\varphi_{ij}| = \left| \int \varphi_i(p) \varphi_j(p) \, dp \right|.$$

The function $\varphi(p)$ is said to be *normalized* on S if

$$\int \varphi^2(p) \, dp = 1.$$

Any continuous function except 0 can be normalized by dividing it by a proper constant, not 0.

Exercise.

3. Show that the functions of any normalized orthogonal set are independent.

Two sets of functions are said to be *linearly equivalent* if any function of either set is a linear homogeneous combination of the functions of the other set, with constant coefficients. In using the terms defined above, we may omit the word *linearly* if danger of misunderstanding is precluded, as it will be in the following.

A set consisting of two rows of n functions each,

$$\varphi_1(p), \ \varphi_2(p), \ldots, \varphi_n(p),$$
$$\psi_1(p), \ \psi_2(p), \ldots, \psi_n(p),$$

is called a *biorthogonal* set, if

$$\int \varphi_i(p) \psi_j(p) \, dp = 0, \quad i \neq j, \ i,j = 1, 2, \ldots, n.$$

If, in addition, this integral is 1 when $i = j$, for all j, the set is called a *normalized* biorthogonal set.

Exercise.

4. Show that in a normalized biorthogonal set, the functions of either row are independent.

Given two sets of n functions each,

$$[\varphi_i]: \quad \varphi_1, \varphi_2, \ldots, \varphi_n,$$
$$[\psi_i]: \quad \psi_1, \psi_2, \ldots, \psi_n,$$

such that no homogeneous linear combination of the φ_i, with constant coefficients not all 0, is orthogonal to all the ψ_i, it is possible to find a set $[\Phi_i]$ equivalent to $[\varphi_i]$, and a set $[\Psi_i]$ equivalent to $[\psi_i]$, such that

$$[\Phi_i]: \quad \Phi_1, \Phi_2, \ldots, \Phi_n,$$
$$[\Psi_i]: \quad \Psi_1, \Psi_2, \ldots, \Psi_n,$$

is a normalized biorthogonal set.

We remark first that if a function is orthogonal to all the functions of a set, it is orthogonal to all the functions of any equivalent set.

By hypothesis, φ_1 is not orthogonal to all the ψ_i. Let these functions be permuted, if necessary, and the notations interchanged, so that φ_1 is not orthogonal to ψ_1. We then choose $\Phi_1 = \varphi_1$, and $\Psi_1 = \psi_1$.

We next write $\Phi_2 = \varphi_2 - c\Phi_1$, and choose c so that this function is orthogonal to Ψ_1. This is possible, because the equation determining c is

$$\int \varphi_2 \Psi_1 \, dp - c \int \Phi_1 \Psi_1 \, dp = 0,$$

and the coefficient of c is not 0. Then Φ_2, a linear combination of the φ_i, is orthogonal to ψ_1, and therefore, by hypothesis, not to all the remaining ψ_i. Let the ordering and notation be chosen so that Φ_2 is not orthogonal to ψ_2. We then write $\Psi_2 = \psi_2 - c'\Psi_1$, choosing c' so that Ψ_2 is orthogonal to Φ_1. Then the set Φ_1, Φ_2, is equivalent to the set φ_1, φ_2, for $\Phi_1 = \varphi_1$, $\Phi_2 = \varphi_2 - c\varphi_1$, and $\varphi_1 = \Phi_1$, $\varphi_2 = \Phi_2 + c\Phi_1$. Similarly, the set Ψ_1, Ψ_2, is equivalent to ψ_1, ψ_2. Moreover,

$$\int \Phi_1 \Psi_1 \, dp \neq 0, \quad \int \Phi_2 \Psi_2 \, dp = \int \Phi_2 \psi_2 \, dp \neq 0.$$

Continuing in this way, we form a biorthogonal set of n pairs of functions, in which no Φ_i is orthogonal to its companion Ψ_i. If then each Ψ_i be divided by the non-vanishing number

$$\int \Phi_i(p) \Psi_i(p) \, dp,$$

the set becomes a normalized biorthogonal set.

It will be remarked that in a normalized biorthogonal set, the order of the pairs is unessential. The pairing, however, is essential.

Exercises.

5. Complete the above proof by an argument from k to $k + 1$.

6. Show as a corollary to the theorem that any set of n independent functions is equivalent to a normalized orthogonal set.

7. The Homogeneous Integral Equations.

If λ_0 is a root of $\delta(\lambda) = 0$, the associated homogeneous integral equations, obtained from (3) and (4) by setting $f(p) = 0$,

$$(18) \qquad \varphi(p) = \lambda_0 \int \varphi(q) K(p, q) \, dq \, ,$$

$$(19) \qquad \psi(p) = \lambda_0 \int \psi(q) K(q, p) \, dq \, ,$$

have solutions. In fact, the equation (17) shows that for any fixed q, $N(p, q; \lambda_0)$ is a solution of (18), and (16) shows that for any fixed q, $N(q, p; \lambda_0)$ is a solution of (19).

However, 0 is a solution of any homogeneous equation, and for most purposes, a valueless solution. By a solution of a homogeneous equation is usually meant one which does not vanish identically. We do not know that the above solutions are different from 0. But it is still true that these equations have non-trivial solutions. To see this, we note that from the equations (13) and (14), it follows that

$$\int N(r, r; \lambda) \, dr = -\frac{d}{d\lambda} \delta(\lambda) \, .$$

Hence, if λ_0 is a root of order n of $\delta(\lambda)$, so that the nth derivative of $\delta(\lambda)$ is not 0 for $\lambda = \lambda_0$, $N(p, q; \lambda)$ cannot contain $(\lambda - \lambda_0)^n$ as a factor for all p and q. Accordingly, *every zero of $\delta(\lambda)$ is a pole of the resolvent $R(p, q; \lambda)$*. The poles of $R(p, q; \lambda)$ are called the *characteristics*, or *characteristic numbers* of the kernel.

In a neighborhood of such a pole λ_0, $R(p, q; \lambda)$ has a development

$$(20) \qquad R(p, q; \lambda) = \frac{A_m(p, q)}{(\lambda - \lambda_0)^m} + \frac{A_{m-1}(p, q)}{(\lambda - \lambda_0)^{m-1}} + \cdots$$
$$+ \frac{A_1(p, q)}{\lambda - \lambda_0} + B(p, q; \lambda),$$

where $m \leq n$, the coefficients $A_i(p, q)$ being continuous, $A_m(p, q)$ not identically 0, and $B(p, q; \lambda)$ being a power series in $\lambda - \lambda_0$, uniformly convergent in a neighborhood of λ_0, with coefficients which are continuous in p and q. It is readily verified that $A_m(p, q)$ and $A_m(q, p)$ are, for any fixed q for which these functions are not identically 0 in p, non-trivial solutions of the equations (18) and (19), respectively.

Since the solutions we have found for the homogeneous equations depend upon a parameter point q, which may be chosen in infinitely many ways, it might appear that these equations have infinitely many solutions. *There are, however, only a finite number of linearly independent real continuous solutions for any real characteristic number.* The kernel is assumed to be real, here, and throughout the chapter.

To show this, let $\varphi_1, \varphi_2, \ldots, \varphi_n$ denote a set of real, continuous, independent solutions of the equation (18). Clearly, any equivalent set of functions are solutions, and so by Exercise 6 of the last section, we may assume the given set to be a normalized orthogonal one. Now

$$\int [\lambda_0 K(p,r) - \varphi_1(p)\varphi_1(r) - \varphi_2(p)\varphi_2(r) - \cdots - \varphi_n(p)\varphi_n(r)]^2 dr \geqq 0.$$

Expanding the square, carrying out the integration, and keeping in mind the hypothesis on the solutions, we have

$$\lambda_0^2 \int K^2(p,r)\,dr - 2\sum_1^n \varphi_i(p)\lambda_0 \int \varphi_i(r)K(p,r)\,dr + \sum_1^n \varphi_i^2(p)$$

$$= \lambda_0^2 \int K^2(p,r)\,dr - \sum_1^n \varphi_i^2(p) \geqq 0.$$

Integrating the last inequality with respect to p, we obtain

$$n \leqq \lambda_0^2 \iint K^2(p,r)\,dr\,dp.$$

Hence the number of linearly independent real continuous solutions of (18) is limited, as asserted. It is the same with the solutions of (19).

If a characteristic is real, the real and imaginary parts of a complex solution are solutions of the homogeneous equation, and it follows at once that the number of independent complex solutions is bounded.

If λ_0 is not a pole of the resolvent, the homogeneous equations (18) *and* (19) *have no non-trivial solutions.* This is seen by putting $f(p) = 0$ in the unique solutions (10) and (11).

Relationships between the Solutions of the Associated Homogeneous Equations. We show first that *any solution of one of the homogeneous equations for a characteristic λ_i, is orthogonal to any solution of the associated homogeneous equation for a different characteristic λ_j.* Suppose

$$\varphi(p) = \lambda_i \int \varphi(q) K(p,q)\,dq,$$

$$\psi(p) = \lambda_j \int \psi(q) K(q,p)\,dq.$$

If these equations be multiplied by $\psi(p)$ and $\varphi(p)$, respectively, and integrated with respect to p, the resulting integrals on the right will be equal. Accordingly

$$\left(\frac{1}{\lambda_i} - \frac{1}{\lambda_j}\right)\int \psi(p)\varphi(p)\,dp = 0,$$

division by the characteristics being justified since 0 is never a characteristic ($\delta(0) = 1$). As $\lambda_i \neq \lambda_j$, $\varphi(p)$ and $\psi(p)$ are orthogonal, as stated.

The Case of a Simple Pole. Here the relation (20) takes the form

$$(21) \qquad R(p,q;\lambda) = \frac{A(p,q)}{\lambda - \lambda_0} + B(p,q;\lambda), \qquad A(p,q) \not\equiv 0.$$

If this expression for the resolvent be substituted in the equations (8) and (9), we find by comparing the coefficients of $(\lambda - \lambda_0)^{-1}$ and the terms free from $\lambda - \lambda_0$, the equations

$$(22) \qquad A(p,q) = \lambda_0 \int A(p,r) K(r,q) dr,$$

$$(23) \qquad A(p,q) = \lambda_0 \int A(r,q) K(p,r) dr,$$

$$(24) \qquad K(p,q) = B(p,q;\lambda_0) - \int A(p,r) K(r,q) dr \\ - \lambda_0 \int B(p,r;\lambda_0) K(r,q) dr,$$

$$(25) \qquad K(p,q) = B(p,q;\lambda_0) - \int A(r,q) K(p,r) dr \\ - \lambda_0 \int B(r,q;\lambda_0) K(p,r) dr.$$

As already remarked, and as now shown by equation (23), $A(p,q)$ is, for any fixed q, a solution of (18). But that equation has only a finite number of real independent solutions, so that if $\varphi_1(p), \varphi_2(p), \ldots, \varphi_n(p)$ denotes a set of independent solutions in terms of which any solution can be expressed, $A(p,q)$ must be a linear homogeneous combination of these functions with coefficients independent of p, and so, functions of q:

$$(26) \quad A(p,q) = \varphi_1(p) \psi_1(q) + \varphi_2(p) \psi_2(q) + \cdots + \varphi_n(p) \psi_n(q).$$

That the functions $\psi_i(q)$ are continuous can be seen by assigning to p n suitable values and solving the resulting equations for the $\psi_i(q)$. The selection of the values $p_1, p_2, \ldots, p_n$ can be made so that the determinant involved is not 0, otherwise the $\varphi_i(p)$ could be shown to be dependent. The functions $\psi_i(q)$ then appear as linear homogeneous functions of the continuous functions $A(p_1,q), A(p_2,q), \ldots, A(p_n,q)$, and so are continuous.

Now let $\varphi(p)$ be any continuous solution of (18). Inserting in this equation the expression (24) for $K(p,q)$, and simplifying the result by (18) and (22), we find

$$(27) \qquad \varphi(p) = - \int \varphi(q) A(p,q) dq = \sum_1^n c_i \varphi_i(p), \\ c_i = - \int \varphi(q) \psi_i(q) dq.$$

Thus we verify what we already know, that any solution of (18) can be expressed in terms of the functions $\varphi_i(p)$. But a similar process involving the equations (19), (25) and (23) shows that *any solution of (19) is a homogeneous linear combination with constant coefficients of the functions $\psi_i(q)$ occurring in the expression (26) for $A(p,q)$.*

Let us now identify $\varphi(p)$ in the equation (27) with $\varphi_j(p)$. Since the $\varphi_i(p)$ are independent, this means that $c_j = 1$, and $c_i = 0$ for $i \neq j$. We have, accordingly

$$\int \varphi_j(q) \left[-\psi_i(q) \right] dq = \begin{cases} 0, & i \neq j, \\ 1, & i = j, \end{cases}$$

so that *the functions $\varphi_i(p)$ and the functions $-\psi_i(q)$ occurring in the expression (26) for the residue $A(p, q)$ at the pole λ_0 form a normalized biorthogonal set.* It follows from Exercise 4, page 293, that the functions $\psi_i(q)$ as well as the $\varphi_i(p)$ form independent sets. Thus, *in the case of a simple pole, the two associated homogeneous equations (18) and (19) have the same number of linearly independent solutions. These can be so chosen as to form a normalized biorthogonal set.*

Poles of Higher Order. These do not occur in the applications which we shall make. In order to establish the fact, however, we shall have need of one result. If the expression (20) for $R(p, q; \lambda)$ is substituted in the equation (8), and coefficients of powers of $\lambda - \lambda_0$ compared, as before, we find

$$A_m(p, q) = \lambda_0 \int A_m(p, r) K(r, q) \, dr,$$

$$A_{m-1}(p, q) = \int A_m(p, r) K(r, q) \, dr + \lambda_0 \int A_{m-1}(p, r) K(r, q) \, dr.$$

From these equations, we see that *if λ_0 is a pole of $R(p, q; \lambda)$, of order higher than one, the simultaneous integral equations*

$$(28) \qquad \begin{cases} \psi_1(q) = \lambda_0 \int \psi_1(r) K(r, q) \, dr, \\ \psi_2(q) = \int \psi_1(r) K(r, q) \, dr + \lambda_0 \int \psi_2(r) K(r, q) \, dr \end{cases}$$

have a continuous solution $\psi_1(q)$, $\psi_2(q)$, in which $\psi_1(q)$ (and therefore also $\psi_2(q)$) does not vanish identically.

8. The Non-homogeneous Equation; Summary of Results for Continuous Kernels.

It remains to consider the non-homogeneous equations (3) and (4) when λ is a characteristic λ_0 of the kernel. We shall suppose that it is a simple pole of the resolvent. We may confine ourselves to the equation (3), since the treatment of (4) is similar. Let us suppose first that it has a solution $\varphi(p)$. Then

$$(29) \qquad f(p) = \varphi(p) - \lambda_0 \int \varphi(q) K(p, q) \, dq.$$

The function (10) then has a pole at λ_0, unless $f(p)$ is orthogonal to $A(p, q)$. This suggests the following steps. We change p to r in (29), multiply by $A(p, r)$, and integrate with respect to r. In the resulting equation, the right hand member vanishes, by (22). Accordingly

$$\int f(r)\,A\,(p,r)\,dr = \sum_{1}^{n}\varphi_i\,(p)\int f(r)\,\psi_i\,(r)\,dr = 0\,.$$

This equation can hold only if all the integrals vanish, because of the independence of the $\varphi_i\,(p)$. Hence *a necessary condition that the non-homogeneous equation* (3) *have a solution when λ is a characteristic, is that $f\,(p)$ shall be orthogonal to all the solutions of the associated homogeneous equation for the same value of λ.*

If the equation (29), with p replaced by r, is multiplied by $B\,(p,r;\lambda_0)$ and integrated with respect to r, it is found, with the help of equations (24), (22) and (29) that when the necessary condition is fulfilled, the solution must have the form

$$\varphi\,(p) = f\,(p) + \lambda_0\int f\,(q)\,B\,(p,q;\,\lambda_0)\,dq + \sum_{1}^{n}c_i\,\varphi_i\,(p)\,.$$

Clearly the constants c_i may have any values, for they multiply solutions of the homogeneous equation, and so contribute nothing to the right hand member of (29). Conversely, it may be proved by substitution that this is a solution. *The necessary condition is therefore also sufficient.*

Summary. Hypotheses: the kernel $K\,(p,\,q)$ and the function $f\,(p)$ are real and continuous. The characteristics are real, and simple poles of the resolvent $R\,(p,\,q;\,\lambda)$.

(a) λ is not a characteristic.

The associated integral equations

(I)　　　　　　　$f\,(p) = \varphi\,(p) - \lambda\int\varphi\,(q)\,K\,(p,q)\,dq\,,$

(I')　　　　　　$f\,(p) = \psi\,(p) - \lambda\int\psi\,(q)\,K\,(q,p)\,dq\,,$

have each one and only one continuous solution, namely

$$\varphi\,(p) = f\,(p) + \lambda\int f\,(q)\,R\,(p,q;\,\lambda)\,dq\,,$$
$$\psi\,(p) = f\,(p) + \lambda\int f\,(q)\,R\,(q,p;\,\lambda)\,dq\,,$$

respectively.

The corresponding associated homogeneous integral equations

(II)　　　　　　　$\varphi\,(p) = \lambda\int\varphi\,(q)\,K\,(p,q)\,dq\,,$

(II')　　　　　　$\psi\,(p) = \lambda\int\psi\,(q)\,K\,(q,p)\,dq\,,$

have no non-trivial solutions.

(b) λ is a characteristic.

The equations (II) and (II') have the same number of linearly independent solutions. These may be so selected as to form a normalized biorthogonal set.

A necessary and sufficient condition that (I) or (I') have solutions is that $f(p)$ be orthogonal to all the solutions of the associated homogeneous equation (II') or (II). The solution is then determined, except for an additive solution of the corresponding homogeneous equation, (II) or (II').

If, the other hypotheses being maintained, $\lambda = \lambda_0$ is a pole of higher order of the resolvent, the simultaneous equations (28) have a non-trivial solution.

9. Preliminary Study of the Kernel of Potential Theory.

For the first and second fundamental existence theorems in two dimensions, the above discussion suffices, provided the region under consideration has a boundary with continuous curvature. But in three dimensions, the kernel becomes infinite when p and q tend toward coincidence. We first examine the nature and some consequences of this discontinuity, and then show how the results for continuous kernels may be extended to hold for the kernel which interests us.

Recalling the conditions imposed on the surface S in § 2, the results of Chapter VI are available. We find there, developing z in the numerator of the expression (2), page 169, in a Taylor series with remainder about the point (ξ, η), that

$$\left| \frac{\partial}{\partial \nu} \frac{1}{r} \right| \leqq \frac{M r'^2}{r^3}$$

where r' is the projection of r on the tangent plane to S at p. As this is less than r, we infer that

(30) $$|K(p, q)| \leqq \frac{M}{r}, \quad r = \overline{pq} \neq 0.$$

This result was obtained only for q in a neighborhood of p, but all the materials were given for the proof that such an inequality held uniformly over S, that is, that there is one constant a, and one constant M, such that (30) holds whenever $r \leqq a$. Also, the last restriction may be dropped. For, for $r > a$, $|K(p, q)|$ is bounded, say by B, and if we increase M, if necessary, so that

$$\frac{M}{R} \geqq B,$$

where R is the greatest chord of S, the inequality (30) will hold without restriction.

A further study of the function (2) of Chapter VI shows that $K(p, q)$ has continuous derivatives of the first order with respect to the coördinates of the projection of p or q on any fixed plane tangent to S at a point near the variable point, for $r \neq 0$. It follows that the derivative of $K(p, q)$ with respect to the distance s measured along any regular arc on S to p, or q, is continuous for r not 0. Moreover, such a derivative is subject to an inequality

$$(31) \qquad \left| \frac{\partial K(p,q)}{\partial s} \right| \leqq \frac{M}{r^2}, \qquad\qquad r \neq 0,$$

first uniformly for r less than some constant a, and then, by increasing M, if necessary, for the whole of S. It is unnecessary to distinguish between the constants M in (30) and (31). The larger will serve for both.

We now prove

Lemma I. *If $\varphi(p)$ and $\psi(p)$ are continuous on S, the integrals*

$$\varPhi(p) = \int \varphi(q) K(p,q) \, dq \quad and \quad \varPsi(p) = \int \psi(q) K(q,p) \, dq$$

satisfy a uniform Hölder condition on S. Moreover, if F is a bound for $|\varphi(p)|$ and $|\psi(p)|$, there is a constant C, independent of these functions, such that

$$|\varPhi(p)| \leqq C F, \qquad |\varPsi(p)| \leqq C F.$$

We need consider only $\varPhi(p)$. The same considerations will apply to $\varPsi(q)$. Let a be a number such that the portion of S in the sphere of radius a about any point p of S admits the representation $z = f(x, y)$ when referred to a tangent-normal system of axes at p, in which there is a bound for the absolute values of the derivatives of first and second orders, independent of the position of p.

Let p and p_0 be two points of S a distance η apart, not greater than a. We refer the portion of S within a sphere of radius a about p_0 to axes tangent and normal to S at p_0, taking the (x, z)-plane through p. Then, by (31),

$$|K(p,q) - K(p_0,q)| = \left| \int_0^x \frac{\partial K(p,q)}{\partial s} \cdot \frac{ds}{dx} \, dx \right| \leqq \max \sqrt{1 + f_x^2} \, \frac{M}{r^2} |x|$$

$$\leqq \frac{M'}{\bar{r}^2} \eta,$$

where we have differentiated along the curve γ in which the (x, z)-plane cuts S near p_0, where M' is a constant which is the same for all positions of p_0, and where $\bar{r}$ is the distance of q from the nearest point of the curve γ between p_0 and p.

Let c be less than a, and less than $\frac{1}{2\sqrt{2}}$, and let η be restricted to be not greater than c. We divide S into the part σ inside the sphere about p_0 of radius $\eta^{\frac{1}{3}}$, and the rest, $S - \sigma$. Then when q is on $S - \sigma$, $\bar{r} > \eta^{\frac{1}{3}} - \eta$, and hence, if S be used to denote the whole area of S,

$$\left| \iint_{S-\sigma} \varphi(q) \left[K(p,q) - K(p_0,q) \right] dq \right| \leqq F S M' \frac{\eta}{(\eta^{\frac{1}{3}} - \eta)^2} \leqq 4 F S M' \eta^{\frac{1}{3}},$$

since $\eta < c < \frac{1}{2}\sqrt{2}$. Also

$$\left| \int_\sigma \varphi(q) [K(p,q) - K(p_0,q)] dq \right| \leqq F \iint_\sigma \left(\frac{M}{r} + \frac{M}{r_0} \right) dS, \qquad r_0 = \overline{p_0 q},$$

where we have used the inequality (30). If we change the region of integration to the projection on the (x, y)-plane, and use the Lemma III (b) of § 2, Chapter VI (p. 149), we find that this integral is less than

$$2 M' F \int_0^{2\pi} \int_0^{\eta^{\frac{1}{3}}} dr' \, d\vartheta = 4 \pi M' F \eta^{\frac{1}{3}}.$$

Thus the integral giving $|\Phi(p) - \Phi(p_0)|$ is composed of two parts, each less in absolute value than a uniform constant times $\eta^{\frac{1}{3}}$. If A is the sum of these constants, we have, writing r in place of η,

$$|\Phi(p) - \Phi(p_0)| \leqq A r^{\frac{1}{3}}, \quad \text{for} \quad \overline{p p_0} = r \leqq c.$$

Thus the existence of the uniform Hölder condition is established.

For the second part of the lemma, we have

$$|\Phi(p)| \leqq F M \int \frac{dq}{r} = F M \left[\iint_{S-\sigma} \frac{dS}{r} + \iint_\sigma \frac{dS}{r} \right]$$

where σ denotes the portion of S in a sphere of radius a about p. The first integral on the right is not more than $\frac{S}{a}$, and the second is not greater than a uniform constant times a, as is seen by integrating over the projection on the tangent plane at p. If C be the sum of these two bounds for the integrals, multiplied by M, we have

$$|\Phi(p)| \leqq C F,$$

where C is independent of p and of the function $\varphi(p)$.

Lemma II. *The iterated kernel $K_2(p, q)$ is continuous.*

We first consider $K_1(p, q)$, showing that it is continuous for $p \neq q$. To do this, we write it as the sum of two integrals

$$I_1 = \int_{S-\sigma_p-\sigma_q} K(p,r) K(r,q) \, dr, \quad I_2 = \int_{\sigma_p+\sigma_q} K(p,r) K(r,q) \, dr,$$

where σ_p and σ_q are the portions of S within small spheres of radius α about the points p_0 and q_0 at which the continuity is to be investigated. The method of proof follows the lines of Chapter VI. The continuity at (p_0, q_0) is established by showing that $|I_2|$ can be made arbitrarily small, independently of p and q, by taking α sufficiently small, and by showing that I_1 is continuous at $(p_0 q_0)$ for any fixed α. If, for instance $\overline{p p_0} < \frac{\alpha}{2}$ and $\overline{q q_0} < \frac{\alpha}{2}$ the integrands in I_1 are continuous in all variables, and so, therefore, is I_1.

As to I_2, if we subject α to the first restriction that it shall be less than one third the distance $\eta = p_0\, q_0$, then for r in σ_p,

$$|K(p,r)| \leq \frac{M}{\varrho}, \quad \text{and} \quad |K(r,q)| \leq \frac{M}{\eta - 2\alpha} \leq \frac{3M}{\eta},$$

by (30), ϱ being the distance pr. Similar inequalities hold when r is in σ_q. Accordingly, integrating over the projections of σ_p and σ_q on the tangent planes at p and q respectively, we have, if ϱ' is the projection of ϱ,

$$|I_2| \leq 2 \int\limits_0^{2\pi}\int\limits_0^{a} \frac{3M}{\eta} \cdot \frac{M}{\varrho'} \sec\gamma\, \varrho'\, d\varrho'\, d\vartheta \leq \frac{6M^2}{\eta} 2\pi \max \sec\gamma \cdot \alpha,$$

which shows that $|I_2|$ has the stated property. Thus $K_1(p, q)$ is continuous at (p_0, q_0), these points being distinct.

We next seek a bound for $K_1(p, q)$ when p and q are close together. We think of q as fixed, and describe a sphere about q of radius a. Let σ be the portion it cuts from S. With $\overline{pq} = \eta \leq \frac{a}{2}$, the integral

$$I_1 = \int\limits_{S-\sigma} K(p,r)\, K(r,q)\, dr$$

has an integrand less in absolute value than $\frac{4M^2}{a^2}$, and the integral is uniformly bounded. And

$$|I_2| = \left| \int\limits_\sigma K(p,r)\, K(r,q)\, dr \right| \leq M^2 \iint\limits_{\sigma'} \frac{1}{\varrho\,\varrho'} \sec\gamma\, dS',$$

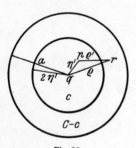

Fig. 28.

where ϱ and ϱ' are the projections on the tangent plane at q of the distances rq and pr, respectively, and the integration is over the projection σ' of σ. Thus

$$|I_2| \leq M' \iint\limits_C \frac{dS'}{\varrho\,\varrho'},$$

where $M' = M^2 \max \sec\gamma$ is a constant, independent of the positions of p, q, or r, and C is a circle of radius a about q (fig. 28). Let η' be the projection of pq. We suppose it less than $\frac{a}{2}$. We now divide the field C of integration into two parts, namely, a circle c of radius $2\eta'$ about q, and the remaining annular region $C - c$.

As to

$$\iint\limits_c \frac{dS'}{\varrho\,\varrho'},$$

it is obviously unchanged by a transformation which changes all distances in a fixed ratio, and hence, being convergent, it is equal to a fixed constant A'.

As to

$$\iint_{C-c} \frac{dS'}{\varrho \varrho'},$$

since for r in $C - c$, $\varrho \geqq 2\eta'$, $\varrho' \geqq \varrho - \eta'$, and hence $\varrho' \geqq \frac{\varrho}{2}$, this integral is not greater than

$$2 \int_0^{2\pi} \int_{2\eta'}^{a} \frac{d\varrho \, d\vartheta}{\varrho} = 4\pi \log \frac{a}{2\eta'}.$$

Hence, assembling the inequalities, we see that for $\eta' \leqq \frac{a}{2}$,

$$|K_1(p, q)| \leqq A + B \log \frac{a}{2\eta'},$$

where A and B are two constants, uniform over all of S. Since $\eta = \overline{pq}$ is less than $\frac{a}{2}$, η' will be also. And as $\eta' \geqq \eta \cos \overline{\gamma}$, $\overline{\gamma}$ being the greatest angle between the normals to σ at q and at any other point, $\log \left(\frac{a}{2\eta'} \right) \leqq \log \left(\frac{a \sec \overline{\gamma}}{2\eta} \right)$. Therefore, adopting now the usual notation r for the distance $\eta = \overline{pq}$, we have, for $r \leqq \frac{a}{2}$,

$$|K_1(p, q)| \leqq A + B \log \left(\frac{a \sec \overline{\gamma}}{2r} \right).$$

The constants may be selected so as to be independent of the positions of p and q, as long as $r \leqq \frac{a}{2}$. Then, since $|K_1(p, q)|$ is continuous, and therefore bounded for $r \geqq \frac{a}{2}$, we may select M, and increase B, if necessary, so that the inequality

$$(32) \qquad |K_1(p, q)| \leqq B \log \frac{M}{r}$$

holds uniformly on S.

This, with the continuity for p and q distinct, is the information we need about $K_1(p, q)$.

Coming now to $K_2(p, q)$, the reasoning, used to show $K_1(p, q)$ continuous when p and q are distinct, holds for $K_2(p, q)$, since the inequality (32) is stronger than (30). Hence it remains only to establish the continuity when p and q coincide, say at p_0. Let σ denote the portion of S within a sphere of radius $\alpha < \frac{a}{2}$ about p_0, and let p and q be restricted to the interior of a concentric sphere of half the radius. Then

$$I_1 = \int_{S-\sigma} K_1(p, r) K(r, q) \, dr$$

is continuous in p and q. As to the integral over σ, we have

$$|I_2| = \left|\int_\sigma K_1(p,r)\,K(r,q)\,dr\right| \leqq 2 \int_0^{2\pi}\!\!\int_0^a B \log\frac{M}{\varrho}\cdot\frac{M}{\varrho}\sec\gamma\,\varrho\,d\varrho\,d\vartheta$$

$$= 4\pi\,B\,M\sec\overline{\gamma}\left(1 + \log\frac{M}{\alpha}\right)\alpha,$$

for first,

$$\frac{M}{\varrho'}\log\frac{M}{\varrho} \leqq \frac{M}{\varrho}\log\frac{M}{\varrho} + \frac{M}{\varrho'}\log\frac{M}{\varrho'},$$

ϱ and ϱ' being the projections of $\overline{pr}$ and $\overline{rq}$, respectively, on the tangent plane at p_0, the left-hand member being dominated by the first term on the right, where $\varrho \leqq \varrho'$, and by the second where $\varrho' \leqq \varrho$. Secondly, the integral of one of these terms over a circle of fixed radius is greatest when the distance involved is measured from the center of that circle (see the proof of Lemma III, on page 148).

Thus $|I_2|$ vanishes with α, uniformly as to p and q, and the continuity of $K_2(p,q)$ at all points is established.

It will be of service later to notice that the same considerations would have applied had the kernel been replaced by its absolute value, with the understanding that $K_1(p,q)$ and $K_2(p,q)$ would then have meant the iterated kernels for the kernel $|K(p,q)|$.

Lemma III. *The order of integrations in iterated integrals over integrands containing $K(p,q)$ as a factor may be inverted* in the cases which arise in the theory of integral equations of this chapter.

Let us consider, for instance, the iterated integral

$$K_2(p,q) = \int\left[\int K(p,r)\,K(r,s)\,dr\right]K(s,q)\,ds,$$

taking first p and q distinct. It is not a question of decomposing the integral with respect to r, or the integral with respect to s, each in reality a double integral over the surface S; the problem is to show that the above integral, which is expressed as a double integral with respect to s of a double integral with respect to r, can be evaluated in the reverse order.

Now the coördinates ξ_1, η_1, ζ_1, of s, and the coördinates ξ_2, η_2, ζ_2, of r, may together be regarded as the coördinates of a point P in space of six dimensions, and if s and r be confined to S, the corresponding point P will be confined to a certain four dimensional locus, which we shall denote by V. The product $K(p,r)\,K(r,s)\,K(s,q)$ becomes infinite at certain points of V, but if these points be cut out by the subtraction of a suitable region v, the product will be continuous in $V - v$. The integral over this region of the product may be defined as the limit of a sum, that is; as a multiple (quadruple) integral, which we shall denote by $S(V-v)$. We shall show first that this multiple integral has a limit, as the content of v approaches 0, that is, that the improper multiple integral $S(V)$ is convergent. We shall then show that the above iterated integral for $K_2(p,q)$, which we denote by $I(V)$, is equal to $S(V)$. As the same reasoning will apply to the iterated integral in the reverse order, it will follow that the iterated integrals in the two orders are equal.

We cut out the singularities of the integrand by the following inequalities:

(33) $$\overline{sp} \geqq \alpha, \quad \overline{sq} \geqq \alpha, \quad \overline{rp} \geqq \alpha', \quad \overline{rs} \geqq \alpha',$$

where $\overline{sp}$, etc. denote the ordinary distances in space of three dimensions between the points s and p, etc. on S, and where $0 < \alpha < a, 0 < \alpha' < a$. Here a is such that the part of S in the sphere of radius a about any point of S is a regular surface element. Let $V-v$ denote the portion of V in which these inequalities are all satisfied. Then v denotes the portion in which at least one is not satisfied.

If σ_p and σ_q denote the portions of S in spheres of radius α about p and q, respectively, and σ_p' and σ_s' the portions in spheres of radius α' about p and s, respectively, the iterated integral

$$I(V-v) = \int_{S-\sigma_p-\sigma_q} \left[\int_{S-\sigma_p'-\sigma_s'} K(p,r) K(r,s) \, dr \right] K(s,q) \, ds$$

is equal to the multiple integral

$$S(V-v) = \iint_{V-v} K(p,r) K(r,s) K(s,q) \, dV,$$

for the regions of integration covered are the same, by (33), and the integrand is continuous[1].

Furthermore, if we distinguish by bars the corresponding integrals obtained from the above by replacing the integrand by its absolute value, we have likewise

$$\bar{I}(V-v) = \bar{S}(V-v).$$

Now $\bar{I}(V)$ exists, as follows from a remark made in connection with the proof of Lemma II. Moreover, $\bar{I}(V-v) \leqq \bar{I}(V)$, since the integrand is never negative. Hence $\bar{S}(V-v)$ is bounded, and as it never decreases as α and α' decrease, it is a simple matter to show that it has a limit as α and α' approach 0. It follows (see Lemma II, Chapter VI, page 147) that $S(V)$ is convergent. Thus the first step is complete.

---

[1] See, for instance, OSGOOD, *Advanced Calculus*, New York, 1925, p. 50.

From the convergence of $S(V)$ and the equality of $S(V-v)$ with $I(V-v)$, it follows that α and α' may be given such initial restrictions that

$$(34) \qquad |I(V-v)-S(V)| < \frac{\varepsilon}{3},$$

ε being any fixed positive quantity. Then we may further restrict α, if necessary, so that

$$(35) \qquad \left|I(V) - \int_{S-\sigma_p-\sigma_q} K_1(p,s)\,K(s,q)\,ds\right| < \frac{\varepsilon}{3},$$

for the first term on the left is the limit of the second as α approaches 0. Next, with α fixed so that these inequalities are in force, we further restrict α', if necessary, so that

$$\left|K_1(p,s) - \int_{S-\sigma'_p-\sigma'_s} K(p,r)\,K(r,s)\,dr\right| \leqq \frac{\varepsilon\alpha}{3MS},$$

where M is the constant of the inequality (30), and S the area of the surface S. If the functions on the left are multiplied by $K(s,q)$, which in $S-\sigma_p-\sigma_q$ is not greater in absolute value than $\dfrac{M}{\alpha}$, and integrated with respect to s over this region, the result is

$$(36) \qquad \left|\int_{S-\sigma_p-\sigma_q} K_1(p,s)\,K(s,q)\,ds - I(V-v)\right| < \frac{\varepsilon}{3}.$$

We conclude from (34), (35) and (36) that

$$|I(V)-S(V)| < \varepsilon.$$

But the difference on the left is independent of ε, and as ε is any positive constant, the difference must be 0. This completes the second step in the reasoning.

Thus the iterated integrals in the two orders are equal when p and q are distinct. But we have seen in connection with the previous lemma that one of them is continuous in p and q for all positions of these points, and the same reasoning applies also to the other. It follows that they are equal when p and q coincide.

It is now clear that the other iterated integrals which occur in the theory of integral equations as presented are independent of order, for they are over products containing $K(p,q)$ or iterated kernels, or continuous functions, and these only. In any case, the factors will be dominated by the inequality for $|K(p,q)|$, so that the proof still will be valid. From this, in particular, follows the extension of Lemma I:

Lemma I holds also if in the integrals there considered, any iterated kernel $K_i\,(p,\,q)$ be substituted for $K\,(p,\,q)$. This is seen by carrying out the integration with respect to the variable entering $\varphi\,(p)$ or $\psi\,(p)$ under the integral sign first, applying Lemma I, and repeating the process until all integrations have been carried out.

10. The Integral Equation with Discontinuous Kernel.

We shall now show that the results obtained with respect to the solutions of the integral equations (I), (I'), (II) and (II'), § 8 (p. 298), continue to hold for the kernel just studied. It is true that the Fredholm series for $\delta\,(\lambda)$ and $N\,(p,\,q;\,\lambda)$ no longer exist in the same form, since they involve the now meaningless symbol $K\,(p,\,p)$. However, the resolvent function still exists. Let us consider the series (7) for the resolvent, first as to the character of the terms. We see that *after the second they are all continuous functions of p and q.* How about convergence? We saw that $K_2\,(p,\,q)$ was continuous. Let K^3 denote the maximum of $|\,K_2\,(p,\,q)\,|$ and S the area of the surface S. Then

$$|\,K_5\,(p,q)\,| = |\,\textstyle\int K_2\,(p,r)\,K_2\,(r,q)\,dr\,| \leqq S\,K^6,\qquad |\,K_8\,(p,q)\,| \leqq S^2 K^9,\;\ldots$$

Thus the series consisting of every third term of (7), is dominated by the series

$$\frac{1}{|\,\lambda\,|\,S}\,[\,|\,\lambda\,|^3 K^3 S + |\,\lambda\,|^6 K^6 S^2 + |\,\lambda\,|^9 K^9 S^3 + \cdots\,],$$

which converges for $|\lambda| < \dfrac{1}{\sqrt[3]{S\,K}}$. By Lemma I, the series consisting of the 4th, 7th, 10th, $\ldots$ terms of (7) is dominated by the series whose terms are $|\lambda|\,C$ times those of the above, and the series consisting of the remaining terms of (7) is dominated by the series whose terms are $|\lambda|^2\,C^2$ times those of the above. Thus the series for the resolvent converges absolutely and uniformly for $|\lambda| \leqq \lambda_1$, if $\lambda_1 < \dfrac{1}{\sqrt[3]{S\,K}}$. *The resolvent is equal to $K\,(p,\,q) + \lambda\,K_1\,(p,\,q)$ plus a power series in λ with continuous coefficients, uniformly convergent for $|\lambda| \leqq \lambda_1$.* It satisfies the characteristic equations (8) and (9) for $|\lambda| \leqq \lambda_1$.

Furthermore, the resolvent can be expressed as the quotient of two always convergent series in λ. Consider the resolvent for the continuous kernel $K_2\,(p,\,q)$:

$$R_2\,(p,q;\,\lambda) = K_2\,(p,q) + \lambda\,K_5\,(p,q) + \lambda^2 K_8\,(p,q) + \cdots.$$

We see that the function $\lambda^2 R_2\,(p,\,q;\,\lambda^3)$ gives exactly the series of the 3^{d}, 6th, 9th, $\ldots$ terms of (7). The series of the next following terms of (7) is therefore given by

$$\lambda^3 \int R_2\,(p,r;\,\lambda^3)\,K\,(r,q)\,dr,$$

and the series of the next following terms, by

$$\lambda^4 \int R_2 (p,r;\lambda^3) K_1 (r,q) \, dr.$$

Hence we have the identity, valid for $|\lambda| < \lambda_1$,

$$R (p,q;\lambda) = K (p,q) + \lambda K_1 (p,q) + \lambda^2 R_2 (p,q;\lambda^3)$$
$$+ \lambda^3 \int R_2 (p,r;\lambda^3) [K (r,q) + \lambda K_1 (r,q)] \, dr.$$

Now the resolvent $R_2 (p,q;\lambda)$ corresponding to the continuous kernel $K_2 (p, q)$ is the quotient of two always convergent power series, $\dfrac{N_2(p,q;\lambda)}{\delta_2 (\lambda)}$, the coefficients of $N_2 (p,q;\lambda)$ being continuous. Hence

$$R (p,q;\lambda) = \frac{[K (p,q) + \lambda K_1 (p,q)] \, \eta (\lambda) + M (p,q;\lambda)}{\eta (\lambda)},$$

where

$$M (p,q;\lambda) = \lambda^2 N_2 (p,q;\lambda^3) + \lambda^3 \int N_2 (p,r;\lambda^3) [K (r,q) + \lambda K_1 (r,q)] \, dr,$$
$$\eta (\lambda) = \delta_2 (\lambda^3).$$

Thus the resolvent for $K (p, q)$ is a quotient of two always convergent power series, as stated. Moreover, if $R (p, q; \lambda)$ is expressed in the form

$$R (p,q;\lambda) = K (p,q) + \lambda K_1 (p,q) + \frac{M (p,q;\lambda)}{\eta (\lambda)},$$

we see that *the residues $A (p, q)$ at the poles are continuous functions, and that the functions $B (p, q; \lambda_0)$ are linear combinations of $K (p, q)$ and $K_1 (p, q)$ plus continuous functions of p and q.*

We are not able to conclude that all the roots of $\eta (\lambda)$ are poles of $R (p, q; \lambda)$, but this is not important for our purposes. The important thing for us is whether a given value of λ is a pole of $R (p, q; \lambda)$. It is for this reason that we defined the characteristics of a kernel as the poles of its resolvent. This definition is independent of the particular quotient form given to $R (p, q; \lambda)$.

The above resolvent satisfies the equations (8) and (9) and when these equations are multiplied by $\eta (\lambda)$, they become identities known to be valid for small $|\lambda|$, but since they are identities between always convergent series, they are valid for all λ.

If $\lambda = \lambda_0$ is not a characteristic of $K (p, q)$, whether $\eta (\lambda)$ is 0 or not, the numerator and denominator are developable in always convergent series in $\lambda - \lambda_0$, and if a power of $\lambda - \lambda_0$ is a factor of the denominator, it is always a factor of the numerator, since λ_0 is not a pole of the resolvent. If this factor is removed, and the resolvent defined at λ_0 by the value of the resulting quotient, it will be continuous in all its variables for λ near λ_0, (except for the two terms in $K (p, q)$ and $K_1 (p, q)$), and since it satisfies the equations (8) and (9) can be used, just as in the case of continuous kernels, to solve the non-homogeneous equations (I) and (I'). If $f(p)$ is continuous, we see by the form of the solutions in § 8, by means of Lemma I of the last section, that these solutions are continuous. In the present case, the homogeneous equations (II) and (II') have no non-trivial solutions.

If $\lambda = \lambda_0$ is a pole of the resolvent, we have a continuous residue, and all the theory for this case goes through, just as in § 7. Thus *the statements of the summary in § 8 hold unaltered if we substitute for the hypothesis that $K(p,q)$ be continuous, the hypothesis that it be the kernel of the potential theory problem. Furthermore, the solutions of the homogeneous equations all satisfy uniform Hölder conditions on S.* This follows from Lemma I.

11. The Characteristic Numbers of the Special Kernel.

Reverting to § 2, we found there that the potentials

$$W(P) = \frac{1}{2\pi} \int \varphi(q) \frac{\partial}{\partial \nu} \frac{1}{r} \, dq , \quad V(P) = \frac{1}{2\pi} \int \psi(q) \frac{1}{r} \, dq$$

satisfies the following boundary conditions

$$(37) \qquad -W_- = \varphi(p) - \int \varphi(q) K(p,q) \, dq ,$$

$$(38) \qquad +W_+ = \varphi(p) + \int \varphi(q) K(p,q) \, dq ,$$

$$(39) \qquad +\frac{\partial V}{\partial n_-} = \psi(p) + \int \psi(q) K(q,p) \, dq ,$$

$$(40) \qquad -\frac{\partial V}{\partial n_+} = \psi(p) - \int \psi(q) K(q,p) \, dq .$$

If we multiply (37) by $\frac{(1+\lambda)}{2}$ and (38) by $\frac{(1-\lambda)}{2}$ and add, we have

$$(41) \qquad \frac{1-\lambda}{2} W_+ - \frac{1+\lambda}{2} W_- = \varphi(p) - \lambda \int \varphi(q) K(p,q) \, dq ,$$

and treating (39) and (40) similarly, we have

$$(42) \qquad \frac{1-\lambda}{2} \frac{\partial V}{\partial n_-} - \frac{1+\lambda}{2} \frac{\partial V}{\partial n_+} = \psi(p) - \lambda \int \psi(q) K(q,p) \, dq .$$

The characteristics of $K(p,q)$ are real. For if $\lambda = \alpha + i\beta$ is a characteristic (α and β real), there will be a function $\psi_1(p) + i\psi_2(p)$ for which the right hand member of (42) vanishes identically. This function is not identically 0, and satisfies a uniform Hölder condition, by Lemma I, § 9, so that the corresponding potential $V_1(P) + i V_2(P)$ has continuous derivatives of the first order in the region R, and also in the region R'. Thus, separating real and imaginary parts in the left hand member of (42), we have

$$(43) \qquad (1-\alpha)\frac{\partial V_1}{\partial n_-} - (1+\alpha)\frac{\partial V_1}{\partial n_+} + \beta \frac{\partial V_2}{\partial n_-} + \beta \frac{\partial V_2}{\partial n_+} = 0 ,$$

$$(44) \qquad (1-\alpha)\frac{\partial V_2}{\partial n_-} - (1+\alpha)\frac{\partial V_2}{\partial n_+} - \beta \frac{\partial V_1}{\partial n_-} - \beta \frac{\partial V_1}{\partial n_+} = 0 .$$

If we multiply these equations respectively by V_2 and V_1, subtract, and integrate over S, the terms in α drop out, by Theorem VI (page 216). There remains

(45) $$\beta(J_1 + J_2) - \beta(J_1' + J_2') = 0,$$

where J denotes a Dirichlet integral (see page 279), formed for V_1 or V_2, and extended over the region R or R'. If we multiply the equations (43) and (44) by V_1 and V_2 respectively, add and integrate, we find

(46) $$(1 - \alpha)(J_1 + J_2) + (1 + \alpha)(J_1' + J_2') = 0.$$

We have, in (45) and (46), what may be regarded as two equations for the two sums of Dirichlet integrals in the parentheses. The determinant of the coefficients is 2β. Therefore either $\beta = 0$ or all four of the Dirichlet integrals vanish, for none of them is susceptible of negative values. The latter condition would mean that V_1 and V_2 were constant in R and constant in R'. But since these functions are regular at infinity, and continuous at the points of S, they would have to vanish identically. Then $\psi_1(p) \equiv \psi_2(p) \equiv 0$. But this is contrary to the hypothesis that the solution is non-trivial. There is nothing left but that β shall be 0, and this means that the characteristic is real, as was to be proved.

We may draw another conclusion from the equation (46). Suppose now that β is 0, that α is a real characteristic, and that $\psi_1(p)$ is a real non-trivial solution of the equation (42) with left hand member set equal to 0. We have then only to set V_2 and therefore J_2 and J_2' equal to 0 in (46) in order to obtain the valid equation

$$(1 - \alpha)J_1 + (1 + \alpha)J_1' = 0.$$

Solving this equation for α, we find

$$\alpha = \frac{J_1 + J_1'}{J_1 - J_1'},$$

from which it appears that *the characteristics are never less than 1 in absolute value.*

The Characteristics are Poles of the Resolvent of Order Never Greater than 1. For, if λ_0 were a pole of order greater than 1, the equations (28) would have a solution in which neither $\psi_1(p)$ nor $\psi_2(p)$ vanished identically. The corresponding potentials would satisfy the boundary conditions

$$(1 - \lambda_0)\frac{\partial V_1}{\partial n_-} - (1 + \lambda_0)\frac{'\partial V_1}{\partial n_+} = 0,$$

$$(1 - \lambda_0)\frac{\partial V_2}{\partial n_-} - (1 + \lambda_0)\frac{\partial V_2}{\partial n_+} = \frac{\partial V_1}{\partial n_-} + \frac{\partial V_1}{\partial n_+},$$

the latter being derived by means of (42), (39) and (40). If these equations be multiplied by $-V_2$ and V_1, respectively, added, and integrated over S, the result is

$$J_1 - J_1' = 0,$$

whereas if the first be multiplied by V_1 and integrated over S, the result is

$$(1 - \lambda_0)\, J_1 + (1 + \lambda_0)\, J_1' = 0.$$

These equations are compatible only if $J_1 = J_1' = 0$. From this would follow $V_1 = 0$ and hence $\psi_1\,(p) = 0$. But this contradicts the assumption that the pole was of higher order. Hence the poles are simple, as we wished to show.

12. Solution of the Boundary Value Problems.

We shall now somewhat extend the scope of the problems to be discussed. In order to include the problem of the existence of static charges on a number of different conductors in the field at once, we suppose that R is not necessarily a single region, but k closed regions without common points, bounded by k smooth surfaces of the kind we have been considering, and that R' is the region exterior to these k surfaces, together with the surfaces themselves. This assumption impairs none of the results derived in the foregoing sections.

Suppose now that $\lambda = 1$ were a characteristic of $K\,(p, q)$. There would then be a function $\psi\,(p)$, continuous, and not identically 0, for which the right hand member of (40) vanished identically. This solution of the homogeneous equation satisfies a uniform Hölder condition on S, by Lemma I, p. 300. The corresponding potential V would then be continuously differentiable in R and R', by Theorem VII, Chapter VI (p. 165). But by (40), its normal derivatives on S, regarded as the boundary of R', would vanish everywhere. Hence V would vanish throughout R'. But the potential of a simple distribution is continuous everywhere. Hence V would vanish on the boundary of R, and therefore throughout R. This could only be if the function $\psi\,(p)$ were identically 0. This is contrary to the assumption, and so $\lambda = 1$ is not a characteristic.

It follows that the equations (37) and (40) have continuous solutions for any continuous values of the left-hand members, and we therefore have the results

I. *The Dirichlet problem is solvable for the finite regions R for any continuous boundary values.*

II. *The Neumann problem is solvable for the infinite region R' for any continuous values of the normal derivative on the boundary.*

The solutions are given as the potentials of double and simple distributions on the boundary, respectively.

We now show that $\lambda = -1$ is a characteristic of the kernel. Suppose, in fact, that W denotes the double distribution whose moment on the surface S_i is 1, and on the remaining surfaces, is 0. Then in R', $W \equiv 0$, for the potential of a double distribution with constant moment on a closed regular surface is always 0 in the infinite region bounded by that surface. Thus the homogeneous equation, (38) with left-hand member set equal to 0, has a non-trivial solution. So $\lambda = -1$ must be a characteristic.

We can easily set up a complete set of independent solutions of this homogeneous equation. Let $\varphi_i (p) = 1$ on S_i and vanish on the other surfaces. Then any solution of the homogeneous equation is a linear homogeneous combination of $\varphi_1 (p)$, $\varphi_2 (p)$, ... $\varphi_k (p)$ with constant coefficients. In fact, let $\varphi (p)$ be any solution. Since the corresponding potential W is 0 on the boundary of R', it is 0 throughout R', and so has vanishing normal derivatives in R'. Hence, by Theorem X, page 170, the normal derivatives of W approach 0 along the normals. This implies that the normal derivatives on S_i exist, as one sided limits, and are 0, as may be seen by the law of the mean. Keeping in mind the character of the surfaces S_i (page 286), we see that the hypotheses of Exercise 9, page 244, are in force, and that W must be constant in each region R_i. Hence its moment must be constant on each surface S_i, and consequently can be represented as a linear homogeneous combination of the $\varphi_i (p)$ with constant coefficients, as asserted.

It follows that the associated homogeneous integral equation, (39) with left-hand member set equal to 0, has also exactly k linearly independent solutions $\psi_i (p)$, $i = 1, 2, ... k$. Since the potentials V_i to which these functions give rise have normal derivatives which vanish on the boundary of R, they must be constant in each region R_i of which R is composed. These potentials are linearly independent, for a relation

$$c_1 V_1 + c_2 V_2 + \cdots + c_k V_k = 0$$

would give rise, by means of the relationship between densities and normal derivatives of simple distributions, to the same relation with the potentials replaced by the $\psi_i (p)$, and such a relation does not exist unless all the constants are 0, the $\psi_i (p)$ being independent.

Since the potentials V_i are linearly independent, any set of linear homogeneous combinations of them which are independent, will be an equivalent set. Since the V_i are constant on each surface S_i, and linearly independent, it is possible to form the equivalent set V_i', such that V_i' is 1 on S_i, and 0 on all the remaining surfaces bounding R; this for $i = 1, 2, ... k$. These potentials are a solution of the problem: *given k conductors in a homogeneous medium, to find the potential when* *all but one of the conductors are grounded, and that one is at the constant potential* 1.

Suppose now that the conductors are not grounded, and that charges e_1, e_2, ... e_k are imparted to them. Let us see whether we can find the potential of these charges, when in equilibrium on the conductors, in the form $V = \sum_j c_j V_j$. The density of the distribution producing V will be given by $\psi(p) = \sum_j c_j \psi_j(p)$. The problem is to determine whether the c_j can be selected so that the charge on S_i is the given e_i, for all i. Since $\varphi_i(p) = 1$ on S_i, and is 0 on the remaining surfaces, we may obtain the charge on S_i by multiplying the equation $\psi(p) = \sum_j c_j \psi_j(p)$ by $\varphi_i(p)$ and integrating over all the surfaces. The equations to be fulfilled are

$$\sum_j c_j \int \varphi_i(p)\, \psi_j(p)\, dp = e_i, \qquad i = 1, 2, \ldots k.$$

These equations are compatible. For otherwise the equations obtained by replacing the right hand members by 0 would have a solution c_1, c_2, ... c_k in which all the c_i were not 0, and this would mean that there was a linear combination of the $\psi_i(p)$, namely $\sum c_j \psi_j(p)$, which was orthogonal to all the functions $\varphi_i(p)$. But this is impossible, since the $\varphi_i(p)$ and the $\psi_i(p)$ are equivalent to sets which together form a normalized biorthogonal set (see the end of p. 298). Hence we have the proof of the possibility of the electrostatic problems:

III. *Given either the constant values of the potential on the conductors* $R_1, R_2, \ldots R_k$, *or, given the total charge on each of them, it is possible to determine the densities of charges in equilibrium on the conductors, producing, in the first case, a potential with the given constant values on the conductors, or having, in the second case, the given total charges on the conductors.*

We may now consider the non-homogeneous equations (38) and (39). A necessary and sufficient condition that (38) be solvable is that the values assigned to W_+ constitute a function which shall be orthogonal to $\psi_i(p)$, $\psi_2(p)$, ... $\psi_k(p)$. We shall now suppose that these functions are chosen so as to form with the $\varphi_i(p)$ a normalized biorthogonal set. Then the function

$$W_+(p) - \sum_j c_j \varphi_j(p), \quad c_j = \int W_+(p)\, \psi_j(p)\, dp$$

is certainly orthogonal to all the $\psi_i(p)$. With W_+ replaced by this value, the equation (38) is solvable, and there exists a double distribution on S whose potential in R' assumes the boundary values $W_+(p) - \sum_j c_j \varphi_j(p)$. But the function $\sum_j c_j \varphi_j(p)$, being constant on each surface S_i, can be represented as the boundary values of a conductor potential. We therefore have the result

IV. *The Dirichlet problem is solvable for the infinite region R' for any continuous boundary values.* The solution may be expressible as the potential of a double distribution, or it may not. If not, it is expressible as the sum of the potential of a double distribution and a conductor potential.

Passing to the equation (39), we see at once that a necessary and sufficient condition that it be solvable for given continuous boundary values of the normal derivative of V is that these values be orthogonal to a set of independent functions constant on each surface S_i, that is that

$$\iint_{S_i} \frac{\partial V}{\partial n_-} dS = 0, \qquad i = 1, 2, \ldots k.$$

These are not conditions on the mode of representation of a solution, but are essential restrictions on any function harmonic in the regions R_i. As the regions R_i are not connected, there is no difference in content in the statement that the Neumann problem is solvable for a single one of them, or for all together. We therefore state the result

V. *The Neumann problem is solvable for a single one of the bounded regions R_i under the essential condition that the integral over the bounding surface of the values assigned to the normal derivative vanishes.*

Finally, let us consider the problem of heat conduction, or the *third boundary value problem of potential theory*. It is required to find a function V, harmonic in R, such that on S

$$\frac{\partial V}{\partial n_-} + h(p) V_- = f(p),$$

where $h(p)$ and $f(p)$ satisfy a uniform Hölder condition on S (now assumed to be a single surface), and where $h(p) \geqq 0$, the inequality sign holding at some point of S. If we seek to represent V as the potential of a simple distribution on S, — that is as the stationary temperatures due to a distribution of heat sources on S —, we are led to the integral equation

$$f(p) = \psi(p) + \int \psi(q) \left[K(q, p) + \frac{h(p)}{2} \frac{1}{r} \right] dq, \quad r = \overline{pq}.$$

This equation is always solvable unless the homogeneous equation obtained by replacing $f(p)$ by 0 has a solution not identically 0. But § 1 of Chapter VIII (p. 214) in the proof of Theorem V, shows that the potential of the corresponding distribution would vanish in R and consequently in the infinite region R' bounded by S. This cannot be unless the density is everywhere 0. So the homogeneous equation has no nontrivial solutions.

The non-homogeneous equation therefore has a continuous solution $\psi(p)$. Referring to that equation, we note that the integral

$$\int \psi(q) K(p, q) \, dq$$

satisfies a uniform Hölder condition on S, and so does the term

$$\frac{h(p)}{2} \int \psi(p) \frac{1}{r} \, dq,$$

since first, $\frac{1}{r}$ satisfies all the requirements imposed on $K(p, q)$ in the proof of Lemma I, § 9, and secondly, the product of two functions satisfying a uniform Hölder condition also satisfies one. Finally, by hypothesis, $f(p)$ satisfies one, and therefore $\psi(p)$ must. Hence the potential V has continuous derivatives in R, and satisfies the boundary conditions. Thus is proved the possibility of the problem

VI. *Given the functions* $f(p)$, $h(p)$, *satisfying the above conditions, there exists a function* V, *harmonic in* R, *and satisfying on the boundary of* R *the condition*

$$\frac{\partial V}{\partial n_-} + h(p) V_- = f(p).$$

13. Further Consideration of the Dirichlet Problem; Superharmonic and Subharmonic Functions.

The possibility of the Dirichlet problem has now been established for any region, finite or infinite, with a finite boundary S with the required smoothness. This is sufficient for many purposes, but the theory of functions of a complex variable demands a broader existence theorem in two dimensions, and recent developments are sufficiently interesting to warrant some attention to them. We shall see that there are limitations on the problem in the nature of some domains, and we shall find methods for constructing the solution whenever it exists.

The notion of superharmonic and subharmonic functions will be useful. We shall confine ourselves to continuous functions of these types, although they may be more broadly defined. The function W, continuous in a region R is said to be *superharmonic* in R, if, for any closed region R' in R, and any function U harmonic in R',

$$W \geqq U$$

throughout R' whenever this inequality obtains at all boundary points of R'. A *subharmonic* function is similarly defined, with the inequality reversed. Harmonic functions belong to both classes; they are the only functions which do. We now develop those properties of superharmonic functions which we shall need.

1. *If W is superharmonic in R, it is, at the center of any sphere in R, greater than or equal to its arithmetic mean on the surface of the sphere.* It is understood here, and in what follows, that the sphere together with its whole interior, lies in R.

Given a point P of R, and a sphere in R with P as center, let us denote by $AW(P)$ the arithmetic mean of the values of W on the surface of the sphere, as formulated in Chapter VIII (p. 224). We have to show that always $W(P) \geqq AW(P)$.

Let U be that function, harmonic in the sphere, which, on the surface of the sphere, coincides with W. Then, by the definition of superharmonic functions, by Gauss' theorem, and by the construction of U, we have the successive inequalities

$$W(P) \geqq U(P), \quad U(P) = AU(P), \quad AU(P) = AW(P),$$

from which follows the desired inequality, holding for any P and sphere about P in R.

The second property is a converse of the first.

2. *If W is continuous in R, and if to every point P within R there corresponds a number $\alpha > 0$, such that $W(P) \geqq AW(P)$ for all spheres about P of radius less than α, then W is superharmonic in R.*

Let R' be any closed region in R, and let U be any function, harmonic in R', and such that $W \geqq U$ on the boundary of R'. Since $U(P) = AU(P)$ in R', for spheres in R', it follows that

$$W(P) - U(P) \geqq A[W(P) - U(P)]$$

for spheres in R' of radius less than the value of α corresponding to P. This difference is continuous in R', and the reasoning of the proof of Theorem X, p. 223, is applicable to show that it can have no minimum in the interior of R'. As it is not negative on the boundary, it cannot be negative in the interior. Hence, by the definition, W is superharmonic.

3. *If W is superharmonic in R and if its derivatives of the second order exist and are continuous in the interior of R, then $V^2 W \leqq 0$ in the interior of R.* Thus such a function W is the potential of a volume distribution in R with non-negative density, plus possible harmonic functions. Conversely, *if W has continuous derivatives of the second order in the interior of R, is continuous in R, and if $V^2 W \leqq 0$, W is superharmonic in R.*

Exercise.

1. Prove these statements, first deriving from Green's first identity the relation

$$\int_0^a \frac{1}{4\pi\varrho^2} \iiint_{\Sigma_\varrho} V^2 W \, dV \, d\varrho = AW(P) - W(P),$$

as a basis for the proof, Σ_ϱ being the sphere about P of radius ϱ, and a the radius of the sphere used for averaging.

4. *Let W be continuous and superharmonic in a region R. Let R' be a closed region in R, and U a function, harmonic in R', and coinciding with W on the boundary of R'. Then the function W_1, defined as equal to U in R' and equal to W in the rest of R, is superharmonic in R.*

We show this by means of the property 2. If P is interior to R', $W_1(P) = AW_1(P)$ for all spheres about P of radius less than the distance from P to the nearest boundary point of R'. If P is in R but not in R', $W_1(P) \geq AW_1(P)$ for small enough spheres about P. If P is on the boundary of R', $W_1(P) = W(P) \geq AW(P) \geq AW_1(P)$, since $W \geq W_1$ wherever the two differ. Thus the sufficient condition of property 2 is fulfilled.

Exercise.

2. Establish the property: 5. *If $W_1, W_2, W_3, \ldots W_n$ are continuous and super-harmonic in R, the function W, defined at each point P of R as the least of the values assumed at that point by the W_i, is superharmonic in R.*

14. Approximation to a Given Domain by the Domains of a Nested Sequence.

A sequence $T_1, T_2, T_3, \ldots$ will be said to be *nested*, if for each n, T_n and its boundary is in T_{n+1}. The domains will be said to *approximate* to T if they are in T, and if any given point of T lies in T_n for large enough n.

We proceed to show how such a sequence can be constructed for any given bounded domain T. We begin by forming approximating closed regions, $R_1, R_2, R_3, \ldots$. When these are stripped of their boundaries, they will yield the required domains.

Let P_0 be a point of T. Let C be a cube with P_0 as center, in T. We construct a lattice of cubes, of side a, equal to one third the side of C, so placed that the faces of C lie in the planes of the lattice. We assign to R_1 the cube of this lattice in which P_0 lies, and also every other cube of the lattice with the properties

(*a*) c and all the 26 adjacent cubes of the lattice are in T,

(*b*) c is one of a succession of cubes, each having a face in common with the next, and the cube containing P_0 being one of the succession.

Then R_1 will be a closed region, in the sense of the definition, p. 93. To form R_2, we form a second lattice by adding the parallel planes bisecting the edges of the cubes of the first. R_2 shall consist of the cubes of the second lattice with the properties (*a*) and (*b*) with respect to that lattice. It should be observed that R_1 is entirely *interior* to R_2. For if c is a cube of R_1, it is entirely surrounded by cubes of the first lattice in T. It is therefore entirely surrounded by cubes of the second lattice which, in turn are also surrounded by cubes of the second lattice in T, so that they possess the qualification (*a*) for membership in R_2. Evidently they possess the qualification (*b*). Thus *c* is interior to R_2. By continued subdivision of the lattice we construct similarly $R_3, R_4, \ldots, R_n$ being made of the cubes of side $\frac{a}{2^{n-1}}$ of the nth lattice with properties (*a*) and (*b*) for that lattice. Each region is interior to the next.

We now show that they approximate *T*. Obviously, they are in *T*. Let *P* be any point of *T*. Then *P* can be joined to P_0 by a polygonal line γ in *T*. Let $3d$ denote the least distance of a point of γ from the boundary of *T*. If then *n* is chosen so that the diagonal of the nth lattice is less than *d*, *P* will lie in R_n. To see this, we substitute two sides for one, where necessary, changing γ to a new polygonal line γ', joining *P* to P_0, which nowhere meets an edge of the lattice, except possibly at *P*. This can be done so that γ' remains within a distance *d* of γ, and hence so that γ' remains at a distance greater than $2d$ from the boundary of *T*. It follows that all the cubes containing points of γ' have property (*a*). But since γ' passes from one cube to the next through a face, these cubes have also property (*b*), and so belong to R_n. As *P* is in one of them, it is in R_n, as stated.

As *P* is *interior* to R_{n+1}, it follows that the set of nested domains, $T_1, T_2, T_3, \ldots$ consisting of the interiors of the regions $R_1, R_2, R_3, \ldots$, also approximate to *T*. We note also that if *R* is any closed region in *T*, *R* also lies in some T_n. For every point of *R* is in one of the domains T_i, and hence, by the Heine-Borel theorem, *R* lies in a finite number of these domains. Obviously then, it lies in that one of them with the greatest index.

We now make several applications of the above construction. In the first place, we had need, in Chapter VIII, to know that if R' was interior to *R*, we could interpolate any desired number of regions between the two, each interior to the next. To do this, we need only construct a nested sequence approximating to the interior of *R*. One of them will contain R', and between this and *R* there will be as many regions as we care to select from the sequence.

As a second application, let us consider the possibility of constructing the set of spheres needed in Poincaré's *méthode de balayage*. About the centers of the cubes of R_1, we construct spheres with diameters one per cent greater than the diameters of the cubes. These spheres are well within *T*, and each point of R_1 is interior to at least one of them. Call them $S_1, S_2, \ldots S_{n_1}$. About the cubes of R_2 which are not in R_1, we construct in the same way the spheres $S_{n_1+1}, S_{n_1+2}, \ldots S_{n_2}$, and so on. We obtain an infinite sequence of spheres, all in *T*, and such that every point of *T* is interior to at least one of the sequence.

We next remark that *it is possible to construct a sequence of nested domains $A_1, A_2, A_3, \ldots$, whose boundaries are analytic surfaces without* *singular points, and which approximate to* T. We form A_n from R_n as follows. We form an integral analogous to the potential of a spread of density 1 on the polyhedral boundary S_n of R_n:

$$F(P) = \iint\limits_{S_n} \frac{dS}{r^2},$$

where r is the distance from P to the point of integration. The use of the minus second power of r has as consequence that $F(P)$ becomes positively infinite as P approaches any point of S_n. It is easy to show by the methods used for Newtonian potentials, that $F(P)$ is analytic everywhere except on S_n. Since R_{n-1} is interior to R_n, $F(P)$ has a maximum M in R_{n-1}, and so for any constant $K > M$, the set of points for which $F(P) < K$ contains R_{n-1}. This is an open set, and so it is made up of two (since it also contains points outside of S_n) or more domains. Let A denote the one containing R_{n-1}.

Now A is bounded by the analytic surface $F(P) = K$, and the reasoning used to prove Theorem XIV, p. 276 is applicable here. It shows us that in any neighborhood of K, there is a number K' such that the surface $F(P) = K'$ is free from singularities. If we choose $K' > K$, the domain A becomes the required member A_n of the sequence. It lies strictly between R_{n-1} and R_n, and has a non-singular analytic boundary.

As the Fredholm method establishes the possibility of the Dirichlet problem for what we shall call the *analytic domains* $A_1, A_2, A_3, \ldots$, we see that *any bounded domain whatever can be approximated to by a sequence of nested domains for which the Dirichlet problem is possible*.

A fourth application is to the theorem of LEBESGUE *on the extension of the definition of a continuous function*: *If* t *is a closed bounded set, and if* $f(p)$ *is defined and continuous on* t, *there exists a function* $F(P)$, *defined and continuous throughout space, and coinciding on* t *with* $f(p)$. We begin by showing that if t is the boundary of a bounded domain T, the extension of the definition of $f(p)$ to the domain T is possible.

We form a system of cubes, consisting of the cubes of the first lattice in R_1, the cubes of the second lattice in R_2 which are not in R_1, the cubes of the third lattice in R_3 but not in R_2, and so on. We define $F(P)$ first at the vertices of these cubes. Let P be such a vertex, and σ the smallest sphere about P containing points of t. The points of t on the surface of σ form a closed set, and so the values of $f(p)$ on this set have a minimum. This minimum is the value assigned to $F(P)$. Thus $F(P)$ is defined at all the vertices of the cubes, and, in the case of cubes adjacent only to cubes of the same or larger size, only at the vertices. No cube will be adjacent to a cube of side less than half its own, but there will be cubes adjacent to cubes of side half their own. For such cubes $F(P)$ will have been defined at at least one mid-point of an edge or face.

We now define $F(P)$ at the remaining points of the cubes by linear interpolation. Let C denote a cube for which $F(P)$ has been defined only at the vertices. Then there is one and only one function, linear in x, y and z separately (the axes being parallel to the sides of C)

$$F(P) = axyz + byz + czx + dxy + ex + fy + gz + h$$

which assumes the values already assigned to $F(P)$ at the vertices of C. We let $F(P)$ have this definition in the closed cube. We note that it assigns to the mid-point of any edge, the arithmetic mean of the values at the ends of the edge; and to the mid-point of any face, the arithmetic mean of the values at the four corners of the face. Suppose now that C is one of the cubes for which $F(P)$ has been defined, in assigning values at the vertices, at a mid-point of an edge or face, as well, in virtue of being adjacent to a cube of side half its own. We then define $F(P)$ at the following points, *provided it has not already been defined at the point in question*, namely, at the mid-point of a side, as the arithmetic mean of the values at the ends of that side; at the mid-point of a face, as the arithmetic mean of its values at the four corners of the face; at the center, as the arithmetic mean of its values at the eight vertices. In each of the eight equal cubes of which C is composed, $F(P)$ is then defined by linear interpolation, as above.

This manner of definition is consistent, for on a face which a cube has in common with a cube of the same size, or in common with a quarter of the face of a cube of larger size, the interpolating functions agree at four vertices, and therefore over the whole face. $F(P)$, thus defined, is accordingly continuous throughout T. It remains to show that if $F(P)$ is defined on t as equal to $f(p)$, it is continuous there also. Let q be a point of t, and σ a sphere about q within which $f(p)$ differs from $f(q)$ by less than ε. Then there is a second sphere σ' about q, such that all cubes with points in σ' lie completely in a concentric sphere of radius less than half that of σ. The vertices of these cubes will then be nearer to points of t in σ than outside of σ, so that the values of $F(P)$ at the vertices will differ from $f(q)$ by less than ε. As the values assigned by linear interpolation are intermediate between the values at the vertices, it follows that throughout σ', $F(P)$ differs from $f(q)$ by less than ε, and the continuity of $F(P)$ is established.

Suppose now that t is any bounded closed set. The set E of points not in t is an open set. Let T denote any one of the domains of which E is made up. If T is bounded, $f(p)$ is defined and continuous on its boundary, which is in t, and by the method just indicated, $F(P)$ may be defined in T. If T is infinite, we consider the portion T' of T in a sphere, containing t in its interior. We assign to $F(P)$, on and outside this sphere the arithmetic mean of the extremes of $f(p)$, and then extend the definition to T' by the usual method. The continuity of $F(P)$, thus defined for all of space, is then established in the same manner as in the special case of a single domain with its boundary. We note that it lies between the extremes of $f(p)$, and is uniformly continuous in the whole of space.

We close with a proof of a theorem we shall need, namely the theorem of WEIERSTRASS *on approximation by polynomials: If $F(P)$ is continuous in a closed bounded region R, and ε any positive number, there exists a polynomial $G(P)$, such that throughout R,*

$$|G(P) - F(P)| < \varepsilon.$$

We give the proof in two dimensions. The method holds in any number of dimensions, but the integrals employed are slightly simpler to handle in two. Let $f(x, y)$ be continuous in R. We regard its definition as extended to the whole of the plane so as to be uniformly continuous. Let M denote a bound for its absolute value.

Consider the integral extended to a circle of radius a about the origin

$$\Phi(a) \doteq \frac{1}{\pi} \iint_{C_a} e^{-\varrho^2}\, dS = \frac{1}{\pi} \int_0^{2\pi} \int_0^a e^{-\varrho^2} \varrho\, d\varrho\, d\varphi = (1 - e^{-a^2}).$$

By means of a change of variable, we verify that

$$\frac{h^2}{\pi} \iint_{C_a} e^{-h^2 \varrho^2}\, dS = \Phi(ha).$$

We now form the function

$$F(x, y) = \frac{h^2}{\pi} \iint f(\xi, \eta)\, e^{-h^2 r^2}\, dS, \qquad r^2 = (x - \xi)^2 + (y - \eta)^2,$$

the integral being extended over the whole plane. This function reduces to 1 when $f(x, y)$ is 1, so that we may write

$$F(x, y) - f(x, y) = \frac{h^2}{\pi} \iint [f(\xi, \eta) - f(x, y)]\, e^{-h^2 r^2}\, dS$$
$$= [f(\bar{\xi}, \bar{\eta}) - f(x, y)]\, \Phi(ha) + \vartheta\, 2M\, [1 - \Phi(ha)], \qquad -1 \leqq \vartheta \leqq 1,$$

as we see by breaking the integral into the sum of an integral over the surface of the circle of radius a about (x, y) and one over the rest of the plane, and employing the law of the mean. As $f(x, y)$ is uniformly continuous, we can, given any $\varepsilon > 0$, so restrict a that the first term on the right is uniformly less in absolute value than $\frac{\varepsilon}{6}$, since $0 < \Phi(ha) < 1$. With a thus fixed, h can be taken so large that the second term is less in absolute value than $\frac{\varepsilon}{6}$. Thus $F(x, y)$ differs from $f(x, y)$ throughout the plane by less than $\frac{\varepsilon}{3}$. Hereafter h is kept fixed.

We next take a circle C with R in its interior, and denote by b the distance to the circumference from the nearest point of R. If C' denotes the region outside this circle, then, when (x, y) is in R,

$$\left| \frac{h^2}{\pi} \iint_{C'} f(\xi, \eta) e^{-h^2 r^2} dS \right| \le M[1 - \Phi(h\,b)],$$

and this can be made less than $\dfrac{\varepsilon}{3}$ by taking C, and with it b, large enough. Hence if

$$F_1(x, y) = \frac{h^2}{\pi} \iint_{C} f(\xi, \eta) e^{-h^2 r^2} dS,$$

$F_1(x, y)$ differs from $F(x, y)$ in R by less than $\dfrac{\varepsilon}{3}$, and so from $f(x, y)$ by less than $\dfrac{2\varepsilon}{3}$.

Finally, $e^{-h^2 r^2}$ is equal, by Taylor's theorem with remainder, to a polynomial in r^2, plus a function which can be made uniformly less than $\dfrac{\varepsilon \pi}{3 h^2 A M}$ for (x, y) in R and (ξ, η) in C, where A is the area of C. Thus the integral $F_1(x, y)$ becomes a polynomial $G(x, y)$ plus a function uniformly less than $\dfrac{\varepsilon}{3}$ in R. Therefore in R

$$|G(x, y) - f(x, y)| < \varepsilon,$$

and the theorem is proved.

15. Construction of a Sequence Defining the Solution of the Dirichlet Problem.

Let T be any bounded domain, and $G(P)$ a superharmonic polynomial. We proceed to form a sequence whose limit is the solution of the corresponding Dirichlet problem, if the problem is possible for T. We shall investigate the possibility later.

Let $R_1, R_2, R_3, \ldots$ be a sequence of closed regions in the closed region R consisting of T and its boundary t, with the two properties

(a) the Dirichlet problem is possible for each,

(b) any point of T is the center of a sphere which is in infinitely many of the regions R_i.

They need not all be distinct. For instance, R might consist of two ellipsoids with some common interior points. Then R_1 might be one ellipsoid and R_2 the second, R_3 the first, R_4 the second, and so on. Or the sequence might be a nested set of analytic regions approximating to R. Or, it might be the system of spheres of Poincaré's method. In the first case the method we shall develop reduces, in large degree, to the *"alternierendes Verfahren"*, of SCHWARZ[1]; in the second to a method devised by the author[2]; in the third, to the *méthode de balayage*.

We now form the sequence W_0, W_1, W_2, W_3, . . . :

W_0, identical in R with $G(P)$;

W_1, identical in $R - R_1$ with W_0,

identical in R_1 with the function harmonic in R_1 with the same values on the boundary of R_1 as W_0;

. . .   .

W_n, identical in $R - R_n$ with W_{n-1},

identical in R_n with the function harmonic in R_n with the same values on the boundary of R_n as W_{n-1};

. . .   .

These functions are continuous superharmonic functions, by property 4, p. 317. Furthermore, the sequence is a monotone decreasing one, by the definition of superharmonic functions. Finally, its terms are never less than the minimum of $G(P)$ in R. *Hence the sequence converges at every point of R.*

Let P be any point of T. Then by hypothesis, there is a sphere σ about P which lies in infinitely many of the regions R_i. If n_1, n_2, n_3, . . . are the indices of these regions, W_{n_1}, W_{n_2}, W_{n_3}, . . . are harmonic in σ. Hence, by Harnack's second convergence theorem (Theorem VIII, p. 263), they converge uniformly, say in a concentric sphere of half the radius of σ, to a harmonic limit. But as the whole sequence is monotone, it also converges uniformly in the same sphere to the same limit.

If R' is any closed region in T, every point of R' is interior to a sphere within which the convergence is uniform. Hence, by the Heine-Borel theorem, R' lies in a finite number of spheres in each of which the convergence is uniform. The limit is harmonic in each. Thus we have established

Theorem I. *The sequence W_0, W_1, W_2, . . . converges at every point of R to a function U which is harmonic in the interior or R, the convergence being uniform in any closed region interior to R.*

16. Extensions; Further Properties of U.

We first remove the restriction that the polynomial $G(P)$ be superharmonic. The Laplacian $V^2 G(P)$ is a polynomial, and so is bounded

---

[1] *Gesammelte Mathematische Abhandlungen*, Vol. II, pp. 133—143. It should be added, however that the method in this case is more general than the alternierendes Verfahren, in that not only two, but any number—even an infinite number—of regions may be employed.

[2] Proceedings of the American Academy, Vol. LVIII (1923), pp. 528—529. The method was suggested by a construction of Green's function, by HARNACK.

in absolute value in R, say by M. The Laplacian of the polynomial $\varrho^2 = x^2 + y^2 + z^2$ is 6, so that if we write $G(P) = G'(P) - G''(P)$, where

$$G'(P) = \left[G(P) - \frac{M\varrho^2}{6}\right], \qquad G''(P) = \left[-\frac{M^2}{6}\right],$$

$\nabla^2 G'(P) \leqq 0$ and $\nabla^2 G''(P) \leqq 0$, and $G(P)$ is thus exhibited as the difference of two superharmonic polynomials. The sequences defined by writing first $W_0 = G'(P)$ and then $W_0 = G''(P)$ are subject to Theorem I, and therefore so also is the sequence defined by taking $W_0 = G(P)$.

We next remove all restrictions on R, whose interior we denote by T. The case in which the boundary t extends to infinity may be reduced to the case of a bounded boundary by an inversion in a point of T. Then if T has an exterior point, it may be reduced by an inversion to a bounded domain. But it need not have. Thus, the conductor problem for a circular lamina leads to a Dirichlet problem for a domain without exterior points. In such a case we cannot take for W_0 a polynomial. We can, however, take a function whose boundary values are those of any given polynomial, and which is the difference of two superharmonic functions; this is all that is essential to the method of sequences.

Suppose then that T is an infinite domain, whose boundary is interior to a sphere σ_1 of radius R about O, and that $G(P)$ is any polynomial. We define $H(P)$ as equal to $G(P)$ in σ_1, as equal to 0 outside the sphere σ_2 of radius $2R$ about O, while between the two we take

$$H(P) = G(P)\left(4 - 9\frac{\varrho}{R} + 6\frac{\varrho^2}{R^2}\right)\left(2 - \frac{\varrho}{R}\right)^3,$$

ϱ being the distance $\overline{OP}$. Then $H(P)$ coincides with $G(P)$ on t, has continuous derivatives of the second order satisfying a Hölder condition everywhere, and is 0 outside σ_2. The function

$$h(P) = -\frac{1}{4\pi}\iiint\limits_{\sigma_2} |\nabla^2 H(P)|\frac{1}{r}dV$$

has as Laplacian the absolute value of that of $H(P)$, so that in

$$H(P) = [H(P) - h(P)] - [-h(P)]$$

we have a representation of $H(P)$ as the difference of two superharmonic functions. We remark that if $F(P)$ is any function, continuous throughout space, the function formed from $F(P)$ just as was $H(P)$ from $G(P)$, can be approximated to by functions of the type $H(P)$ just as closely as desired, uniformly throughout space.

We now generalize the boundary values to any continuous function $f(p)$. We form a continuous extension $f(P)$ of $f(p)$ to all of space (possible, by the theorem of Lebesgue), and having described concentric spheres σ_1 and σ_2 containing the boundary t of T, modify $f(P)$ as $G(P)$ was modified to form $H(P)$. Let us call the resulting function $F(P)$. Then, given any $\varepsilon > 0$, we form a polynomial $G(P)$ which differs from $F(P)$ in σ_2 by less than $\frac{\varepsilon}{3}$ (possible by the theorem of Weierstrass). Finally, we form from $G(P)$ the function $H(P)$, everywhere the difference of two superharmonic functions, using the same spheres and multiplying function as in the formation of $F(P)$ from $f(P)$. We then have, throughout space

$$H(P) - \frac{\varepsilon}{3} \leqq F(P) \leqq H(P) + \frac{\varepsilon}{3}.$$

We now compare the sequences $W_0 = F(P)$, $W_1, W_2, \ldots$ and $W_0' = H(P)$, $W_1', W_2', \ldots$. By considering differences, we see that

$$W_n' - \frac{\varepsilon}{3} \leqq W_n \leqq W_n' + \frac{\varepsilon}{3}, \text{ for all } n.$$

Since, by Theorem I, $W_0', W_1', W_2', \ldots$ converges uniformly throughout any closed region R', in T, there will be an N such that for $n \geqq N$, $m \geqq N$,

$$|W_m' - W_n'| < \frac{\varepsilon}{3}[,$$

and hence, by the preceding inequalities,

$$|W_m - W_n| < \varepsilon.$$

As there is such an N for any positive ε, this shows that the sequence $W_0', W_1', W_2', \ldots$ converges uniformly in R'. As the terms of the sequence are all equal on the boundary of R, we see that *Theorem I holds for any region with bounded boundary and any continuous boundary values, extended as indicated above. Even the restriction that the boundary be bounded will be removed.* Before taking up this question, however, we establish

Theorem II. *The harmonic function U arrived at by the sequence method is independent, both of the particular choice of the regions $R_1, R_2, R_3, \ldots$ employed, and of the particular choice of the continuous extension of the boundary values $f(p)$.*

First, let one set of regions lead to the sequence $W_0, W_1, W_2, \ldots$, and a second set to $W_0, W_1', W_2', \ldots$, with limits U and U', respectively, the initial function being in both cases the same superharmonic function. As the sequences are monotone decreasing,

$$U' \leqq W_0, \qquad U \leqq W_0.$$

Since the terms of both sequences are superharmonic, with the same boundary values, it follows from these inequalities that

$$U' \leqq W_n, \qquad U \leqq W_n',$$

and hence, in the limit, we must have $U' = U$. The extension to the case in which W_0 is any continuous function follows immediately.

Secondly, let W_0 and W_0' denote any two continuous extensions of the same boundary values, leading to the limits U and U'. Then the function $W_0' - W_0$ will lead to the limit $U' - U$. As we have already seen that the limits are independent of the regions R_i, we may choose for these a nested set approaching R. As $W_0' - W_0$ has the boundary values 0, it will be less in absolute value than a given $\varepsilon > 0$ at all points outside some region R' in T. Then as soon as n is great enough so that R_n contains R', the values on the boundary of R_n of

$$W_n' - W_n$$

will be. less in absolute value than ε, and as this function is harmonic in R_n, it is less in absolute value than ε throughout R_n. This is therefore true of $U' - U$, and as ε is arbitrary, $U' = U$ in T. As $U' = U = W_0$ on the boundary, the equality holds in R. The theorem is thus proved. Moreover, the proof brings to light the fact that in the case of an infinite domain it is not necessary that the continuous extension of $f(p)$ have the character of the function $H(P)$, vanishing outside some sphere.

If, finally, we have to deal with an unbounded boundary t, we may transform the domain T by an inversion to one T' in which the boundary t' is bounded, transform the boundary values $f(p)$ to values $f'(p)$ by the corresponding Kelvin transformation, and employ the sequence method to form a function U' for T'. Then transforming back again, we have the sequence, and the limiting function U corresponding to the domain T. In all this, we understand by continuity at infinity a property which is invariant under a Kelvin transformation. In particular, all functions harmonic at infinity vanish there.

Thus Theorems I und II hold for any domains whatever. It remains to consider whether U takes on the required boundary values. It does, if the Dirichlet problem, as set, is possible. And in any case, the method attaches to any domain and any continuous boundary values, a single harmonic function U.[1] We turn now to the question of the boundary values of U.

Exercise.

Show that if the solution V of the Dirichlet problem exists, it must coincide with the above function U.

17. Barriers.

An effective instrument for studying the behavior of U on the boundary is the barrier. Barriers were used by POINCARÉ, and their

---

[1] It can be shown that the method of the calculus of variations, and the method of mediation (see LEBESGUE: *Sur le problème de Dirichlet*, Comptes Rendus de l'Académie de Paris, Vol. 154 (1912), p. 335) lead in every case to this same function.

importance was recognized by Lebesgue[1], who gave the name to the concept, and extended it. We adopt the following definition. Given a domain T, and a boundary point q, the function $V(P, q)$ is said to be a *barrier for T at the boundary point q* if it is continuous and superharmonic in T, if it approaches 0 at q, and if outside of any sphere about q, it has in T a positive lower bound. We now prove

Theorem III. *A necessary and sufficient condition that the Dirichlet problem for T, and arbitrarily assigned continuous boundary values, is possible, is that a barrier for T exist at every boundary point of T.*

The condition is necessary. For if the Dirichlet problem is possible for all continuous boundary functions, it is possible for the boundary values of the continuous function $F(P) = r = \overline{qP}$. By calculating its Laplacian, it is seen that this function is subharmonic in T, so that the harmonic function $V(P, q)$ with the same boundary values is never less than r. As $V(P, q)$ approaches the boundary value 0 at q, it is a barrier at q.

Now suppose that a barrier exists for every boundary point of T. We shall prove that at any such point q, the function U, which is the limit of the sequence determined by the continuous extension $F(P)$ of the assigned boundary values, approaches the limit $F(q)$. If T is infinite, we assume that $F(P) \equiv 0$ outside some sphere containing t in its interior. Theorem II shows that such an assumption does not restrict the generality.

Given $\varepsilon > 0$, there is a sphere σ about q within which

$$|F(P) - F(q)| < \frac{\varepsilon}{2}.$$

For P outside σ, the difference quotient

$$\frac{F(P) - F(q)}{r}, \qquad r = \overline{Pq},$$

is bounded, say by M, so that $F(P) \leqq F(q) + Mr$. On the other hand, in T and outside σ, the barrier $V(P, q)$ has a positive lower bound, and so therefore has $\dfrac{V(P, q)}{r}$, if T is bounded. Otherwise, it has such a bound in the portion T' of T, outside of which $F(P) \equiv 0$. Let b denote a bound. Then, outside σ and in T, if bounded, otherwise in T',

$$Mr \leqq \frac{M}{b} V(P, q).$$

Hence, keeping in mind the inequalities on $F(P)$ and the fact that

---

[1] *Sur le problème de Dirichlet*, Comptes Rendus de l'Académie des sciences de Paris, Vol. 154 (1912, I), p. 335; *Conditions de régularité, conditions d'irrégularité, conditions d'impossibilité dans le problème de Dirichlet*, ibid. Vol. 178 (1924, I), pp. 352—354.

$V(P, q) \geqq 0$, we see that at all points of T or T'

$$(47) \qquad F(P) \leqq F(q) + \frac{M}{b} V(P, q) + \frac{\varepsilon}{2}.$$

But if T is infinite, this inequality holds on the boundary of the domain $T'' = T - T'$, and as $V(P, q)$ is superharmonic and the other terms are constant, it holds also throughout T'', and so in any case throughout T. It holds therefore throughout R, that is, T and its boundary.

Now the right hand member of the inequality (47) is superharmonic, and hence if the function on the left be replaced, in any closed region in R, by the harmonic function which coincides with it on the boundary of the region, the inequality still subsists. Thus it subsists for all the terms of the sequence $W_0 = F(P)$, W_1, W_2, . . ., and so also for the limit U. If then σ' is a sphere about q, in σ, and in which $V(P, q) < \frac{b\,\varepsilon}{2M}$, then in σ', $U < F(q) + \varepsilon.$

Similarly, in a sphere σ'' about q,

$$U > F(q) - \varepsilon.$$

These two inequalities, holding in the smaller of the two spheres, show that U has the limit $F(q)$ at q, and the proof of the theorem is complete.

But the proof shows more than this. The points of t at which a barrier exists, are called *regular points* of the boundary, and all other boundary points, *exceptional*. The above proof establishes

Theorem IV. *The harmonic function U, established by the method of sequences, approaches the given boundary values at every regular point.*

18. The Construction of Barriers.

The progress made through the introduction of the idea of barrier lies in this: the Dirichlet problem has been reduced to a study of the boundary in an arbitrarily small neighborhood of each of its points, that is to a problem *im Kleinen*. For it is obvious that a barrier for T at q is also a barrier for any domain in T which has q as a boundary point. On the other hand, if T'' includes T, but coincides with T within any sphere σ about q, however small, from the barrier $V(P, q)$ for T can at once be constructed one for T''. We do this as follows. Let b denote the greatest lower bound of $V(P, q)$ in T outside σ. We then define $V''(P, q)$ in T'' as the less of the two functions $V(P, q)$ and b, in σ, and outside σ as b. $V''(P, q)$ is then superharmonic, by Exercise 2 (p. 317), and it is clear that it has the other requisite properties[1]. Thus

---

[1] The exercise shows that $V(P, q)$ is superharmonic in T. Then, as it has property 2 (p. 316) in T'', it is superharmonic in this domain also.

the regularity of q depends only on the boundary in its immediate neighborhood.

We now construct some examples of barriers. The first is a barrier for T at any boundary point q which lies on a sphere none of whose points are in T. Let σ denote such a sphere for q and let σ' be a smaller sphere internally tangent to σ at q. Then if r denotes the distance from the center of σ' to P, and a the radius of σ',

$$V(P, q) = \frac{1}{r} - \frac{1}{a}$$

is readily seen to be a barrier. We thus have Poincaré's criterion: *the Dirichlet problem is possible for the domain T if each of its boundary points lies on a sphere with no points in T.*

From the potential of a charge in equilibrium on an ellipsoidal conductor, we can, by allowing the least axis of the ellipsoid to approach 0, construct the potential of a charge in equilibrium on an elliptic plate. If the charge is chosen so that the potential V is 1 on the plate, then $1 - V$ is harmonic in any bounded domain including no points of the plate, and is positive except on the plate. Hence *any boundary point q of T is regular provided it lies on an ellipse with no other points in common with T or its boundary.* The word ellipse here includes, of course, the curve together with all points of its plane within the curve. The resulting criterion for the possibility of the Dirichlet problem is also due to Poincaré.

The spherical harmonics $\varrho^n P_n (\cos \vartheta)$ are positive between $\vartheta = 0$ and the first root of the function, for $\varrho > 0$. For large n, this region is only that in a rather sharp cone. But if n is made fractional, a solution of Legendre's equation exists of the form $\varrho^n P_n (\cos \vartheta)$, which is positive and harmonic *outside* a cone of one nappe, as sharp as we please. Thus, in virtue of the remark at the beginning of this section, we may state that q is a regular point of the boundary of T if it is the vertex of any right circular cone, which has no points in the portion of T in any sphere about q, however small. The resulting criterion for the Dirichlet problem is due to ZAREMBA. It follows from this that the cubical regions $R_1, R_2, R_3, \ldots$ of page 317 are regions for which the Dirichlet problem is possible for all continuous boundary values.

We have spoken of the Dirichlet problem for a given domain and for *all* continuous boundary values, because for any domain whatever the Dirichlet problem is possible for *some* continuous boundary values. We have, for instance, in the case of a bounded domain, only to assign as boundary values those of a terminating series of spherical harmonics.

19. Capacity.

Still more general types of barriers are possible[1]. Before continuing in this direction, however, let us consider briefly another notion which has been most fruitful.

In electrostatics, the *capacity* of an isolated conductor is defined as the ratio of the charge in equilibrium on it to the value of the potential at its surface. This definition may be restated as follows. Assuming the domain outside the conductor to have only regular boundary points, we form the conductor potential V, namely the solution of the Dirichlet problem for that domain, with boundary values 1. The charge producing this potential is given by Gauss' integral

$$c = -\frac{1}{4\pi}\iint \frac{\partial V}{\partial n} dS,$$

extended over any smooth surface enclosing the conductor. Then c is the capacity of the conductor.

The notion of capacity may be extended to any bounded set of points[2] B. We adjoin to B all its limit points to form the set B'. Then the set of points not in B' contains an infinite domain T, all of whose boundary points are in B'. We form, by the method of sequences, the function V, harmonic in T, for the boundary values 1, and call this the *conductor potential* of T, or of B, irrespective of whether it approaches the boundary values 1 or not. The *capacity* of B is then defined by Gauss' integral, above.

WIENER[3] has given the following general criterion as to the regularity of a boundary point q of T. Let λ be a fixed number, $0 < \lambda < 1$. Let γ_n denote the capacity of the set of points not in T and in the closed region between the spheres σ_n and σ_{n+1} about q, of radii λ^n and λ^{n+1}. *Then q is a regular or an exceptional boundary point of T according as the series*

(48) $$\frac{\gamma_0}{1} + \frac{\gamma_1}{\lambda} + \frac{\gamma_2}{\lambda^2} + \cdots$$

diverges or converges.

To prove this theorem, we have need of a number of lemmas on capacity, which are well adapted to serve as exercises.

---

[1] See, for instance, LEBESGUE, Comptes Rendus, Vol. 178 (1924), p. 352; BOULIGAND, Bulletin des sciences mathématiques, Ser. 2, Vol. 48 (1924), p. 205.

[2] WIENER, N., Journal of Mathemat cs and Physics of the Massachusetts Institute of Technology, Vol. III (1924), p. 49, p. 127. The concept is there defined for n dimensions $n \geqq 2$. It is somewhat more complicated in the plane than in space.

[3] L. c., p. 130.

Exercises.

1. Let $c(E)$ denote the capacity of E (which we shall always assume to be bounded), and let $E' + E''$ denote, as is customary, the set of all points in either E' or E''. Show that

$$c(E') \leqq c(E' + E'') \leqq c(E') + c(E'') .$$

Suggestion. Recall the uniform convergence of the sequences defining the conductor potentials, and use..Harnack's theorem (page 248) to establish the convergence of Green's integral.

2. Given a bounded set E and a number $\varepsilon > 0$, the set E can be enclosed within a set of equal spheres whose capacity differs from that of E by less than ε.

Suggestion. Apply Exercise 1 to the boundary of T_n, after showing, by the Heine-Borel theorem, that the spheres may be taken outside T_n.

3. Show that the normal derivatives of the conductor potential of the set of spheres of Exercise 1 exist and are continuous on the spheres, except possibly at their intersections (see Exercises 3 and 4, page 262), and that they are bounded in absolute value by those of the conductor potential of a single one of the spheres. Thus show that there is an actual distribution of mass on the spheres producing the conductor potential.

4. Show that the conductor potential V of E at any point P not on E satisfies the inequalities

$$\frac{c(E)}{r''} \leqq V \leqq \frac{c(E)}{r'} ,$$

where r' and r'' are the greatest lower and least upper bounds of the distances from P to the points of E.

5. Show that the capacity of a sphere is equal to its radius, and that the capacity of a circular disk is $\dfrac{2}{\pi}$ times its radius. Show that the capacity of a finite number of regular analytic arcs is 0. Suggestion. Show that the conductor potential of each arc is dominated by the potential of a distribution of constant density k on the arc, no matter how small k.

6. The capacity of the sum of a finite number of sets of 0 capacity is 0. This is not always true for infinite sums [1]. Prove these statements.

7. If E and E' are similar, *i. e.* are such that there is a one-to-one correspondence between their points, such that the distance between any two points of E' is k times the distance between the corresponding points of E, then $c(E') = k\,c(E)$.

8. If to every point of E corresponds a point of E' (the correspondence not being necessarily one-to-one) such that the distance between any two points of E is not less than the distance between the corresponding points of E', then $C(E) \geqq C(E')$.

We now take up the proof of Wiener's theorem, observing first, that if it holds for any value of λ, $0 < \lambda < 1$, it then holds for values as near the extremities of this interval as we please. This is easily verified by comparing the series with that formed for $\mu = \lambda^2$, and showing that the two converge or diverge together, by means of Exercise 1.

Let E denote the set of points not in T. We prove the lemma: *a necessary and sufficient condition that the boundary point q of T be regular,*

---

[1] The statement is true, however, for an infinite sum of *closed* sets, provided the limiting set is closed. This is proved by VASILESCO, Journal de mathématiques pures et appliquées, in a paper soon to appear.

is that the conductor potential V_α, of the portion E_α of E in any sphere about q, approaches 1 as P approaches q. The condition is necessary, since if q is regular for T, it is also regular for the domain bounded by E_α (page 328) and the conductor potential V_α approaches 1 at every regular boundary point. The condition is also sufficient. Let the radius α of the sphere cutting off E_a take on values α_n approaching 0. Let v_n be the conductor potential of E_{a_n}. We form the function

$$V = \frac{1}{2} v_1 + \frac{1}{4} v_2 + \frac{1}{8} v_3 + \cdots .$$

This function never exceeds 1, and is definitely less than 1 outside the sphere of radius α_n, for any n. For the sum of the first $n + 1$ terms cannot exceed $1 - \frac{1}{2^{n+1}}$, while the remaining terms define a function never greater than $\frac{1}{2^{n+1}}$ on the boundary of the domain in which it is harmonic. As this boundary is inside the sphere of radius α_n, the function is definitely less than $\frac{1}{2^{n+1}}$ on and outside the sphere of radius α_n. On the other hand, since V is a uniformly convergent series of functions approaching 1 at q, V does also. It follows that $1 - V$ is a barrier for T at q, and so q is regular.

Suppose now that the series (48) diverges. We show that V_α approaches 1 at q for any $\alpha > 0$. Then by the lemma, q will be regular. Given ε, $0 < \varepsilon < \frac{1}{3}$, we choose $\lambda = 1 - \frac{\varepsilon}{3}$, and consider the series

$$\sum_0^\infty \frac{\gamma_{ki}}{\lambda^{ki}}, \quad \sum_0^\infty \frac{\gamma_{ki+1}}{\lambda^{ki+1}}, \quad \cdots, \quad \sum_0^\infty \frac{\gamma_{k(i+1)-1}}{\lambda^{k(i+1)-1}},$$

where k is chosen so that $\lambda^{k-1} < \frac{\varepsilon}{3}$.

At least one of them must be divergent. We may assume that it is the first, since the other cases may be reduced to this by means of Exercise 7. We then choose m so that $\lambda^{km} < \alpha$. Let e_i denote the points of E in the closed region between the spheres σ_i and σ_{i+1} of radii λ^i and λ^{i+1} about q, and let v_i denote the conductor potential of e_i. We construct the function

$$V_{m,m'} = \sum_{i=m}^{m'} v_{ki},$$

where m' will be determined presently.

This function is harmonic except at the points of

$$e_{m,m'} = \sum_{i=m}^{m'} e_{ki},$$

and so is never greater than any bound which it has at the points of this set. On e_{kn}, $v_{kn} \leqq 1$, while for $i \neq n$, we find, by using Exercise 4, that

$$v_{ki} \leqq \frac{1}{\lambda (1 - \lambda^{k-1})} \frac{\gamma_{ki}}{\lambda^{ki}}.$$

Hence always

$$V_{m,m'} \leqq 1 + \frac{1}{\lambda (1 - \lambda^{k-1})} \sum_{i=m}^{m'} \frac{\gamma_{ki}}{\lambda^{ki}} < \frac{1 + \sum_{i=m}^{m'} \frac{\gamma_{ki}}{\lambda^{ki}}}{\lambda (1 - \lambda^{k-1})},$$

and hence the function

$$V_{m,m'} = \frac{\lambda (1 - \lambda^{k-1}) V_{m,m'}}{1 + \sum_{i=m}^{m'} \frac{\gamma_{ki}}{\lambda^{ki}}}$$

is always less than 1.

This function, harmonic in a domain including that in which V_α is harmonic, is therefore dominated by the functions of the sequence defining V_a, and so $V_\alpha \geqq V'_{m,m'}$. On the other hand, also by Exercise 4, if P is at a distance r from q,

$$V_{m,m'} \geqq \sum_{i=m}^{m'} \frac{\gamma_{ki}}{r + \lambda^{ki}},$$

and so

$$V_\alpha > \lambda (1 - \lambda^{k-1}) \frac{\sum_{i=m}^{m'} \frac{\gamma_{ki}}{r + \lambda^{ki}}}{1 + \sum_{i=m}^{m'} \frac{\gamma_{ki}}{\lambda^{ki}}}.$$

Calling the denominator D, m' can be chosen so great that $D > \frac{6}{\varepsilon}$, because of the divergence of the corresponding infinite series. Then, since the numerator approaches $D - 1$ as r approaches 0, there is an $\eta > 0$ such that for $r < \eta$, the numerator exceeds $D - 2$. We find then that for r so restricted

$$V_\alpha > 1 - \varepsilon,$$

from which we conclude that V_α approaches 1 at q, and q is regular, as was to be proved.

Now suppose that the series (48) converges. We choose m so that

$$\sum_{i=m}^{\infty} \frac{\gamma_i}{\lambda^i} < \frac{\lambda}{4},$$

and show that the conductor potential V_m of the points of E in the closed sphere σ_m does not approach 1 at q. In fact, if it did, there would be a sphere σ about q in which $V_m > \frac{3}{4}$. We then choose $m' > m$, such that $V_{m'} < \frac{1}{4}$ on σ, which is possible by Exercise 4. If now $V_{m,\,m'}$ denote the conductor potential of the portion of E in the closed region bounded by σ_m and $\sigma_{m'}$, we have by the reasoning of Exercise 1,

$$V_m \leqq V_{m'} + V_{m,m'},$$

so that on σ, we should have

$$\frac{3}{4} < \frac{1}{4} + V_{m,m'}, \quad \text{or} \quad V_{m,m'} > \frac{1}{2}.$$

The sequence defining the conductor potential $V_{m,\,m'}$ is monotone decreasing, so its terms would be greater than $\frac{1}{2}$ on σ, while inside σ their boundary values are 1. Hence they, and therefore their limiting function $V_{m,\,m'}$ would be greater than $\frac{1}{2}$ at all points within σ.

On the other hand we have at q, by Exercises 1 and 4,

$$V_{m,\,m'} \leqq \sum_{i=m}^{m'} v_i \leqq \sum_{i=m}^{m'} \frac{\gamma_i}{\lambda^{i+1}} \leqq \frac{1}{\lambda} \sum_{i=m}^{\infty} \frac{\gamma_i}{\lambda^i} < \frac{1}{4},$$

and we arrive at a contradiction. Hence V_m cannot approach 1 at q, so that by the lemma, q is exceptional.

Exercises.

9. Obtain by means of Exercise 7 the criterion of Zaremba. Generalize this to the case where the surface of a triangle with vertex at q contains no other points of R.

Suggestion. Use Exercises 1 and 5.

10. Show that if q is the vertex of a spine of Lebesgue, generated by rotating about the x-axis the curve

$$y = e^{-\frac{1}{x}}, \qquad 0 < x,$$

T lying outside the spine and bounded by it in the neighborhood of q, then q is an exceptional point. Suggestion. Obtain from Equation (27), page 189 the capacity of a prolate spheroid, and enclose the set e_i within such a surface.

11. Show that if q lies on a surface separating two domains T and T', q may be regular for both T and T', but it can never be exceptional for both. (BOULIGAND).

12. Show that the vertex of an algebraic spine formed by rotating about the x-axis the curve

$$y = x^n, \qquad x \geqq 0,$$

is regular for both domains bounded near the vertex by the spine. (LEBESGUE).

20. Exceptional Points.

The question now arises as to how exceptional exceptional points really are. We consider first portions of the boundary of 0 capacity. We have seen (page 271) that a regular isolated arc is the locus of only removable singularities of a bounded harmonic function. If we form the sequence for continuous values on the boundary of a domain, the boundary of which contains such an arc, the limit of the sequence will be harmonic and bounded in the neighborhood of the arc, and so will have only a removable singularity; we may say that the limiting function simply ignores the exceptional points of which the arc is composed. We shall see presently that the notion of capacity enables us to characterize, completely, removable singularities.

First we prove

Theorem V. *If M is the least upper bound of the function U in a domain T, in which U is harmonic, the set of boundary points at which the upper limit of U is greater than or equal to $M - \varepsilon$, for any $\varepsilon > 0$, has positive capacity.* It is understood that if T is infinite, so that U vanishes at infinity, $M > 0$. A similar result is at once inferred for the greatest lower bound.

Suppose that for some $\varepsilon > 0$ the theorem were false, and that the set E of boundary points, for each of which the limit of U for some manner of approach was greater than or equal to $M - \varepsilon$, had the capacity 0. Let $T_1, T_2, T_3, \ldots$ denote an infinite sequence of nested domains approximating to the infinite domain in which the conductor potential of E is harmonic. Let u_n be the conductor potential of T_n. For the points common to T and T_n, an open set, U has boundary values not greater than those of

$$M - \varepsilon + \varepsilon u_n$$

for all n. Hence, throughout this set of points, U is dominated by this harmonic function. The same relation holds in the limit, as n becomes infinite. But if the capacity of E were 0, its conductor potential would be 0 at all points not in E, and so certainly throughout T. That is

$$U \leqq M - \varepsilon .$$

But this would show that the least upper bound of U was not M, but at most $M - \varepsilon$. Thus the assumption that $c(E) = 0$ is untenable.

We see then that sets of capacity 0 are incapable of holding up a harmonic function to assigned values against the drag of lower boundary values elsewhere. We now complement the above theorem by the following:

Theorem VI. *Let T be any domain, and let B be any set of points taken from the boundary of T, with the properties (a) the set $T' = T + B$ is a domain, and (b) the part of B in any closed region in T' has capacity 0. Then any function U, bounded and harmonic in T, can have at most removable singularities at the points of B.*

Conversely, *if B is a set with the property (a), and if any function which is bounded and harmonic in T can have only removable singularities at the points of B, then B has the property (b).*

Let P_0 be any point of B. It is interior to T', by (a). Let σ denote a sphere about P_0, entirely in T'. We denote by e the set of points of B on the surface of σ. Now the function $f(p)$, defined on σ as equal to an upper bound M of U at the points of e, and as equal to U on the rest of σ, is continuous, except at the points of e, and bounded. It is therefore integrable, since its discontinuities can be enclosed by a set of circles on σ of arbitrarily small capacity, and so of arbitrarily small area[1]. It follows that Poisson's integral, formed for the boundary values $f(p)$, defines a function V, harmonic within σ, bounded by M, and like U, bounded below.

Now $U - V$ is harmonic in the domain S, consisting of the points within σ not in B, and has the upper limit 0 at all boundary points of S not in B, that is, except at points of a set of capacity 0. Hence by the preceding theorem, $U - V \leqq 0$. As the same argument applies to $V - U$, $U = V$ in S. But V is harmonic in the whole interior of σ, so that if U is redefined as equal to V at the points of B within σ, it becomes harmonic at all these points. Thus the singularities of U in a neighborhood of P_0 are removable, and as P_0 was any point of B, at all points of B.

To prove the converse, let R be any closed region in T', and let e denote the set of points of B in R. Let V be the conductor potential of e. It is harmonic except at points of e, and is bounded. Hence its singularities are removable, by hypothesis. When redefined, it becomes harmonic throughout all of space, and so (see Exercise 1, page 222) is 0. It follows that $c(e) = 0$, as was to be proved.

Boundary values at points of the set B have no influence on the Dirichlet problem. They are one type of exceptional point, namely those *at which the boundary E of T is of capacity* 0,[2] by which we mean that each is the center of some sphere the part of E within which has capacity 0. If such points are removed from E, the resulting set is said to be *reduced*, and it is essentially the same as E for purposes of the Dirichlet problem. A reduced set may have exceptional points, as in the case of the spine of Lebesgue, but these cannot, in general, be removed without altering the situation essentially.

It is natural to ask whether exceptional points can occur in sufficient frequency on the boundary to affect the solution of the Dirichlet problem. More precisely, can two different functions, harmonic and bounded in T, approach the same boundary values at all regular bound-

---

[1] To prove the area infinitesimal, we project it onto a plane, using Exercise 8, page 331. If E is a plane set, bounded by a finite number of regular arcs, and of area A, we prove by Lemma III (b), page 149, comparing the conductor potential of E with the potential of a spread of unit density on E, that $2\sqrt{\pi}\,c(E) \geq \sqrt{A}$. Since $c(E)$ is infinitesimal, A is.

[2] VASILESCO, l. c. page 331.

ary points? If so, their difference would be harmonic in T, bounded, and approach 0 at every regular boundary point. Call this difference W, in an order of subtraction which makes W somewhere positive. If M is the least upper bound of W, the set e of boundary points of T at which the upper limit of W is greater than or equal to $\frac{M}{2}$ must have positive capacity, by Theorem V, page 335. Now this set is closed, and consists only of exceptional points of the boundary. We should therefore have a contradiction if it were possible to establish the following lemma: *Every closed bounded set of positive capacity contains a regular point.* The corresponding lemma in two dimensions has been established[1], so that in the plane, there is for any given domain T and any continuous boundary values, one and only one function, bounded and harmonic in T and approaching the given boundary values at every regular point. In space of three or more dimensions, the lemma is still in doubt.

In all questions of uniqueness, the hypothesis on the harmonic function that it be bounded, is apt to play an essential part. Consider, for instance the harmonic function $U = x$, in the domain in which $x > 0$. Its boundary values are everywhere 0, yet it is not unique, since $U = c x$ has, for any c, the same boundary values. If, however, U is required to be bounded, we must have $c = 0$, and uniqueness is reestablished. By an inversion and a Kelvin transformation, this example yields an example for a bounded domain.

Literature. The literature of the subject matter of this chapter is so extensive, that we can only give some indications. On integral equations, the original paper of FREDHOLM, six pages in length, is a gem. *Öfversigt af Kongl. Svenska Vetenscaps Akademiens Förhandingar*, Vol. 57 (1900), pp. 39 to 46 (in French). Brief treatments of the more developed theory are to be found in BÔCHER, *An Introduction to the Study of Integral Equations*, Cambridge Tract No. 10, 1909 and 1914, and in KOWALEWSKI, *Einführung in die Determinantentheorie*, Leipzig, 1909, Chapter 18. For a more extended treatment one may consult LALESCO, *Introduction à la théorie des équations intégrales*, Paris, 1912; also HEYWOOD and FRECHET, *L'équation de Fredholm et ses applications à la physique mathématique*, Paris, 1912, and KNESER, *Die Integralgleichung und ihre Anwendung in der mathematischen Physik*, Braunschweig, 1911 and 1922.

As to the fundamental existence theorems, most books on Potential Theory give more or less attention to them (see the general list of books on page 377). For further literature, see the *Encyklopädie der Mathematischen Wissenschaften*, particularly II, C, 3, LICHTENSTEIN, *Neuere Entwickelungen der Potentialtheorie*. References to more recent work

---

[1] KELLOGG, Comptes Rendus de l'Académie de Paris, Vol. 187 (1928), p. 526, on the basis of a theorem of VASILESCO, l. c. footnote, p. 331.

will be found in a report of the author, *Recent Progress with the Dirich-let Problem*, Bulletin of the American Mathematical Society, Vol. 32 (1926), pp. 601—625, and in BOULIGAND, *Fonctions Harmoniques, Principes de Picard et de Dirichlet*, Fascicule 11 of the Mémorial des Sciences Mathématiques, Paris, 1926. The problem of attaching a harmonic function to discontinuous boundary values has also received much attention. Among recent contributions to this study may be mentioned those of PERRON, *Mathematische Zeitschrift*, Vol. 18 (1923), REMAK, ibid. Vol. 20 (1924), RADÓ and F. RIESZ, ibid. Vol. 22 (1925), WIENER, *Transactions of the American Mathematical Society*, Vol. 25 (1923), and EVANS, in his book (see p. 377) and EVANS, BRAY and MILES in recent numbers of the *Transactions* and the *American Journal of Mathematics*.

Exercises on the Logarithmic Potential.

1. Show that the kernel for the existence theorems in two dimensions is continuous, if properly defined when p and q coincide, provided the boundary curve C when given in parametric form in terms of the length of arc, $x = x(s)$, $y = y(s)$, is such that $x(s)$ and $y(s)$ have continuous derivatives of second order corresponding to all points of C.

2. Solve the Dirichlet problem for the circle by means of integral equations.

3. Develop existence theorems for plane regions by means of integral equations.

4. Examine the question as to whether the more general proofs of the possibility of the Dirichlet problem given in §§ 13—18 need any alterations in order to be applicable to the problem in two dimensions. Establish any facts needed to make them applicable.

5. Construct a barrier which is 0 on a straight line segment, everywhere continuous, and positive and harmonic except on the segment. Thus show that in the plane the Dirichlet problem is possible for any region which can be touched at any boundary point by one end of a straight line segment, however short, having no other point in common with the region.

Chapter XII.

The Logarithmic Potential.

1. The Relation of Logarithmic to Newtonian Potentials.

We have seen in Chapter VI, § 7 (p. 172), that logarithmic potentials are limiting forms of Newtonian potentials. We have seen also that harmonic functions in two dimensions, being special cases of harmonic functions in space, in that they are independent of one coördinate, partake of the properties of harmonic functions in space. The only essential differences arise from a change in the definition of regularity at infinity, and the character of these differences has been amply illustrated in the exercises at the close of Chapter IX (p. 248).

An acquaintance with the theory of Newtonian potentials, and with the exercises on logarithmic potentials in the preceding chapters,

will give a good understanding of the foundations of the theory of logarithmic potentials, except that the connection of this theory with that
of functions of a complex variable will have been left untouched. Accordingly, this chapter will be devoted a study of this connection. The
object will not be to develop the theory of functions of a complex variable in any systematic manner, except as it touches potential theory.
At the same time, no previous knowledge of the theory of functions
on the part of the reader will be assumed. We shall expect him to be
acquainted with the preceding chapters of this book, and with complex
numbers as treated in Chapter XX of OSGOOD's *Advanced Calculus*, or
in any good book on algebra. The following remarks and exercises may
serve as a review and for practice.

For the purposes of the rational operations of algebra, we may
think of the complex number $a + ib$, where a and b are real numbers,
as a linear polynomial in i, subject to the usual rules of algebra, with
the additional provision that expressions may be simplified by means
of the equation $i^2 + 1 = 0$. The number $a + ib$ may be pictured
as the point in the plane whose coördinates in an ordinary cartesian
system are (a, b). Or it may be pictured as the vector from $(0, 0)$ to
(a, b). It is understood that $a + ib = 0$ means $a = 0$ and $b = 0$.

Exercises.

1. A rational function of a finite number of complex numbers is a complex number, if no denominator is 0. Suggestion. Show that if c and c' are complex numbers,
$c + c'$, $c - c'$, cc' and $\dfrac{c}{c'}$ $(c' \neq 0)$ are complex numbers (*i.e.* can be expressed in
the form $a + ib$, a and b real), and then generalize.

2. Show that $c = a + ib$ can be written in the form

$$\varrho \left(\cos \varphi + i \sin \varphi \right).$$

Here ϱ is called the magnitude, or the absolute value of c (written $|c|$), and φ is
called the angle of c (written arc c). Arc c is determined, for $c \neq 0$, except for an
additive multiple of 2π.

3. Show that $a)$ $|c + c'| \leq |c| + |c'|$, $b)$ $|cc'| = |c| \, |c'|$, $c)$ arc $(cc') =$
arc c + arc c', if the proper branch of one of the three many-valued functions is
selected.

4. If n is a positive integer, show that there are n and only n distinct complex
numbers whose n^{th} power is a given complex number $c \neq 0$.

If $w = f(z)$ is a complex number, determined when $z = x + iy$ is given, we
call w a function of z. We say that w approaches w_0 as z approaches $z_0 = x_0 + iy_0$
if the real function $|w - w_0|$ of x and y approaches 0 as x approaches x_0 and y
approaches y_0. This may be expressed

$$\lim_{z = z_0} w = w_0.$$

The function $w = f(z)$ is said to be continuous at z_0 if

$$\lim_{z = z_0} f(z) = f(z_0).$$

5. Show that any polynomial $P(z)$ is continuous at all points z_0, and that if the coefficients are real, $P(z)$ approaches, at any point of the axis of reals, $y = 0$, the real polynomial $P(x)$. Show the same for the general rational function $\dfrac{P(z)}{Q(z)}$, exception being made for the points at which $Q(z) = 0$.

2. Analytic Functions of a Complex Variable.

The last exercise shows how the definition of a real rational function may be extended to the whole plane of z (with possible exception of a finite number of points at which $Q(z) = 0$), namely by substituting z for x. Other extensions, however, are possible. Thus to x^2 corresponds

$$z^2 = (x^2 - y^2) + i\,2\,xy,$$

but

$$f(z) = (x^2 + y^2) - i\,2\,xy$$

is also defined for all points of the z-plane and reduces to x^2 for $y = 0$. The first is a rational function of z. The second is not. These examples illustrate two types of functions of z. Both belong to a broader class of functions $u(x, y) + i\,v(x, y)$, in which u and v are any real functions of x and y. The first belongs to a narrower class, of which the rational functions of $z = x + iy$ are examples. What general property, applicable to other known functions, has the restricted class, to which the rational functions belong, and which distinguishes it from the broader class?

RIEMANN[1] found the answer to this question in the *existence of a derivative*. It will be recalled that the derivative of a real function of a real variable is not regarded as existing unless the difference quotient approaches a limit, no matter how the increment of the independent variable approaches 0. The first of the above functions has the difference quotient

$$\frac{\varDelta z^2}{\varDelta z} = 2\,z_0 + \varDelta z, \qquad (\varDelta z \neq 0),$$

and this approaches the limit $2z_0$ as $\varDelta z$ approaches 0 in any way. Thus z^2 has a derivative at every point z_0. On the other hand, the second function has the difference quotient

$$\frac{\varDelta f(z)}{\varDelta z} = \frac{(2\,x_0 - i\,2\,y_0 + \varDelta x)\,\varDelta x + (2\,y_0 - i\,2\,x_0 + \varDelta y - i\,2\,\varDelta x)\,\varDelta y}{\varDelta x + i\,\varDelta y}.$$

If first $\varDelta y$, and then $\varDelta x$, approaches 0, the limit is $2(x_0 - i\,y_0)$, whereas if the order is reversed, the limit is $2(y_0 - i\,x_0)$. It is therefore impossible that the function $f(z)$ have a derivative in the required sense, save pos-

---

[1] *Grundlagen für eine allgemeine Theorie der Funktionen einer komplexen veränderlichen Größe*, Inauguraldissertation, Werke, I, p. 3.

sibly at points of the line $y = x$, that is at points which fill no domain of the plane.

It is a function which, in some domain of the plane, has a derivative at every point, which is usually meant by the expression function of a complex variable, or, to exclude ambiguity, *analytic function of a complex variable*. We formulate the definition as follows.

The function $w = u + iv$ is said to be an analytic function of the complex varible $z = x + iy$ in the domain T of the z-plane, if the real functions u and v of x and y have continuous partial derivatives of the first order in T, and if w has a derivative with respect to z at every point of T.

To say that a function is *analytic at a point* means that it is analytic in a neighborhood of the point. We shall understand by the expression *analytic in a closed region*, analytic at every point of that region.

It may seem striking that analytic functions occupy the position they do, as opposed to the broader class of complex functions of which they constitute a sub-class. The reason is two-fold. The theory of the broader class amounts merely to a theory of pairs of real functions, in which a complex variable plays no essential role. On the other hand, the class of analytic functions includes all the elementary functions of analysis, and it is a class with a wealth of general properties, all of which have their source in this quality of differentiability. We shall see presently that among these properties is that of developability in convergent power series, and that this property is characteristic. Thus the term *analytic* is not being used here in a new sense (see page 135).

3. The Cauchy-Riemann Differential Equations.

If we employ the law of the mean for real functions of two variables, the difference quotient for the function $w = f(z) = u + iv$, analytic at $z_0 = x_0 + iy_0$, can be given the form

$$\frac{\varDelta w}{\varDelta z} = \frac{\left(\frac{\partial u}{\partial x_0} \varDelta x + \frac{\partial u}{\partial y_0} \varDelta y\right) + i \left(\frac{\partial v}{\partial x_0} \varDelta x + \frac{\partial v}{\partial y_0} \varDelta y\right)}{\varDelta x + i \varDelta y} + \eta,$$

$$|\eta| = \frac{\eta_1 \varDelta x + \eta_2 \varDelta y}{\sqrt{(\varDelta x)^2 + (\varDelta y)^2}},$$

where η_1 and η_2 are the differences between values of partial derivatives of u and v at (x_0, y_0) and at a point between this and $(x_0 + \varDelta x, y_0 + \varDelta y)$, so that they vanish as $\varDelta z$ approaches 0. If first $\varDelta y$ and then $\varDelta x$ approaches 0, this quotient approaches

$$\frac{\partial u}{\partial x_0} + i \frac{\partial v}{\partial x_0},$$

whereas if the order be reversed, the limit is

$$- i \frac{\partial u}{\partial y_0} + \frac{\partial v}{\partial y_0}.$$

The derivative cannot exist unless these limits are equal. Hence a necessary condition that the derivative exist at $z_0 = x_0 + i y_0$ is that the equations

(1) $$\frac{\partial u}{\partial x} = \frac{\partial v}{\partial y}, \qquad \frac{\partial u}{\partial y} = - \frac{\partial v}{\partial x}$$

are satisfied at (x_0, y_0). They are known as the *Cauchy-Riemann equations*[1]. We now show that the condition is sufficient. In fact, if these equations are satisfied, the difference quotient assumes the form

$$\frac{\Delta w}{\Delta z} = \left(\frac{\partial u}{\partial x} + i \frac{\partial v}{\partial x}\right)_0 + \eta \doteq - i \left(\frac{\partial u}{\partial y} + i \frac{\partial v}{\partial y}\right)_0 + \eta,$$

and since η approaches 0 as Δx and Δy approach 0 in any way whatever, it appears that the derivative exists and is given by

$$\frac{dw}{dz} = \frac{\partial}{\partial x}(u + iv) = - i \frac{\partial}{\partial y}(u + iv).$$

Theorem I. *If u and v have continuous derivatives of the first order in T, a necessary and sufficient condition that u + iv be an analytic function of x + iy in T is that the Cauchy-Riemann differential equations are satisfied.*

Exercises.

1. Show that if $f_1(z)$ and $f_2(z)$ are analytic in T, then the following are also: a) $c f_1(z)$, b) $f_1(z) + f_2(z)$, c) $f_1(z) f_2(z)$, d) $\frac{f_1(z)}{f_2(z)}$ except at the points where $f_2(z) = 0$. Show that the rules of the differential calculus hold for the derivatives of these combinations of functions.

2. Show that an analytic function of an analytic function is analytic. More specifically, if $\zeta = f(z)$ is one-valued and analytic in a domain T, if the values of ζ corresponding to the points of T form a domain S, and if $w = \varphi(\zeta)$ is analytic in S, then $w = \varphi(f(z))$ is an analytic function of z in T.

3. If we write $\zeta = \xi + i\eta = a + ib + (\cos\alpha + i\sin\alpha) z$, this linear function is analytic in the whole plane, and the points ζ correspond to the points z by a Euclidean motion of the plane. Thus show that the Cauchy-Riemann differential equations are invariant under a Euclidean motion of the plane.

4. If $w = f(z)$ is analytic in T, and if $f'(z) = 0$ at all points of T, show that $f(z)$ is constant in T.

5. Show that the inverse of an analytic function is analytic. More specifically, show if that $w = f(z)$ is analytic in a neighborhood of z_0, and if $f'(z_0) \neq 0$, there is a neighborhood of the point $w_0 = f(z_0)$ in which the inverse function $z = \varphi(w)$ exists and is analytic.

---

[1] For historical indications, see the Encyklopädie der mathematischen Wissenschaften, II, B, 1, *Allgemeine Theorie der analytischen Funktionen einer komplexen Größe*, Osgood, p. 13. We refer also for the rest of this chapter for bibliographical notes to this article, to Osgood's *Funktionentheorie*, and to the articles II, C, 4 by Bieberbach and II, C, 3 by Lichtenstein, in the same Encyklopädie.

4. Geometric Significance of the Existence of the Derivative.

A geometric representation of a function of a complex variable requires four dimensions, as four real variables are involved. It is customary to meet this situation by using two planes, a z-plane and a w-plane, between the points of which the function $w = f(z)$ sets up a correspondence. It is said to *map* the z-plane (or a portion thereof) on the w-plane (or a portion thereof). A good way in which to identify the corresponding points is to draw in the z-plane a set of numbered coördinate lines or curves, and to draw and number the corresponding lines or curves in the w-plane. Corresponding points then appear as the intersections of corresponding curves.

We now seek the geometric significance of the existence of the derivative. Let $w = f(z)$ be analytic in a neighborhood of z_0, at which the derivative does not vanish. We shall see (page 352) that the derivative can vanish only at isolated points in a neighborhood of z_0, unless w is constant. Then from the equation

$$dw = f'(z_0)\, dz$$

we infer that

$$\text{arc } dw = \text{arc } dz + \text{const.},$$

so that if two curves C_1, C_2 of the z-plane pass through z_0 and the differentials of z corresponding to their tangents at z_0 are dz_1 and dz_2, while the differentials of w corresponding to the tangents to the curves of the w-plane on which C_1 and C_2 are mapped are dw_1 and dw_2, then

$$\text{arc } dw_2 - \text{arc } dw_1 = \text{arc } dz_2 - \text{arc } dz_1,$$

so that *the angle between two curves is preserved by the mapping*. We note also that the *sense* of the angle is preserved. In the above considerations, possible additive multiples of 2π in the angles have been omitted as having no geometric significance.

A small triangle in one plane is mapped on a small triangle, in general curvilinear, in the second plane, with the same angles. Thus the shape of figures is the more nearly preserved the smaller the figures. The mapping is for this reason called *conformal*. It can be shown that the converse is true, namely that if u and v are real functions of x and y with continuous partial derivatives of the first order in T, with Jacobian different from 0, and if the transformation $u = u(x, y)$, $v = v(x, y)$ maps T on a domain of the plane of u and v, in such a way that angles are preserved in magnitude and sense, then $u + iv$ is an analytic function of $x + iy$. Thus the conformality of the mapping characterizes analytic functions.

Exercise.

Study the mapping of the function $w = z^2$, by drawing the lines $x = $ const. and $y = $ const. and their maps in the w-plane. Explain the existence of a point at which the mapping is not conformal.

The Point ∞. An analytic function may be regarded as a transformation, carrying points of the plane into points of the same plane. Let us consider the transformation brought about by the function

$$w = \frac{1}{z}.$$

If we write $z = \varrho\,(\cos\varphi + i\sin\varphi)$, $w = r\,(\cos\vartheta + i\sin\vartheta)$, the transformation may be written

$$r = \frac{1}{\varrho}, \qquad \vartheta = -\varphi.$$

It can therefore be brought about by an inversion in the unit circle and a reflection of the plane in the axis of real numbers. It can readily be seen that this is a transformation of great value in the study of functions at great distances from the origin. As the correspondence it establishes is one-to-one, except that the origin is left unpaired, we find it convenient to adjoin to the plane an ideal element which we call the *point infinity*, or the point ∞. We then say that any set of points has a property with respect to ∞, if the set on which it is mapped by $w = \frac{1}{z}$ has this property with respect to the point 0. For instance, if a set has a point other than the point ∞ outside every circle about the origin, then ∞ is called a limit point of the set. We say that a function $w = f(z)$ is analytic at infinity, if the function $f\left(\frac{1}{z}\right)$ can be so defined at $z = 0$ as to be analytic there. The value which it must have at $z = 0$ is the value assigned to w at ∞.

5. Cauchy's Integral Theorem.

The divergence theorem in the plane may be written in the form

$$(2) \qquad \iint_R \left(\frac{\partial P}{\partial x} + \frac{\partial Q}{\partial y}\right) dS = \int_C (P\,dy - Q\,dx)$$

(see Exercise 2, page 88, noting the extension provided by the rest of Chapter IV), where R is a regular region of the plane, C its boundary, described in the positive sense when R lies to the left, and where P and Q are piecewise continuously differentiable in R. By means of this theorem and the Cauchy-Riemann equations, we infer that *if $f(z) = u + iv$ is analytic in a simply connected domain T, the integral*

$$\int f(z)\,dz = \int (u\,dx - v\,dy) + i\int(v\,dx + u\,dy)$$

vanishes when extended over any closed regular curve in T. The justification of the breaking of the integral into real and imaginary parts is an immediate consequence of its definition as the limit of a sum.

The above theorem is known as *Cauchy's integral theorem.* We shall make a number of applications of it. The first will be to prove

Theorem II. *If $f(z)$ is analytic in the simply connected domain T which contains the point z_0, then*

$$F(z) = U + iV = \int_{z_0}^{z} f(z)\,dz$$

is analytic in T.

In the first place, Cauchy's integral theorem assures us that the integral is independent of the path. We find for the derivatives of U and V

$$\frac{\partial U}{\partial x} = u, \quad \frac{\partial U}{\partial y} = -v, \quad \frac{\partial V}{\partial x} = v, \quad \frac{\partial V}{\partial y} = u,$$

so that these derivatives are continuous in T and satisfy the Cauchy-Riemann equations. Hence, by Theorem I, $F(z)$ is analytic in T, as was to be proved.

We note, moreover, that U and V have continuous partial derivatives of the second order in T. Hence

$$\frac{\partial^2 U}{\partial x^2} + \frac{\partial^2 U}{\partial y^2} = \frac{\partial u}{\partial x} - \frac{\partial v}{\partial y} = 0,$$

so that U is harmonic in T. It therefore has continuous derivatives of all orders in T, and as these are also harmonic, we have established the first part of

Theorem III. *The real and imaginary parts of a function which is analytic in T are harmonic in T.* Conversely, *if u is harmonic in the simply connected domain T, there exists a function v such that $u + iv$ is an analytic function of $x + iy$ in T.*

The function v is exhibited by the formula

$$v = \int_{z_0}^{z} \left(-\frac{\partial u}{\partial y}\,dx + \frac{\partial u}{\partial x}\,dy \right).$$

An application of the divergence theorem (2) shows that this integral is independent of the path if u is harmonic, and the derivatives of v are seen to be connected with those of u by the Cauchy-Riemann equations. Thus, by Theorem I, $u + iv$ is analytic, as was to be proved.

The function v is said to be *conjugate* to u, the conjugate, or the harmonic conjugate[1] of u. As $if(z) = v - iu$ is analytic when $f(z)$ is, $-u$ is conjugate to v.

---

[1] This use of the word, applied only to real functions, is to be distinguished from that applied to two complex numbers: $a + ib$ and $a - ib$ are said to be conjugate numbers.

We are assuming in this chapter, as heretofore, that functions are one-valued unless the contrary is stated. In Theorem III it is necessary to assume that T is simply connected if we are to be sure that v is one-valued. We shall meet in the logarithm of z an instance in which v is many-valued.

Theorem III shows us that the theory of analytic functions of a complex variable may be regarded as a theory of pairs of real harmonic functions. However, to assume this point of view exclusively would be most unfortunate, for there is great gain in simplicity in uniting these pairs of functions into single objects of thought.

The Definition of the Elementary Functions for Complex Values of the Variable. We have already indicated how the rational functions may be defined. For the other elementary functions we shall confine ourselves to indications on the extension of the definition of the logarithm, supplemented by some exercises on related functions. Here Cauchy's integral theorem is fundamental, for we choose as definition

$$\log z = \int\limits_1^z \frac{dz}{z}.$$

If the path of integration, for real positive z, is restricted to the segment joining the point 1 to z, this function coincides with the Naperian logarithm of z. Now the integrand is analytic everywhere except at 0. We introduce a *cut* along the negative axis of reals between 0 and ∞, and let T denote the set of all points of the plane except those of the cut. Then T is simply connected, and the integral gives us a one-valued analytic function in T. It thus constitutes an extension of the definition of the logarithm to complex values of z.

To gain a better insight into the character of this function, let us specialize the path of integration as follows: first along the axis of reals from 1 to the point ϱ, where $z = \varrho\,(\cos\varphi + i\sin\varphi)$; then from ϱ to z along the circle about O through these points. We find then

$$\log z = \int\limits_1^\varrho \frac{dx}{x} + \int\limits_0^\varphi \frac{(-\sin\vartheta + i\cos\vartheta)}{\cos\vartheta + i\sin\vartheta}\,d\vartheta = \log\varrho + i\,\varphi.$$

Thus the real part of $\log z$ is the logarithm of the absolute value of z, and the imaginary part is i times the angle of z, $-\pi < \text{arc } z < \pi$. This is in T.

But the integral defining $\log z$ is an analytic function in the domain obtained from I by warping the cut in any way. The logarithm may therefore be defined also at points of the negative axis of reals. Only, the values on this line will differ, according as the path of integration approaches it from below or above, by $2\pi i$. Thus a *continuous* extension of the definition is possible only if we admit multiple values for the function. This is customary, and the last equation gives the definition for unrestricted values of arc z.

Exercises.

1. Show from the above definition that $\log z_1 z_2 = \log z_1 + \log z_2$ if the angle of one of the arguments is suitably chosen. Study the mapping of the function $w = \log z$, drawing, in particular, the rays $\varphi = $ const. and the circles $\varrho = $ const. in the z-plane, and their maps in the w-plane. Show that the whole plane of z, regarded as bounded by the negative axis of reals, is mapped on a certain strip of the w-plane, and consider what part of the boundary should be regarded as part of the strip if every point z other than 0 and ∞ are to be represented.

2. Study the function $z = \varphi(w)$ inverse to $w = \log z$, showing, in particular, that it is an extension, analytic in the whole plane of w except at ∞, of the real function $x = e^u$. Show also that a) e^w as thus extended has the imaginary period $2\pi i$, b) that $e^{w_1} \cdot e^{w_2} = e^{w_1 + w_2}$, c) that $e^{iv} = \cos v + i \sin v$, and d) that $\dfrac{d e^w}{d w} = e^w$.

We note that the equation (c) enables us to express a complex number in polar coördinate form more compactly than heretofore, namely by $z = \varrho e^{i\varphi}$.

3. From equation (c), infer Euler's expressions

$$\cos v = \frac{e^{iv} + e^{-iv}}{2}, \quad \sin v = \frac{e^{iv} - e^{-iv}}{2 i},$$

and by means of these study the extensions to complex values of the variables of the definitions of the trigonometric functions and their inverses.

4. By means of the identity

$$\frac{1}{x^2 + a^2} = \frac{1}{2 a i} \left(\frac{1}{x - i a} - \frac{1}{x + i a} \right)$$

integrate the left hand member in terms of logarithms, and reconcile the result with the usual integral in terms of the inverse tangent.

The Evaluation of Definite Integrals. Another use to which Cauchy's integral theorem may be put is in the evaluation of definite integrals. If such an integral can be expressed as the real part of the integral of an analytic function, the path of integration can sometimes be so deformed as to reduce the integral to one easily evaluated. We shall here confine ourselves to a single example, referring to books on analytic functions, or on definite integrals, for further illustrations.

The example we shall select is that of the integral needed in Exercise 9, page 64:

$$I = \int_0^{2\pi} \log(1 - k \cos \varphi)\, d\varphi, \qquad 0 < k < 1.$$

Consider the function

$$f(z) = \log(a - z)\frac{1}{z},$$

where a is a real number greater than 1. If we cut the z-plane along the positive axis of reals from a to ∞, any branch of $\log(a - z)$ is one-valued and analytic in the domain consisting of the points of the plane not on the cut. We select the branch which reduces to the real logarithm of a for $z = 0$. Then $f(z)$ is one-valued and analytic in a domain containing the annular region between the circles C, $|z| = 1$, and c, $|z| = \varepsilon$, where $0 < \varepsilon < 1$. The integral of $f(z)$ over the boundary of this region vanishes, if the sense of integration is such as to leave the region always to the left. For if we integrate around C in the counter-clockwise sense, then along a radius to c, then around c in the clockwise sense, and then back along the radius to C, we shall have integrated around a closed path bounding a simply connected domain in which $f(z)$ is analytic, and the integrals over the radius will destroy each other. Hence the integrals over c and C in the counter-clockwise sense are equal:

$$i \int_0^{2\pi} \log (a - \cos \varphi - i \sin \varphi)\, d\varphi = i \int_0^{2\pi} \log (a - \varepsilon \cos \varphi - i \varepsilon \sin \varphi)\, d\varphi.$$

The integrand is continuous, and the right hand member approaches $i\, 2\pi \log a$ as ε approaches 0. Hence the left hand member, which is independent of ε, has this limit as its value. Dividing by i, and taking the real parts of both sides of the resulting equation, we have

$$\int_0^{2\pi} \log |\, a - \cos \varphi - i \sin \varphi\, |\, d\varphi = \int_0^{2\pi} \log \sqrt{1 + a^2 - 2 a \cos \varphi}\, d\varphi$$
$$= 2\pi \log a.$$

This leads at once, on writing $k = \dfrac{2a}{1 + a^2}$ to the desired result,

$$\int_0^{2\pi} \log (1 - k \cos \varphi)\, d\varphi = 2\pi \log \frac{1 + \sqrt{1 - k^2}}{2}.$$

6. Cauchy's Integral.

Our next application of Cauchy's integral theorem is to the derivation of a formula analogous to the third identity of Green. Let $f(\zeta)$ be analytic in the bounded domain T of the ζ-plane, and let R be a closed regular region in T. Let z be an interior point of R. Then the function of ζ

$$\frac{f(\zeta)}{\zeta - z}$$

is analytic in the region R' consisting of the points of R not interior to a small circle c, of radius ε, about z. We infer, just as in the preceding section, that the integral of this function over the boundary C of R is equal to the integral over c, both times in the counter-clockwise sense:

$$\int_c \frac{f(\zeta)}{\zeta - z}\, d\zeta = \int_C \frac{f(\zeta)}{\zeta - z}\, d\zeta.$$

If on c we write $\zeta - z = \varepsilon e^{i\varphi}$, the left hand member becomes

$$i \int_0^{2\pi} f(z + \varepsilon e^{i\varphi}) \, d\varphi,$$

and because of the continuity of the integrand, the limit of this expression as ε approaches 0 is $i\, 2\pi f(z)$. We thus obtain *Cauchy's integral*:

$$(3) \qquad f(z) = \frac{1}{2\pi i} \int_C \frac{f(\zeta)}{\zeta - z} \, d\zeta.$$

It gives $f(z)$ at any interior point of R in terms of its values on the boundary of R. It is thus analogous to Green's integral (page 237). If, however, the integral be separated into real and imaginary parts, the real part of $f(z)$ will be given, not in terms of its boundary values alone, but in terms of these and the boundary values of its conjugate. In this respect, Cauchy's integral is more nearly analogous to the expression for a harmonic function in terms of its boundary values and those of its normal derivative, as indicated above. In fact, Green's third identity for the plane can be derived from (3). We have only to keep in mind that the Cauchy-Riemann equations are invariant under a rigid motion, so that we have the relations

$$\frac{\partial u}{\partial n} = \frac{\partial v}{\partial s}, \quad \frac{\partial u}{\partial s} = -\frac{\partial v}{\partial n}.$$

We have, in equation (3), a striking illustration of the advantages of considering analytic functions of a complex variable as wholes, rather than as pairs of harmonic functions. For the equation representing $f(z)$ in terms of its boundary values is possible in a most simple form, without the use of Green's function, depending on the special character of the region.

Power Series for Analytic Functions. It is not difficult to verify that the theorem stating that the integral of a real function may be differentiated with respect to a parameter by differentiating under the integral sign, provided the derivative of the integrand is continuous in all the variables, holds also for functions of a complex variable. We have then, z still being interior to R,

$$(4) \qquad f'(z) = \frac{1}{2\pi i} \int_C \frac{f(\zeta)}{(\zeta - z)^2} \, d\zeta, \ldots, f^{(n)}(z) = \frac{n!}{2\pi i} \int_C \frac{f(\zeta)}{(\zeta - z)^{n+1}} \, d\zeta, \ldots.$$

Let a denote a point of T, and c a circle about a lying with its interior in T. Let z be interior to c. Then, from the algebraic identity

$$\frac{1}{\zeta - z} = \frac{1}{\zeta - a} + \frac{z - a}{(\zeta - a)^2} + \cdots + \frac{(z-a)^n}{(\zeta - a)^{n+1}} + \frac{(z-a)^{n+1}}{(\zeta - z)(\zeta - a)^{n+1}},$$

and equation (3), we derive the formula

(5) $$f(z) = \sum_{0}^{n} a_k (z - a)^k + R_n,$$

where

$$a_k = \frac{1}{2 \pi i} \int_c \frac{f(\zeta)}{(\zeta - a)^{k+1}} d\zeta, \quad R_n = \frac{(z - a)^{n+1}}{2 \pi i} \int_c \frac{f(\zeta) d\zeta}{(\zeta - z)(\zeta - a)^{n+1}}.$$

Comparing the coefficients a_k with the formulas (4), we see that what we have here is a Taylor series for $f(z)$ with remainder. In order to obtain an infinite series, let us seek a bound for the remainder. As $|\zeta - a|$ is constant, equal to the radius ϱ of c, we see that

$$|R_n| \leqq \left| \frac{z - a}{\varrho} \right|^{n+1} \frac{1}{2 \pi} \int_c \left| \frac{f(\zeta)}{\zeta - z} \right| d\zeta.$$

As n becomes infinite, R_n approaches 0, and we have the first part of

Theorem IV. *If $f(z)$ is analytic in T, it is developable in a power series about any point a of T, convergent in the interior of any circle about a which lies in T. Conversely, any convergent power series in $z - a$ represents a function which is analytic in the interior of any circle about a, in which the series is convergent.*

As an instrument for the proof of the second part of the theorem, we derive a theorem analogous to Koebe's converse of Gauss' theorem, in that an analytic function is characterized, by means of it, in terms of integrals. It is a converse of Cauchy's integral theorem, and is

Morera's Theorem. Let $f(z)$ be continuous in the simply connected domain T, and let the integral

$$\int f(z) dz$$

vanish when taken over the boundary of any regular region in T. Then $f(z)$ is analytic in T.

The hypothesis implies that the integral, from the point z_0 of T to z, is independent of the path. Its derivatives, given on page 345, are continuous and satisfy the Cauchy-Riemann equations. Thus the indefinite integral of $f(z)$ is analytic in T, and we readily verify that its derivative is $f(z)$. From the formulas (4), we infer that the derivative of an analytic function is analytic. Hence $f(z)$ is analytic in T.

Returning to the proof of the second part of Theorem IV, we note that if the power series

$$\sum_{0}^{\infty} a_k (z - a)^k$$

is convergent for $z = z_0$, $|z_0 - a| = \varrho$, its terms are necessarily bounded in absolute value, so that for some constant B, $|a_k| \leqq \dfrac{B}{\varrho^k}$. It follows that for $|z - a| \leqq \lambda \varrho$, $0 < \lambda < 1$, the series is dominated by the geometric series

$$\sum_0^\infty B \lambda^k,$$

and so converges uniformly and absolutely. The rest of the proof of Theorem IV then follows the lines of that of Harnack's theorem (p. 249).

Thus analytic functions, in the sense in which we have defined them, are identical with functions which can be developed in convergent power series. It was on the power series that WEIERSTRASS founded his theory of functions of a complex variable.

Infinite Series of Analytic Functions. In § 2 of Chapter V (p. 125), we had need of the fact that a certain infinite series of polynomials could be represented as a power series. This fact is established in

Theorem V. *Let*

(6) $$w_1(z) + w_2(z) + w_3(z) + \cdots$$

be an infinite series of functions of z, all analytic in a domain T and let the series converge uniformly in T. Then the sum w (z) is analytic in any closed region R in T. Furthermore, if a is in R, if

$$w_k(z) = \sum_{n=0}^\infty a_{kn}(z - a)^n, \qquad k = 1, 2, 3, \ldots$$

is the development in powers of (z — a) of $w_k(z)$, and if

$$w(z) = \sum_{n=0}^\infty a_n (z - a)^n$$

is the development of w (z), then

$$a_n = \sum_{k=1}^\infty a_{kn}, \qquad n = 1, 2, 3, \ldots.$$

The fact that $w(z)$ is analytic in R' follows from Morera's theorem, since the series (6) may be integrated termwise. For the same reason we have, integrating around a circle c about a, and in T,

$$a_n = \frac{1}{2\pi i} \int_c \frac{w(\zeta)}{(\zeta - a)^{n+1}} d\zeta = \sum_{k=1}^\infty \frac{1}{2\pi i} \int_c \frac{w_k(\zeta)}{(\zeta - a)^{n+1}} d\zeta = \sum_{k=1}^\infty a_{kn}.$$

Exercise.

Show that the derivative of a power series, convergent in a circle c, may be obtained, in the interior of c, by termwise differentiation.

7. The Continuation of Analytic Functions.

The theorems of § 5, Chapter X, on the continuation of the domain of definition of harmonic functions, yield at once theorems on the continuation of analytic functions. From Theorem IV, we infer that an analytic function is completely determined by its values in a domain, however small (see also Theorem VI, below). From Theorem V, we infer that if two analytic functions agree in an overlapping portion of their domains of definition, each constitutes a continuation of the other. Theorem VI has an analogue for analytic functions which makes no hypothesis on the normal derivatives: *Let T_1 and T_2 be two domains without common points, but whose boundaries contain a common isolated regular arc. If $w_1(z)$ is analytic in T_1 and $w_2(z)$ in T_2, if they agree and form a continuous function at the points of the arc, when defined there by their limiting values, then they define a function which is analytic in the domain $T_1 + T_2 + \gamma$, where γ denotes the set of interior points of the arc.* The proof follows that of Theorem VI, Cauchy's integral and integral theorem playing the roles of Green's identities.

We have seen that if a function U, harmonic in a domain T in space, vanishes, together with its normal derivatives, on a regular surface element in T, it is identically 0 in T. Corresponding to this we have a result for analytic functions of which we shall have need:

Theorem VI. *If $w(z)$ is analytic in a closed region R, and vanishes at infinitely many points of R, it vanishes at all points of R.*

In fact, if $w(z)$ has infinitely many zeros in R, these zeros will have a limit point a in R, by the Bolzano-Weierstrass theorem. As $w(z)$ is analytic at a, it is developable in a power series in $z - a$, convergent in a circle c about a. Because of its continuity, $w(z)$ vanishes at a, so that the constant term in the power series is absent. Let a_k denote the first coefficient not 0, on the assumption that $w(z)$ is not identically 0 in c. Then the function

$$\frac{w(z)}{(z-a)^k} = a_k + a_{k+1}(z-a) + a_{k+2}(z-a)^2 + \cdots,$$

is analytic within c, and by hypothesis, vanishes at points arbitrarily near a. Hence, because of continuity, it vanishes at a, and we have $a_k = 0$. Thus we are led to a contradiction, and $w(z) = 0$ throughout the interior of c. By the argument used for the proof of Theorem IV, page 259, we infer that $w(z) = 0$ throughout R.

An analytic function, defined in a domain, may, or may not, be continuable beyond that domain. The obstacles to continuation lie in the function itself. It may become infinite at a point; it cannot then be analytic in any domain containing the point. If defined in a domain, and if continuable along a path which leaves and returns to this domain and which contains a point at which the function is not analytic, the function may not return to its initial value, and so of necessity be several-valued. When we speak of an analytic function, we usually have reference to the function continued in every possible way[1].

---

[1] For further details on this point, the reader may consult OSGOOD's *Funktionentheorie*, particularly § 3, Chapter IX.

Exercises.

1. Show that the function

$$f(z) = \sum_{1}^{\infty} z^{n!},$$

defined and analytic in the unit circle, cannot be continued beyond this circle. Suggestion. Show that $f(z)$ becomes infinite as z approaches the circumference of the unit circle along any ray $\varphi = \left(\dfrac{p}{q}\right)\pi$, where p and q are integers. The unit circle is a *natural boundary* for $f(z)$.

2. Show that if a function $f(x)$, defined and one-valued on an interval of the axis of reals, is susceptible of being defined in a neighborhood of a point of this interval so as to be analytic there, this definition is possible in only one way.

8. Developments in Fourier Series.

The analogue of a series of surface spherical harmonics is, in two dimensions, a Fourier series.

We shall devote this and the following section to them. Let $f(z)$ be analytic in a domain including the unit circle. The infinite series

$$f(z) = \sum_{0}^{\infty} a_n z^n$$

will then be uniformly convergent within and on the circle, and so also will be the series obtained by taking the real and imaginary parts of its terms. The coefficients are given by the formulas (5), with $a = 0$. We write

$$z = \varrho\, e^{i\varphi}, \quad \zeta = e^{i\vartheta}, \quad f(z) = u + iv, \quad a_n = \alpha_n - i\beta_n,$$

and find

(7)
$$u(\varrho, \varphi) = \sum_{0}^{\infty} (\alpha_n \cos n\varphi + \beta_n \sin n\varphi)\, \varrho^n,$$

$$v(\varrho, \varphi) = \sum_{0}^{\infty} (\alpha_n \sin n\varphi - \beta_n \cos n\varphi)\, \varrho^n,$$

where

(8)
$$\alpha_n = \frac{1}{2\pi} \int_{0}^{2\pi} [u(1, \vartheta) \cos n\vartheta + v(1, \vartheta) \sin n\vartheta]\, d\vartheta,$$

$$\beta_n = \frac{1}{2\pi} \int_{0}^{2\pi} [u(1, \vartheta) \sin n\vartheta - v(1, \vartheta) \cos n\vartheta]\, d\vartheta.$$

Thus, the real and imaginary parts of $f(z)$ can be expanded in uniformly convergent Fourier series for $\varrho \leqq 1$.

We remark that if $f(z)$ is analytic only in the interior of the circle and bounded on the circumference, the series (7) still converge uniformly in any closed region within the circle. Also, that if we know the series for the harmonic function u, that for the conjugate function v may be obtained by interchanging the coefficients of $\cos n\varphi$ and $\sin n\varphi$ and then reversing the sign of the coefficient of $\cos n\varphi$, for every positive n. This leaves undetermined the constant term, but we know that this is not determined by the fact that v is conjugate to u.

Suppose now that the real harmonic function u is given, without its conjugate. It is desirable to eliminate from the formulas (8), for the coefficients, the function v. This may be done by applying Cauchy's integral theorem to the function $f(z) z^{n-1}$ $(n \geqq 1)$, analytic in a domain including the unit circle. We find, on integrating around this circle, the equations

$$\int_0^{2\pi} [u(1, \vartheta) \cos n\vartheta - v(1, \vartheta) \sin n\vartheta] d\vartheta = 0,$$

$$\int_0^{2\pi} [u[1, \vartheta) \sin n\vartheta + v(1, \vartheta) \cos n\vartheta] d\vartheta = 0,$$

by means of which we are enabled to write the expansion in the form

$$(9) \qquad u(\varrho, \varphi) = \frac{1}{2}\alpha_0 + \sum_1^\infty \varrho^n (\alpha_n \cos n\varphi + \beta_n \sin n\varphi),$$

where

$$(10) \quad \alpha_n = \frac{1}{\pi} \int_0^{2\pi} u(1, \vartheta) \cos n\vartheta \, d\vartheta, \qquad \beta_n = \frac{1}{\pi} \int_0^{2\pi} u(1, \vartheta) \sin n\vartheta \, d\vartheta.$$

The series is uniformly convergent in the unit circle if u is harmonic in an including domain. Suppose, however, that instead of the boundary values of u being given, we have an arbitrary function $f(\vartheta)$, with period 2π, integrable and bounded, and that we form the coefficients

$$(11) \qquad \alpha_n = \frac{1}{\pi} \int_0^{2\pi} f(\vartheta) \cos n\vartheta \, d\vartheta, \qquad \beta_n = \frac{1}{\pi} \int_0^{2\pi} f(\vartheta) \sin n\vartheta \, d\vartheta.$$

The series (9), with these coefficients, will still converge uniformly in any closed region within the unit circle, and so, by Harnack's theorem, represent a harmonic function. We have thus a means of assigning to any function of the type $f(\vartheta)$ (and to even more general ones, in fact), a function which is harmonic within the circle. The result is a sort of generalization of the Dirichlet problem for discontinuous boundary values for the circle. The question as to the sense in which the harmonic function approaches the given boundary values, and the question as to the sense in which they uniquely determine the harmonic function, have received much study[1].

---

[1] The reader will find the matter treated in EVANS' *The Logarithmic Potential* (see page 377).

Exercises.

1. Show that if, in deriving the series (9), we had integrated over the circle $|z| = a < 1$, the coefficients would have been given in the form

$$\alpha_n = \frac{1}{\pi a^n} \int\limits_0^{2\pi} u\,(a,\,\vartheta)\cos n\,\vartheta\,d\,\vartheta\,, \quad \beta_n = \frac{1}{\pi a^n} \int\limits_0^{2\pi} u\,(a,\,\vartheta)\sin n\,\vartheta\,d\,\vartheta\,.$$

Show that these expressions are independent of a for $0 < a < 1$.

2. Show, on the hypothesis $\varrho < 1$, that the sum of the series (9), with the coefficients (11), is given by Poisson's integral

$$u\,(\varrho,\,\varphi) = \frac{1-\varrho^2}{2\,\pi} \int\limits_0^{2\pi} \frac{f\,(\vartheta)\,d\,\vartheta}{1 - 2\,\varrho\cos(\vartheta-\varphi) + \varrho^2}\,,$$

and thus that if $f(\vartheta)$ is merely continuous and periodic, the series represents a function which is harmonic in the closed unit circle, and has the boundary values $f(\varphi)$.

9. The Convergence of Fourier Series.

Because of their usefulness in studying the behavior of harmonic functions and of analytic functions on the boundary of circles in which they are harmonic or analytic, as well as for their importance in physical applications, we shall be justified in a brief consideration of the convergence of Fourier series for $\varrho = 1$. We take, then the series

$$(12) \qquad \frac{1}{2}\alpha_0 + \sum_1^\infty (\alpha_n \cos n\,\varphi + \beta_n \sin n\,\varphi)$$

obtained from (9) by setting $\varrho = 1$, the coefficients being given by (11). We shall assume that $f(\vartheta)$ has the period $2\,\pi$, and that it is integrable in the sense of Riemann. Products and sums of such functions have the same property. We first show that the sum of the squares of the coefficients (11) is convergent. This follows from the identity

$$\int\limits_0^{2\pi} [f(\vartheta) - \frac{1}{2}\alpha_0 - \sum_1^m (\alpha_n \cos n\,\vartheta + \beta_n \sin n\,\vartheta)]^2\,d\,\vartheta$$

$$= \int\limits_0^{2\pi} f^2(\vartheta)\,d\,\vartheta - \pi\Big[\frac{\alpha_0^2}{2} + \sum_1^m (\alpha_n^2 + \beta_n^2)\Big].$$

The form of the left hand member shows that the right hand member is never negative and it follows that *if $f(\varphi)$ is periodic and integrable, the series*

$$\frac{\alpha_0^2}{2} + \sum_1^\infty (\alpha_n^2 + \beta_n^2)$$

is convergent. As a corollary, we note that α_n *and* β_n *approach* 0 *as* n *becomes infinite.*

Returning to the question of convergence of the series (12), let $s_m = s_m(\varphi)$ denote the sum of the first $n + 1$ terms. Introducing the values of the coefficients and the notation $\gamma = \vartheta - \varphi$, we may write

$$s_m = \frac{1}{\pi} \int_0^{2\pi} f(\vartheta) \left[\frac{1}{2} + \cos\gamma + \cos 2\gamma + \cdots + \cos n\gamma \right] d\vartheta.$$

The function in brackets may be written

$$\frac{1}{2} \left[e^{-in\gamma} + e^{-i(n-1)\gamma} + \cdots + e^{-i\gamma} + 1 + e^{i\gamma} + \cdots + e^{in\gamma} \right]$$

$$= \frac{1}{2} \frac{e^{-i(n+\frac{1}{2})\gamma} - e^{i(n+\frac{1}{2})\gamma}}{e^{-i\frac{\gamma}{2}} - e^{i\frac{\gamma}{2}}} = \frac{1}{2} \frac{\sin\left(n + \frac{1}{2}\right)\gamma}{\sin\frac{1}{2}\gamma}.$$

We thus obtain, if we use γ as the variable of integration,

$$s_m = \frac{1}{2\pi} \int_{-\pi}^{\pi} f(\varphi + \gamma) \frac{\sin(2n+1)\frac{\gamma}{2}}{\sin\frac{\gamma}{2}} d\gamma,$$

the change in the limits of integration being allowable because of the periodicity of the integrand. Finally, writing $\gamma = 2t$, we have

$$s_m = \frac{1}{\pi} \int_{-\frac{\pi}{2}}^{\frac{\pi}{2}} f(\varphi + 2t) \frac{\sin(2n+1)t}{\sin t} dt,$$

which may be written

$$(13) \qquad s_m = \frac{1}{\pi} \int_0^{\frac{\pi}{2}} [f(\varphi + 2t) + f(\varphi - 2t)] \frac{\sin(2n+1)t}{\sin t} dt.$$

Applying this identity to the function $f(\varphi) = 1$, we have, since the series (12) then reduces to its first term,

$$(14) \qquad 1 = \frac{2}{\pi} \int_0^{\frac{\pi}{2}} \frac{\sin(2n+1)t}{\sin t} dt.$$

We multiply this equation by $f(\varphi)$, which is independent of t, and subtract the result from (13):

$$(15) \qquad s_m(\varphi) - f(\varphi)$$

$$= \frac{1}{\pi} \int_0^{\frac{\pi}{2}} [f(\varphi + 2t) + f(\varphi - 2t) - 2f(\varphi)] \frac{\sin(2n+1)t}{\sin t} dt.$$

We have here a convenient formula for the discussion of the convergence. To establish convergence at a point φ_0, further hypotheses on $f(\varphi)$ at φ_0 are necessary. Even continuity is not sufficient[1]. A simple condition which suffices is this: there exist two constants, a and A, such that

$$(16) \quad |f(\varphi_0 + 2t) + f(\varphi_0 - 2t) - 2f(\varphi_0)| \leq At, \qquad \text{for } 0 \leq t \leq a.$$

Not every continuous function satisfies this condition. Thus, if near φ_0, $f(\varphi) = (\varphi - \varphi_0)^{\frac{2}{3}}$, $f(\varphi)$ does not. On the other hand, a discontinuous function may satisfy it. For instance if $f(\varphi)$ has piecewise continuous derivatives, and at any point of discontinuity has as value the arithmetic mean of the limits approached from right and left, then $f(\varphi)$ satisfies the condition.

Consider the formula (15), on the hypothesis that $f(\varphi)$ satisfies (16). We note first that

$$\left| \int_0^\eta [f(\varphi_0 + 2t) + f(\varphi_0 - 2t) - 2f(\varphi_0)] \frac{\sin(2n+1)t}{\sin t} dt \right|$$

$$\leq A \int_0^\eta \frac{t}{\sin t} dt < A \frac{\pi}{2} \eta, \qquad 0 < \eta < a, \qquad \eta < \frac{\pi}{2}.$$

Hence, given $\varepsilon > 0$, if we take $\eta \leq \frac{2\varepsilon}{\pi A}$, this portion of the integral in (15) will be less in absolute value than ε. If η is thus fixed, the rest of the integral approaches 0 as n becomes infinite. We may see this as follows. If we define

$$g(t) = \frac{f(\varphi_0 + 2t) + f(\varphi_0 - 2t) - 2f(\varphi_0)}{\sin t}, \qquad \eta \leq t \leq \frac{\pi}{2},$$

$g(t) = 0$ elsewhere in the interval $(0, 2\pi)$,

then $g(t)$ is integrable in the interval, and

$$\int_0^{\frac{\pi}{2}} [f(\varphi_0 + 2t) + f(\varphi_0 - 2t) - 2f(\varphi_0)] \frac{\sin(2n+1)t}{\sin t} dt$$

$$= \int_0^{2\pi} g(t) \sin(2n+1)t\, dt = \pi \beta'_{2n+1}$$

is π times the Fourier constant β'_{2n+1} for $g(t)$. It therefore approaches 0 as n becomes infinite. If n be required to be large enough to make this

---

[1] Examples exhibiting this fact have been given by L. FEJÉR, Journal für reine und angewandte Mathematik, Vol. 137 (1909); Sitzungsberichte der Bayerischen Akademie, 1910.

integral less in absolute value than ε, we shall have

$$|s_m(\varphi_0) - f(\varphi_0)| < \frac{2\varepsilon}{\pi} < \varepsilon,$$

and the series (12) therefore converges at φ_0 to the value $f(\varphi_0)$. It may be noted that except for the condition of integrability, the convergence of the Fourier series at a point depends only on the character of the function in a neighborhood of that point.

Exercise.

1. Show that the condition (16) may be replaced by the milder one that

$$\int_0^a \frac{|f(\varphi_0 + 2t) + f(\varphi_0 - 2t) - 2f(\varphi_0)|}{t} dt$$

is convergent.

Sometimes the fact that a Fourier series may be thought of as giving the boundary values of the real or imaginary part of an analytic function enables us to find in a simple way the sum of the series. Let us take as an example the series

(17) $\sin\varphi + \frac{1}{2}\sin 2\varphi + \frac{1}{3}\sin 3\varphi + \cdots.$

This is, formally, at least, the value, for $\varrho = 1$, of v in the analytic function

$$f(z) = u + iv = z + \frac{1}{2}z^2 + \frac{1}{3}z^3 + \cdots = \log\frac{1}{1-z}.$$

This function, within the unit circle, has as the coefficient of i,

$$v = \text{arc}\frac{1}{1-z} = \tan^{-1}\frac{\varrho\sin\varphi}{1 - \varrho\cos\varphi},$$

where the inverse tangent lies in the interval $\left(-\frac{\pi}{2}, \frac{\pi}{2}\right)$, for $\frac{1}{(1-z)}$ has a positive real part, and v reduces to 0 for $\varrho = 0$. From this expression we see that

$$\lim_{\varrho=1} v = \tan^{-1}\frac{\sin\varphi}{1 - \cos\varphi} = \frac{\pi}{2} - \frac{\varphi}{2}, \qquad 0 < \varphi < 2\pi.$$

The function $f(\varphi)$, equal to this limiting value in the open interval $(0, 2\pi)$, and equal to 0 at the end points, satisfies the condition (16), and so is represented by its Fourier series at every point, by the convergence theorem. If we form its Fourier coefficients, we find that they coincide with those of the series (17), and the function $f(\varphi)$, just defined, is therefore the sum of the series.

Exercises.

2. Determine the Fourier coefficients of the function $f(\varphi)$ above, and thus complete the proof that it represents the sum of the series (17).

3. Determine the sum of the series

$$\cos \varphi - \frac{1}{3} \cos 3\,\varphi + \frac{1}{5} \cos 5\,\varphi - \cdots.$$

4. Given a thermally isotropic homogeneous body in the form of a right circular cylinder whose bases are insulated, and whose curved surface is kept, one half at the temperature 1 and the other at the temperature -1, the two halves being bounded by diametrically opposite generators, determine the stationary temperatures in the interior. Draw the traces of the isothermal surfaces on a plane perpendicular to the axis.

5. Show that if $f(z)$ is analytic in a domain including the closed region R, bounded by two circles about the origin, then $f(z)$ is developable in a *Laurent series*

$$f(z) = \sum_{-\infty}^{\infty} a_n z^n,$$

uniformly convergent in R, where

$$a_n = \frac{1}{2\pi i} \int_c \frac{f(\zeta)}{\zeta^{n+1}} \, d\zeta,$$

c being any circle about the origin between the two given circles. Thus show a) that $f(z)$ is the sum of two functions, one analytic within the outer circle, and the other analytic outside the inner circle; b) that if a function $f(z)$ is analytic and one-valued in a neighborhood of a point, except possibly at that point, and bounded in the neighborhood of the point, it has there at most a removable singularity; c) that the only function which is everywhere analytic (including ∞), is a constant.

Although the Fourier series of a continuous function need not converge at every point, FEJÉR[1] has shown that it is always summable. This means that whereas the partial sums $s_0, s_1, s_2, \ldots$ may not approach a limit, their arithmetic means

$$s_0, \quad \frac{s_0 + s_1}{2}, \quad \frac{s_0 + s_1 + s_2}{2}, \quad \ldots$$

always do, and the limit is, in fact, $f(\varphi)$. We shall not, however, develop the proof. It may be found in the *Funktionentheorie of* HURWITZ and COURANT, Berlin, 1925, p. 305. Further material on Fourier series may be found in LEBESGUE's *Leçons sur les séries trigonométriques*, Paris, 1928, in most works on the theory of functions of real variables, and in the books referred to on page 206.

10. Conformal Mapping.

We have seen that analytic functions map domains of one plane conformally on domains of another. We shall see later that if simply connected domains, one in the z-plane and one in the ζ-plane, are given,

---

[1] *Sur les fonctions bornées et intégrables*, Comptes Rendus de l'Académie de Paris, Vol. **131** (1900), pp. 984—987.

there is essentially only one function $\zeta = f(z)$ which maps the one on the other conformally. Thus analytic functions are characterized by their mapping properties, and the geometric theory of functions, based on this fact, is becoming a more and more important aspect of the subject. We shall consider, in the present section, some special cases of mapping.

A. $\zeta = z + b$. The mapping may be regarded as a translation, any figure in the z-plane being mapped on a congruent figure in the ζ-plane, translated with respect to the axes by a vector displacement b.

B (a). $\zeta = az$, $|a| = 1$, *i. e.* $a = e^{ia}$, α real. The mapping may be regarded as a rotation of the plane through the angle α.

(b). $\zeta = az$, a real and positive. The mapping may be regarded as a uniform dilation or contraction of the plane, the direction of the axes remaining fixed. Or, it may be described as a homothetic transformation.

C. $\zeta = az + b$. The mapping may be described as a homothetic transformation followed by a Euclidean motion of the plane. This may be seen by writing the function in the form

$$z_1 = |a| z, \quad z_2 = e^{ia} z_1, \quad \zeta = z_2 + b, \quad \text{where } \alpha = \text{arc } a.$$

We note that the mapping carries circles and straight lines into circles and straight lines.

D. $\zeta = \dfrac{1}{z}$. We have met this function on page 344. As an inversion in space carries spheres and planes into spheres or planes, straight lines and circles in a plane through the center of inversion will be carried into straight lines or circles. We see that this is therefore a property of the present transformation, a fact otherwise easy of verification.

E. $\zeta = \dfrac{az + b}{cz + d}$, $ad - bc \neq 0$. This is called the general *linear function*, or broken linear function. If $ad - bc$ were 0, ζ would be constant, and the whole plane of z would be mapped on a single point. We assume that this is not the case. The inverse of this function,

$$z = \frac{-d\zeta + b}{c\zeta - a}, \quad (-d)(-a) - bc = ad - bc \neq 0,$$

is also a linear function; each is analytic save at one point. The linear function is a combination of functions of the types C and D. If $c = 0$, this is evident at once. Otherwise, we may write

$$z_1 = z + \left(\frac{d}{c}\right), \quad z_2 = \frac{1}{z_1}, \quad \zeta = \frac{a}{c} + \frac{bc - ad}{c^2} z_2.$$

We see thus that the general linear function maps circles and straight lines on circles or straight lines.

Exercises.

1. Show that

$$\zeta = \frac{z - i}{z + i}$$

maps the upper half-plane $y > 0$ on the interior of the unit circle $|\zeta| < 1$, and the axis of reals on the circumference of this circle.

2. Show that there is a linear function which maps the interior of any circle on the interior of the unit circle; the same for the half-plane to one side of any straight line.

3. Show that there is a linear function which maps any three given distinct points of the z-plane on any three given distinct points of the ζ-plane, and that there is only one such linear function.

4. Show that the linear function maps the upper half-plane $y > 0$ on the upper half-plane $\eta > 0$ if, and only if, the coefficients a, b, c, d all have real ratios, and after they have been made real by division by a suitable factor, $ad - bc > 0$.

5. Show that the function of the preceding exercise is uniquely determined by the demands that a given point a of the upper half-plane of z shall correspond to $\zeta = i$, and a given point of the axis of reals in the z-plane shall correspond to the point ∞ in the ζ-plane. Infer from this and Exercise 2 that there is one and only one linear function which maps the interior of the unit circle on itself in such a way that a given interior point corresponds to the center, and a given point on the circumference to the point 1.

F. $\zeta = z^n$, n real and positive. The mapping is conformal except at 0 and ∞. If n is an integer, each point of the z-plane goes over into a single point of the ζ-plane, but n points of the ζ-plane go over into a single point (other than 0 or ∞) of the z-plane. Thus the inverse function is not one-valued for $n > 1$. The function maps a domain bounded by two rays from 0 on a domain of the same sort. The latter may overlap itself.

G. $\zeta = \cos z$. The mapping is conformal except at the points $z = n\pi$, where n is any integer. Breaking the function into real and imaginary parts, we find

$$\xi = \cos x \cosh y,$$
$$\eta = -\sin x \sinh y.$$

The lines $y = $ const. go over into the ellipses

$$\frac{\xi^2}{\cosh^2 y} + \frac{\eta^2}{\sinh^2 y} = 1,$$

which, since $\cosh^2 y - \sinh^2 y = 1$, constitute a confocal family, with foci at $\zeta = \pm 1$. The lines $x = $ const. are mapped on the hyperbolas

$$\frac{\xi^2}{\cos^2 x} - \frac{\eta^2}{\sin^2 x} = 1$$

with the same foci.

To study the mapping farther, we note that since $\cos z$ has the period 2π, we shall get all the points of the ζ-plane which are given

362   The Logarithmic Potential.

at all, if we consider only the points of the z-plane in a strip of breadth 2π, say the strip $-\pi < x \leq \pi$. Moreover, since $\cos(-z) = \cos z$, we may confine ourselves to the upper half of this strip, provided we include the part $0 \leq x \leq \pi$ of the axis of reals. It will appear that we cannot confine ourselves to any more restricted region and still get all values for ζ which it may assume, so that the partly open region

$$R: \quad -\pi < x \leq \pi, \quad y > 0 \quad \text{and} \quad 0 \leq x \leq \pi, \quad y = 0$$

is a *fundamental region* for the function $\zeta = \cos z$; for this is the usual designation of a region in which an analytic function assumes exactly once all the values it assumes at all. It is clear that the region obtained

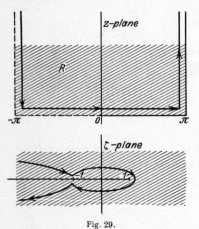

Fig. 29.

from R by a translation $z_1 = z + b$, b real, or by the rotation $z = -z$ is also a fundamental region, and still others may be formed.

The fundamental region R and its map are represented in figure 29. The boundary of R is mapped on the axis of real ζ between $-\infty$ and 1. But the points of the boundary, described with the region to the left, which come before 0, are not points of R. Hence the above portion of the axis of real ζ must be regarded as the map of the boundary of R from 0 on.

We make two applications of the function $\zeta = \cos z$. We note first that inasmuch as the derivative vanishes at no interior point of R, the inverse function exists and is analytic in the whole plane of ζ, if the points of the cut from 1 to $-\infty$ along the real axis are removed. The imaginary part $y = y(\xi, \eta)$ of this inverse function is therefore harmonic in the same domain. But it is also harmonic at the points of the axis of reals to the left of -1, being an even function of ξ. It is thus harmonic and one-valued in the region bounded by the segment from $(-1, 0)$ to $(1, 0)$; it approaches continuously the value 0 on this segment, and is elsewhere positive, as is at once seen by the mapping. It will therefore serve as a barrier of the sort contemplated in Exercise 5, page 338.

An allied application is to elliptic coördinates. The variables x and y may be interpreted as generalized coördinates of a point of the (ξ, η)-plane. The coördinate curves are confocal ellipses and hyperbolas, as we have just seen. As it is convenient to think of x and y as cartesian coördinates, let us interchange these variables with ξ and η. At the same time, we drop a minus sign, and write

$$x = \cos\xi \cosh\eta, \quad y = \sin\xi \sinh\eta.$$

We find

$$ds^2 = |d(x - iy)|^2 = |d\cos\zeta|^2 = |\sin\zeta|^2 |d\zeta|^2$$
$$= [(\sin\xi\cosh\eta)^2 + (\cos\xi\sinh\eta)^2](d\xi^2 + d\eta^2)$$
$$= (\cosh^2\eta - \cos^2\xi)(d\xi^2 + d\eta^2).$$

Laplace's equation may then be written

$$\nabla^2 U = \frac{1}{\cosh^2\eta - \cos^2\xi}\left[\frac{\partial^2 U}{\partial\xi^2} + \frac{\partial^2 U}{\partial\eta^2}\right].$$

Exercises.

6. Show that by means of a function of type F and a linear function, the domain bounded by any two rays from a point can be mapped conformally on the interior of the unit circle.

7. Show that the domain common to any two intersecting circles can be mapped conformally on the interior of the unit circle.

8. Determine the potential and the density of a charge in equilibrium on the infinite elliptic cylinder $\eta = 1$, it being given that the total charge between two planes perpendicular to the generators, and two units apart, is E. Check the result by integrating the density over a suitable region.

9. If $z = \zeta^2$, show that the lines $\xi = $ const. and $\eta = $ const. give two systems of confocal parabolas meeting at right angles. Express the Laplacian of U in terms of the generalized coördinates ξ and η of a point in the z-plane.

10. If $z = f(\zeta)$ is analytic and has a non-vanishing derivative in the domain T of the ζ-plane, show that the element of arc $d\sigma$ in the ζ-plane is connected with the element of arc ds in the z-plane by the relation

$$ds^2 = |f'(\zeta)|^2 d\sigma^2,$$

and that

$$\frac{\partial^2 U}{\partial x^2} + \frac{\partial^2 U}{\partial y^2} = \frac{1}{\mu}\left(\frac{\partial^2 U}{\partial\xi^2} + \frac{\partial^2 U}{\partial\eta^2}\right),$$

where

$$\mu = |f'(\zeta)|^2 = \left(\frac{\partial x}{\partial\xi}\right)^2 + \left(\frac{\partial y}{\partial\xi}\right)^2 = \left(\frac{\partial x}{\partial\xi}\right)^2 + \left(\frac{\partial x}{\partial\eta}\right)^2.$$

Thus the transformation defined by an analytic function carries harmonic functions in the plane into harmonic functions (see the end of § 2, p. 236).

11. Show that the Dirichlet integral

$$\iint\limits_T \left[\left(\frac{\partial u}{\partial x}\right)^2 + \left(\frac{\partial u}{\partial y}\right)^2\right] dS$$

is invariant under the transformation defined by an analytic function of $x + iy$.

11. Green's Function for Regions of the Plane.

It has been stated that the mapping brought about by an analytic function essentially characterizes it. Our aim is now to substantiate this assertion. By way of preparation, we first establish a property of the equipotential lines of Green's function for simply connected regions, and follow this by a study of the relation between Green's function for such regions and the mapping of them on the unit circle.

Green's function for the region R and the pole Q (interior to R) is the function

$$g(P,Q) = \log\frac{1}{r} + v(P,Q), \qquad r = \overline{PQ},$$

which approaches 0 at every boundary point of R, $v(P,Q)$ being harmonic in the closed region R. It will be recalled that a function is harmonic in a closed region if it is continuous in the closed region, and harmonic at all interior points. No hypothesis is made on the behavior of the derivatives in the neighborhood of the boundary. If R is infinite, the function must behave so at infinity that it is carried by an inversion into a function which is harmonic in the region inverse to R. We now prove

Theorem VII. *If R is a simply connected region, the equipotential lines $g = \mu$, $\mu > 0$, are simple closed curves which are analytic at every point.* They have no multiple points.

From § 9, page 273, we infer that the equipotential $g = \mu$ is analytic at every point except at those where the gradient ∇g of g vanishes. Such points can have no limit point in the interior of R. For the analytic function $f(z)$ of which g is the real part becomes infinite at the pole Q, and it is easily verified that its derivative does not vanish in a neighborhood of that point. Now $f'(z) = 0$ means the same thing as $\nabla g = 0$. If the zeros of the derivative had a limit point in the interior of R, the derivative would then vanish throughout the interior of R, by Theorem VI. We conclude that at most a finite number of points at which $\nabla g = 0$ lie on the locus $g = \mu$. In the neighborhood of such a point, $g = \mu$ consists of a finite number of regular arcs passing through the point with equally spaced tangents (see page 276). The analytic pieces, of which $g = \mu$ consists, can terminate only in the points at which $\nabla g = 0$, and are at most finite in number.

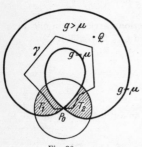

Fig. 30.

Consider now the set of points T where $g > \mu$, in which we count also Q (fig. 30). Because of the continuity of g at all points involved, the boundary points of T all belong to the equipotential $g = \mu$. Conversely, all points of $g = \mu$ are boundary points of T, for g could have only equal or smaller values in the neighborhood of a point $g = \mu$ which was not a boundary point of T. This would be in contradiction with Gauss' theorem of the arithmetic mean.

Suppose that the equipotential $g = \mu$ contained a point P_0 at which $\nabla g = 0$. As we have seen, the equipotential would have at least two branches passing through P_0, and these would divide the plane near

P_0 into domains in which alternately $g < \mu$ and $g > \mu$; for otherwise there would be a point at which $g = \mu$, but in whose neighborhood it was never greater, or else never less. Call T_1 and T_2 two of these domains in which $g > \mu$. They would be parts of T, since T contains all points at which $g > \mu$. If a point of T_1 could not be joined to a point of T_2 by a polygonal line lying in T, T would have to consist of at least two domains without common points. In only one of these could Q lie. The other would be one in which g was harmonic, with boundary values everywhere equal to μ. This is impossible, since it would make g constant. So we can join P_0 to a point in T_1 by a short straight line segment, and join it similarly to a point in T_2, and then join the points in T_1 and T_2 by a polygonal line, the whole constituting a regular closed curve γ lying in T except at the single point P_0. Now such a curve, by the Jordan theorem[1], divides the plane into two distinct domains D_1 and D_2. Near P_0 there would be points at which $g < \mu$ on both sides of γ, that is, in both D_1 and D_2. Then in each there would be regions with interiors defined by $g < \mu$. At the boundaries of these regions g could take on only the values 0 or μ. If, for any such region, 0 were not among these values, g would be constant in that region, and this is impossible. Hence both D_1 and D_2 would have to contain boundary points of the region R. It follows that the closed curve γ could not be shrunk to a point while remaining always in the interior of R, and R could not be simply connected. Thus the assumption that the equipotential $g = \mu$ contains a point at which $\nabla g = 0$ has led to a contradiction, and the equipotential is free from multiple points and is analytic throughout.

If R is an infinite region, and if μ is the value approached by g at infinity, the equipotential $g = \mu$ cannot be bounded. It is, however, a curve of the sort described, in the sense that an inversion about any point not on it carries it into one.

Incidentally, it has emerged that at every interior point of a simply connected region, the gradient of Green's function for that region is different from 0.

12. Green's Function and Conformal Mapping.

We are now in a position to show the relation between Green's function for a simply connected domain and the conformal mapping of that domain on the circle. It is embodied in the next two theorems.

Theorem VIII. *If $\zeta = f(z)$ maps the simply connected domain T of the z-plane on the interior of the unit circle in the ζ-plane in a one-to-one conformal manner, then $- \log |f(z)|$ is Green's function for T, the pole being the point of the z-plane corresponding to $\zeta = 0$.*

---

[1] See the footnote, page 110.

Near the pole z_0, $f(z)$ has the development

$$f(z) = a_1(z - z_0) + a_2(z - z_0)^2 + \cdots,$$

where $a_1 \neq 0$ because the mapping is conformal. Hence

$$\log f(z) = \log(z - z_0) + \log[a_1 + a_2(z - z_0) + \cdots],$$

and

$$-\log|f(z)| = \log\frac{1}{r} + v,$$

where v is harmonic in the neighborhood of z_0. As there is no other point within R at which $f(z)$ vanishes, v is harmonic in T.

As z approaches a boundary point of T, ζ can have no interior point of the unit circle as limit point. For suppose, as z approached the boundary point z_1, the corresponding values of ζ had a limit point ζ_1 interior to the unit circle. This means that no matter how small the circle c about z_1, there would be points within c corresponding to points arbitrarily near ζ_1. But as the inverse of $\zeta = f(z)$ is analytic at ζ_1, the points of the ζ-plane in a sufficiently small closed circle about ζ_1 all correspond to points in a closed region entirely in T, and therefore one which excludes the points of c if c is sufficiently small. We thus have a contradiction. Hence as z approaches the boundary of T in any manner, $|\zeta| = |f(z)|$ approaches 1. Thus $-\log|f(z)|$ approaches 0, and therefore is Green's function, as stated.

Conversely, if Green's function for T is known, we can determine the mapping function:

Theorem IX. *If g is Green's function for the simply connected domain T with pole at the point $z_0 = x_0 + iy_0$, then the function*

$$\zeta = f(z) = e^{-g - ih},$$

where h is conjugate to g, maps T in a one-to-one conformal manner on the interior of the unit circle of the ζ-plane, the pole being mapped on the center of the circle.

In the representation $g = -\log r + v$, v is harmonic in the simply connected domain T and so has a one-valued conjugate. The conjugate of $-\log r$ is $-\varphi$, the many-valued function defined by

$$\cos\varphi = \frac{x - x_0}{r}, \qquad \sin\varphi = \frac{y - y_0}{r}.$$

Thus the conjugate h of g is many-valued in T, decreasing by 2π each time that z makes a circuit in the counter-clockwise sense about the pole z_0. As e^z has the peiod $2\pi i$, the function $f(z)$ of the theorem is one-valued in T.

Near z_0, $g + ih$ has the form

$$-\log(z - z_0) - \psi(z),$$

where $\psi(z)$ is analytic at z_0. Hence

$$f(z) = (z - z_0) e^{\psi(z)},$$

and since

$$f'(z_0) = e^{\psi(z_0)} \neq 0,$$

the mapping is conformal in the neighborhood of z_0. It is also conformal throughout the rest of T, for

$$f'(z) = \frac{\partial f(z)}{\partial x} = -e^{-g-ih}\left(\frac{\partial g}{\partial x} + i\frac{\partial h}{\partial x}\right),$$

and this quantity can vanish at no points near which g is bounded unless $\nabla g = 0$. But we have seen that such points do not occur in simply connected domains. The mapping is therefore conformal throughout T.

Since g is positive in T, $|\zeta| = e^{-g} < 1$, and the function $\zeta = f(z)$ maps T on the whole or a part of the interior of the unit circle. On the other hand, to any interior point ζ_1 of this circle, there corresponds a single point of T. For if we write $\zeta_1 = e^{-\mu-i\alpha}$, the circle $|\zeta| = e^{-\mu}$ on which ζ_1 lies, is the map of a single simple closed analytic curve $g = \mu$. On this curve,

$$\frac{\partial g}{\partial n} = \frac{\partial h}{\partial s} < 0,$$

and h decreases monotonely, the total decrease for a circuit being 2π. Hence there is one and only one point of the curve at which h differs from α by an integral multiple of 2π. Thus there is one and only one point of T corresponding to ζ_1. It follows that $\zeta = f(z)$ maps the whole of T on the whole interior of the unit circle in a one-to-one conformal way, as was to be proved. It is clear that $z = z_0$ corresponds to $\zeta = 0$.

We see, then, that the problem of determining Green's function for T and the problem of mapping T by an analytic function in a one-to-one manner on the interior of the unit circle are equivalent. On the basis of this fact, we proceed to establish RIEMANN's fundamental theorem on mapping:

The interior T of any simply connected region whose boundary contains more than one point, can be mapped in a one-to-one conformal manner on the interior of the unit circle.

The theorem is equivalent to asserting the existence of Green's function for T, and this, in turn, to asserting the existence of the solution v of a certain Dirichlet problem. But this, again, is equivalent to asserting the existence of a barrier for T at every boundary point. We proceed to establish the existence of the barriers.

We remark first, as a lemma, that if the function $z_1 = f(z)$ maps the domain T in a one-to-one conformal manner on the domain T_1, the function being continuous at the boundary point a, then a barrier

$V_1(x_1, y_1)$ for T_1 at the corresponding boundary point a_1 is carried by the transformation defined by the function into a barrier $V(x, y)$ for T at a. Our procedure will be to transform T, by a succession of such functions, into a domain of such a character that the existence of a barrier at the point corresponding to a will be evident.

The boundary of T consists of a single connected set of points, in the sense that no simple closed regular curve can be drawn in T which encloses some but not all the boundary points. For if such a curve could be drawn, it would not be possible to shrink it to a point while remaining in T, and T would not be simply connected.

We provide for the case in which there are no points exterior to T. Since there are at least two boundary points, these may be carried by a linear function into 0 and ∞, respectively. In order not to complicate notation, let us retain the designation T for the new domain. Its boundary contains the points 0 and ∞. We then employ the function $\zeta = z^{1/2}$. Let z_0 be any interior point of T, and ζ_0 either of the square roots of z_0, but a fixed one. Then the branch of the two valued function $\zeta = z^{1/2}$ which reduces to ζ_0 for $z = z_0$ is one valued in T, for if we pass from any point of T by a continuous curve back to that point again, the value of the square root must come back to itself unless the curve makes a circuit about the origin. This it cannot do if it remains in T, since the boundary of T extends from 0 to ∞, for it contains these points and is connected. The branch in question is continuous at all points of T and its boundary, its derivative vanishes nowhere in T, and it therefore fulfills the conditions of the lemma at all boundary points. It is obviously the same for linear functions.

We may thus assume that T has an exterior point; for instance, the point $-\zeta_0$. There is therefore a circle containing no points of T, and if the domain exterior to this circle be mapped by a linear function on the interior of the unit circle, T will be mapped on a region interior to the unit circle.

Now let a denote a boundary point of the simply connected domain T lying in the unit circle, and having more than one boundary point. By a translation, a may be brought to the point 0. T will then lie in the circle $|z| < 2$. Then any selected branch of the function $\zeta = \log z$ will map T on a domain T' of the ζ-plane, lying to the left of the line $\xi = \log 2$, the point a going into the point ∞. As the reciprocal of this branch of $\log z$ vanishes as z approaches 0, the function is to be regarded as continuous at 0 for the purposes of the lemma. If now by a linear function, we map the half of the ζ-plane to the left of the line $\xi = \log 2$ on the interior of the unit circle, the domain T' will go over into a domain T'', in the unit circle, the point ∞ going over into a point of the circumference. The function can be so chosen that this point is the point 1. For such a domain and boundary point, $U = 1 - x''$ is a barrier. The theorem is thus established.

Incidentally, we may draw a further conclusion as to the Dirichlet problem. Since a barrier for a domain, at a point a, is also a barrier for any domain which is a part of the first, and has a as a boundary point, we infer that *the Dirichlet problem is possible for any domain such that any boundary point belongs to a connected set of boundary points containing more than one point.*

We may also state that *given any two simply connected domains, each with more than one boundary point, there exists a function which maps one on the other in a one-to-one conformal manner.* For both domains can be so mapped on the unit circle, and through it, on each other.

Uniqueness of the Mapping Function. If the mapping function be thought of as determined by Green's function, we see that two arbitrary elements enter it. The first is the position of the pole, and the second is the additive constant which enters the conjugate of g. These may be determined, the first so that a preassigned point of T is mapped on the center of the unit circle, and the second so that a preassigned direction through the pole corresponds to the direction of the axis of reals at the center of the circle, for changing h by a constant multiplies the mapping function by a constant of absolute value 1, and the constant can be chosen so as to produce any desired rotation. Thus, although a simply connected domain does not determine quite uniquely a function which maps it on the unit circle, the following theorem of uniqueness justifies our assertion at an earlier point, to the effect that an analytic function is characterized by its mapping properties:

Theorem X. *Given a simply connected domain T with more than one boundary point, and an interior point z_0, there exists one and only one function $\zeta = f(z)$ which maps T on the interior of the unit circle of the ζ-plane in a one-to-one conformal way, and so that z_0 and a given direction through z_0 correspond to the center of the circle and the direction of the positive axis of reals.*

We have seen that there is one such function. Suppose there are two $f_1(z)$ and $f_2(z)$. By Theorem VIII, the negatives of the absolute values of their logarithms are both Green's function for T with the same pole, and hence are identical. This means that the real part of $\log \left(\dfrac{f_1(z)}{f_2(z)} \right)$ is 0 (with a removable singularity at z_0), so that the imaginary part is constant. That is,

$$f_1(z) = e^{i\alpha} f_2(z), \qquad \alpha \text{ real.}$$

Both functions map the same direction at z_0 on the direction of the positive real axis at 0. Let the given direction be that of the vector $e^{i\beta}$.

Then, writing $dz = e^{i\beta} d\varrho$, we must have

$$d\zeta_1 = f_1'(z_0)\, e^{i\beta}\, d\varrho \quad \text{and} \quad d\zeta_2 = f_2'(z_0)\, e^{i\beta}\, d\varrho$$

real and positive. The same must therefore be true of the quotient of these differentials, and hence of the quotient $\dfrac{f_1'(z_0)}{f_2'(z_0)}$. Computing this quotient from the preceding equation, we find it necessary that $e^{i\alpha} = +1$. Thus the two mapping functions must be identical.

Incidentally, we see that the only function mapping the interior of the unit circle on itself is a linear function. This function can be so chosen as to bring an arbitrary interior point to the center, and an arbitrary direction to that of the positive axis of reals. It follows that the function mapping the interior of a simply connected region, with more than one boundary point, on the interior of the unit circle is determined to within a linear substitution.

13. The Mapping of Polygons.

A natural inquiry to make with respect to the characterization of a function by its mapping, is to ask for the simplest domains, and study the properties of the functions which map them on the interior of the unit circle. After the circle itself, polygons would undoubtedly be reckoned among the simplest. The problem of the mapping of polygons was first investigated by CHRISTOFFEL and SCHWARZ[1].

Let T denote a finite domain of the plane of z, bounded by a polygonal line, whose vertices, in order, the line being described with T to the left, are $a_1, a_2, \ldots a_n$. Let the exterior angles, that is the angles through which the vector, with the direction and sense of motion along the polygon, turns at the vertices, be denoted by $\pi\mu_1, \pi\mu_2, \ldots \pi\mu_n$. Instead of seeking the function mapping T on the unit circle, it will be more convenient to attack the equivalent problem of mapping the upper half-plane of ζ on T. Let $z = f(\zeta)$ denote the mapping function, which we know exists, by the last section, and let $\alpha_1, \alpha_2, \ldots \alpha_n$ denote the points of the real axis which it maps on the vertices of T. The function then maps straight line segments of the boundary on straight line segments, and we may prove that it is analytic at all interior points of these segments as follows. If ζ is on the segment (α_{i-1}, α_i), z is on the segment (a_{i-1}, a_i), and for suitable choice of a and b, $az + b$ lies on a segment of the axis of reals, and is analytic in the upper half-plane in the neighborhood of points of the segment. If the definition of such a function is extended to points in the lower half-plane by a reflection, that is, by the convention that at the point $\xi - i\eta$ it has as value the

[1] CHRISTOFFEL, Annali di Matematica, 2d Ser. Vol. I (1867), *Gesammelte Werke*, Vol. I, p. 245 ff.; SCHWARZ, Journal für reine und angewandte Mathematik, Vol. LXX (1869), p. 105 ff., *Gesammelte Abhandlungen*, Vol. II, p. 65 ff.

conjugate of its value at $\xi + i\eta$, it will be analytic in the lower half-plane near the segment of the axis of reals in question, and, by a theorem of § 7, it will be analytic at the interior points of the segment as well. Furthermore, since for ζ on (α_{i-1}, α_i), $az + b$ is real,

$$a \frac{dz}{d\zeta} = a f'(\zeta) \quad \text{and} \quad F(\zeta) = \frac{\dfrac{d^2 z}{d\zeta^2}}{\dfrac{dz}{d\zeta}} = \frac{f''(\zeta)}{f'(\zeta)}$$

are also real. But the second expression is independent of a and b, and hence it is real and analytic on the whole axis of real ζ, except possibly at the points α_i.

Let us now consider the situation in the neighborhood of the vertices. As z goes from the side (a_{i-1}, a_i) to the side (a_i, a_{i+1}) through points of T, arc $(z - a_i)$ decreases by $(1 - \mu_i)\pi$, while arc $(\zeta - \alpha_i)$ decreases by π. If we write

$$z_1 = k (z - a_i)^{\frac{1}{1 - \mu_i}}$$

selecting a definite branch of the many-valued function and then choosing the constant k so that z_1 becomes real and negative when z approaches the side (a_{i-1}, a_i) from within T, then arc z_1 also decreases by π, and z_1, regarded as a function of ζ, maps the upper half-plane of ζ near α_i on the upper half-plane of z_1 near 0. If defined in the lower half-plane near α_i by a reflection, it is analytic in a neighborhood of α_i, except possibly at α_i. But the function is bounded in this neighborhood, and so any possible singularity at α_i is removable. Hence z_1 is developable in a convergent power series

$$z_1 = b_1 (\zeta - \alpha_i) + b_2 (\zeta - \alpha_i)^2 + \cdots,$$

where $b_1 \neq 0$, since the mapping is conformal at α_i. Eliminating z_1 between the last two equations, we find

$$z = a_i + (\zeta - \alpha_i)^{1 - \mu_i} \left[\frac{b_1}{k} + \frac{b_2}{k} (\zeta - \alpha_i) + \cdots \right]^{1 - \mu_i},$$

valid for a choice of the branches of the many-valued functions which maps the upper half of the ζ-plane near α_i on T near a_i. The second factor of the second term is an analytic function near $\zeta = \alpha_i$, which does not vanish at $\zeta = \alpha_i$. We may therefore write

$$z = a_i + (\zeta - \alpha_i)^{1 - \mu_i} [c_0 + c_1 (\zeta - \alpha_i) + \cdots], \qquad c_0 \neq 0.$$

Computing $F(\zeta)$ from this expression, we find

$$F(\zeta) = \frac{-\mu_i}{\zeta - \alpha_i} + P(\zeta - \alpha_i),$$

where $P(\zeta - \alpha_i)$ is a power series in $\zeta - \alpha_i$, convergent in a neighborhood of α_i. In verifying this last statement, it is necessary to note that

$\mu_i \neq 1$. This is true, because if μ_i were 1, T could have no points in a neighborhood of a_i, and this point would not be a boundary point.

Carrying out the same reasoning for the other points α_i, for which we may assume that none is the point ∞ (because a linear transformation would remedy the situation if it existed), we conclude that the function

$$F(\zeta) + \sum_{1}^{n} \frac{\mu_i}{\zeta - \alpha_i}$$

is analytic in the neighborhood of all vertices. It is clearly analytic in the upper half-plane of ζ, and on the real axis. If defined by a reflection at points of the lower half-plane, it is analytic in the whole plane when properly defined at the removable singularities α_i. If we examine its character at ∞ by the substitution $w = \frac{1}{\zeta}$, we find

$$F(\zeta) + \sum_{1}^{n} \frac{\mu_i}{\zeta - \alpha_i} = - \frac{\frac{d^2 z}{d w^2}}{\frac{d z}{d w}} w^2 - 2w + \sum_{1}^{n} \frac{\mu_i w}{1 - \alpha_i w}.$$

For w near 0, $z = f\left(\frac{1}{w}\right)$ maps a portion of the lower half-plane near $w = 0$ on a portion of T near an interior point of the side (a_n, a_1), and so, by a now familiar argument, is analytic in a neighborhood of that point, with a non-vanishing derivative. Thus the above expression is analytic in the whole plane, including the point ∞, and so (Exercise 5, page 359) is constant. As it vanishes at ∞, $(w = 0)$, it is identically 0. We remark that since the first term on the right is w^2 times an analytic function, the sum of the remaining two terms contains the factor w^2, so that we must have $\sum \mu_i = 2$. That this is true is geometrically evident.

We have then in

$$\frac{\frac{d^2 z}{d \zeta^2}}{\frac{d z}{d \zeta}} + \sum_{1}^{n} \frac{\mu_i}{\zeta - \alpha_i} = 0.$$

a differential equation for the mapping function. It is readily integrated, and yields the result

$$(18) \qquad z = A \int_{\zeta_0}^{\zeta} \frac{d\zeta}{\Pi (\zeta - \alpha_i)^{\mu_i}} + B,$$

where A and B are constants depending on the position and size of the domain T, the branches of the many-valued functions in the integrand, and the choice of the lower limit of integration, which may be any point in the upper half-plane of ζ. The symbol Π means the product of the n factors of which a typical one follows.

The problem is not completely solved until not only these constants A and B have been appropriately determined, but also the real constants α_i. We know, however, that the mapping function exists[1], and that it must have the given form. We leave the determination of the constants as a problem to be solved in particular cases.

As an illustration, let us suppose that T is a rectangle. Then $\mu_1 = \mu_2 = \mu_3 = \mu_4 = \frac{1}{2}$. Because of the symmetry of T, it is reasonable to suppose that the four points α_1, α_2, α_3, α_4 can be taken symmetric with respect to 0. We take them as ± 1, $\pm \frac{1}{k}$ $(0 < k < 1)$. We have, then as a tentative mapping function,

$$(19) \qquad z = \int_0^\zeta \frac{d\zeta}{\sqrt{(1 - \zeta^2)(1 - k^2 \zeta^2)}},$$

that is, an elliptic integral of the first kind.

Exercise.

1. Verify, on the understanding that by the radical is meant that branch of the square root which reduces to $+1$ for $\zeta = 0$, that this function maps the upper half-plane of ζ on the interior of the rectangle of the z-plane whose vertices are $\pm K$ and $\pm K + iK'$, where

$$K = \int_0^1 \frac{dt}{\sqrt{(1 - t^2)(1 - k^2 t^2)}}, \qquad K' = \int_1^{\frac{1}{k}} \frac{dt}{\sqrt{(t^2 - 1)(1 - k^2 t^2)}}.$$

The function $\zeta = \varphi(z)$, inverse to the function (19), maps the rectangle on the upper half of the ζ-plane. It is so far defined only in the rectangle. But it is real when z is real and between the vertices $-k$ and k. It can therefore be continued analytically across the axis of reals into the rectangle symmetric to T by a reflection. By similar reflections, $\varphi(z)$ can be continued across the other sides of T, and then across the sides of the new rectangles, until it is defined in the whole plane of z. However, the original rectangle T, together with an ad-

---

[1] When the formula for $z = f(\zeta)$ was first derived, the theorem of Riemann could not be regarded as rigorously established, and the endeavor was made to establish it for polygonal regions, by showing that the constants could be determined so that the given region would be the map of the upper half-plane. The method used was called the method of continuity, and has not only historical interest, but value in allied problems in which an existence theorem would otherwise be lacking. For further information on the method, the reader may consult E. STUDY, *Vorlesungen über ausgewählte Gegenstände der Geometrie*, Heft 2, herausgegeben unter Mitwirkung von W. BLASCHKE, *Konforme Abbildung einfach-zusammenhängender Bereiche*, Leipzig, 1913. An elementary proof by means of the method of continuity is given by A. WEINSTEIN, *Der Kontinuitätsbeweis des Abbildungssatzes für Polygone*, Mathematische Zeitschrift, Vol. XXI (1924), pp. 72—84.

jacent one, suitable portions of the boundary being included, constitutes the map of the whole ζ-plane, and this is therefore a fundamental region for the function. It is an elliptic function. Its inverse is many-valued, corresponding to paths of integration no longer confined to the upper half-plane of ζ.

Exercises.

2. Show that $\varphi(z)$ is doubly periodic, with the periods $4\,K$ and $2\,K'\,i$.

3. Show that as k approaches 0, the rectangle T becomes infinitely high, while retaining a bounded breadth, and that as k approaches 1, the rectangle becomes infinitely broad, while keeping a bounded height. Show thus that a rectangle of any shape can be mapped on the upper half-plane by means of the function (19).

4. Study the mapping on the upper half-plane of the interior of a triangle. Show that if the function $\zeta = \varphi(z)$, with its definition extended by reflections, is to be single valued, the interior angles of the triangle must be each the quotient of π by an integer, and that there are but a finite number of such triangles (as far as shape is concerned). Determine for one such case a fundamental region, the periods of the function $\varphi(z)$, and a period parallelogram, that is, a partly closed region S, such that the value of z for any point in the plane differs, by a homogeneous linear combination of the periods with integral coefficients, from the value of z for one and only one point in S. Determine the number of times $\varphi(z)$ becomes infinite in the period parallelogram, and show that it assumes in this region any other given value the same number of times.

5. Show by means of a linear transformation that if in the mapping of a polygonal domain T on the upper half-plane, one of the vertices of T corresponds to the point ∞, the formula (18) accomplishes the mapping when modified by the suppression of the factor in the denominator which corresponds to this vertex.

6. Show that the function mapping the interior of the unit circle on the polygon T is also given by the formula (18), if the points α_i are on the circumference of the circle.

7. Find the function mapping the square whose vertices are ± 1, $\pm i$ on the unit circle in such a way that the vertices and center keep their positions.

Infinite Regions Bounded by Closed Polygons. For certain physical applications, the case is important in which T is the region outside a a closed polygon. In this case, just as before,

$$F(\zeta) + \sum_1^n \frac{\mu_i}{\zeta - \alpha_i}$$

is analytic on the axis of real ζ, and also in the upper half-plane, except at one point. For since $z = f(\zeta)$ must become infinite at the point β of the ζ-plane corresponding to the infinitely distant point in T, it is not analytic at this point. But this is the only exception. When defined by a reflection in the axis of reals, the above function also becomes infinite at the point $\bar{\beta}$ conjugate to β, and one finds that

$$F(\zeta) + \sum_1^n \frac{\mu_i}{\zeta - \alpha_i} + \frac{2}{\zeta - \beta} + \frac{2}{\zeta - \bar{\beta}}$$

is everywhere analytic. The necessary condition on the angles turns out to be $\Sigma \mu_i = -2$, and this checks with the geometry of the situation, since the polygon must be described in the counter-clockwise sense if T is to be to the left. The mapping function is given by

$$(20) \qquad z = A \int_{\zeta_0}^{\zeta} \frac{d\zeta}{(\zeta - \beta)^2 (\zeta - \bar{\beta})^2 \, \Pi \, (\zeta - \alpha_i)^{\mu_i}} + B.$$

Exercises.

8. Derive from this result the formula

$$z = A \int_{\zeta_0}^{\zeta} \frac{d\zeta}{\zeta^2 \, \Pi \, (\zeta - \gamma_i)^{\mu_i}} + B$$

for the function mapping the interior of the unit circle on the infinite domain T bounded by a closed polygon, the points γ_i being on the circumference of the circle. Show that the same formula gives a function mapping the infinite domain outside the unit circle on the infinite domain T, and that in this case the conditions

$$\sum \mu_i = -2, \qquad \sum \gamma_i \mu_i = 0$$

must be fulfilled in order that the mapping be conformal at ∞. The points γ_i will usually be different in the two cases.

9. Determine a) a function mapping the upper half-plane of ζ on the infinite domain T of the plane of z, bounded by the straight line segment from -1 to $+1$ so that $\zeta = i$ corresponds to the infinite point of the z-plane, b) a function mapping the ζ-plane outside the unit circle on the same domain of the z-plane so that the infinite points correspond. Answers, if $\alpha_1 = -1$, $\alpha_2 = 1$,

$$a) \qquad z = \frac{2\zeta}{1 + \zeta^2}, \qquad b) \qquad z = \frac{1}{2} \left(\zeta + \frac{1}{\zeta} \right).$$

By means of this last exercise, we can find the distribution of a static charge of electricity on an infinite conducting strip. The potential U of such a distribution must be constant on the strip, and at a great distance r from the origin of the z-plane, must become negatively infinite like $e \log \frac{1}{r}$, where e is the charge on a piece of the strip two units long. On the strip in the second part of the exercise, $|\zeta| = 1$, while at great distances $|\zeta|$ becomes infinite like $2 |z|$, that is, like $2r$. Hence the function

$$U = - e \log \frac{|\zeta|}{2},$$

which is harmonic in x and y, since it is the real part of an analytic function, satisfies the requirements on the potential.

To find the density of electrification, we first find

$$\frac{d}{dz} (U + i V) = - \frac{d}{dz} \left(e \log \frac{\zeta}{2} \right) = - \frac{\dfrac{e}{\zeta}}{\dfrac{dz}{d\zeta}} = \frac{2 e \zeta}{1 - \zeta^2}.$$

The magnitude of this derivative is the magnitude of the gradient of U, and this is the magnitude of the normal derivative of U at points of the strip, since here the tangential derivative is 0. Hence

$$\sigma = -\frac{1}{4\pi}\left(\frac{\partial U}{\partial n_+} - \frac{\partial U}{\partial n_-}\right) = \frac{e}{2\pi}\frac{2}{|\zeta - \zeta^{-1}|}.$$

Corresponding to points of the strip, $\zeta = e^{i\vartheta}$, so that $z = x = \cos\vartheta$, and

$$\sigma = \frac{2}{2\pi|\sin\vartheta|} = \frac{e}{2\pi\sqrt{1-x^2}}.$$

Exercises.

10. Show, in the notation of Exercise 8, that the density of a static charge on the surface of an infinite conducting prism, whose cross-section is the polygon bounding T, is

$$\sigma = \frac{e}{4\pi A}\left|\varPi(\zeta - \gamma_i)^{\mu_i}\right|.$$

Since μ_i is negative at any outward projecting edge of the prism, and positive at any inward projecting edge, we see that the density becomes infinite at the former and 0 at the latter.

11. Determine the density of electrification on a prism whose right section is a square, inscribed in the unit circle, with vertices at $\vartheta = \frac{\pi}{4}$, $\frac{3\pi}{4}$, $\frac{5\pi}{4}$ and $\frac{7\pi}{4}$. Answer,

$$\sigma = \frac{e}{8\pi A}|\sec 2\vartheta|, \quad \text{where} \quad \zeta = e^{i\vartheta}, \quad A = \frac{1}{2\int_0^{\pi/4}\sqrt{\cos 2\vartheta}\,d\vartheta}.$$

12. Study the mapping of domains bounded by open polygons, that is, of infinite domains whose polygonal boundaries pass through the point ∞.

For further information concerning the relation between the logarithmic potential and the theory of functions of a complex variable, the reader is referred to OSGOOD'S *Funktionentheorie*, particularly the chapters from XIII on. An excellent idea of the scope of the geometric theory of functions may be had from the third part of the HURWITZ-COURANT *Vorlesungen über allgemeine Funktionentheorie*, Berlin, 1925. Two small volumes which may be recommended are CURTISS, *Analytic Functions of a Complex Variable*, Chicago, 1926, an introduction to the general theory, and BIEBERBACH, *Einführung in die konforme Abbildung*, Berlin, 1927, on conformal mapping. For physical applications, see RIEMANN-WEBER, *Die Differential- und Integralgleichungen der Mechanik und Physik*, Braunschweig, 1925.

Bibliographical Notes.

Among the books on potential theory, the following may be mentioned as either historically important, or of probable use for supplementary reading.

GREEN, G.: *An Essay on the Application of Mathematical Analysis to the Theories of Electricity and Magnetism*, Nottingham, 1828.

HEINE, E.: *Handbuch der Kugelfunktionen*, two volumes, Berlin, 1878.

BETTI, E.: *Teorica delle forze Newtoniane*, Pisa, 1879, translated into German and enlarged by W. F. MEYER under the title *Lehrbuch der Potentialtheorie und ihrer Anwendungen*, Stuttgart, 1885.

HARNACK, A.: *Grundlagen der Theorie des logarithmischen Potentials*, Leipzig, 1887.

LEJEUNE-DIRICHLET, P. G.: *Vorlesungen über die im umgekehrten Verhältnis des Quadrats der Entfernung wirkenden Kräfte.* Edited by P. GRUBE, Leipzig, 1887.

NEUMANN, F.: *Vorlesungen über Potential und Kugelfunktionen*, Leipzig, 1887.

MATHIEU, E.: *Théorie du potential et ses applications à l'électrostatique et au magnétism*, Paris 1885-86. Translated into German by H. MASER, Berlin, 1890.

APPELL, P.: *Leçons sur l'attraction et la fonction potentielle*, Paris, 1892.

POINCARÉ, H.: *Théorie du potential Newtonien*. Paris, 1899.

TARLETON, F. A.: *An Introduction to the Mathematical Theory of Attraction*, London, 1899.

KORN, A.: *Lehrbuch der Potentialtheorie*, two volumes, Berlin, 1899-1901. *Fünf Abhandlungen zur Potentialtheorie*. Berlin, 1902.

PEIRCE, B. O.: *The Newtonian Potential Function*, Boston, 1902.

WANGERIN, A.: *Theorie des Potentials und der Kugelfunktionen*, Leipzig, 1909.

COURANT, R. und D. HILBERT: *Methoden der mathematischen Physik*, Berlin, Vol. I, 1924, Vol. II to appear shortly.

STERNBERG, W.: *Potentialtheorie*, two small volumes. Berlin, 1925-26.

EVANS, G. C.: *The Logarithmic Potential, Discontinuous Dirichlet and Neumann Problems*, Vol. VI of the Colloquium Publications of the American Mathematical Society, New York, 1927.

One or more chapters on potential theory and its applications will be found in each of the following works.

THOMSON and TAIT: *A Treatise on Natural Philosophy*, Cambridge, 1912.

APPELL, P.: *Traité de mécanique rationelle*, Paris, 1902-21.

GOURSAT, E.: *Cours d'analyse*, 1902-27.

PICARD, E.: *Traité d'analyse*, Paris, 1922-28.

HURWITZ-COURANT: *Vorlesungen über allgemeine Funktionentheorie; Geometrische Funktionentheorie*, Berlin, 1925.

RIEMANN-WEBER: *Die Differential- und Integralgleichungen der Mechanik und Physik*, herausgegeben von P. FRANK und R. VON MISES. Braunschweig, 1925-27.

OSGOOD, W. F.: *Lehrbuch der Funktionentheorie*, Leipzig, 1928.

For the applications to physics, in addition to APPELL and RIEMANN-WEBER, cited above, the following may be consulted.

MAXWELL, J. C.: *Electricity and Magnetism*, Oxford, 1904.

LIVENS, G. H.: *The Theory of Electricity*, Cambridge, 1918.

JEANS, J. H.: *The Mathematical Theory of Electricity and Magnetism*, Cambridge, 1925.

KIRCHHOFF, G.: *Vorlesungen über Mechanik*, Leipzig, 1897.

WIEN, W.: *Lehrbuch der Hydrodynamic*, Leipzig, 1900.

ABRAHAM, M. and A. FÖPPL: *Theorie der Elektrizität*, Leipzig, 1923.

LAMB, H.: *Hydrodynamics*, Cambridge, 1924.

LOVE, A. E. H.: *A Treatise on the Mathematical Theory of Elasticity*, Cambridge, 1927.

CLEBSCH, A.: *Theorie der Elastizität fester Körper*, Leipzig, 1862; translated into French by ST. VENANT and FLAMANT, Paris, 1883.

FOURIER, J. B. J.: *Théorie analytic de la chaleur*, Paris, 1822; translated into English by FREEMAN, Cambridge, 1878, into German by WEINSTEIN, Berlin, 1884.

POINCARÉ, H.: *Théorie analytique de la propagation de la chaleur*, Paris, 1895.

HELMHOLZ, H. V.: *Vorlesungen über die Theorie der Wärme*, Leipzig, 1903.

CLARKE, A. R.: *Geodesy*, Oxford, 1880.

HELMERT, F. R.: *Die mathematischen und physikalischen Theorien der höheren Geodäsie*, Leipzig, 1880-84.

For further bibliographical information, see in the first place the *Encyklopädie der mathematischen Wissenschaften*, Leipzig, Vol. II, A, 7, b, *Potentialtheorie*, H. BURKHARDT und F. MEYER, pp. 464-503; Vol. II, C, 3, *Neuere Entwickelungen der Potentialtheorie. Konforme Abbildung*, L. LICHTENSTEIN, pp. 177-377; also articles on the theory of functions, hydrodynamics, elasticity, electricity and magnetism, conduction of heat, and geodesy. A brief bibliography of recent publications is to be found in G. BOULIGAND, *Fonctions harmoniques, principes de Dirichlet et de Picard*, Mémorial des sciences mathématiques, fasc. XI, Paris, 1926.

Index.

CATALOG OF DOVER BOOKS

BOOKS EXPLAINING SCIENCE AND MATHEMATICS

THE COMMON SENSE OF THE EXACT SCIENCES, W. K. Clifford. Introduction by James Newman, edited by Karl Pearson. For 70 years this has been a guide to classical scientific and mathematical thought. Explains with unusual clarity basic concepts, such as extension of meaning of symbols, characteristics of surface boundaries, properties of plane figures, vectors, Cartesian method of determining position, etc. Long preface by Bertrand Russell. Bibliography of Clifford. Corrected, 130 diagrams redrawn. 249pp. 5⅜ x 8.
T61 Paperbound **$1.60**

SCIENCE THEORY AND MAN, Erwin Schrödinger. This is a complete and unabridged reissue of SCIENCE AND THE HUMAN TEMPERAMENT plus an additional essay: "What is an Elementary Particle?" Nobel Laureate Schrödinger discusses such topics as nature of scientific method, the nature of science, chance and determinism, science and society, conceptual models for physical entities, elementary particles and wave mechanics. Presentation is popular and may be followed by most people with little or no scientific training. "Fine practical preparation for a time when laws of nature, human institutions . . . are undergoing a critical examination without parallel," Waldemar Kaempffert, N. Y. TIMES. 192pp. 5⅜ x 8.
T428 Paperbound **$1.35**

PIONEERS OF SCIENCE, O. Lodge. Eminent scientist-expositor's authoritative, yet elementary survey of great scientific theories. Concentrating on individuals—Copernicus, Brahe, Kepler, Galileo, Descartes, Newton, Laplace, Herschel, Lord Kelvin, and other scientists—the author presents their discoveries in historical order adding biographical material on each man and full, specific explanations of their achievements. The clear and complete treatment of the post-Newtonian astronomers is a feature seldom found in other books on the subject. Index. 120 illustrations. xv + 404pp. 5⅜ x 8.
T716 Paperbound **$1.50**

THE EVOLUTION OF SCIENTIFIC THOUGHT FROM NEWTON TO EINSTEIN, A. d'Abro. Einstein's special and general theories of relativity, with their historical implications, are analyzed in non-technical terms. Excellent accounts of the contributions of Newton, Riemann, Weyl, Planck, Eddington, Maxwell, Lorentz and others are treated in terms of space and time, equations of electromagnetics, finiteness of the universe, methodology of science. 21 diagrams. 482pp. 5⅜ x 8.
T2 Paperound **$2.00**

THE RISE OF THE NEW PHYSICS, A. d'Abro. A half-million word exposition, formerly titled THE DECLINE OF MECHANISM, for readers not versed in higher mathematics. The only thorough explanation, in everyday language, of the central core of modern mathematical physical theory, treating both classical and modern theoretical physics, and presenting in terms almost anyone can understand the equivalent of 5 years of study of mathematical physics. Scientifically impeccable coverage of mathematical-physical thought from the Newtonian system up through the electronic theories of Dirac and Heisenberg and Fermi's statistics. Combines both history and exposition; provides a broad yet unified and detailed view, with constant comparison of classical and modern views on phenomena and theories. "A must for anyone doing serious study in the physical sciences," JOURNAL OF THE FRANKLIN INSTITUTE. "Extraordinary faculty . . . to explain ideas and theories of theoretical physics in the language of daily life," ISIS. First part of set covers philosophy of science, drawing upon the practice of Newton, Maxwell, Poincaré, Einstein, others, discussing modes of thought, experiment, interpretations of causality, etc. In the second part, 100 pages explain grammar and vocabulary of mathematics, with discussions of functions, groups, series, Fourier series, etc. The remainder is devoted to concrete, detailed coverage of both classical and quantum physics, explaining such topics as analytic mechanics, Hamilton's principle, wave theory of light, electromagnetic waves, groups of transformations, thermodynamics, phase rule, Brownian movement, kinetics, special relativity, Planck's original quantum theory, Bohr's atom, Zeeman effect, Broglie's wave mechanics, Heisenberg's uncertainty, Eigen-values, matrices, scores of other important topics. Discoveries and theories are covered for such men as Alembert, Born, Cantor, Debye, Euler, Foucault, Galois, Gauss, Hadamard, Kelvin, Kepler, Laplace, Maxwell, Pauli, Rayleigh, Volterra, Weyl, Young, more than 180 others. Indexed. 97 illustrations. ix + 982pp. 5⅜ x 8.
T3 Volume 1, Paperbound **$2.00**
T4 Volume 2, Paperbound **$2.00**

CONCERNING THE NATURE OF THINGS, Sir William Bragg. Christmas lectures delivered at the Royal Society by Nobel laureate. Why a spinning ball travels in a curved track; how uranium is transmuted to lead, etc. Partial contents: atoms, gases, liquids, crystals, metals, etc. No scientific background needed; wonderful for intelligent child. 32pp. of photos, 57 figures. xii + 232pp. 5⅜ x 8.
T31 Paperbound **$1.35**

THE UNIVERSE OF LIGHT, Sir William Bragg. No scientific training needed to read Nobel Prize winner's expansion of his Royal Institute Christmas Lectures. Insight into nature of light, methods and philosophy of science. Explains lenses, reflection, color, resonance, polarization, x-rays, the spectrum, Newton's work with prisms, Huygens' with polarization, Crookes' with cathode ray, etc. Leads into clear statement or 2 major historical theories of light, corpuscle and wave. Dozens of experiments you can do. 199 illus., including 2 full-page color plates. 293pp. 5⅜ x 8.
S538 Paperbound **$1.85**

PHYSICS, THE PIONEER SCIENCE, L. W. Taylor. First thorough text to place all important physical phenomena in cultural-historical framework; remains best work of its kind. Exposition of physical laws, theories developed chronologically, with great historical, illustrative experiments diagrammed, described, worked out mathematically. Excellent physics text for self-study as well as class work. Vol. 1: Heat, Sound: motion, acceleration, gravitation, conservation of energy, heat engines, rotation, heat, mechanical energy, etc. 211 illus. 407pp. 5⅜ x 8. Vol. 2: Light, Electricity: images, lenses, prisms, magnetism, Ohm's law, dynamos, telegraph, quantum theory, decline of mechanical view of nature, etc. Bibliography. 13 table appendix. Index. 551 illus. 2 color plates. 508pp. 5⅜ x 8.

Vol. 1 S565 Paperbound **$2.00**
Vol. 2 S566 Paperbound **$2.00**
The set **$4.00**

FROM EUCLID TO EDDINGTON: A STUDY OF THE CONCEPTIONS OF THE EXTERNAL WORLD, Sir Edmund Whittaker. A foremost British scientist traces the development of theories of natural philosophy from the western rediscovery of Euclid to Eddington, Einstein, Dirac, etc. The inadequacy of classical physics is contrasted with present day attempts to understand the physical world through relativity, non-Euclidean geometry, space curvature, wave mechanics, etc. 5 major divisions of examination: Space; Time and Movement; the Concepts of Classical Physics; the Concepts of Quantum Mechanics; the Eddington Universe. 212pp. 5⅜ x 8.

T491 Paperbound **$1.35**

THE STORY OF ATOMIC THEORY AND ATOMIC ENERGY, J. G. Feinberg. Wider range of facts on physical theory, cultural implications, than any other similar source. Completely non-technical. Begins with first atomic theory, 600 B.C., goes through A-bomb, developments to 1959. Avogadro, Rutherford, Bohr, Einstein, radioactive decay, binding energy, radiation danger, future benefits of nuclear power, dozens of other topics, told in lively, related, informal manner. Particular stress on European atomic research. "Deserves special mention . . . authoritative," Saturday Review. Formerly "The Atom Story." New chapter to 1959. Index. 34 illustrations. 251pp. 5⅜ x 8.

T625 Paperbound **$1.45**

THE STRANGE STORY OF THE QUANTUM, AN ACCOUNT FOR THE GENERAL READER OF THE GROWTH OF IDEAS UNDERLYING OUR PRESENT ATOMIC KNOWLEDGE, B. Hoffmann. Presents lucidly and expertly, with barest amount of mathematics, the problems and theories which led to modern quantum physics. Dr. Hoffmann begins with the closing years of the 19th century, when certain trifling discrepancies were noticed, and with illuminating analogies and examples takes you through the brilliant concepts of Planck, Einstein, Pauli, de Broglie, Bohr, Schroedinger, Heisenberg, Dirac, Sommerfeld, Feynman, etc. This edition includes a new, long postscript carrying the story through 1958. "Of the books attempting an account of the history and contents of our modern atomic physics which have come to my attention, this is the best," H. Margenau, Yale University, in "American Journal of Physics." 32 tables and line illustrations. Index. 275pp. 5⅜ x 8.

T518 Paperbound **$1.45**

SPACE AND TIME, Emile Borel. An entirely non-technical introduction to relativity, by world-renowned mathematician, Sorbonne Professor. (Notes on basic mathematics are included separately.) This book has never been surpassed for insight, and extraordinary clarity of thought, as it presents scores of examples, analogies, arguments, illustrations, which explain such topics as: difficulties due to motion; gravitation a force of inertia; geodesic lines; wave-length and difference of phase; x-rays and crystal structure; the special theory of relativity; and much more. Indexes. 4 appendixes. 15 figures. xvi + 243pp. 5⅜ x 8.

T592 Paperbound **$1.45**

THE RESTLESS UNIVERSE, Max Born. New enlarged version of this remarkably readable account by a Nobel laureate. Moving from sub-atomic particles to universe, the author explains in very simple terms the latest theories of wave mechanics. Partial contents: air and its relatives, electrons & ions, waves & particles, electronic structure of the atom, nuclear physics. Nearly 1000 illustrations, including 7 animated sequences. 325pp. 6 x 9.

T412 Paperbound **$2.00**

SOAP SUBBLES, THEIR COLOURS AND THE FORCES WHICH MOULD THEM, C. V. Boys. Only complete edition, half again as much material as any other. Includes Boys' hints on performing his experiments, sources of supply. Dozens of lucid experiments show complexities of liquid films, surface tension, etc. Best treatment ever written. Introduction. 83 illustrations. Color plate. 202pp. 5⅜ x 8.

T542 Paperbound **95¢**

SPINNING TOPS AND GYROSCOPIC MOTION, John Perry. Well-known classic of science still unsurpassed for lucid, accurate, delightful exposition. How quasi-rigidity is induced in flexible and fluid bodies by rapid motions; why gyrostat falls, top rises; nature and effect on climatic conditions of earth's precessional movement; effect of internal fluidity on rotating bodies, etc. Appendixes describe practical uses to which gyroscopes have been put in ships, compasses, monorail transportation. 62 figures. 128pp. 5⅜ x 8.

T416 Paperbound **$1.00**

MATTER & LIGHT, THE NEW PHYSICS, L. de Broglie. Non-technical papers by a Nobel laureate explain electromagnetic theory, relativity, matter, light and radiation, wave mechanics, quantum physics, philosophy of science. Einstein, Planck, Bohr, others explained so easily that no mathematical training is needed for all but 2 of the 21 chapters. Unabridged. Index. 300pp. 5⅜ x 8.

T35 Paperbound **$1.60**

A SURVEY OF PHYSICAL THEORY, Max Planck. One of the greatest scientists of all time, creator of the quantum revolution in physics, writes in non-technical terms of his own discoveries and those of other outstanding creators of modern physics. Planck wrote this book when science had just crossed the threshold of the new physics, and he communicates the excitement felt then as he discusses electromagnetic theories, statistical methods, evolution of the concept of light, a step-by-step description of how he developed his own momentous theory, and many more of the basic ideas behind modern physics. Formerly "A" Survey of Physics." Bibliography. Index. 128pp. 5⅜ x 8. S650 Paperbound **$1.15**

THE NATURE OF LIGHT AND COLOUR IN THE OPEN AIR, M. Minnaert. Why is falling snow sometimes black? What causes mirages, the fata morgana, multiple suns and moons in the sky? How are shadows formed? Prof. Minnaert of the University of Utrecht answers these and similar questions in optics, light, colour, for non-specialists. Particularly valuable to nature, science students, painters, photographers. Translated by H. M. Kremer-Priest, K. Jay. 202 illustrations, including 42 photos. xvi + 362pp. 5⅜ x 8. T196 Paperbound **$1.95**

THE STORY OF X-RAYS FROM RONTGEN TO ISOTOPES, A. R. Bleich. Non-technical history of x-rays, their scientific explanation, their applications in medicine, industry, research, and art, and their effect on the individual and his descendants. Includes amusing early reactions to Röntgen's discovery, cancer therapy, detections of art and stamp forgeries, potential risks to patient and operator, etc. Illustrations show x-rays of flower structure, the gall bladder, gears with hidden defects, etc. Original Dover publication. Glossary. Bibliography. Index. 55 photos and figures. xiv + 186pp. 5⅜ x 8. T662 Paperbound **$1.35**

TEACH YOURSELF ELECTRICITY, C. W. Wilman. Electrical resistance, inductance, capacitance, magnets, chemical effects of current, alternating currents, generators and motors, transformers, rectifiers, much more. 230 questions, answers, worked examples. List of units. 115 illus. 194pp. 6⅞ x 4¼. Clothbound **$2.00**

TEACH YOURSELF HEAT ENGINES, E. De Ville. Measurement of heat, development of steam and internal combustion engines, efficiency of an engine, compression-ignition engines, production of steam, the ideal engine, much more. 318 exercises, answers, worked examples. Tables. 76 illus. 220pp. 6⅞ x 4¼. Clothbound **$2.00**

TEACH YOURSELF MECHANICS, P. Abbott. The lever, centre of gravity, parallelogram of force, friction, acceleration, Newton's laws of motion, machines, specific gravity, gas, liquid pressure, much more. 280 problems, solutions. Tables. 163 illus. 271pp. 6⅞ x 4¼. Clothbound **$2.00**

GREAT IDEAS OF MODERN MATHEMATICS: THEIR NATURE AND USE, Jagjit Singh. Reader with only high school math will understand main mathematical ideas of modern physics, astronomy, genetics, psychology, evolution, etc., better than many who use them as tools, but comprehend little of their basic structure. Author uses his wide knowledge of non-mathematical fields in brilliant exposition of differential equations, matrices, group theory, logic, statistics, problems of mathematical foundations, imaginary numbers, vectors, etc. Original publication. 2 appendixes. 2 indexes. 65 illustr. 322pp. 5⅜ x 8. S587 Paperbound **$1.55**

MATHEMATICS IN ACTION, O. G. Sutton. Everyone with a command of high school algebra will find this book one of the finest possible introductions to the application of mathematics to physical theory. Ballistics, numerical analysis, waves and wavelike phenomena, Fourier series, group concepts, fluid flow and aerodynamics, statistical measures, and meteorology are discussed with unusual clarity. Some calculus and differential equations theory is developed by the author for the reader's help in the more difficult sections. 88 figures. Index. viii + 236pp. 5⅜ x 8. T440 Clothbound **$3.50**

FREE! All you do is ask for it!

A DOVER SCIENCE SAMPLER, edited by George Barkin. 64-page book, sturdily bound, containing excerpts from over 20 Dover books explaining science. Edwin Hubble, George Sarton, Ernst Mach, A. d'Abro, Galileo, Newton, others, discussing island universes, scientific truth, biological phenomena, stability in bridges, etc. Copies limited, no more than 1 to a customer. FREE

THE FOURTH DIMENSION SIMPLY EXPLAINED, edited by H. P. Manning. 22 essays, originally Scientific American contest entries, that use a minimum of mathematics to explain aspects of 4-dimensional geometry: analogues to 3-dimensional space, 4-dimensional absurdities and curiosities (such as removing the contents of an egg without puncturing its shell), possible measurements and forms, etc. Introduction by the editor. Only book of its sort on a truly elementary level, excellent introduction to advanced works. 82 figures. 251pp. 5⅜ x 8. T711 Paperbound **$1.35**

FAMOUS BRIDGES OF THE WORLD, D. B. Steinman. An up-to-the-minute revised edition of a book that explains the fascinating drama of how the world's great bridges came to be built. The author, designer of the famed Mackinac bridge, discusses bridges from all periods and all parts of the world, explaining their various types of construction, and describing the problems their builders faced. Although primarily for youngsters, this cannot fail to interest readers of all ages. 48 illustrations in the text. 23 photographs. 99pp. 6⅛ x 9¼. T161 Paperbound **$1.00**

THE PRINCIPLES OF SCIENCE, A TREATISE ON LOGIC AND THE SCIENTIFIC METHOD, W. S. Jevons. Treating such topics as Inductive and Deductive Logic, the Theory of Number, Probability, and the Limits of Scientific Method, this milestone in the development of symbolic logic remains a stimulating contribution to the investigation of inferential validity in the natural and social sciences. It significantly advances Boole's logic, and contains a detailed introduction to the nature and methods of probability in physics, astronomy, everyday affairs, etc. In his introduction, Ernest Nagel of Columbia University says, "[Jevons] continues to be of interest as an attempt to articulate the logic of scientific inquiry." Index. liii + 786pp. 5⅜ x 8.   S446 Paperbound **$2.98**

Group theory, algebra, sets

LECTURES ON THE ICOSAHEDRON AND THE SOLUTION OF EQUATIONS OF THE FIFTH DEGREE, Felix Klein. The solution of quintics in terms of rotation of a regular icosahedron around its axes of symmetry. A classic & indispensable source for those interested in higher algebra, geometry, crystallography. Considerable explanatory material included. 230 footnotes, mostly bibliographic. 2nd edition, xvi + 289pp. 5⅜ x 8.   S314 Paperbound **$1.85**

LINEAR GROUPS, WITH AN EXPOSITION OF THE GALOIS FIELD THEORY, L. E. Dickson. The classic exposition of the theory of groups, well within the range of the graduate student. Part I contains the most extensive and thorough presentation of the theory of Galois Fields available, with a wealth of examples and theorems. Part II is a full discussion of linear groups of finite order. Much material in this work is based on Dickson's own contributions. Also includes expositions of Jordan, Lie, Abel, Betti-Mathieu, Hermite, etc. "A milestone in the development of modern algebra," W. Magnus, in his historical introduction to this edition. Index. xv + 312pp. 5⅜ x 8.   S482 Paperbound **$1.95**

INTRODUCTION TO THE THEORY OF GROUPS OF FINITE ORDER, R. Carmichael. Examines fundamental theorems and their application. Beginning with sets, systems, permutations, etc., it progresses in easy stages through important types of groups: Abelian, prime power, permutation, etc. Except 1 chapter where matrices are desirable, no higher math needed. 783 exercises, problems. Index. xvi + 447pp. 5⅜ x 8.   S299 Clothbound **$3.95**
                                                                S300 Paperbound **$2.00**

THEORY OF GROUPS OF FINITE ORDER, W. Burnside. First published some 40 years ago, this is still one of the clearest introductory texts. Partial contents: permutations, groups independent of representation, composition series of a group, isomorphism of a group with itself, Abelian groups, prime power groups, permutation groups, invariants of groups of linear substitution graphical representation, etc. 45pp. of notes. Indexes. xxiv + 512pp. 5⅜ x 8.
                                                                S38 Paperbound **$2.45**

THEORY AND APPLICATIONS OF FINITE GROUPS, G. A. Miller, H. F. Blichfeldt, L. E. Dickson. Unusually accurate and authoritative work, each section prepared by a leading specialist: Miller on substitution and abstract groups, Blichfeldt on finite groups of linear homogeneous transformations, Dickson on applications of finite groups. Unlike more modern works, this gives the concrete basis from which abstract group theory arose. Includes Abelian groups, prime-power groups, isomorphisms, matrix forms of linear transformations, Sylow groups, Galois' theory of algebraic equations, duplication of a cube, trisection of an angle, etc. 2 Indexes. 267 problems. xvii + 390pp. 5⅜ x 8.   S216 Paperbound **$2.00**

CONTINUOUS GROUPS OF TRANSFORMATIONS, L. P. Eisenhart. Intensive study of the theory and geometrical applications of continuous groups of transformations; a standard work on the subject, called forth by the revolution in physics in the 1920's. Covers tensor analysis, Riemannian geometry, canonical parameters, transitivity, imprimitivity, differential invariants, the algebra of constants of structure, differential geometry, contact transformations, etc. "Likely to remain one of the standard works on the subject for many years . . . principal theorems are proved clearly and concisely, and the arrangement of the whole is coherent," MATHEMATICAL GAZETTE. Index. 72-item bibliography. 185 exercises. ix + 301pp. 5⅜ x 8.
                                                                S781 Paperbound **$1.85**

THE THEORY OF GROUPS AND QUANTUM MECHANICS, H. Weyl. Discussions of Schroedinger's wave equation, de Broglie's waves of a particle, Jordan-Hoelder theorem, Lie's continuous groups of transformations, Pauli exclusion principle, quantization of Maxwell-Dirac field equations, etc. Unitary geometry, quantum theory, groups, application of groups to quantum mechanics, symmetry permutation group, algebra of symmetric transformation, etc. 2nd revised edition. Bibliography. Index. xxii + 422pp. 5⅜ x 8.   S268 Clothbound **$4.50**
                                                                S269 Paperbound **$1.95**

ALGEBRAIC THEORIES, L. E. Dickson. Best thorough introduction to classical topics in higher algebra develops theories centering around matrices, invariants, groups. Higher algebra, Galois theory, finite linear groups, Klein's icosahedron, algebraic invariants, linear transformations, elementary divisors, invariant factors; quadratic, bi-linear, Hermitian forms, singly and in pairs. Proofs rigorous, detailed; topics developed lucidly, in close connection with their most frequent mathematical applications. Formerly "Modern Algebraic Theories." 155 problems. Bibliography. 2 indexes. 285pp. 5⅜ x 8.   S547 Paperbound **$1.50**

ALGEBRAS AND THEIR ARITHMETICS, L. E. Dickson. Provides the foundation and background necessary to any advanced undergraduate or graduate student studying abstract algebra. Begins with elementary introduction to linear transformations, matrices, field of complex numbers; proceeds to order, basal units, modulus, quaternions, etc.; develops calculus of linear sets, describes various examples of algebras including invariant, difference, nilpotent, semi-simple. "Makes the reader marvel at his genius for clear and profound analysis," Amer. Mathematical Monthly. Index. xii + 241pp. 5⅜ x 8. **S616 Paperbound $1.35**

THE THEORY OF EQUATIONS WITH AN INTRODUCTION TO THE THEORY OF BINARY ALGEBRAIC FORMS, W. S. Burnside and A. W. Panton. Extremely thorough and concrete discussion of the theory of equations, with extensive detailed treatment of many topics curtailed in later texts. Covers theory of algebraic equations, properties of polynomials, symmetric functions, derived functions, Horner's process, complex numbers and the complex variable, determinants and methods of elimination, invariant theory (nearly 100 pages), transformations, introduction to Galois theory, Abelian equations, and much more. Invaluable supplementary work for modern students and teachers. 759 examples and exercises. Index in each volume. Two volume set. Total of xxiv + 604pp. 5⅜ x 8. **S714 Vol I Paperbound $1.85**
S715 Vol II Paperbound $1.85
The set $3.70

COMPUTATIONAL METHODS OF LINEAR ALGEBRA, V. N. Faddeeva, translated by **C. D. Benster.** First English translation of a unique and valuable work, the only work in English presenting a systematic exposition of the most important methods of linear algebra—classical and contemporary. Shows in detail how to derive numerical solutions of problems in mathematical physics which are frequently connected with those of linear algebra. Theory as well as individual practice. Part I surveys the mathematical background that is indispensable to what follows. Parts II and III, the conclusion, set forth the most important methods of solution, for both exact and iterative groups. One of the most outstanding and valuable features of this work is the 23 tables, double and triple checked for accuracy. These tables will not be found elsewhere. Author's preface. Translator's note. New bibliography and index. x + 252pp. 5⅜ x 8. **S424 Paperbound $1.95**

ALGEBRAIC EQUATIONS, E. Dehn. Careful and complete presentation of Galois' theory of algebraic equations; theories of Lagrange and Galois developed in logical rather than historical form, with a more thorough exposition than in most modern books. Many concrete applications and fully-worked-out examples. Discusses basic theory (very clear exposition of the symmetric group); isomorphic, transitive, and Abelian groups; applications of Lagrange's and Galois' theories; and much more. Newly revised by the author. Index. List of Theorems. xi + 208pp. 5⅜ x 8. **S697 Paperbound $1.45**

THEORY OF SETS, E. Kamke. Clearest, amplest introduction in English, well suited for independent study. Subdivision of main theory, such as theory of sets of points, are discussed, but emphasis is on general theory. Partial contents: rudiments of set theory, arbitrary sets and their cardinal numbers, ordered sets and their order types, well-ordered sets and their cardinal numbers. Bibliography. Key to symbols. Index. vii + 144pp. 5⅜ x 8.
S141 Paperbound $1.35

Number theory

INTRODUCTION TO THE THEORY OF NUMBERS, L. E. Dickson. Thorough, comprehensive approach with adequate coverage of classical literature, an introductory volume beginners can follow. Chapters on divisibility, congruences, quadratic residues & reciprocity, Diophantine equations, etc. Full treatment of binary quadratic forms without usual restriction to integral coefficients. Covers infinitude of primes, least residues, Fermat's theorem, Euler's phi function, Legendre's symbol, Gauss's lemma, automorphs, reduced forms, recent theorems of Thue & Siegel, many more. Much material not readily available elsewhere. 239 problems. Index. J figure. viii + 183pp. 5⅜ x 8. **S342 Paperbound $1.65**

ELEMENTS OF NUMBER THEORY, I. M. Vinogradov. Detailed 1st course for persons without advanced mathematics; 95% of this book can be understood by readers who have gone no farther than high school algebra. Partial contents: divisibility theory, important number theoretical functions, congruences, primitive roots and indices, etc. Solutions to both problems and exercises. Tables of primes, indices, etc. Covers almost every essential formula in elementary number theory! Translated from Russian. 233 problems, 104 exercises. viii + 227pp. 5⅜ x 8. **S259 Paperbound $1.60**

THEORY OF NUMBERS and DIOPHANTINE ANALYSIS, R. D. Carmichael. These two complete works in one volume form one of the most lucid introductions to number theory, requiring only a firm foundation in high school mathematics. "Theory of Numbers," partial contents: Eratosthenes' sieve, Euclid's fundamental theorem, G.C.F. and L.C.M. of two or more integers, linear congruences, etc "Diophantine Analysis": rational triangles, Pythagorean triangles, equations of third, fourth, higher degrees, method of functional equations, much more. "Theory of Numbers": 76 problems. Index. 94pp. "Diophantine Analysis": 222 problems. Index. 118pp. 5⅜ x 8. **S529 Paperbound $1.35**

CONTRIBUTIONS TO THE FOUNDING OF THE THEORY OF TRANSFINITE NUMBERS, Georg Cantor.
These papers founded a new branch of mathematics. The famous articles of 1895-7 are
translated, with an 82-page introduction by P. E. B. Jourdain dealing with Cantor, the background of his discoveries, their results, future possibilities. Bibliography. Index. Notes.
ix + 211 pp. 5⅜ x 8.   S45 Paperbound **$1.25**

See also: **TRANSCENDENTAL AND ALGEBRAIC NUMBERS, A. O. Gelfond.**

Probability theory and information theory

A PHILOSOPHICAL ESSAY ON PROBABILITIES, Marquis de Laplace. This famous essay explains
without recourse to mathematics the principle of probability, and the application of probability to games of chance, natural philosophy, astronomy, many other fields. Translated
from the 6th French edition by F. W. Truscott, F. L. Emory, with new introduction for this
edition by E. T. Bell. 204pp. 5⅜ x 8.   S166 Paperbound **$1.35**

MATHEMATICAL FOUNDATIONS OF INFORMATION THEORY, A. I. Khinchin. For the first time
mathematicians, statisticians, physicists, cyberneticists, and communications engineers are
offered a complete and exact introduction to this relatively new field. Entropy as a measure of
a finite scheme, applications to coding theory, study of sources, channels and codes,
detailed proofs of both Shannon theorems for any ergodic source and any stationary channel
with finite memory, and much more are covered. Bibliography. vii + 120pp. 5⅜ x 8.
                                                                        S434 Paperbound **$1.35**

SELECTED PAPERS ON NOISE AND STOCHASTIC PROCESS, edited by **Prof. Nelson Wax,** U. of
Illinois. 6 basic papers for newcomers in the field, for those whose work involves noise
characteristics. Chandrasekhar, Uhlenbeck & Ornstein, Uhlenbeck & Ming, Rice, Doob. Included is Kac's Chauvenet-Prize winning Random Walk. Extensive bibliography lists 200
articles, up through 1953. 21 figures. 337pp. 6⅛ x 9¼.   S262 Paperbound **$2.35**

THEORY OF PROBABILITY, William Burnside. Synthesis, expansion of individual papers presents numerous problems in classical probability, offering many original views succinctly,
effectively. Game theory, cards, selections from groups; geometrical probability in such
areas as suppositions as to probability of position of point on a line, points on surface
of sphere, etc. Includes methods of approximation, theory of errors, direct calculation of
probabilities, etc. Index. 136pp. 5⅜ x 8.   S567 Paperbound **$1.00**

Vector and tensor analysis, matrix theory

VECTOR AND TENSOR ANALYSIS, A. P. Wills. Covers the entire field of vector and tensor
analysis from elementary notions to dyads and non-Euclidean manifolds (especially detailed),
absolute differentiation, the Lamé operator, the Riemann-Christoffel and Ricci-Einstein
tensors, and the calculation of the Gaussian curvature of a surface. Many illustrations from
electrical engineering, relativity theory, astro-physics, quantum mechanics. Presupposes only
a good working knowledge of calculus. Exercises at end of each chapter. Intended for
physicists and engineers as well as pure mathematicians. 44 diagrams. 114 problems.
Bibliography. Index. xxxii + 285pp. 5⅜ x 8.   S454 Paperbound **$1.75**

APPLICATIONS OF TENSOR ANALYSIS, A. J. McConnell. (Formerly APPLICATIONS OF THE
ABSOLUTE DIFFERENTIAL CALCULUS.) An excellent text for understanding the application
of tensor methods to familiar subjects such as dynamics, electricity, elasticity, and hydrodynamics. Explains the fundamental ideas and notation of tensor theory, the geometrical
treatment of tensor algebra, the theory of differentiation of tensors, and includes a wealth
of practical material. Bibliography. Index. 43 illustrations. 685 problems. xii + 381pp.
5⅜ x 8.   S373 Paperbound **$1.85**

VECTOR AND TENSOR ANALYSIS, G. E. Hay. One of the clearest introductions to this increasingly important subject. Start with simple definitions, finish the book with a sure mastery
of oriented Cartesian vectors, Christoffel symbols, solenoidal tensors, and their applications. Complete breakdown of plane, solid, analytical, differential geometry. Separate chapters on application. All fundamental formulae listed & demonstrated. 195 problems, 66
figures. viii + 193pp. 5⅜ x 8.   S109 Paperbound **$1.75**

VECTOR ANALYSIS, FOUNDED UPON THE LECTURES OF J. WILLARD GIBBS, by E. B. Wilson.
Still a first-rate introduction and supplementary text for students of mathematics and
physics. Based on the pioneering lectures of Yale's great J. Willard Gibbs, can be followed
by anyone who has had some calculus. Practical approach, stressing efficient use of combinations and functions of vectors. Worked examples from geometry, mechanics, hydrodynamics, gas theory, etc., as well as practice examples. Covers basic vector processes, differential
and integral calculus in relation to vector functions, and theory of linear vector functions,
forming an introduction to the study of multiple algebra and matrix theory. While the notation is not always modern, it is easily followed. xviii + 436pp. 5⅜ x 8.
                                                                        S656 Paperbound **$2.00**

PROBLEMS AND WORKED SOLUTIONS IN VECTOR ANALYSIS, L. R. Shorter. More pages of fully-worked-out examples than any other text on vector analysis. A self-contained course for home study or a fine classroom supplement. 138 problems and examples begin with fundamentals, then cover systems of coordinates, relative velocity and acceleration, the commutative and distributive laws, axial and polar vectors, finite displacements, the calculus of vectors, curl and divergence, etc. Final chapter treats applications in dynamics and physics: kinematics of a rigid body, equipotential surfaces, etc. "Very helpful . . . very comprehensive. A handy book like this . . . will fill a great want," MATHEMATICAL GAZETTE. Index. List of 174 important equations. 158 figures. xiv + 356pp. 5⅜ x 8. S135 Paperbound **$2.00**

THE THEORY OF DETERMINANTS, MATRICES, AND INVARIANTS, H. W. Turnbull. 3rd revised, corrected edition of this important study of virtually all the salient features and major theories of the subject. Covers Laplace identities, linear equations, differentiation, symbolic and direct methods for the reduction of invariants, seminvariants, Hilbert's Basis Theorem, Clebsch's Theorem, canonical forms, etc. New appendix contains a proof of Jacobi's lemma, further properties of symmetric determinants, etc. More than 350 problems. New references to recent developments. xviii + 374pp. 5⅜ x 8. S699 Paperbound **$2.00**

Differential equations, ordinary and partial, and integral equations

INTRODUCTION TO THE DIFFERENTIAL EQUATIONS OF PHYSICS, L. Hopf. Especially valuable to the engineer with no math beyond elementary calculus. Emphasizing intuitive rather than formal aspects of concepts, the author covers an extensive territory. Partial contents: Law of causality, energy theorem, damped oscillations, coupling by friction, cylindrical and spherical coordinates, heat source, etc. Index. 48 figures. 160pp. 5⅜ x 8. S120 Paperbound **$1.25**

INTRODUCTION TO THE THEORY OF LINEAR DIFFERENTIAL EQUATIONS, E. G. Poole. Authoritative discussions of important topics, with methods of solution more detailed than usual, for students with background of elementary course in differential equations. Studies existence theorems, linearly independent solutions; equations with constant coefficients; with uniform analytic coefficients; regular singularities; the hypergeometric equation; conformal representation; etc. Exercises. Index. 210pp. 5⅜ x 8. S629 Paperbound **$1.65**

DIFFERENTIAL EQUATIONS FOR ENGINEERS, P. Franklin. Outgrowth of a course given 10 years at M. I. T. Makes most useful branch of pure math accessible for practical work. Theoretical basis of D.E.'s; solution of ordinary D.E.'s and partial derivatives arising from heat flow, steady-state temperature of a plate, wave equations; analytic functions; convergence of Fourier Series. 400 problems on electricity, vibratory systems, other topics. Formerly "Differential Equations for Electrical Engineers." Index. 41 illus. 307pp. 5⅜ x 8. S601 Paperbound **$1.65**

DIFFERENTIAL EQUATIONS, F. R. Moulton. A detailed, rigorous exposition of all the non-elementary processes of solving ordinary differential equations. Several chapters devoted to the treatment of practical problems, especially those of a physical nature, which are far more advanced than problems usually given as illustrations. Includes analytic differential equations; variations of a parameter; integrals of differential equations; analytic implicit functions; problems of elliptic motion; sine-amplitude functions; deviation of formal bodies; Cauchy-Lipschitz process; linear differential equations with periodic coefficients; differential equations in infinitely many variations; much more. Historical notes. 10 figures. 222 problems. Index. xv + 395pp. 5⅜ x 8. S451 Paperbound **$2.00**

LECTURES ON CAUCHY'S PROBLEM, J. Hadamard. Based on lectures given at Columbia, Rome, this discusses work of Riemann, Kirchhoff, Volterra, and the author's own research on the hyperbolic case in linear partial differential equations. It extends spherical and cylindrical waves to apply to all (normal) hyperbolic equations. Partial contents: Cauchy's problem, fundamental formula, equations with odd number, with even number of independent variables; method of descent. 32 figures. Index. iii + 316pp. 5⅜ x 8. S105 Paperbound **$1.75**

PARTIAL DIFFERENTIAL EQUATIONS OF MATHEMATICAL PHYSICS, A. G. Webster. A keystone work in the library of every mature physicist, engineer, researcher. Valuable sections on elasticity, compression theory, potential theory, theory of sound, heat conduction, wave propagation, vibration theory. Contents include: deduction of differential equations, vibrations, normal functions, Fourier's series, Cauchy's method, boundary problems, method of Riemann-Volterra. Spherical, cylindrical, ellipsoidal harmonics, applications, etc. 97 figures. vii + 440pp. 5⅜ x 8. S263 Paperbound **$2.00**

ORDINARY DIFFERENTIAL EQUATIONS, E. L. Ince. A most compendious analysis in real and complex domains. Existence and nature of solutions, continuous transformation groups, solutions in an infinite form, definite integrals, algebraic theory, Sturmian theory, boundary problems, existence theorems, 1st order, higher order, etc. "Deserves the highest praise, a notable addition to mathematical literature," BULLETIN, AM. MATH. SOC. Historical appendix. Bibliography. 18 figures. viii + 558pp. 5⅜ x 8. S349 Paperbound **$2.55**

THEORY OF DIFFERENTIAL EQUATIONS, A. R. Forsyth. Out of print for over a decade, the complete 6 volumes (now bound as 3) of this monumental work represent the most comprehensive treatment of differential equations ever written. Historical presentation includes in 2500 pages every substantial development. Vol. 1, 2: EXACT EQUATIONS, PFAFF'S PROBLEM; ORDINARY EQUATIONS, NOT LINEAR: methods of Grassmann, Clebsch, Lie, Darboux; Cauchy's theorem; branch points; etc. Vol. 3, 4: ORDINARY EQUATIONS, NOT LINEAR; ORDINARY LINEAR EQUATIONS: Zeta Fuchsian functions, general theorems on algebraic integrals, Brun's theorem, equations with uniform periodic coffiecients, etc. Vol. 4, 5: PARTIAL DIFFERENTIAL EQUATIONS: 2 existence-theorems, equations of theoretical dynamics, Laplace transformations, general transformation of equations of the 2nd order, much more. Indexes. Total of 2766pp. 5⅜ x 8.   S576-7-8 Clothbound: the set **$15.00**

DIFFERENTIAL AND INTEGRAL EQUATIONS OF MECHANICS AND PHYSICS (DIE DIFFERENTIAL-UND INTEGRALGLEICHUNGEN DER MECHANIK UND PHYSIK), edited by P. Frank and R. von Mises. Most comprehensive and authoritative work on the mathematics of mathematical physics available today in the United States: the standard, definitive reference for teachers, physicists, engineers, and mathematicians—now published (in the original German) at a relatively inexpensive price for the first time! Every chapter in this 2,000-page set is by an expert in his field: Caratheodory, Courant, Frank, Mises, and a dozen others. Vol. I, on mathematics, gives concise but complete coverages of advanced calculus, differential equations, integral equations, and potential, and partial differential equations. Index. xxiii + 916pp. Vol. II (physics): classical mechanics, optics, continuous mechanics, heat conduction and diffusion, the stationary and quasi-stationary electromagnetic field, electromagnetic oscillations, and wave mechanics. Index. xxiv + 1106pp. Two volume set. Each volume available separately. 5⅝ x 8⅜.   S787 Vol I Clothbound **$7.50**
                                                S788 Vol II Clothbound **$7.50**
                                                The set **$15.00**

MATHEMATICAL ANALYSIS OF ELECTRICAL AND OPTICAL WAVE-MOTION, Harry Bateman. Written by one of this century's most distinguished mathematical physicists, this is a practical introduction to those developments of Maxwell's electromagnetic theory which are directly connected with the solution of the partial differential equation of wave motion. Methods of solving wave-equation, polar-cylindrical coordinates, diffraction, transformation of coordinates, homogeneous solutions, electromagnetic fields with moving singularities, etc. Index. 168pp. 5⅜ x 8.   S14 Paperbound **$1.60**

See also: **THE ANALYTICAL THEORY OF HEAT, J. Fourier; INTRODUCTION TO BESSEL FUNCTIONS, F. Bowman.**

Statistics

ELEMENTARY STATISTICS, WITH APPLICATIONS IN MEDICINE AND THE BIOLOGICAL SCIENCES, F. E. Croxton. A sound introduction to statistics for anyone in the physical sciences, assuming no prior acquaintance and requiring only a modest knowledge of math. All basic formulas carefully explained and illustrated; all necessary reference tables included. From basic terms and concepts, the study proceeds to frequency distribution, linear, non-linear, and multiple correlation, skewness, kurtosis, etc. A large section deals with reliability and significance of statistical methods. Containing concrete examples from medicine and biology, this book will prove unusually helpful to workers in those fields who increasingly must evaluate, check, and interpret statistics. Formerly titled "Elementary Statistics with Applications in Medicine." 101 charts. 57 tables. 14 appendices. Index. iv + 376pp. 5⅜ x 8.
                                                S506 Paperbound **$1.95**

METHODS OF STATISTICS, L. H. C. Tippett. A classic in its field, this unusually complete systematic introduction to statistical methods begins at beginner's level and progresses to advanced levels for experimenters and poll-takers in all fields of statistical research. Supplies fundamental knowledge of virtually all elementary methods in use today by sociologists, psychologists, biologists, engineers, mathematicians, etc. Explains logical and mathematical basis of each method described, with examples for each section. Covers frequency distributions and measures, inference from random samples, errors in large samples, simple analysis of variance, multiple and partial regression and correlation, etc. 4th revised (1952) edition. 16 charts. 5 significance tables. 152-item bibliography. 96 tables. 22 figures. 395pp. 6 x 9.
                                                S228 Clothbound **$7.50**

STATISTICS MANUAL, E. L. Crow, F. A. Davis, M. W. Maxfield. Comprehensive collection of classical, modern statistics methods, prepared under auspices of U. S. Naval Ordnance Test Station, China Lake, Calif. Many examples from ordnance will be valuable to workers in all fields. Emphasis is on use, with information on fiducial limits, sign tests, Chi-square runs, sensitivity, quality control, much more. "Well written . . . excellent reference work," Operations Research. Corrected edition of NAVORD Report 3360 NOTS 948. Introduction. Appendix of 32 tables, charts. Index. Bibliography. 95 illustrations. 306pp. 5⅜ x 8.
                                                S599 Paperbound **$1.55**

ANALYSIS & DESIGN OF EXPERIMENTS, H. B. Mann. Offers a method for grasping the analysis of variance and variance design within a short time. Partial contents: Chi-square distribution and analysis of variance distribution, matrices, quadratic forms, likelihood ration tests and tests of linear hypotheses, power of analysis, Galois fields, non-orthogonal data, interblock estimates, etc. 15pp. of useful tables. x + 195pp. 5 x 7⅜. S180 Paperbound **$1.45**

Numerical analysis, tables

PRACTICAL ANALYSIS, GRAPHICAL AND NUMERICAL METHODS, F. A. Willers. Translated by R. T. Beyer. Immensely practical handbook for engineers, showing how to interpolate, use various methods of numerical differentiation and integration, determine the roots of a single algebraic equation, system of linear equations, use empirical formulas, integrate differential equations, etc. Hundreds of shortcuts for arriving at numerical solutions. Special section on American calculating machines, by T. W. Simpson. 132 illustrations. 422pp. 5⅜ x 8.
S273 Paperbound **$2.00**

NUMERICAL SOLUTIONS OF DIFFERENTIAL EQUATIONS, H. Levy & E. A. Baggott. Comprehensive collection of methods for solving ordinary differential equations of first and higher order. All must pass 2 requirements: easy to grasp and practical, more rapid than school methods. Partial contents: graphical integration of differential equations, graphical methods for detailed solution. Numerical solution. Simultaneous equations and equations of 2nd and higher orders. "Should be in the hands of all in research in applied mathematics, teaching," NATURE. 21 figures. viii + 238pp. 5⅜ x 8. S168 Paperbound **$1.75**

NUMERICAL INTEGRATION OF DIFFERENTIAL EQUATIONS, Bennett, Milne & Bateman. Unabridged republication of original monograph prepared for National Research Council. New methods of integration of differential equations developed by 3 leading mathematicians: THE INTERPOLATIONAL POLYNOMIAL and SUCCESSIVE APPROXIMATIONS by A. A. Bennett; STEP-BY-STEP METHODS OF INTEGRATION by W. W. Milne; METHODS FOR PARTIAL DIFFERENTIAL EQUATIONS by H. Bateman. Methods for partial differential equations, transition from difference equations to differential equations, solution of differential equations to non-integral values of a parameter will interest mathematicians and physicists. 288 footnotes, mostly bibliographic; 235-item classified bibliography. 108pp. 5⅜ x 8. S305 Paperbound **$1.35**

INTRODUCTION TO RELAXATION METHODS, F. S. Shaw. Fluid mechanics, design of electrical networks, forces in structural frameworks, stress distribution, buckling, etc. Solve linear simultaneous equations, linear ordinary differential equations, partial differential equations, Eigen-value problems by relaxation methods. Detailed examples throughout. Special tables for dealing with awkwardly-shaped boundaries. Indexes. 253 diagrams. 72 tables. 400pp. 5⅜ x 8. S244 Paperbound **$2.45**

TABLES OF INDEFINITE INTEGRALS, G. Petit Bois. Comprehensive and accurate, this orderly grouping of over 2500 of the most useful indefinite integrals will save you hours of laborious mathematical groundwork. After a list of 49 common transformations of integral expressions, with a wide variety of examples, the book takes up algebraic functions, irrational monomials, products and quotients of binomials, transcendental functions, natural logs, etc. You will rarely or never encounter an integral of an algebraic or transcendental function not included here; any more comprehensive set of tables costs at least $12 or $15. Index. 2544 integrals. xii + 154pp. 6⅛ x 9¼. S225 Paperbound **$1.65**

A TABLE OF THE INCOMPLETE ELLIPTIC INTEGRAL OF THE THIRD KIND, R. G. Selfridge, J. E. Maxfield. The first complete 6 place tables of values of the incomplete integral of the third kind, prepared under the auspices of the Research Department of the U.S. Naval Ordnance Test Station. Calculated on an IBM type 704 calculator and thoroughly verified by echo-checking and a check integral at the completion of each value of **a**. Of inestimable value in problems where the surface area of geometrical bodies can only be expressed in terms of the incomplete integral of the third and lower kinds; problems in aero-, fluid-, and thermodynamics involving processes where nonsymmetrical repetitive volumes must be determined; various types of seismological problems; problems of magnetic potentials due to circular current; etc. Foreword. Acknowledgment. Introduction. Use of table. xiv + 805pp. 5⅝ x 8⅜. S501 Clothbound **$7.50**

MATHEMATICAL TABLES, H. B. Dwight. Unique for its coverage in one volume of almost every function of importance in applied mathematics, engineering, and the physical sciences. Three extremely fine tables of the three trig functions and their inverse functions to thousandths of radians; natural and common logarithms; squares, cubes; hyperbolic functions and the inverse hyperbolic functions; $(a^2 + b^2)$ exp. $\frac{1}{2}a$; complete elliptic integrals of the 1st and 2nd kind; sine and cosine integrals; exponential integrals $Ei(x)$ and $Ei(-x)$; binomial coefficients; factorials to 250; surface zonal harmonics and first derivatives; Bernoulli and Euler numbers and their logs to base of 10; Gamma function; normal probability integral; over 60 pages of Bessel functions; the Riemann Zeta function. Each table with formulae generally used, sources of more extensive tables, interpolation data, etc. Over half have columns of differences, to facilitate interpolation. Introduction. Index. viii + 231pp. 5⅜ x 8.
S445 Paperbound **$1.75**

TABLES OF FUNCTIONS WITH FORMULAE AND CURVES, E. Jahnke & F. Emde. The world's most comprehensive 1-volume English-text collection of tables, formulae, curves of transcendent functions. 4th corrected edition, new 76-page section giving tables, formulae for elementary functions—not in other English editions. Partial contents: sine, cosine, logarithmic integral; factorial function; error integral; theta functions; elliptic integrals, functions; Legendre, Bessel, Riemann, Mathieu, hypergeometric functions, etc. Supplementary books. Bibliography. Indexed. "Out of the way functions for which we know no other source," SCIENTIFIC COMPUTING SERVICE, Ltd. 212 figures. 400pp. 5⅜ x 8. **S133 Paperbound $2.00**

JACOBIAN ELLIPTIC FUNCTION TABLES, L. M. Milne-Thomson. An easy to follow, practical book which gives not only useful numerical tables, but also a complete elementary sketch of the application of elliptic functions. It covers Jacobian elliptic functions and a description of their principal properties; complete elliptic integrals; Fourier series and power series expansions; periods, zeros, poles, residues, formulas for special values of the argument; transformations, approximations, elliptic integrals, conformal mapping, factorization of cubic and quartic polynomials; application to the pendulum problem; etc. Tables and graphs form the body of the book: Graph, 5 figure table of the elliptic function sn (u m); cn (u m); dn (u m). 8 figure table of complete elliptic integrals K, K', E, E', and the nome q. 7 figure table of the Jacobian zeta-function Z(u). 3 figures. xi + 123pp. 5⅜ x 8.

S194 Paperbound $1.35

PHYSICS

General physics

FOUNDATIONS OF PHYSICS, R. B. Lindsay & H. Margenau. Excellent bridge between semi-popular works & technical treatises. A discussion of methods of physical description, construction of theory; valuable for physicist with elementary calculus who is interested in ideas that give meaning to data, tools of modern physics. Contents include symbolism, mathematical equations; space & time foundations of mechanics; probability; physics & continua; electron theory; special & general relativity; quantum mechanics; causality. "Thorough and yet not overdetailed. Unreservedly recommended," NATURE (London). Unabridged, corrected edition. List of recommended readings. 35 illustrations. xi + 537pp. 5⅜ x 8.

S377 Paperbound $2.45

FUNDAMENTAL FORMULAS OF PHYSICS, ed. by D. H. Menzel. Highly useful, fully inexpensive reference and study text, ranging from simple to highly sophisticated operations. Mathematics integrated into text—each chapter stands as short textbook of field represented. Vol. 1: Statistics, Physical Constants, Special Theory of Relativity, Hydrodynamics, Aerodynamics, Boundary Value Problems in Math. Physics; Viscosity, Electromagnetic Theory, etc. Vol. 2: Sound, Acoustics; Geometrical Optics, Electron Optics, High-Energy Phenomena, Magnetism, Biophysics, much more. Index. Total of 800pp. 5⅜ x 8.

Vol. 1 S595 Paperbound $2.00
Vol. 2 S596 Paperbound $2.00

MATHEMATICAL PHYSICS, D. H. Menzel. Thorough one-volume treatment of the mathematical techniques vital for classic mechanics, electromagnetic theory, quantum theory, and relativity. Written by the Harvard Professor of Astrophysics for junior, senior, and graduate courses, it gives clear explanations of all those aspects of function theory, vectors, matrices, dyadics, tensors, partial differential equations, etc., necessary for the understanding of the various physical theories. Electron theory, relativity, and other topics seldom presented appear here in considerable detail. Scores of definitions, conversion factors, dimensional constants, etc. "More detailed than normal for an advanced text . . . excellent set of sections on Dyadics, Matrices, and Tensors," JOURNAL OF THE FRANKLIN INSTITUTE. Index. 193 problems, with answers. x + 412pp. 5⅜ x 8. **S56 Paperbound $2.00**

THE SCIENTIFIC PAPERS OF J. WILLARD GIBBS. All the published papers of America's outstanding theoretical scientist (except for "Statistical Mechanics" and "Vector Analysis"). Vol I (thermodynamics) contains one of the most brilliant of all 19th-century scientific papers—the 300-page "On the Equilibrium of Heterogeneous Substances," which founded the science of physical chemistry, and clearly stated a number of highly important natural laws for the first time; 8 other papers complete the first volume. Vol II includes 2 papers on dynamics, 8 on vector analysis and multiple algebra, 5 on the electromagnetic theory of light, and 6 miscellaneous papers. Biographical sketch by H. A. Bumstead. Total of xxxvi + 718pp. 5⅝ x 8⅜.

S721 Vol I Paperbound $2.00
S722 Vol II Paperbound $2.00
The set $4.00

Relativity, quantum theory, nuclear physics

THE PRINCIPLE OF RELATIVITY, A. Einstein, H. Lorentz, M. Minkowski, H. Weyl. These are the 11 basic papers that founded the general and special theories of relativity, all translated into English. Two papers by Lorentz on the Michelson experiment, electromagnetic phenomena. Minkowski's SPACE & TIME, and Weyl's GRAVITATION & ELECTRICITY. 7 epoch-making papers by Einstein: ELECTROMAGNETICS OF MOVING BODIES, INFLUENCE OF GRAVITATION IN PROPAGATION OF LIGHT, COSMOLOGICAL CONSIDERATIONS, GENERAL THEORY, and 3 others. 7 diagrams. Special notes by A. Sommerfeld. 224pp. 5⅜ x 8.
S81 Paperbound **$1.75**

SPACE TIME MATTER, Hermann Weyl. "The standard treatise on the general theory of relativity," (Nature), written by a world-renowned scientist, provides a deep clear discussion of the logical coherence of the general theory, with introduction to all the mathematical tools needed: Maxwell, analytical geometry, non-Euclidean geometry, tensor calculus, etc. Basis is classical space-time, before absorption of relativity. Partial contents: Euclidean space, mathematical form, metrical continuum, relativity of time and space, general theory. 15 diagrams. Bibliography. New preface for this edition. xviii + 330pp. 5⅜ x 8.
S267 Paperbound **$1.85**

PRINCIPLES OF QUANTUM MECHANICS, W. V. Houston. Enables student with working knowledge of elementary mathematical physics to develop facility in use of quantum mechanics, understand published work in field. Formulates quantum mechanics in terms of Schroedinger's wave mechanics. Studies evidence for quantum theory, for inadequacy of classical mechanics, 2 postulates of quantum mechanics; numerous important, fruitful applications of quantum mechanics in spectroscopy, collision problems, electrons in solids; other topics. "One of the most rewarding features . . . is the interlacing of problems with text," Amer. J. of Physics. Corrected edition. 21 illus. Index. 296pp. 5⅜ x 8.   S524 Paperbound **$1.85**

PHYSICAL PRINCIPLES OF THE QUANTUM THEORY, Werner Heisenberg. A Nobel laureate discusses quantum theory; Heisenberg's own work, Compton, Schroedinger, Wilson, Einstein, many others. Written for physicists, chemists who are not specialists in quantum theory, only elementary formulae are considered in the text; there is a mathematical appendix for specialists. Profound without sacrifice of clarity. Translated by C. Eckart, F. Hoyt. 18 figures. 192pp. 5⅜ x 8.   S113 Paperbound **$1.25**

SELECTED PAPERS ON QUANTUM ELECTRODYNAMICS, edited by J. Schwinger. Facsimiles of papers which established quantum electrodynamics, from initial successes through today's position as part of the larger theory of elementary particles. First book publication in any language of these collected papers of Bethe, Bloch, Dirac, Dyson, Fermi, Feynman, Heisenberg, Kusch, Lamb, Oppenheimer, Pauli, Schwinger, Tomonoga, Weisskopf, Wigner, etc. 34 papers in all, 29 in English, 1 in French, 3 in German, 1 in Italian. Preface and historical commentary by the editor. xvii + 423pp. 6⅛ x 9¼.   S444 Paperbound **$2.45**

THE FUNDAMENTAL PRINCIPLES OF QUANTUM MECHANICS, WITH ELEMENTARY APPLICATIONS, E. C. Kemble. An inductive presentation, for the graduate student or specialist in some other branch of physics. Assumes some acquaintance with advanced math; apparatus necessary beyond differential equations and advanced calculus is developed as needed. Although a general exposition of principles, hundreds of individual problems are fully treated, with applications of theory being interwoven with development of the mathematical structure. The author is the Professor of Physics at Harvard Univ. "This excellent book would be of great value to every student . . . a rigorous and detailed mathematical discussion of all of the principal quantum-mechanical methods . . . has succeeded in keeping his presentations clear and understandable," Dr. Linus Pauling, J. of the American Chemical Society. Appendices: calculus of variations, math. notes, etc. Indexes. 611pp. 5⅜ x 8.
S472 Paperbound **$2.95**

ATOMIC SPECTRA AND ATOMIC STRUCTURE, G. Herzberg. Excellent general survey for chemists, physicists specializing in other fields. Partial contents: simplest line spectra and elements of atomic theory, building-up principle and periodic system of elements, hyperfine structure of spectral lines, some experiments and applications. Bibliography. 80 figures. Index. xii + 257pp. 5⅜ x 8.   S115 Paperbound **$1.95**

THE THEORY AND THE PROPERTIES OF METALS AND ALLOYS, N. F. Mott, H. Jones. Quantum methods used to develop mathematical models which show interrelationship of basic chemical phenomena with crystal structure, magnetic susceptibility, electrical, optical properties. Examines thermal properties of crystal lattice, electron motion in applied field, cohesion, electrical resistance, noble metals, para-, dia-, and ferromagnetism, etc. "Exposition . . . clear . . . mathematical treatment . . . simple," Nature. 138 figures. Bibliography. Index. xiii + 320pp. 5⅜ x 8.   S456 Paperbound **$1.85**

FOUNDATIONS OF NUCLEAR PHYSICS, edited by R. T. Beyer. 13 of the most important papers on nuclear physics reproduced in facsimile in the original languages of their authors: the papers most often cited in footnotes, bibliographies. Anderson, Curie, Joliot, Chadwick, Fermi, Lawrence, Cockcroft, Hahn, Yukawa. UNPARALLELED BIBLIOGRAPHY. 122 double-columned pages, over 4,000 articles, books classified. 57 figures. 288pp. 6⅛ x 9¼.
S19 Paperbound **$1.75**

MESON PHYSICS, R. E. Marshak. Traces the basic theory, and explicitly presents results of experiments with particular emphasis on theoretical significance. Phenomena involving mesons as virtual transitions are avoided, eliminating some of the least satisfactory predictions of meson theory. Includes production and study of π mesons at nonrelativistic nucleon energies, contrasts between π and μ mesons, phenomena associated with nuclear interaction of π mesons, etc. Presents early evidence for new classes of particles and indicates theoretical difficulties created by discovery of heavy mesons and hyperons. Name and subject indices. Unabridged reprint. viii + 378pp. 5⅜ x 8.   S500 Paperbound **$1.95**

See also: **STRANGE STORY OF THE QUANTUM, B. Hoffmann; FROM EUCLID TO EDDINGTON, E. Whittaker; MATTER AND LIGHT, THE NEW PHYSICS, L. de Broglie; THE EVOLUTION OF SCIENTIFIC THOUGHT FROM NEWTON TO EINSTEIN, A. d'Abro; THE RISE OF THE NEW PHYSICS, A. d'Abro; THE THEORY OF GROUPS AND QUANTUM MECHANICS, H. Weyl; SUBSTANCE AND FUNCTION, & EINSTEIN'S THEORY OF RELATIVITY, E. Cassirer; FUNDAMENTAL FORMULAS OF PHYSICS, D. H. Menzel.**

Hydrodynamics

HYDRODYNAMICS, H. Dryden, F. Murnaghan, Harry Bateman. Published by the National Research Council in 1932 this enormous volume offers a complete coverage of classical hydrodynamics. Encyclopedic in quality. Partial contents: physics of fluids, motion, turbulent flow, compressible fluids, motion in 1, 2, 3 dimensions; viscous fluids rotating, laminar motion, resistance of motion through viscous fluid, eddy viscosity, hydraulic flow in channels of various shapes, discharge of gases, flow past obstacles, etc. Bibliography of over 2,900 items. Indexes. 23 figures. 634pp. 5⅜ x 8.   S303 Paperbound **$2.75**

A TREATISE ON HYDRODYNAMICS, A. B. Basset. Favorite text on hydrodynamics for 2 generations of physicists, hydrodynamical engineers, oceanographers, ship designers, etc. Clear enough for the beginning student, and thorough source for graduate students and engineers on the work of d'Alembert, Euler, Laplace, Lagrange, Poisson, Green, Clebsch, Stokes, Cauchy, Helmholtz, J. J. Thomson, Love, Hicks, Greenhill, Besant, Lamb, etc. Great amount of documentation on entire theory of classical hydrodynamics. Vol I: theory of motion of frictionless liquids, vortex, and cyclic irrotational motion, etc. 132 exercises. Bibliography. 3 Appendixes. xii + 264pp. Vol II: motion in viscous liquids, harmonic analysis, theory of tides, etc. 112 exercises. Bibliography. 4 Appendixes. xv + 328pp. Two volume set. 5⅜ x 8.
S724 Vol I Paperbound **$1.75**
S725 Vol II Paperbound **$1.75**
The set **$3.50**

HYDRODYNAMICS, Horace Lamb. Internationally famous complete coverage of standard reference work on dynamics of liquids & gases. Fundamental theorems, equations, methods, solutions, background, for classical hydrodynamics. Chapters include Equations of Motion, Integration of Equations in Special Gases, Irrotational Motion, Motion of Liquid in 2 Dimensions, Motion of Solids through Liquid-Dynamical Theory, Vortex Motion, Tidal Waves, Surface Waves, Waves of Expansion, Viscosity, Rotating Masses of liquids. Excellently planned, arranged; clear, lucid presentation. 6th enlarged, revised edition. Index. Over 900 footnotes, mostly bibliographical. 119 figures. xv + 738pp. 6⅛ x 9¼.   S256 Paperbound **$2.95**

See also: **FUNDAMENTAL FORMULAS OF PHYSICS, D. H. Menzel; THEORY OF FLIGHT, R. von Mises; FUNDAMENTALS OF HYDRO- AND AEROMECHANICS, L. Prandtl and O. G. Tietjens; APPLIED HYDRO- AND AEROMECHANICS, L. Prandtl and O. G. Tietjens; HYDRAULICS AND ITS APPLICATIONS, A. H. Gibson; FLUID MECHANICS FOR HYDRAULIC ENGINEERS, H. Rouse.**

Acoustics, optics, electromagnetics

ON THE SENSATIONS OF TONE, Hermann Helmholtz. This is an unmatched coordination of such fields as acoustical physics, physiology, experiment, history of music. It covers the entire gamut of musical tone. Partial contents: relation of musical science to acoustics, physical vs. physiological acoustics, composition of vibration, resonance, analysis of tones by sympathetic resonance, beats, chords, tonality, consonant chords, discords, progression of parts, etc. 33 appendixes discuss various aspects of sound, physics, acoustics, music, etc. Translated by A. J. Ellis. New introduction by Prof. Henry Margenau of Yale. 68 figures. 43 musical passages analyzed. Over 100 tables. Index. xix + 576pp. 6⅛ x 9¼.
S114 Paperbound **$2.95**

THE THEORY OF SOUND, Lord Rayleigh. Most vibrating systems likely to be encountered in practice can be tackled successfully by the methods set forth by the great Nobel laureate, Lord Rayleigh. Complete coverage of experimental, mathematical aspects of sound theory. Partial contents: Harmonic motions, vibrating systems in general, lateral vibrations of bars, curved plates or shells, applications of Laplace's functions to acoustical problems, fluid friction, plane vortex-sheet, vibrations of solid bodies, etc. This is the first inexpensive edition of this great reference and study work. Bibliography. Historical introduction by R. B. Lindsay. Total of 1040pp. 97 figures. 5⅜ x 8.
S292, S293, Two volume set, paperbound, **$4.00**

THE DYNAMICAL THEORY OF SOUND, H. Lamb. Comprehensive mathematical treatment of the physical aspects of sound, covering the theory of vibrations, the general theory of sound, and the equations of motion of strings, bars, membranes, pipes, and resonators. Includes chapters on plane, spherical, and simple harmonic waves, and the Helmholtz Theory of Audition. Complete and self-contained development for student and specialist; all fundamental differential equations solved completely. Specific mathematical details for such important phenomena as harmonics, normal modes, forced vibrations of strings, theory of reed pipes, etc. Index. Bibliography. 86 diagrams. viii + 307pp. 5⅜ x 8.
S655 Paperbound **$1.50**

WAVE PROPAGATION IN PERIODIC STRUCTURES, L. Brillouin. A general method and application to different problems: pure physics, such as scattering of X-rays of crystals, thermal vibration in crystal lattices, electronic motion in metals; and also problems of electrical engineering. Partial contents: elastic waves in 1-dimensional lattices of point masses. Propagation of waves along 1-dimensional lattices. Energy flow. 2 dimensional, 3 dimensional lattices. Mathieu's equation. Matrices and propagation of waves along an electric line. Continuous electric lines. 131 illustrations. Bibliography. Index. xii + 253pp. 5⅜ x 8.
S34 Paperbound **$1.85**

THEORY OF VIBRATIONS, N. W. McLachlan. Based on an exceptionally successful graduate course given at Brown University, this discusses linear systems having 1 degree of freedom, forced vibrations of simple linear systems, vibration of flexible strings, transverse vibrations of bars and tubes, transverse vibration of circular plate, sound waves of finite amplitude, etc. Index. 99 diagrams. 160pp. 5⅜ x 8.
S190 Paperbound **$1.35**

LOUD SPEAKERS: THEORY, PERFORMANCE, TESTING AND DESIGN, N. W. McLachlan. Most comprehensive coverage of theory, practice of loud speaker design, testing; classic reference, study manual in field. First 12 chapters deal with theory, for readers mainly concerned with math. aspects; last 7 chapters will interest reader concerned with testing, design. Partial contents: principles of sound propagation, fluid pressure on vibrators, theory of moving-coil principle, transients, driving mechanisms, response curves, design of horn type moving coil speakers, electrostatic speakers, much more. Appendix. Bibliography. Index. 165 illustrations, charts. 411pp. 5⅜ x 8.
S588 Paperbound **$2.25**

MICROWAVE TRANSMISSION, J. S. Slater. First text dealing exclusively with microwaves, brings together points of view of field, circuit theory, for graduate student in physics, electrical engineering, microwave technician. Offers valuable point of view not in most later studies. Uses Maxwell's equations to study electromagnetic field, important in this area. Partial contents: infinite line with distributed parameters, impedance of terminated line, plane waves, reflections, wave guides, coaxial line, composite transmission lines, impedance matching, etc. Introduction. Index. 76 illus. 319pp. 5⅜ x 8.
S564 Paperbound **$1.50**

THE ANALYSIS OF SENSATIONS, Ernst Mach. Great study of physiology, psychology of perception, shows Mach's ability to see material freshly, his "incorruptible skepticism and independence." (Einstein). Relation of problems of psychological perception to classical physics, supposed dualism of physical and mental, principle of continuity, evolution of senses, will as organic manifestation, scores of experiments, observations in optics, acoustics, music, graphics, etc. New introduction by T. S. Szasz, M. D. 58 illus. 300-item bibliography. Index. 404pp. 5⅜ x 8.
S525 Paperbound **$1.75**

APPLIED OPTICS AND OPTICAL DESIGN, A. E. Conrady. With publication of vol. 2, standard work for designers in optics is now complete for first time. Only work of its kind in English; only detailed work for practical designer and self-taught. Requires, for bulk of work, no math above trig. Step-by-step exposition, from fundamental concepts of geometrical, physical optics, to systematic study, design, of almost all types of optical systems. Vol. 1: all ordinary ray-tracing methods; primary aberrations; necessary higher aberration for design of telescopes, low-power microscopes, photographic equipment. Vol. 2: (Completed from author's notes by R. Kingslake, Dir. Optical Design, Eastman Kodak.) Special attention to high-power microscope, anastigmatic photographic objectives. "An indispensable work," J., Optical Soc. of Amer. "As a practical guide this book has no rival," Transactions, Optical Soc. Index. Bibliography. 193 diagrams. 852pp. 6⅛ x 9¼.
Vol. 1 T611 Paperbound **$2.95**
Vol. 2 T612 Paperbound **$2.95**

THE THEORY OF OPTICS, Paul Drude. One of finest fundamental texts in physical optics, classic offers thorough coverage, complete mathematical treatment of basic ideas. Includes fullest treatment of application of thermodynamics to optics; sine law in formation of images, transparent crystals, magnetically active substances, velocity of light, apertures, effects depending upon them, polarization, optical instruments, etc. Introduction by A. A. Michelson. Index. 110 illus. 567pp. 5⅜ x 8.
S532 Paperbound **$2.45**

OPTICKS, Sir Isaac Newton. In its discussions of light, reflection, color, refraction, theories of wave and corpuscular theories of light, this work is packed with scores of insights and discoveries. In its precise and practical discussion of construction of optical apparatus, contemporary understandings of phenomena it is truly fascinating to modern physicists, astronomers, mathematicians. Foreword by Albert Einstein. Preface by I. B. Cohen of Harvard University. 7 pages of portraits, facsimile pages, letters, etc. cxvi + 414pp. 5⅜ x 8.
S205 Paperbound **$2.00**

OPTICS AND OPTICAL INSTRUMENTS: AN INTRODUCTION WITH SPECIAL REFERENCE TO PRACTICAL APPLICATIONS, B. K. Johnson. An invaluable guide to basic practical applications of optical principles, which shows how to set up inexpensive working models of each of the four main types of optical instruments—telescopes, microscopes, photographic lenses, optical projecting systems. Explains in detail the most important experiments for determining their accuracy, resolving power, angular field of view, amounts of aberration, all other necessary facts about the instruments. Formerly "Practical Optics." Index. 234 diagrams. Appendix. 224pp. 5⅜ x 8.
S642 Paperbound **$1.65**

PRINCIPLES OF PHYSICAL OPTICS, Ernst Mach. This classical examination of the propagation of light, color, polarization, etc. offers an historical and philosophical treatment that has never been surpassed for breadth and easy readability. Contents: Rectilinear propagation of light. Reflection, refraction. Early knowledge of vision. Dioptrics. Composition of light. Theory of color and dispersion. Periodicity. Theory of interference. Polarization. Mathematical representation of properties of light. Propagation of waves, etc. 279 illustrations, 10 portraits. Appendix. Indexes. 324pp. 5⅜ x 8.
S178 Paperbound **$1.75**

FUNDAMENTALS OF ELECTRICITY AND MAGNETISM, L. B. Loeb. For students of physics, chemistry, or engineering who want an introduction to electricity and magnetism on a higher level and in more detail than general elementary physics texts provide. Only elementary differential and integral calculus is assumed. Physical laws developed logically, from magnetism to electric currents, Ohm's law, electrolysis, and on to static electricity, induction, etc. Covers an unusual amount of material; one third of book on modern material: solution of wave equation, photoelectric and thermionic effects, etc. Complete statement of the various electrical systems of units and interrelations. 2 Indexes. 75 pages of problems with answers stated. Over 300 figures and diagrams. xix +669pp. 5⅜ x 8.
S745 Paperbound **$2.75**

THE ELECTROMAGNETIC FIELD, Max Mason & Warren Weaver. Used constantly by graduate engineers. Vector methods exclusively: detailed treatment of electrostatics, expansion methods, with tables converting any quantity into absolute electromagnetic, absolute electrostatic, practical units. Discrete charges, ponderable bodies, Maxwell field equations, etc. Introduction. Indexes. 416pp. 5⅜ x 8.
S185 Paperbound **$2.00**

ELECTRICAL THEORY ON THE GIORGI SYSTEM, P. Cornelius. A new clarification of the fundamental concepts of electricity and magnetism, advocating the convenient m.k.s. system of units that is steadily gaining followers in the sciences. Illustrating the use and effectiveness of his terminology with numerous applications to concrete technical problems, the author here expounds the famous Giorgi system of electrical physics. His lucid presentation and well-reasoned, cogent argument for the universal adoption of this system form one of the finest pieces of scientific exposition in recent years. 28 figures. Index. Conversion tables for translating earlier data into modern units. Translated from 3rd Dutch edition by L. J. Jolley. x + 187pp. 5½ x 8¾.
S909 Clothbound **$6.00**

THEORY OF ELECTRONS AND ITS APPLICATION TO THE PHENOMENA OF LIGHT AND RADIANT HEAT, H. Lorentz. Lectures delivered at Columbia University by Nobel laureate Lorentz. Unabridged, they form a historical coverage of the theory of free electrons, motion, absorption of heat, Zeeman effect, propagation of light in molecular bodies, inverse Zeeman effect, optical phenomena in moving bodies, etc. 109 pages of notes explain the more advanced sections. Index. 9 figures. 352pp. 5⅜ x 8.
S173 Paperbound **$1.85**

TREATISE ON ELECTRICITY AND MAGNETISM, James Clerk Maxwell. For more than 80 years a seemingly inexhaustible source of leads for physicists, mathematicians, engineers. Total of 1082pp. on such topics as Measurement of Quantities, Electrostatics, Elementary Mathematical Theory of Electricity, Electrical Work and Energy in a System of Conductors, General Theorems, Theory of Electrical Images, Electrolysis, Conduction, Polarization, Dielectrics, Resistance, etc. "The greatest mathematical physicist since Newton," Sir James Jeans. 3rd edition. 107 figures, 21 plates. 1082pp. 5⅜ x 8.   S636-7, 2 volume set, paperbound **$4.00**

See also: FUNDAMENTAL FORMULAS OF PHYSICS, D. H. Menzel; MATHEMATICAL ANALYSIS OF ELECTRICAL & OPTICAL WAVE MOTION, H. Bateman.

Mechanics, dynamics, thermodynamics, elasticity

MECHANICS VIA THE CALCULUS, P. W. Norris, W. S. Legge. Covers almost everything, from linear motion to vector analysis: equations determining motion, linear methods, compounding of simple harmonic motions, Newton's laws of motion, Hooke's law, the simple pendulum, motion of a particle in 1 plane, centers of gravity, virtual work, friction, kinetic energy of rotating bodies, equilibrium of strings, hydrostatics, sheering stresses, elasticity, etc. 550 problems. 3rd revised edition. xii + 367pp. 6 x 9.
S207 Clothbound **$3.95**

MECHANICS, J. P. Den Hartog. Already a classic among introductory texts, the M.I.T. professor's lively and discursive presentation is equally valuable as a beginner's text, an engineering student's refresher, or a practicing engineer's reference. Emphasis in this highly readable text is on illuminating fundamental principles and showing how they are embodied in a great number of real engineering and design problems: trusses, loaded cables, beams, jacks, hoists, etc. Provides advanced material on relative motion and gyroscopes not usual in introductory texts. "Very thoroughly recommended to all those anxious to improve their real understanding of the principles of mechanics." MECHANICAL WORLD. Index. List of equations. 334 problems, all with answers. Over 550 diagrams and drawings. ix + 462pp. 5⅜ x 8.
S754 Paperbound **$2.00**

THEORETICAL MECHANICS: AN INTRODUCTION TO MATHEMATICAL PHYSICS, J. S. Ames, F. D. Murnaghan. A mathematically rigorous development of theoretical mechanics for the advanced student, with constant practical applications. Used in hundreds of advanced courses. An unusually thorough coverage of gyroscopic and baryscopic material, detailed analyses of the Coriolis acceleration, applications of Lagrange's equations, motion of the double pendulum, Hamilton-Jacobi partial differential equations, group velocity and dispersion, etc. Special relativity is also included. 159 problems. 44 figures. ix + 462pp. 5⅜ x 8.
S461 Paperbound **$2.00**

THEORETICAL MECHANICS: STATICS AND THE DYNAMICS OF A PARTICLE, W. D. MacMillan. Used for over 3 decades as a self-contained and extremely comprehensive advanced undergraduate text in mathematical physics, physics, astronomy, and deeper foundations of engineering. Early sections require only a knowledge of geometry; later, a working knowledge of calculus. Hundreds of basic problems, including projectiles to the moon, escape velocity, harmonic motion, ballistics, falling bodies, transmission of power, stress and strain, elasticity, astronomical problems. 340 practice problems plus many fully worked out examples make it possible to test and extend principles developed in the text. 200 figures. xvii + 430pp. 5⅜ x 8.
S467 Paperbound **$2.00**

THEORETICAL MECHANICS: THE THEORY OF THE POTENTIAL, W. D. MacMillan. A comprehensive, well balanced presentation of potential theory, serving both as an introduction and a reference work with regard to specific problems, for physicists and mathematicians. No prior knowledge of integral relations is assumed, and all mathematical material is developed as it becomes necessary. Includes: Attraction of Finite Bodies; Newtonian Potential Function; Vector Fields, Green and Gauss Theorems; Attractions of Surfaces and Lines; Surface Distribution of Matter; Two-Layer Surfaces; Spherical Harmonics; Ellipsoidal Harmonics; etc. "The great number of particular cases . . . should make the book valuable to geophysicists and others actively engaged in practical applications of the potential theory," Review of Scientific Instruments. Index. Bibliography. xiii + 469pp. 5⅜ x 8.
S486 Paperbound **$2.25**

THEORETICAL MECHANICS: DYNAMICS OF RIGID BODIES, W. D. MacMillan. Theory of dynamics of a rigid body is developed, using both the geometrical and analytical methods of instruction. Begins with exposition of algebra of vectors, it goes through momentum principles, motion in space, use of differential equations and infinite series to solve more sophisticated dynamics problems. Partial contents: moments of inertia, systems of free particles, motion parallel to a fixed plane, rolling motion, method of periodic solutions, much more. 82 figs. 199 problems. Bibliography. Indexes. xii + 476pp. 5⅜ x 8.
S641 Paperbound **$2.00**

MATHEMATICAL FOUNDATIONS OF STATISTICAL MECHANICS, A. I. Khinchin. Offering a precise and rigorous formulation of problems, this book supplies a thorough and up-to-date exposition. It provides analytical tools needed to replace cumbersome concepts, and furnishes for the first time a logical step-by-step introduction to the subject. Partial contents: geometry & kinematics of the phase space, ergodic problem, reduction to theory of probability, application of central limit problem, ideal monatomic gas, foundation of thermo-dynamics, dispersion and distribution of sum functions. Key to notations. Index. viii + 179pp. 5⅜ x 8.
S147 Paperbound **$1.35**

ELEMENTARY PRINCIPLES IN STATISTICAL MECHANICS, J. W. Gibbs. Last work of the great Yale mathematical physicist, still one of the most fundamental treatments available for advanced students and workers in the field. Covers the basic principle of conservation of probability of phase, theory of errors in the calculated phases of a system, the contributions of Clausius, Maxwell, Boltzmann, and Gibbs himself, and much more. Includes valuable comparison of statistical mechanics with thermodynamics: Carnot's cycle, mechanical definitions of entropy, etc. xvi + 208pp. 5⅜ x 8.
S707 Paperbound **$1.45**

THE DYNAMICS OF PARTICLES AND OF RIGID, ELASTIC, AND FLUID BODIES; BEING LECTURES ON MATHEMATICAL PHYSICS, A. G. Webster. The reissuing of this classic fills the need for a comprehensive work on dynamics. A wide range of topics is covered in unusually great depth, applying ordinary and partial differential equations. Part I considers laws of motion and methods applicable to systems of all sorts; oscillation, resonance, cyclic systems, etc. Part 2 is a detailed study of the dynamics of rigid bodies. Part 3 introduces the theory of potential; stress and strain, Newtonian potential functions, gyrostatics, wave and vortex motion, etc. Further contents: Kinematics of a point; Lagrange's equations; Hamilton's principle; Systems of vectors; Statics and dynamics of deformable bodies; much more, not easily found together in one volume. Unabridged reprinting of 2nd edition. 20 pages of notes on differential equations and the higher analysis. 203 illustrations. Selected bibliography. Index. xi + 588pp. 5⅜ x 8.
S522 Paperbound **$2.35**

A TREATISE ON DYNAMICS OF A PARTICLE, E. J. Routh. Elementary text on dynamics for beginning mathematics or physics student. Unusually detailed treatment from elementary definitions to motion in 3 dimensions, emphasizing concrete aspects. Much unique material important in recent applications. Covers impulsive forces, rectilinear and constrained motion in 2 dimensions, harmonic and parabolic motion, degrees of freedom, closed orbits, the conical pendulum, the principle of least action, Jacobi's method, and much more. Index. 559 problems, many fully worked out, incorporated into text. xiii + 418pp. 5⅜ x 8.
$$\text{S696 Paperbound \$2.25}$$

DYNAMICS OF A SYSTEM OF RIGID BODIES (Elementary Section), E. J. Routh. Revised 7th edition of this standard reference. This volume covers the dynamical principles of the subject, and its more elementary applications: finding moments of inertia by integration, foci of inertia, d'Alembert's principle, impulsive forces, motion in 2 and 3 dimensions, Lagrange's equations, relative indicatrix, Euler's theorem, large tautochronous motions, etc. Index. 55 figures. Scores of problems. xv + 443pp. 5⅜ x 8.
$$\text{S664 Paperbound \$2.35}$$

DYNAMICS OF A SYSTEM OF RIGID BODIES (Advanced Section), E. J. Routh. Revised 6th edition of a classic reference aid. Much of its material remains unique. Partial contents: moving axes, relative motion, oscillations about equilibrium, motion. Motion of a body under no forces, any forces. Nature of motion given by linear equations and conditions of stability. Free, forced vibrations, constants of integration, calculus of finite differences, variations, precession and nutation, motion of the moon, motion of string, chain, membranes. 64 figures. 498pp. 5⅜ x 8.
$$\text{S229 Paperbound \$2.35}$$

DYNAMICAL THEORY OF GASES, James Jeans. Divided into mathematical and physical chapters for the convenience of those not expert in mathematics, this volume discusses the mathematical theory of gas in a steady state, thermodynamics, Boltzmann and Maxwell, kinetic theory, quantum theory, exponentials, etc. 4th enlarged edition, with new material on quantum theory, quantum dynamics, etc. Indexes. 28 figures. 444pp. 6⅛ x 9¼.
$$\text{S136 Paperbound \$2.45}$$

FOUNDATIONS OF POTENTIAL THEORY, O. D. Kellogg. Based on courses given at Harvard this is suitable for both advanced and beginning mathematicians. Proofs are rigorous, and much material not generally avialable elsewhere is included. Partial contents: forces of gravity, fields of force, divergence theorem, properties of Newtonian potentials at points of free space, potentials as solutions of Laplace's equations, harmonic functions, electrostatics, electric images, logarithmic potential, etc. One of Grundlehren Series. ix + 384pp. 5⅜ x 8.
$$\text{S144 Paperbound \$1.98}$$

THERMODYNAMICS, Enrico Fermi. Unabridged reproduction of 1937 edition. Elementary in treatment; remarkable for clarity, organization. Requires no knowledge of advanced math beyond calculus, only familiarity with fundamentals of thermometry, calorimetry. Partial Contents: Thermodynamic systems; First & Second laws of thermodynamics; Entropy; Thermodynamic potentials: phase rule, reversible electric cell; Gaseous reactions: van't Hoff reaction box, principle of LeChatelier; Thermodynamics of dilute solutions: osmotic & vapor pressures, boiling & freezing points; Entropy constant. Index. 25 problems. 24 illustrations. x + 160pp. 5⅜ x 8.
$$\text{S361 Paperbound \$1.75}$$

THE THERMODYNAMICS OF ELECTRICAL PHENOMENA IN METALS and A CONDENSED COLLECTION OF THERMODYNAMIC FORMULAS, P. W. Bridgman. Major work by the Nobel Prizewinner: stimulating conceptual introduction to aspects of the electron theory of metals, giving an intuitive understanding of fundamental relationships concealed by the formal systems of Onsager and others. Elementary mathematical formulations show clearly the fundamental thermodynamical relationships of the electric field, and a complete phenomenological theory of metals is created. This is the work in which Bridgman announced his famous "thermomotive force" and his distinction between "driving" and "working" electromotive force. We have added in this Dover edition the author's long unavailable tables of thermodynamic formulas, extremely valuable for the speed of reference they allow. Two works bound as one. Index. 33 figures. Bibliography. xviii + 256pp. 5⅜ x 8. S723 Paperbound **$1.65**

REFLECTIONS ON THE MOTIVE POWER OF FIRE, by Sadi Carnot, and other papers on the 2nd law of thermodynamics by E. Clapeyron and R. Clausius. Carnot's "Reflections" laid the groundwork of modern thermodynamics. Its non-technical, mostly verbal statements examine the relations between heat and the work done by heat in engines, establishing conditions for the economical working of these engines. The papers by Clapeyron and Clausius here reprinted added further refinements to Carnot's work, and led to its final acceptance by physicists. Selections from posthumous manuscripts of Carnot are also included. All papers in English. New introduction by E. Mendoza. 12 illustrations. xxii + 152pp. 5⅜ x 8.
$$\text{S661 Paperbound \$1.50}$$

TREATISE ON THERMODYNAMICS, Max Planck. Based on Planck's original papers this offers a uniform point of view for the entire field and has been used as an introduction for students who have studied elementary chemistry, physics, and calculus. Rejecting the earlier approaches of Helmholtz and Maxwell, the author makes no assumptions regarding the nature of heat, but begins with a few empirical facts, and from these deduces new physical and chemical laws. 3rd English edition of this standard text by a Nobel laureate. xvi + 297pp. 5⅜ x 8.
$$\text{S219 Paperbound \$1.75}$$

THE THEORY OF HEAT RADIATION, Max Planck. A pioneering work in thermodynamics, providing basis for most later work. Nobel Laureate Planck writes on Deductions from Electrodynamics and Thermodynamics, Entropy and Probability, Irreversible Radiation Processes, etc. Starts with simple experimental laws of optics, advances to problems of spectral distribution of energy and irreversibility. Bibliography. 7 illustrations, xiv + 224pp. 5⅜ x 8.
S546 Paperbound **$1.50**

A HISTORY OF THE THEORY OF ELASTICITY AND THE STRENGTH OF MATERIALS, I. Todhunter and K. Pearson. For over 60 years a basic reference, unsurpassed in scope or authority. Both a history of the mathematical theory of elasticity from Galileo, Hooke, and Mariotte to Saint Venant, Kirchhoff, Clebsch, and Lord Kelvin and a detailed presentation of every important mathematical contribution during this period. Presents proofs of thousands of theorems and laws, summarizes every relevant treatise, many unavailable elsewhere. Practically a book apiece is devoted to modern founders: Saint Venant, Lame, Boussinesq, Rankine, Lord Kelvin, F. Neumann, Kirchhoff, Clebsch. Hundreds of pages of technical and physical treatises on specific applications of elasticity to particular materials. Indispensable for the mathematician, physicist, or engineer working with elasticity. Unabridged, corrected reprint of original 3-volume 1886-1893 edition. Three volume set. Two indexes. Appendix to Vol. I. Total of 2344pp. 5⅜ x 8⅜.
S914–916 The set, Clothbound **$12.50**

THE MATHEMATICAL THEORY OF ELASTICITY, A. E. H. Love. A wealth of practical illustration combined with thorough discussion of fundamentals—theory, application, special problems and solutions. Partial Contents: Analysis of Strain & Stress, Elasticity of Solid Bodies, Elasticity of Crystals, Vibration of Spheres, Cylinders, Propagation of Waves in Elastic Solid Media, Torsion, Theory of Continuous Beams, Plates. Rigorous treatment of Volterra's theory of dislocations, 2-dimensional elastic systems, other topics of modern interest. "For years the standard treatise on elasticity," AMERICAN MATHEMATICAL MONTHLY. 4th revised edition. Index. 76 figures. xviii + 643pp. 6⅛ x 9¼.
S174 Paperbound **$2.95**

RAYLEIGH'S PRINCIPLE AND ITS APPLICATIONS TO ENGINEERING, G. Temple & W. Bickley. Rayleigh's principle developed to provide upper and lower estimates of true value of fundamental period of a vibrating system, or condition of stability of elastic systems. Illustrative examples; rigorous proofs in special chapters. Partial contents: Energy method of discussing vibrations, stability. Perturbation theory, whirling of uniform shafts. Criteria of elastic stability. Application of energy method. Vibrating systems. Proof, accuracy, successive approximations, application of Rayleigh's principle. Synthetic theorems. Numerical, graphical methods. Equilibrium configurations, Ritz's method. Bibliography. Index. 22 figures. ix + 156pp. 5⅜ x 8.
S307 Paperbound **$1.50**

INVESTIGATIONS ON THE THEORY OF THE BROWNIAN MOVEMENT, Albert Einstein. Reprints from rare European journals. 5 basic papers, including the Elementary Theory of the Brownian Movement, written at the request of Lorentz to provide a simple explanation. Translated by A. D. Cowper. Annotated, edited by R. Fürth. 33pp. of notes elucidate, give history of previous investigations. Author, subject indexes. 62 footnotes. 124pp. 5⅜ x 8.
S304 Paperbound **$1.25**

See also: FUNDAMENTAL FORMULAS OF PHYSICS, D. H. Menzel.

ENGINEERING

THEORY OF FLIGHT, Richard von Mises. Remains almost unsurpassed as balanced, well-written account of fundamental fluid dynamics, and situations in which air compressibility effects are unimportant. Stressing equally theory and practice, avoiding formidable mathematical structure, it conveys a full understanding of physical phenomena and mathematical concepts. Contains perhaps the best introduction to general theory of stability. "Outstanding," Scientific, Medical, and Technical Books. New introduction by K. H. Hohenemser. Bibliographical, historical notes. Index. 408 illustrations. xvi + 620pp. 5⅜ x 8⅜.
S541 Paperbound **$2.85**

THEORY OF WING SECTIONS, I. H. Abbott, A. E. von Doenhoff. Concise compilation of subsonic aerodynamic characteristics of modern NASA wing sections, with description of their geometry, associated theory. Primarily reference work for engineers, students, it gives methods, data for using wing-section data to predict characteristics. Particularly valuable: chapters on thin wings, airfoils; complete summary of NACA's experimental observations, system of construction families of airfoils. 350pp. of tables on Basic Thickness Forms, Mean Lines, Airfoil Ordinates, Aerodynamic Characteristics of Wing Sections. Index. Bibliography. 191 illustrations. Appendix. 705pp. 5⅜ x 8.
S558 Paperbound **$2.95**

SUPERSONIC AERODYNAMICS, E. R. C. Miles. Valuable theoretical introduction to the supersonic domain, with emphasis on mathematical tools and principles, for practicing aerodynamicists and advanced students in aeronautical engineering. Covers fundamental theory, divergence theorem and principles of circulation, compressible flow and Helmholtz laws, the Prandtl-Busemann graphic method for 2-dimensional flow, oblique shock waves, the Taylor-Maccoll method for cones in supersonic flow, the Chaplygin method for 2-dimensional flow, etc. Problems range from practical engineering problems to development of theoretical results. "Rendered outstanding by the unprecedented scope of its contents . . . has undoubtedly filled a vital gap," AERONAUTICAL ENGINEERING REVIEW. Index. 173 problems, answers: 106 diagrams. 7 tables. xii + 255pp. 5⅜ x 8.
S214 Paperbound **$1.45**

WEIGHT-STRENGTH ANALYSIS OF AIRCRAFT STRUCTURES, F. R. Shanley. Scientifically sound methods of analyzing and predicting the structural weight of aircraft and missiles. Deals directly with forces and the distances over which they must be transmitted, making it possible to develop methods by which the minimum structural weight can be determined for any material and conditions of loading. Weight equations for wing and fuselage structures. Includes author's original papers on inelastic buckling and creep buckling. "Particularly successful in presenting his analytical methods for investigating various optimum design principles," AERONAUTICAL ENGINEERING REVIEW. Enlarged bibliography. Index. 199 figures. xiv + 404pp. 5⅝ x 8⅜.   S660 Paperbound **$2.45**

INTRODUCTION TO THE STATISTICAL DYNAMICS OF AUTOMATIC CONTROL SYSTEMS, V. V. Solodovnikov. First English publication of text-reference covering important branch of automatic control systems—random signals; in its original edition, this was the first comprehensive treatment. Examines frequency characteristics, transfer functions, stationary random processes, determination of minimum mean-squared error, of transfer function to a finite period of observation, much more. Translation edited by J. B. Thomas, L. A. Zadeh. Index. Bibliography. Appendix. xxii + 308pp. 5⅜ x 8.   S420 Paperbound **$2.25**

TENSORS FOR CIRCUITS, Gabriel Kron. A boldly original method of analysing engineering problems, at center of sharp discussion since first introduced, now definitely proved useful in such areas as electrical and structural networks on automatic computers. Encompasses a great variety of specific problems by means of a relatively few symbolic equations. "Power and flexibility . . . becoming more widely recognized," Nature. Formerly "A Short Course in Tensor Analysis." New introduction by B. Hoffmann. Index. Over 800 diagrams. xix + 250pp. 5⅜ x 8.   S534 Paperbound **$1.85**

DESIGN AND USE OF INSTRUMENTS AND ACCURATE MECHANISM, T. N. Whitehead. For the instrument designer, engineer; how to combine necessary mathematical abstractions with independent observation of actual facts. Partial contents: instruments & their parts, theory of errors, systematic errors, probability, short period errors, erratic errors, design precision, kinematic, semikinematic design, stiffness, planning of an instrument, human factor, etc. Index. 85 photos, diagrams. xii + 288pp. 5⅜ x 8.   S270 Paperbound **$1.95**

APPLIED ELASTICITY, J. Prescott. Provides the engineer with the theory of elasticity usually lacking in books on strength of materials, yet concentrates on those portions useful for immediate application. Develops every important type of elasticity problem from theoretical principles. Covers analysis of stress, relations between stress and strain, the empirical basis of elasticity, thin rods under tension or thrust, Saint Venant's theory, transverse oscillations of thin rods, stability of thin plates, cylinders with thin walls, vibrations of rotating disks, elastic bodies in contact, etc. "Excellent and important contribution to the subject, not merely in the old matter which he has presented in new and refreshing form, but also in the many original investigations here published for the first time," NATURE. Index. 3 Appendixes. vi + 672pp. 5⅜ x 8.   S726 Paperbound **$2.95**

STRENGTH OF MATERIALS, J. P. Den Hartog. Distinguished text prepared for M.I.T. course, ideal as introduction, refresher, reference, or self-study text. Full clear treatment of elementary material (tension, torsion, bending, compound stresses, deflection of beams, etc.), plus much advanced material on engineering methods of great practical value: full treatment of the Mohr circle, lucid elementary discussions of the theory of the center of shear and the "Myosotis" method of calculating beam deflections, reinforced concrete, plastic deformations, photoelasticity, etc. In all sections, both general principles and concrete applications are given. Index. 186 figures (160 others in problem section). 350 problems, all with answers. List of formulas. viii + 323pp. 5⅜ x 8.   S755 Paperbound **$1.95**

PHOTOELASTICITY: PRINCIPLES AND METHODS, H. T. Jessop, F. C. Harris. For the engineer, for specific problems of stress analysis. Latest time-saving methods of checking calculations in 2-dimensional design problems, new techniques for stresses in 3 dimensions, and lucid description of optical systems used in practical photoelasticity. Useful suggestions and hints based on on-the-job experience included. Partial contents: strained and stress-strain relations, circular disc under thrust along diameter, rectangular block with square hole under vertical thrust, simply supported rectangular beam under central concentrated load, etc. Theory held to minimum, no advanced mathematical training needed. Index. 164 illustrations. viii + 184pp. 6⅛ x 9¼.   S137 Clothbound **$3.75**

MECHANICS OF THE GYROSCOPE, THE DYNAMICS OF ROTATION, R. F. Deimel, Professor of Mechanical Engineering at Stevens Institute of Technology. Elementary general treatment of dynamics of rotation, with special application of gyroscopic phenomena. No knowledge of vectors needed. Velocity of a moving curve, acceleration to a point, general equations of motion, gyroscopic horizon, free gyro, motion of discs, the damped gyro, 103 similar topics. Exercises. 75 figures. 208pp. 5⅜ x 8.   S66 Paperbound **$1.65**
                                                                                S144 Paperbound **$1.98**

A TREATISE ON GYROSTATICS AND ROTATIONAL MOTION: THEORY AND APPLICATIONS, Andrew Gray. Most detailed, thorough book in English, generally considered definitive study. Many problems of all sorts in full detail, or step-by-step summary. Classical problems of Bour, Lottner, etc.; later ones of great physical interest. Vibrating systems of gyrostats, earth as a top, calculation of path of axis of a top by elliptic integrals, motion of unsymmetrical top, much more. Index. 160 illus. 550pp. 5⅜ x 8.   S589 Paperbound **$2.75**

FUNDAMENTALS OF HYDRO- AND AEROMECHANICS, L. Prandtl and O. G. Tietjens. The well-known standard work based upon Prandtl's lectures at Goettingen. Wherever possible hydrodynamics theory is referred to practical considerations in hydraulics, with the view of unifying theory and experience. Presentation is extremely clear and though primarily physical, mathematical proofs are rigorous and use vector analysis to a considerable extent. An Enginering Society Monograph, 1934. 186 figures. Index. xvi + 270pp. 5⅜ x 8.
S374 Paperbound **$1.85**

APPLIED HYDRO- AND AEROMECHANICS, L. Prandtl and O. G. Tietjens. Presents, for the most part, methods which will be valuable to engineers. Covers flow in pipes, boundary layers, airfoil theory, entry conditions, turbulent flow in pipes, and the boundary layer, determining drag from measurements of pressure and velocity, etc. "Will be welcomed by all students of aerodynamics," NATURE. Unabridged, unaltered. An Engineering Society Monograph, 1934. Index. 226 figures, 28 photographic plates illustrating flow patterns. xvi + 311pp. 5⅜ x 8.
S375 Paperbound **$1.85**

HYDRAULICS AND ITS APPLICATIONS, A. H. Gibson. Excellent comprehensive textbook for the student and thorough practical manual for the professional worker, a work of great stature in its area. Half the book is devoted to theory and half to applications and practical problems met in the field. Covers modes of motion of a fluid, critical velocity, viscous flow, eddy formation, Bernoulli's theorem, flow in converging passages, vortex motion, form of effluent streams, notches and weirs, skin friction, losses at valves and elbows, siphons, erosion of channels, jet propulsion, waves of oscillation, and over 100 similar topics. Final chapters (nearly 400 pages) cover more than 100 kinds of hydraulic machinery: Pelton wheel, speed regulators, the hydraulic ram, surge tanks, the scoop wheel, the Venturi meter, etc. A special chapter treats methods of testing theoretical hypotheses: scale models of rivers, tidal estuaries, siphon spillways, etc. 5th revised and enlarged (1952) edition. Index. Appendix. 427 photographs and diagrams. 95 examples, answers. xv + 813pp. 6 x 9.
S791 Clothbound **$8.00**

FLUID MECHANICS FOR HYDRAULIC ENGINEERS, H. Rouse. Standard work that gives a coherent picture of fluid mechanics from the point of view of the hydraulic engineer. Based on courses given to civil and mechanical engineering students at Columbia and the California Institute of Technology, this work covers every basic principle, method, equation, or theory of interest to the hydraulic engineer. Much of the material, diagrams, charts, etc., in this self-contained text are not duplicated elsewhere. Covers irrotational motion, conformal mapping, problems in laminar motion, fluid turbulence, flow around immersed bodies, transportation of sediment, general charcteristics of wave phenomena, gravity waves in open channels, etc. Index. Appendix of physical properties of common fluids. Frontispiece + 245 figures and photographs. xvi + 422pp. 5⅜ x 8.
S729 Paperbound **$2.25**

THE MEASUREMENT OF POWER SPECTRA FROM THE POINT OF VIEW OF COMMUNICATIONS ENGINEERING, R. B. Blackman, J. W. Tukey. This pathfinding work, reprinted from the "Bell System Technical Journal," explains various ways of getting practically useful answers in the measurement of power spectra, using results from both transmission theory and the theory of statistical estimation. Treats: Autocovariance Functions and Power Spectra; Direct Analog Computation; Distortion, Noise, Heterodyne Filtering and Pre-whitening; Aliasing; Rejection Filtering and Separation; Smoothing and Decimation Procedures; Very Low Frequencies; Transversal Filtering; much more. An appendix reviews fundamental Fourier techniques. Index of notation. Glossary of terms. 24 figures. XII tables. Bibliography. General index. 192pp. 5⅜ x 8.
S507 Paperbound **$1.85**

MICROWAVE TRANSMISSION DESIGN DATA, T. Moreno. Originally classified, now rewritten and enlarged (14 new chapters) for public release under auspices of Sperry Corp. Material of immediate value or reference use to radio engineers, systems designers, applied physicists, etc. Ordinary transmission line theory; attenuation; capacity; parameters of coaxial lines; higher modes; flexible cables; obstacles, discontinuities, and injunctions; tuneable wave guide impedance transformers; effects of temperature and humidity; much more. "Enough theoretical discussion is included to allow use of data without previous background," Electronics. 324 circuit diagrams, figures, etc. Tables of dielectrics, flexible cable, etc., data. Index. Ix + 248pp. 5⅜ x 8.
S459 Paperbound **$1.50**

GASEOUS CONDUCTORS: THEORY AND ENGINEERING APPLICATIONS, J. D. Cobine. An indispensable text and reference to gaseous conduction phenomena, with the engineering viewpoint prevailing throughout. Studies the kinetic theory of gases, ionization, emission phenomena; gas breakdown, spark characteristics, glow, and discharges; engineering applications in circuit interrupters, rectifiers, light sources, etc. Separate detailed treatment of high pressure arcs (Suits); low pressure arcs (Langmuir and Tonks). Much more. "Well organized, clear, straightforward," Tonks, Review of Scientific Instruments. Index. Bibliography. 83 practice problems. 7 appendices. Over 600 figures. 58 tables. xx + 606pp. 5⅜ x 8.
S442 Paperbound **$2.85**

See also: BRIDGES AND THEIR BUILDERS, D. Steinman, S. R. Watson; A DIDEROT PICTORIAL ENCYCLOPEDIA OF TRADES AND INDUSTRY; MATHEMATICS IN ACTION, O. G. Sutton; THE THEORY OF SOUND, Lord Rayleigh; RAYLEIGH'S PRINCIPLE AND ITS APPLICATION TO ENGINEERING, G. Temple, W. Bickley; APPLIED OPTICS AND OPTICAL DESIGN, A. E. Conrady; HYDRODYNAMICS, Dryden, Murnaghan, Bateman; LOUD SPEAKERS, N. W. McLachlan; HISTORY OF THE THEORY OF ELASTICITY AND OF THE STRENGTH OF MATERIALS, I. Todhunter,

K. Pearson; THEORY AND OPERATION OF THE SLIDE RULE, J. P. Ellis; DIFFERENTIAL EQUATIONS FOR ENGINEERS, P. Franklin; MATHEMATICAL METHODS FOR SCIENTISTS AND ENGINEERS, L. P. Smith; APPLIED MATHEMATICS FOR RADIO AND COMMUNICATIONS ENGINEERS, C. E. Smith; MATHEMATICS OF MODERN ENGINEERING, E. G. Keller, R. E. Doherty; THEORY OF FUNCTIONS AS APPLIED TO ENGINEERING PROBLEMS, R. Rothe, F. Ollendorff, K. Pohlhausen.

CHEMISTRY AND PHYSICAL CHEMISTRY

ORGANIC CHEMISTRY, F. C. Whitmore. The entire subject of organic chemistry for the practicing chemist and the advanced student. Storehouse of facts, theories, processes found elsewhere only in specialized journals. Covers aliphatic compounds (500 pages on the properties and synthetic preparation of hydrocarbons, halides, proteins, ketones, etc.), alicyclic compounds, aromatic compounds, heterocyclic compounds, organophosphorus and organometallic compounds. Methods of synthetic preparation analyzed critically throughout. Includes much of biochemical interest. "The scope of this volume is astonishing," INDUSTRIAL AND ENGINEERING CHEMISTRY. 12,000-reference index. 2387-item bibliography. Total of x + 1005pp. 5⅜ x 8. Two volume set.
S700 Vol I Paperbound **$2.00**
S701 Vol II Paperbound **$2.00**
The set **$4.00**

THE PRINCIPLES OF ELECTROCHEMISTRY, D. A. MacInnes. Basic equations for almost every subfield of electrochemistry from first principles, referring at all times to the soundest and most recent theories and results; unusually useful as text or as reference. Covers coulometers and Faraday's Law, electrolytic conductance, the Debye-Hueckel method for the theoretical calculation of activity coefficients, concentration cells, standard electrode potentials, thermodynamic ionization constants, pH, potentiometric titrations, irreversible phenomena, Planck's equation, and much more. "Excellent treatise," AMERICAN CHEMICAL SOCIETY JOURNAL. "Highly recommended," CHEMICAL AND METALLURGICAL ENGINEERING. 2 Indices. Appendix. 585-item bibliography. 137 figures. 94 tables. ii + 478pp. 5⅜ x 8⅜.
S52 Paperbound **$2.35**

THE CHEMISTRY OF URANIUM: THE ELEMENT, ITS BINARY AND RELATED COMPOUNDS, J. J. Katz and E. Rabinowitch. Vast post-World War II collection and correlation of thousands of AEC reports and published papers in a useful and easily accessible form, still the most complete and up-to-date compilation. Treats "dry uranium chemistry," occurrences, preparation, properties, simple compounds, isotopic composition, extraction from ores, spectra, alloys, etc. Much material available only here. Index. Thousands of evaluated bibliographical references. 324 tables, charts, figures. xxi + 609pp. 5⅜ x 8.
S757 Paperbound **$2.95**

KINETIC THEORY OF LIQUIDS, J. Frenkel. Regarding the kinetic theory of liquids as a generalization and extension of the theory of solid bodies, this volume covers all types of arrangements of solids, thermal displacements of atoms, interstitial atoms and ions, orientational and rotational motion of molecules, and transition between states of matter. Mathematical theory is developed close to the physical subject matter. 216 bibliographical footnotes. 55 figures. xi + 485pp. 5⅜ x 8.
S94 Clothbound **$3.95**
S95 Paperbound **$2.45**

POLAR MOLECULES, Pieter Debye. This work by Nobel laureate Debye offers a complete guide to fundamental electrostatic field relations, polarizability, molecular structure. Partial contents: electric intensity, displacement and force, polarization by orientation, molar polarization and molar refraction, halogen-hydrides, polar liquids, ionic saturation, dielectric constant, etc. Special chapter considers quantum theory. Indexed. 172pp. 5⅜ x 8.
S64 Paperbound **$1.50**

Dover publishes books on art, music, philosophy, literature, languages, history, social sciences, psychology, handcrafts, orientalia, puzzles and entertainments, chess, pets and gardens, books explaining science, intermediate and higher mathematics, mathematical physics, engineering, biological sciences, earth sciences, classics of science, etc. Write to:

Dept. catrr.
Dover Publications, Inc.
180 Varick Street, N. Y. 14, N. Y.